כתבי האקדמיה הלאומית הישראלית למדעים

PUBLICATIONS OF THE ISRAEL ACADEMY OF SCIENCES AND HUMANITIES

SECTION OF SCIENCES

———

FLORA PALAESTINA

EQUISETACEAE TO UMBELLIFERAE

by

MICHAEL ZOHARY

ERICACEAE TO ORCHIDACEAE

by

NAOMI FEINBRUN-DOTHAN

FLORA PALAESTINA

PART TWO · TEXT

PLATANACEAE TO UMBELLIFERAE

BY

MICHAEL ZOHARY

JERUSALEM 1987

THE ISRAEL ACADEMY OF SCIENCES AND HUMANITIES

First Printing 1972
Second Printing 1987

ISBN 965-208-000-4
ISBN 965-208-002-0

Printed in Israel

CONTENTS

SPERMATOPHYTA

ANGIOSPERMAE

DICOTYLEDONEAE

(continued)

SYNOPSIS OF FAMILIES IN PART TWO

Rosales
48 Platanaceae
49 Crassulaceae
50 Saxifragaceae
51 Rosaceae
52 Neuradaceae
53 Mimosaceae
54 Caesalpiniaceae
55 Papilionaceae

Geraniales
56 Oxalidaceae
57 Geraniaceae
58 Zygophyllaceae
59 Linaceae
60 Euphorbiaceae

Callitrichales
61 Callitrichaceae

Rutales
62 Rutaceae
63 Polygalaceae

Sapindales
64 Anacardiaceae
65 Aceraceae

Celastrales
66 Salvadoraceae

Rhamnales
67 Rhamnaceae

Malvales
68 Tiliaceae
69 Malvaceae

Thymelaeales
70 Thymelaeaceae
71 Elaeagnaceae

Violales
72 Violaceae
73 Cistaceae
74 Tamaricaceae
75 Frankeniaceae
76 Elatinaceae

Myrtiflorae
77 Lythraceae
78 Myrtaceae
79 Onagraceae
80 Haloragaceae
81 Theligonaceae

Umbelliflorae
82 Araliaceae
83 Umbelliferae

Rosales

48. PLATANACEAE

Monoecious trees. Leaves alternate, stipulate, petiolate, simple; petiole dilated at base, enclosing the axillary bud. Inflorescences of 1–7 unisexual heads arranged along a naked rhachis, with staminate heads below and pistillate above. Perianth inconspicuous, 3 (–6)- or 4 (–8)-merous, (1–) 2-whorled. Staminate flowers: calyx cupular or 0; petals minute; stamens (3–) 4–6 (–7), free, alternating with petals, anthers subsessile, 2-celled, dehiscing longitudinally; small staminodes often present. Pistillate flowers: calyx cupular, lobed or with free sepals; petals usually 0; staminodes usually present; carpels (3–) 5–6 (–9), free, each with 1–2 ovules – or ovary 1-celled and placentation parietal, ovules orthotropous, pendulous, each carpel with 1 style and a stigma along the inner face. Fruiting heads composed of 1-seeded, tetragonous or obpyramidal achenes surrounded at base by long hairs. Seeds linear; endosperm scanty; embryo straight.

One genus and some 6–7 species in S. E. Europe, S. W. Asia and N. America.

1. PLATANUS L.

Description as for family.

1. Platanus orientalis L., Sp. Pl. 999 (1753); Boiss., Fl. 4 : 1161 (1879). [Plate 1]

Tall tree up to 20 m. or more, with a wide, ovoid or ellipsoidal crown and wrinkled bark peeling in sheets. Leaves up to 10–25 cm., long-petioled; stipules small; blade truncate or subcordate at base, palmately 3–5 (–7)-lobed; lobes lanceolate, sinuate or lobulate, mucronulate, upper surface glabrous, lower tomentellous and later glabrescent. Flowers 4-merous. Fruiting heads about 2–3.5 cm. in diam. Achenes about 3 mm., with a low style and a tuft of long bristles. Fl. April–May.

Hab.: River banks. Upper Galilee, Judean Mts., Dan Valley, Hula Plain, Upper Jordan Valley, Gilead, Ammon.

Area: Mainly E. Mediterranean, extending westwards as far as Italy and eastwards up to the Himalayan mountains.

The עַרְמוֹן of the Bible (Gen. xxx : 37 and elsewhere).

49. CRASSULACEAE

Herbs or shrubs, usually succulent. Leaves alternate, opposite or in whorls, exstipulate, usually entire, sometimes crenate, lobed or pinnate. Inflorescences mostly cymose. Flowers mostly hermaphrodite, rarely unisexual (plants then usually dioecious), actinomorphic, mostly 5-merous, rarely 3-, 4-, 6- and up to 32-merous. Calyx of (3–) 4–30, usually free sepals. Petals as many as sepals, free or united. Stamens as many to twice as many as petals, mostly in 2 whorls, free or adnate to petals; anthers 2-celled, dehiscing longitudinally, introrse. Carpels as many as petals, free or con-

nate at base, each subtended by a nectariferous scale, 1-celled, with many, sometimes few or 1, anatropous, mostly erect ovules; placentation parietal; styles and
stigmas as many as carpels. Fruit apocarpous, with follicles opening along the ventral
suture. Seeds minute, elongated; endosperm scanty, fleshy or sometimes 0; embryo
straight.

Up to 30 genera and 1,400 species, most of them in temperate regions, pre-
ponderantly in S. Africa, S. and C. Asia, the Mediterranean region and Mexico.

Literature: A. Berger, Crassulaceae, in: Engl. & Prantl, *Nat. Pflznfam.* ed 2, 18a : 352–
483, 1930.

1. Leaves opposite, connate at base, not succulent (in ours). Petals 3–4.   **1. Crassula**
– Leaves alternate or rosulate, succulent (in ours)   2
2. Petals free or somewhat connate at the base only.   **4. Sedum**
– Petals connate, corolla tubular or urceolate   3
3. Lower leaves spatulate, sessile.   **3. Rosularia**
– Lower leaves orbicular and peltate, petiolate.   **2. Umbilicus**

1. CRASSULA L.

Annuals, half-shrubs or shrubs, with opposite, mostly entire leaves. Inflorescences
umbellate, corymbose or head-like – or flowers solitary. Flowers (3–4–) 5 (–6–9)-merous,
minute. Sepals almost free. Petals shortly connate at base or free, white, whitish-yellow
or pinkish. Stamens free or inserted on corolla tube; filaments filiform. Carpels mostly
free, many-ovuled; styles short, subulate; stigmas minute. Nectariferous scales as many
as other floral parts, minute. Follicles 5, with 2 or many seeds.

About 300 species, chiefly in Africa, some in Asia and S. America.

1. Crassula alata (Viv.) Berger in Engl. et Prantl, Nat. Pflznfam. ed. 2, 18a : 389
(1930). *Tillaea alata* Viv., Pl. Aeg. 16, no. 19 (1831). *T. trichopoda* Fenzl ex Boiss.,
Fl. 2 : 767 (1872). [Plate 2]

Small, often tufted, glabrous annual, 5–10 cm. Stems ascending, with short, densely
clustered branches. Leaves 1–3 mm., connate at base, oblong-lanceolate, mucronate.
Flowers crowded in leaf axils, on conspicuous pedicels. Sepals 3–4, about 3 mm.,
ovate to oblong, acuminate. Petals 3–4, nearly half as long as sepals, hyaline. Nectariferous scales inconspicuous. Follicles 2-seeded. Seeds minutely striate. Fl. February–
May.

Hab.: Shady, more or less damp places, walls and rocks. Sharon Plain, Philistean
Plain, Mt. Carmel, Mt. Gilboa, Shefela, Judean Mts., Judean Desert, Upper Jordan
Valley, Gilead. Rather rare.

Area: Mainly E. Mediterranean.

The relation between this species and *C. muscosa* (L.) Roth, Enum. Pl. Phaen. Germ.
1 : 994 (1827), is still to be elucidated.

2. UMBILICUS DC.

Perennial herbs with fleshy rhizomes or tubers. Stems usually simple. Leaves alternate, petiolate, peltate, umbilicate in centre. Inflorescence a narrow raceme or panicle. Calyx 5-parted; lobes acute. Corolla gamopetalous, tubular or urceolate, 5-lobed. Stamens 10(5); filaments rather short, inserted on upper part of corolla. Carpels 5, free, many-ovuled; styles short, filiform; stigmas capitate. Nectariferous scales small. Fruit apocarpous, with 5 many-seeded follicles.

About 16 species in the Mediterranean and Macaronesian regions, W. Asia and C. Europe.

1. Umbilicus intermedius Boiss., Fl. 2 : 769 (1872). *Cotyledon intermedius* (Boiss.) Bornm., Bot. Jahrb. 33 : 427 (1903). [Plate 3]

Erect, glabrous perennial, 10–50(–60) cm., with an underground, depressed-globular tuber. Leaves fleshy; lower leaves rosulate, long-petioled, blade 2–6 cm. in diam., peltate, orbicular, repand-crenate; upper leaves 0.5–2 cm., sessile, cuneate-lanceolate, more or less dentate-crenate. Flowers pendulous, horizontal (or erect when young), forming more or less dense racemes. Pedicels half as long as lanceolate bracts 4–6 mm. Corolla 0.6–1 cm., 4 to 6 times as long as calyx, yellowish-white (sometimes reddish at apex), tubular-urceolate, more or less deeply 5-cleft. Nectariferous scales oblong to linear-lanceolate, more or less emarginate. Seeds many, minutely and longitudinally striate. Fl. March–May.

Hab. : Walls, fences and rock crevices. Coastal Galilee, Acco Plain, Sharon Plain, Upper and Lower Galilee, Mt. Carmel, Esdraelon Plain, Mt. Gilboa, Samaria, Shefela, Judean Mts., Judean Desert, Negev, Dan Valley, Hula Plain, Upper Jordan Valley, Gilead, Ammon, Moav, Edom.

Area : E. Mediterranean and W. Irano-Turanian.

Further studies are needed to clarify the relation between this species and *U. horizontalis* (Guss.) DC., Prodr. 3 : 400 (1828).

A leading plant of the *Umbilicus-Allium subhirsutum* community on old stone fences.

3. ROSULARIA (DC.) Stapf

Perennial, glabrous or hirsute herbs, forming rosettes or cushions. Leaves sessile, more or less spatulate. Inflorescences terminal and/or axillary, more or less paniculate. Flowers 5-merous. Sepals often rather fleshy. Corolla gamopetalous, tubular-cylindrical, with somewhat reflexed, acute lobes. Stamens 10; filaments inserted on tube of corolla, the epipetalous at a higher level than the episepalous. Carpels free, tapering into a style; stigmas short, capitate. Nectariferous scales almost rectangular. Fruit apocarpous, of 5 many-seeded follicles.

About 20 species from E. Mediterranean to C. Asia.

1. Leaves up to 6 cm. Inflorescence consisting of 6–10 lateral branches. Calyx cylindrical-conical; fruiting calyx 2 mm. Corolla lobes almost as long as tube.   **1. R. libanotica**

– Leaves up to 3 cm. Inflorescence consisting of 2–4 lateral branches. Calyx globular-conical; fruiting calyx 4 mm. Corolla lobes half as long as tube.   **2. R. lineata**

1. Rosularia libanotica (L.) Sam. ex Rech. f., Ark. Bot. ser. 2, 5, 1 : 186 (1959). *Sedum libanoticum* L., Sp. Pl. ed. 2, 617 (1762). *Cotyledon libanotica* Labill., Ic. Pl. Syr. Dec. 3 : 3 (1809). *Umbilicus libanoticus* (Labill.) DC., Prodr. 3 : 399 (1828); Boiss., Fl. 2 : 772 (1872). [Plate 4]

Perennial, puberulous-glandular, 15–30 cm. Leaves 4–6 cm., rosulate, fleshy, spatulate, cuneate at base, obtuse; younger leaves finely short-ciliolate. Inflorescence a loose racemose panicle, made of 6–10 lateral branches and borne on a scape-like peduncle 15–20 cm. Pedicels longer than calyx. Calyx cylindrical-conical; lobes acute-acuminate, with reflexed tip. Corolla 0.8–1 cm., up to two and a half times as long as calyx, rose-pink, tubular, cleft to about half its length into 5 oblong-lanceolate, mucronate, recurved lobes. Nectariferous scales rectangular, obtuse, emarginate. Fruiting calyx 2 mm. across. Follicles oblong-lanceolate, gradually tapering into a style, not ciliate at margin. Fl. March–April.

Hab. : Cliffs. Upper and Lower Galilee, Mt. Carmel, Gilead.
Area : E. Mediterranean and W. Irano-Turanian.

2. Rosularia lineata (Boiss.) Berger in Engl. et Prantl, Nat. Pflznfam. ed. 2, 18a : 466 (1930). *Umbilicus lineata* Boiss., Diagn. ser. 1, 10 : 14 (1849) et Fl. 2 : 773 (1872; "*lineatus*"). *Cotyledon lineatus* (Boiss.) Dinsmore in Post, Fl. Syr. Pal. Sin. ed. 2, 1 : 490 (1932). [Plate 5]

Perennial, hirsute-glandular, 8–15 cm. Leaves 2–3 cm., rosulate, fleshy; radical leaves spatulate-lingulate, obtuse; younger leaves long-ciliate. Inflorescences consisting of 2–4 lateral branches, borne on scape-like peduncle up to 10 cm. Calyx globular-conical; lobes acute, not reflexed at tip. Corolla 7–9 mm., by one and one third longer than calyx, rose-pink, broadly campanulate, cleft to one third its length into triangular-ovate lobes. Nectariferous scales lingulate, entire. Fruiting calyx 4 mm. across. Follicles ovoid, abruptly ending in a style, ciliate along margin and midrib. Fl. March–April.

Hab. : Cliffs. Upper and Lower Galilee, Mt. Carmel, Samaria, C. Negev, Upper Jordan Valley, Golan, Gilead.
Area : E. Mediterranean.

4. SEDUM L.

Perennial or annual glabrous herbs, various in habit. Stems mostly fleshy, sometimes somewhat woody. Leaves mostly alternate, sometimes opposite or whorled, simple, fleshy. Flowers mostly hermaphrodite, sometimes unisexual through abortion (plants then dioecious), mostly 5-merous, sometimes 3–4- or 6–10-merous, in mono- to pleiochasial cymes. Sepals usually 5, free or shortly united at base, somewhat fleshy. Petals 5 (rarely 4 or 6–10), mostly free or slightly united at base. Stamens 10 (rarely 5 or 5–12), the epipetalous stamens adnate to base of petals. Carpels free or shortly connate at base; styles short. Nectariferous scales mostly 5, small, of various shapes, entire, toothed or lobed. Fruit apocarpous, composed of a group of many-seeded, sometimes 1-seeded follicles, dehiscing at ventral suture. Seeds minute.

About 500 species chiefly in the northern hemisphere, especially in Mediterranean region, S. W. Asia and the Sino-Japanese region, some in C. Africa and S. America.

Literature : R. L. Praeger, An account of the genus *Sedum* as found in cultivation, *Journ. Roy. Hort. Soc.* 46 : 1–314 (1921). J. A. Huber, Zur Systematik der Gattung *Sedum*, *Ber. Naturw. Ver. Landshut* 20 : 9–118 (1929). H. Fröderström, The genus *Sedum* L.; a systematic essay, 4 pts., *Acta Hort. Gotob. App.* 5–7, 10 (1930–1936).

1. Perennial evergreens   2
 − Annual ephemerals   3
2. Leaves small, up to 1 × 0.1 cm., semiterete. Flowers yellow.   **1. S. laconicum**
 − Leaves up to 2.5 × 0.3–0.4 cm., more or less terete. Flowers greenish or yellowish-white.
                                                                           2. S. nicaeense
3 (1). Follicles 1-seeded. Leaves and stems reddish. Corolla about 1–1.5 mm.
                                                                          9. S. microcarpum
 − Follicles many-seeded. Leaves and corolla not as above   4
4. Flowers white, pink or red   5
 − Flowers yellow or pale yellow   8
5. Leaves broadly elliptical to obovate. Flowers 4–5-merous. Stamens 5 (4). Corolla twice as long as calyx or longer, white to somewhat reddish.   **3. S. caespitosum**
 − Not as above   6
6. Flowers (4–)6–7(–9)-merous. Nectariferous scales deeply and irregularly lobed.
                                                                           6. S. hispanicum
 − Flowers 5-merous. Nectariferous scales not lobed   7
7. Plants glandular-pubescent throughout. Petals long-acuminate, pink or reddish, with purple midrib. Follicles keeled. Stamens 5.   **5. S. rubens**
 − Plants glabrous, at least in lower part. Petals abruptly cuspidate, white to pink. Stamens 10.   **4. S. pallidum**
8 (4). Petals acute, equal to or a little longer than calyx. Stamens usually 5.
                                                                           7. S. litoreum
 − Petals abruptly cuspidate, 6 times as long as calyx or longer. Stamens 10–14.
                                                                          8. S. palaestinum

1. Sedum laconicum Boiss. et Heldr. in Boiss., Diagn. ser. 1, 6 : 55 (1846–1847) et Fl. 2 : 784 (1872). [Plate 6]

Glabrous, tufted perennial, 5–15 cm. Stems ascending or creeping and rooting at base. Leaves 4–8 mm., alternate, imbricated, semiterete, spurred at base, incurved above, more or less mammillate at tip, pale green. Inflorescences consisting of axillary, 2–4-flowered cymules up to 1.5 cm. Flowers subsessile or short-pedicelled. Calyx lobes 5, erect, oblong, obtuse. Petals 5, somewhat longer than calyx, yellow, lanceolate, acuminate. Stamens 10. Nectariferous scales subspatulate-rectangular, emarginate at apex. Fl. May–July.

Hab. : Rocks. Upper and Lower Galilee. Rare.

Area : E. Mediterranean.

Our specimens differ markedly from the original description in their longer calyx, which is only slightly shorter than the corolla, and in their pedicellate flowers.

2. Sedum nicaeense All., Fl. Pedem. 2 : 122, t. 90, f. 1 (1785); Greuter et Rech. f., Boissiera 13 : 68 (1967). *S. sediforme* (Jacq.) Pau, Acta Mem. Prim. Congr. Nat. Esp. Zaragoza 1908 : 246 (1909) *obiter* et *pro syn.* non *S. sediforme* (Schweinf.) Hamet, Rev. Gen. Bot. 24 : 148 (1912). *Sempervivum sediforme* Jacq., Hort. Bot. Vindob. 1 : 35 (1770). *Sedum altissimum* Poir. in Lam., Encycl. 4 : 634 (1798); Boiss., Fl. 2 : 785 (1872). [Plate 7]

Glaucous, glabrous perennial, woody at base. Sterile stems numerous, ascending; flowering stems erect, 15–60 cm. Leaves 1.2–2(–2.5) cm., closely imbricated, subterete, lanceolate to oblong, short-spurred, mucronate. Inflorescences corymbose, with recurved scorpioid branches. Flowers 5–8-merous, short-pedicelled. Calyx lobes 5, 2–3 mm., ovate. Petals 5–8 mm., pale yellow or greenish-white, linear-lanceolate to oblong, obtuse. Stamens 10–16, ciliate at base. Nectariferous scales rectangular. Follicles pale yellow. Fl. June–July.

Hab.: Stony ground. Sharon Plain, Upper and Lower Galilee, Mt. Carmel, Mt. Gilboa, Judean Mts.

Area: Mediterranean, with slight peripheral extensions.

Sometimes cultivated as an ornamental; eaten as a pot herb.

3. Sedum caespitosum (Cav.) DC., Prodr. 3 : 405 (1828); Boiss., Fl. 2 : 794 (1872). *Crassula caespitosa* Cav., Ic. 1 : 50, t. 69, f. 2 (1791). *S. rubrum* (L.) Thell., Repert. Sp. Nov. 10 : 290 (1912) non Royle ex Edgew., Trans. Linn. Soc. Lond. 20 : 47 (1851). *Tillaea rubra* L., Sp. Pl. 129 (1753). [Plate 8]

Annual, glabrous, 2–6 cm. Leaves 2–5 mm., imbricated, broadly elliptical to obovate. Inflorescences 2–3-forked, erect, stiff. Flowers (4–)5-merous, sessile. Calyx 1–2 mm.; lobes broadly triangular. Petals 3–4 mm., white to somewhat reddish, lanceolate, mucronate. Stamens 5 (or 4). Nectariferous scales linear-subspatulate, obtuse. Follicles about 4 mm., divergent, shortly connate at base. Fl. March–April.

Hab.: Sandy and rocky places. Sharon Plain, Upper Galilee, Shefela, Judean Mts., Upper Jordan Valley, Gilead.

Area: Mediterranean, extending slightly northwards.

4. Sedum pallidum M.B., Fl. Taur.-Cauc. 1 : 353 (1808); Boiss., Fl. 2 : 790 (1872). [Plate 9]

Annual, glabrous in lower part, glandular-pubescent above, 5–15 cm. Stems almost erect, simple below, branched above. Leaves 0.8–1 cm., semiterete to oblong. Inflorescences 2–3-forked into scorpioid cymes. Bracts shorter than the almost sessile, 5-merous flowers. Calyx one fifth or one third as long as corolla; lobes 1–1.5 mm., broadly triangular. Petals 5–6 mm., white to pink, oblong, abruptly cuspidate, slightly glandular-hairy along midrib. Stamens 10, papillose at base of filaments. Nectariferous scales spatulate-obtriangular, minutely dentate. Follicles compressed, lanceolate, puberulent. Fl. March–April.

Hab.: Stony ground. Sharon Plain, Upper and Lower Galilee, Shefela, Judean Mts., Gilead.

Area: E. Mediterranean and W. Irano-Turanian.

5. Sedum rubens L., Sp. Pl. 432 (1753); Boiss., Fl. 2 : 794 (1872). [Plate 10]

Annual, glandular-hairy throughout, 5–15 cm. Stems almost erect, branched above. Leaves 0.5–1.5 cm., semiterete, lanceolate. Inflorescences of 2–3 scorpioid branches. Flowers 5-merous, short-pedicelled. Calyx lobes 1.5–2 mm., ovate-triangular, acute. Petals 4–6 mm., reddish-pink with purple midrib, lanceolate, acuminate-aristate. Stamens usually 5, a little more than half as long as petals. Nectariferous scales rectangular-trapezoidal, somewhat repand at apex. Follicles divergent, tuberculate, frequently glandular. Fl. March–April.

Hab.: Rocky ground. Mt. Carmel.

Area: Mediterranean and S. W. Euro-Siberian.

6. Sedum hispanicum L., Cent. Pl. 1 : 12 (1755) et Amoen. Acad. 4 : 273 (1759). *S. glaucum* Waldst. et Kit., Pl. Rar. Hung. 2 : 198, t. 181 (1804); Boiss., Fl. 2 : 789 (1872). [Plate 11]

Annual, glaucous, hairy above, 5–15 cm. Leaves 0.4–2 cm., terete or semiterete, somewhat flattened. Inflorescences 2–3 (–5)-forked into scorpioid cymes. Bracts slightly shorter than flowers. Flowers anisomerous, 6–7 (rarely 4–9)-merous. Calyx lobes 1–1.5 mm., broadly triangular to semiorbicular, glabrous to glandular-pubescent. Petals 5–6 mm., usually white, with or without a reddish midrib, lanceolate, acuminate, more or less pubescent along midrib. Stamens 12–14. Nectariferous scales deeply lobed. Follicles somewhat compressed, conical, frequently tuberculate. Fl. March–May.

Hab.: Rocks. Upper Galilee, Esdraelon Plain, Shefela, Judean Mts., Hula Plain, Upper Jordan Valley, Gilead.

Area: E. Mediterranean and W. Euro-Siberian.

Var. *polypetalum* (Boiss.) Dinsmore in Post, Fl. Syr. Pal. Sin. ed. 2, 1 : 493 (1932), recorded by Rech. f., Ark. Bot. ser. 2, 2, 5 : 353 (1952) from Upper Galilee, seems not to be separable from the type.

7. Sedum litoreum Guss., Pl. Rar. 185 (1826); Boiss., Fl. 2 : 793 (1872). [Plate 12]

Glabrous annual, 2–10 cm. Stems simple or sparingly branched. Leaves 2–5 mm., semiterete (more or less flattened above) to spatulate or oblong, somewhat gibbous, obtuse. Inflorescences shortly 1–3-branched. Flowers subsessile. Calyx lobes 5, unequal, ovate-oblong, obtuse. Petals 5, 3.5–4 mm., pale yellow, becoming white, lanceolate, acute, equalling or somewhat exceeding calyx. Stamens 5, rarely 10. Nectariferous scales spatulate-obovate, sometimes emarginate. Follicles erect-divergent, muticous, glabrous. Fl. April–May.

Hab.: Coastal sandstone. Coastal Galilee, Sharon Plain, Philistean Plain.

Area: N. and E. Mediterranean.

8. Sedum palaestinum Boiss., Diagn. ser. 1, 10 : 18 (1849) et Fl. 2 : 793 (1872). [Plate 13]

Annual, glabrous and minutely glandular above, 5–10 cm. Stems erect, branching from base, slender. Leaves 6–9 mm., semiterete. Inflorescences 2–3-branched; branches scorpioid. Flowers 5–7-merous, sessile. Calyx lobes minute, ovate-triangular, more or less acute. Petals 5.5–7 mm., 6 times as long as calyx or more, pale yellow, often reddish at keel, lanceolate to oblong, abruptly cuspidate. Stamens 10–14. Nectariferous scales spatulate-rectangular, emarginate. Follicles covered with subsessile glands. Fl. March–April.

Hab.: Rocky ground. Sharon Plain, Philistean Plain, Upper and Lower Galilee, Mt. Carmel, Samaria, Judean Mts., Judean Desert, Gilead.

Area: E. Mediterranean (Palestine-Lebanon).

9. Sedum microcarpum (Sm.) Schönl. in Engl. et Prantl, Nat. Pflznfam. III, 2a : 31 (1890). *Crassula microcarpa* Sm. in Sibth. et Sm., Fl. Gr. Prodr. 1 : 217 (1806). *Telmissa microcarpa* (Sm.) Boiss., Fl. 2 : 795 (1872). [Plate 14]

Annual, glabrous, reddish, 3–10 cm. Stems usually much branched. Leaves terete, obtuse. Inflorescences 2–3-branched; branches rigid, leafy. Flowers 3- to 5-merous, sessile along the branches. Calyx lobes minute, semiovate, 1-nerved. Petals 1.3–1.5 mm., 3 times as long as calyx or more, connate at base, pinkish-white, ovate. Stamens 3–5, nearly equalling petals. Nectariferous scales rectangular, slightly emarginate. Follicles 1-seeded. Fl. January–April.

Hab.: Moist shallow cavities on flat rocks. Sharon Plain, Philistean Plain, Upper and Lower Galilee, Mt. Carmel, Esdraelon Plain, Mt. Gilboa, Samaria, Shefela, Judean Mts., Judean Desert, Dan Valley, Hula Plain, Upper Jordan Valley, Transjordan. Fairly common.

Area: E. Mediterranean, with slight eastward extensions.

50. SAXIFRAGACEAE

Herbs, shrubs or low trees. Leaves usually alternate, simple, with or without small stipules adnate to petiole. Inflorescences axillary or terminal, racemose or paniculate, or flowers solitary. Flowers hermaphrodite or sometimes unisexual (plants then dioecious), actinomorphic or very rarely zygomorphic, 5-merous, rarely 4–12-merous. Calyx gamosepalous, with 5, rarely 4–12 lobes. Petals free, mostly of same number as calyx lobes, rarely less or 0. Disk present. Stamens as many or twice as many as petals or more; filaments mostly free. Carpels 2, sometimes 3–5 (rarely 6–12), usually united (sometimes only at base) or rarely 4–6 and free; ovary superior or more or less inferior, free or more or less adnate to calyx tube; placentation axile, parietal or basal; ovules anatropous; styles as many as carpels, free or more or less connate; stigmas capitate, rarely lobed. Fruit a capsule or berry, rarely a follicle or nutlet. Seeds mostly numerous and minute, sometimes solitary; endosperm mostly copious, fleshy, sometimes scanty or 0; embryo small; cotyledons flat, leaf-like.

About 80 genera and 1,200 species, mostly in arctic and temperate regions.

1. Saxifraga L.

Perennial, rarely annual or biennial herbs. Leaves mostly alternate, rarely opposite, or all radical and rosulate, entire, lobed or divided. Flowers usually 5-merous, bracteolate, mostly in panicles or corymbs. Stamens 10, rarely 8 or 5; filaments thread-like; anthers 2-lobed. Carpels 2, rarely 3–5, more or less united at base into a 2-celled, superior or half-inferior ovary 2-lobed at apex, very rarely carpels free; placentation axile; ovules numerous; styles free, spreading; stigmas capitate or lobed. Fruit a many-seeded capsule, 2-beaked by the persistent styles, opening by 2 valves between the beaks. Seeds numerous, small, tuberculate.

About 350 species, mostly in arctic and temperate regions of the northern hemisphere.

1. Saxifraga hederacea L., Sp. Pl. 405 (1753); Boiss., Fl. 2 : 812 (1872). [Plate 15]

Annual, glabrous or glandular-hairy, 10–20 cm. Stems erect, almost simple, filiform. Leaves alternate, long-petioled, rhombic to broadly triangular or broadly ovate, sometimes reniform, shallowly palmately (3–)5–7(–9)-lobed, lower leaves 1.5–2.5 cm. across, upper leaves smaller, 3-lobed or undivided; base of leaf truncate to subcordate, sometimes cuneate; lobes broadly triangular, mucronulate; margin glandular-ciliate. Flowers solitary, 5–8 mm. across, long-pedicelled. Calyx lobes erect-spreading, ovate, acute. Petals one and a half times as long as calyx lobes or less, white, obovate, abruptly short-clawed. Ovary free. Capsule more or less globular, hardly exceeding calyx; styles more or less spreading. Seeds ovoid. Fl. April.

Hab.: Maquis. Upper Galilee, Mt. Carmel. Very rare.

Area: E. Mediterranean.

51. ROSACEAE

Trees, shrubs (sometimes thorny) or herbs, sometimes climbing. Leaves deciduous or persistent, usually alternate, stipulate, simple or compound. Flowers usually hermaphrodite, rarely unisexual, actinomorphic, often large, solitary or in various types of inflorescences. Epicalyx (bracteoles) present or absent. Perianth usually double, sometimes simple, with basal portions usually adnate to receptacle or calyx tube (hypanthium), or inserted at margin of receptacle. Sepals 5, rarely 4, persistent, imbricated or valvate in bud. Petals usually as many as sepals or 0, caducous, alternating with sepals, imbricated or rarely convolute. Receptacle flat, convex, concave or urceolate, free or adnate to the ovary, sometimes inflated or fleshy in fruit, often with a nectariferous glandular disk. Stamens usually 2 to 4 times as many as sepals, rarely indefinite or 1–5 only. Ovary superior or inferior; carpels 1 to many, 1-celled or spuriously 2-celled, free or connate on a common receptacle or within it (hypanthium); ovules usually 2 in each cell, sometimes 1 or several, anatropous; styles as many as carpels, free, rarely more or less connate. Fruit an achene, pome or drupe, or composed of a group of dry or fleshy carpels or follicles. Seeds with a small embryo and usually without endosperm; cotyledons mostly fleshy.

About 100 genera and over 3,000 species mostly in temperate regions.

1. Fruit with prickles or spines.   4. **Agrimonia**
– Fruit unarmed   2
2. Petals 0   3
– Petals 5 or more   5

3. Leaves palmately lobed. Flowers in sessile, axillary clusters half-enclosed by the stipular cup. Dwarf, unarmed annuals. **3. Aphanes**
– Leaves pinnate. Flowers in terminal clusters or spikes 4
4. Unarmed perennial herbs. Fruit ovoid or spherical, dry, tuberculate. **5. Sanguisorba**
– Spiny half-shrubs. Fruit globular, pulpy, smooth. **6. Sarcopoterium**
5 (2). Low perennial herbs. Leaves digitate, with 5–7 leaflets. Flowers yellow. **2. Potentilla**
– Shrubs or trees, with simple or compound leaves. Flowers white, pink or reddish 6
6. Leaves compound, with 3–7 leaflets. Branches covered with prickles 7
– Leaves simple, entire or lobed. Unarmed or spinescent shrubs or trees 8
7. Ovary superior. Receptacle convex, bearing numerous, 1-seeded druplets. **1. Rubus**
– Ovary inferior. Receptacle concave (hypanthium), enclosing numerous, 1-seeded achenes. **7. Rosa**
8 (6). Leaves more or less deeply lobed 9
– Leaves entire or dentate-crenate or serrulate, not lobed 10
9. Styles 5; ovary 5-celled. Unarmed trees. Flowers 3–5 cm. across. **9. Eriolobus**
– Styles 1–3; ovary 1–3-celled. Thorny trees or shrubs. Flowers 1–1.5 cm. across. **10. Crataegus**
10 (8). Carpels several, united with each other and with the receptacle. Fruit a pome (i.e. a many-seeded, dry or fleshy, false berry). **8. Pyrus**
— Carpel 1, free. Fruit a 1 (–2)-seeded drupe 11
11. Drupe ovoid-globular, less than 1 cm. across. Leaves 0.5–1.2 cm. **12. Cerasus**
— Drupe and leaves larger 12
12. Drupe ovoid, flattened, greyish-green, velvety-canescent. **11. Amygdalus**
— Drupe globular, violet-red to yellow. **13. Prunus**

Subfam. ROSOIDEAE. Carpels numerous (rarely few), 1–2-ovuled, on or within a convex, conical or concave receptacle (hypanthium), mostly free, rarely united with one another and with the receptacle.

1. RUBUS L.

Shrubs or perennial herbs, erect or climbing. Branches armed with sharp prickles and often bearing stipitate glands. Leaves deciduous or persistent, alternate, pinnate or palmate with 3–7 distinct segments or leaflets, rarely simple or lobed; stipules adnate to petiole. Flowers in axillary or terminal cymes, rarely solitary. Calyx persistent, free, deeply (4–)5-lobed; lobes imbricated. Petals 5 (–8), caducous, sometimes 0, white, pink or purple. Stamens usually numerous, free, inserted on edge of calyx. Carpels numerous, free, spirally arranged, with 2 pendulous ovules; style subterminal, short, marcescent; stigmas simple or capitate. Fruit a cylindrical or spherical compound berry, of many 1-seeded druplets with fleshy pericarp and wrinkled stone adherent to the convex or conical dry receptacle.

Between 400 and 600 species almost in all regions of the world.

1. Flowers white. Pedicels with many straight and slender prickles. Petals 6–9 mm. **2. R. tomentosus**

– Flowers pink (rarely white). Pedicels unarmed or with 1–2 curved prickles. Petals 1–1.5 cm.   **1. R. sanguineus**

1. Rubus sanguineus Frivaldszk., Flora 18 : 334 (1835). *R. sanctus* auct. plur. non Schreb., Ic. Descr. Pl. 15, t. 8 (1766). *R. discolor* sensu Boiss., Fl. 2 : 695 (1872) non Weihe et Nees, Rub. Germ. 46, t. 20 (1825). [Plate 16]

Evergreen shrub, up to 1.5 m., with decumbent or nearly erect, arcuate shoots. Flowering branches angular-canaliculate, glabrous or pubescent, with short, strong, straight or curved prickles. Leaves usually 3-foliolate, lowermost leaves or those of sterile branches often 5-foliolate; petiole plano-convex, with small prickles; leaflets 2–8 × 2–5 cm., somewhat leathery, orbicular-ovate to oblong, acute or often obtuse, unequally serrate, pale green, usually more or less pilose above, tomentose-canescent beneath, terminal leaflets larger and sometimes abruptly acuminate. Racemes terminal, compound, divaricate, elongated, appressed-tomentose. Bracts linear, 3-fid, tomentose. Pedicels with small, hooked prickles. Calyx lobes 5–8 mm., reflexed, ovate, mucronulate, tomentose-canescent. Petals 1–1.5 cm., pink, sometimes white, obovate-orbicular, notched, wrinkled, tapering abruptly to a short claw. Stamens pink. Fruit black. Fl. April–September.

Hab. : River banks, by springs and swamps. Acco Plain, Sharon Plain, Philistean Plain, Upper and Lower Galilee, Mt. Carmel, Esdraelon Plain, Samaria, Shefela, Judean Mts., Dan Valley, Hula Plain, Upper and Lower Jordan Valley.

Area : Mediterranean and W. Irano-Turanian, extending into W. Euro-Siberian regions.

Main component of the *Rubus-Dorycnium rectum* community, on elevated river banks. Berries edible.

2. Rubus tomentosus Borkh. in Roem., Neues Mag. Bot. 1 : 2 (1794). [Plate 17]

Evergreen, low, prickly shrub up to 1 m., with weak, decumbent to nearly erect shoots. Flowering branches angular-canaliculate, glabrous or pubescent, with short, weak, somewhat curved or hooked prickles, usually with stipitate glands. Leaves 3–5-foliolate; petiole furrowed on upper side, with small, hooked prickles and with or without stipitate glands; leaflets 2–5 × 1.5–3.5 cm., oblong-rhombic to ovate and obovate, acute or obtuse, coarsely and unequally serrate, green, glabrous or sparingly stellately tomentose above and densely tomentose-canescent beneath; lower leaflets nearly sessile. Racemes terminal, compound, rigid, elongated, villose-tomentose, glandular or not; main axis usually prickly. Bracts lanceolate, 3-fid. Pedicels with many slender, straight prickles. Calyx lobes 4–7 mm., triangular to oblong, mucronulate, tomentose-canescent, reflexed after flowering. Petals 6–9 mm., white, tapering at base. Stamens white, about as long as the green style. Fruit black. Fl. April–June.

Var. **tomentosus**. *R. tomentosus* Borkh., l.c.: Boiss., Fl. 2 : 694 (1872). Leaflets more or less tomentose above.

Hab. : Maquis and garigue. Upper Galilee, Gilead.

Var. **glabratus** Godr., Monogr. Rub. 27 (1843). Leaflets glabrous or with few stellate hairs above.

Hab.: As above.

Area of species: N. Mediterranean, extending into W. Irano-Turanian and Euro-Siberian regions.

R. collinus DC., Cat. Hort. Monsp. 139 (1813), recorded by Dinsmore in Post, Fl. Syr. Pal. Sin. ed. 2, 1 : 462 (1932), from Galilee, has not been found by us.

2. POTENTILLA L.

Perennial, rarely annual herbs or small shrubs. Leaves alternate, floral leaves sometimes opposite; stipules adnate to the base of petiole; blade digitate or pinnate, with 3–8 (or more) leaflets. Flowers usually hermaphrodite, axillary and solitary or in cymes, pedicellate. Calyx persistent; tube short; lobes 5 (4–3), erect or spreading, alternating with the persistent bracteoles of the epicalyx. Petals as many as calyx lobes, usually large, yellow or white, rarely red or purple, obcordate or oblanceolate. Stamens 10–30 (often about 20). Carpels 10 to many, free, inserted on the convex or conical, hairy or glabrous receptacle; ovules solitary in each carpel, pendulous; styles caducous, somewhat lateral. Fruit an apocarpium composed of numerous 1-seeded achenes on the dry or spongy receptacle surrounded by the calyx.

Over 300 species, mostly in the northern hemisphere.

1. Corolla about 1 cm. across. Inflorescences cymose, dichotomously branched.
                                                                                  1. P. geranioides
– Corolla 1.5–2 cm. across. Flowers solitary, axillary.   **2. P. reptans**

1. Potentilla geranioides Willd., Sp. Pl. 2 : 1101 (1799); Boiss., Fl. 2 : 721 (1872). [Plate 18]

Perennial, caespitulose herb, 10–30 cm. Roots and stems woody. Branches decumbent. Leaves small, digitate, lower leaves long-petioled, upper sessile; stipules lanceolate to ovate, entire; leaflets 5–7, pinnatipartite into linear, obtuse segments, lateral leaflets smaller, nearly sessile, the others petiolate. Inflorescences dichotomously cymose, few-flowered, hirsute-canescent. Calyx lobes up to 7 mm., unequal, lanceolate, acute. Corolla about 1 cm. across; petals yellow, obcordate. Achenes few, oblong, not reniform, smooth, somewhat hairy at base. Fl. May–June.

Hab.: Rather damp places. Upper Galilee, Gilead. Rare.

Area: E. Mediterranean and W. Irano-Turanian.

2. Potentilla reptans L., Sp. Pl. 499 (1753); Boiss., Fl. 2 : 723 (1872). [Plate 19]

Perennial herb, patulous-hairy, 10–15 cm. Stems many, rooting at nodes, decumbent to ascending, leafy. Leaves long-petioled to almost sessile; stipules 0.5–1 cm., free, oblong, entire; blade 1–5 × 2–6 cm., palmately divided into 3–7 obovate to oblong, cuneate, acute or obtuse, incised lobes. Flowers axillary, solitary, borne on pedicels 2–5 cm. Epicalyx of elliptical to oblong, mostly obtuse bracteoles, later accrescent. Calyx lobes up to 1 cm., much broader than the bracteoles of the epicalyx, equal, ovate, acute to acuminate. Corolla 1.5–2 cm. across, yellow; petals longer than calyx, broad, obcordate to obovate. Carpels numerous. Achenes about 1–1.5 mm., reniform, glabrous, brown, smooth. Fl. May–July.

Hab.: Roadsides and damp places. Gilead (Burma to Jarash, after Dinsmore in Post, Fl. Syr. Pal. Sin. ed. 2, 1 : 464, 1932).

Area: Euro-Siberian and Mediterranean, extending into the Irano-Turanian territories.

3. APHANES L.

Annual herbs. Leaves alternate, palmate or palmately lobed; stipules large, sheathing. Flowers small, hermaphrodite, often in dense, cymose clusters opposite leaves. Calyx tube persistent, campanulate-urceolate, constricted at throat; lobes (4–)5, alternating with the (4–)5 bracteoles of the epicalyx. Petals 0. Stamens 1 (–2–3), opposite sepals, inserted on inner margin of hypanthium; anthers extrorse. Ovary inferior; carpel 1, with filiform style and capitate stigma; ovule 1, erect. Fruit a membranous achene, included in the indurated hypanthium.

About 20 species, almost cosmopolitan.

1. Aphanes arvensis L., Sp. Pl. 123 (1753). *Alchemilla arvensis* (L.) Scop., Fl. Carn. ed. 2, 1 : 115 (1771); Boiss., Fl. 2 : 731 (1872). [Plate 20]

Annual or biennial, greyish-green, 5–30 cm. Stems decumbent to ascending, usually much branched and pilose. Leaves 0.4–1 × 0.6–1 cm.; radical leaves evanescent; stipules leaf-like, connate up to two thirds their length into a cup and adnate to petiole, hairy, free part triangular-ovate, 5–7-incised-dentate; blade fan-shaped, 3-sect into 2–5-lobed segments, hairy on both sides or ciliate only, tapering to a petiole 2–8 mm. Flowers about 2 mm., opposite the leaves in sessile clusters of 10–20, the cluster half-enclosed by the stipular cup. Calyx tube campanulate, hairy; lobes 4, erect, ovate, acute, alternating with the 4 minute outer bracteoles of the epicalyx. Stamens 1 (–2–3). Achenes about 1 mm., included within calyx (hypanthium), flat, ovate, acute, glabrous. Fl. April–May.

Hab.: In rock crevices. Judean Mts. Very rare.

Area: Mediterranean and Euro-Siberian.

4. AGRIMONIA L.

Tall perennial herbs with oblique or creeping rootstock. Leaves alternate, petiolate, imparipinnate with unequal leaflets; stipules large, adnate to petiole. Flowers hermaphrodite, in terminal spike-like racemes, with pedicels bracteolate at middle. Calyx tube (hypanthium) turbinate or hemispherical, constricted at throat, and covered above with small hooked prickles indurating in fruit; calyx lobes 5, persistent. Petals 5, imbricated, longer than calyx lobes. Stamens 10–20, mostly 15, free. Carpels 2, free; ovules solitary, pendulous; styles terminal; stigmas 2-lobed. Fruit a 1-seeded achene enclosed in the indurated hypanthium.

About 20 species in north-temperate regions and S. America.

1. Agrimonia eupatoria L., Sp. Pl. 448 (1753); Boiss., Fl. 2 : 727 (1872). [Plate 21]

Perennial herb, 30–70 cm. Stems erect, usually simple, densely leafy below, sparingly so above, villose and more or less glandular. Leaves 10–18 cm., appressed-hirsute above, canescent beneath; stipules 1–2(–3) cm., leaf-like, obliquely ovate, coarsely 1–5-dentate; leaflets of two kinds : 3–6 pairs of larger leaflets (2–5 × 1–2.5 cm.), petiolulate, elliptical, coarsely serrate, and 2–3 pairs of smaller, ovate, entire or dentate leaflets between each pair of the larger leaflets; upper leaves smaller, with fewer leaflets. Racemes 10–20(–30) cm., spike-like, elongated, interrupted below, with erect flowers. Bracts 5–6 mm., 3-fid. Pedicels short, 0.5–3 mm. Calyx lobes 4–6 × 2–3 mm., ovate-triangular. Petals golden-yellow, obovate, net-veined. Fruit pendulous, obconical, deeply 10-grooved almost to base, villose, covered above with several rings of hooked prickles. Fl. June.

Hab. : Damp places. Upper Galilee.

Area : Euro-Siberian and Mediterranean, with extensions into adjacent Irano-Turanian territories.

Formerly used as folk remedy : astringent, vermifuge, etc.

5. Sanguisorba L.

Perennial or rarely annual unarmed herbs. Leaves alternate, imparipinnate; stipules sheathing, adnate to petiole. Inflorescences terminal, densely capitate or spicate. Flowers hermaphrodite or the upper flowers in each inflorescence pistillate, 2–3-bracteolate. Calyx tube persistent, top-shaped, constricted at throat; lobes 4(–5–6), caducous, petaloid. Petals 0. Stamens 4 or more, rarely 2; filaments exserted, thread-like or dilated above; anthers short. Ovary inferior, of 1(–2–3) free 1-ovuled carpels enclosed in calyx tube (hypanthium); style terminal, thread-like; stigmas feathery or capitate. Achenes 1(–2–3), enclosed in the dry, corky, angular or more or less winged, tuberculate hypanthium. Seeds pendulous.

About 30 species in north-temperate regions.

1. Sanguisorba minor Scop., Fl. Carn. ed. 2, 1 : 110 (1771) ssp. **verrucosa** (Link ex G. Don) Holmboe, Bergens Mus. Skr. ser. 2, 1, 2 : 100 (1914). *S. verrucosa* (Link ex G. Don) A. Braun et Bouché, Ind. Sem. Hort. Berol. App. 1 : 11 (1867). *Poterium verrucosum* Link ex G. Don, Gen. Syst. 2 : 595 (1832). *P. verrucosum* Ehrenb., Ind. Sem. Hort. Berol. (1829) *nom. nud.*; Ehrenb. ex Decne., Ann. Sci. Nat. Bot. ser. 2, 3 : 263 (1835); Boiss., Fl. 2 : 734 (1872). [Plate 22]

Unarmed perennial herb, 30–60 cm., with an underground rootstock and ascending or erect annual stems and branches. Stems angular, densely leafy below, leafless above, pubescent, later glabrous. Leaves linear, the lower leaves 10–30 cm., the upper leaves shorter; leaflets 3–12 pairs, orbicular, ovate or oblong, incised-serrate, sparsely hairy to glabrous above, densely hairy beneath. Bracteoles 2–3 mm., membranous, orbicular-obovate or ovate, ciliate, pubescent on upper face. Flowers sessile in terminal, dense, globular or ovoid heads. Calyx 4-fid, reddish-green; lobes 5 mm., spreading, broadly elliptical. Stamens numerous. Fruit 4–5 mm., indurated, obsoletely tetragonous, ovoid or spherical, densely covered with obtuse, elongated tubercles. Fl. April–May.

Hab.: Batha and fallow fields. Acco Plain, Sharon Plain, Philistean Plain, Upper and Lower Galilee, Mt. Carmel, Esdraelon Plain, Mt. Gilboa, Samaria, Shefela, Judean Mts., W. and N. Negev, Upper Jordan Valley, Ammon.

Area : Mediterranean.

6. SARCOPOTERIUM Sp.

Spiny half-shrubs. Leaves alternate, imparipinnate; stipules sheathing, adnate to petiole. Flowers unisexual or hermaphrodite (plants monoecious or polygamous), sessile in spicate inflorescences, pistillate flowers in upper part, hermaphrodite and staminate ones in lower, each flower with 2–3 ciliate bracteoles. Calyx persistent; tube in pistillate and hermaphrodite flowers top-shaped, constricted at throat; lobes 4, sepaloid, imbricated. Petals 0. Stamens numerous, inserted on the glandular ring of the calyx throat; filaments thread-like. Ovary inferior, of 2–3 carpels enclosed in calyx tube (hypanthium) and adnate to it; ovules solitary in each carpel, deflexed; styles with feathery, pinkish stigmas. Fruit berry-like, globular, coloured, smooth, consisting of 2–3 coriaceous achenes enclosed in the somewhat pulpy hypanthium.

One species, Mediterranean.

1. Sarcopoterium spinosum (L.) Sp., Ann. Sci. Nat. Bot. ser. 3, 5 : 43 (1846). *Poterium spinosum* L., Sp. Pl. 994 (1753); Boiss., Fl. 2 : 734 (1872). [Plate 23]

Spiny, intricately branched dwarf shrub, 30–60 cm., with branches densely tomentose when young, ending in divaricate, dichotomous, leafless thorns. Leaves 2–8 cm., linear; leaflets 4–7 pairs, small, oblong-ovate or obovate, entire or incised-dentate in upper part, sparingly hairy, or glabrous above, whitish and densely hirsute beneath. Inflorescences up to 6 cm., terminal, spicate, short-peduncled or sessile, oblong, usually interrupted at base. Bracteoles 2–4 mm., membranous, ovate-oblong, acuminate, ciliate, tomentose on upper surface. Calyx 4-fid; lobes about 4 mm., spreading, green, broadly elliptical. Stamens numerous. Carpels 2. Fruit 3–5 mm., globular, somewhat pulpy, reddish, smooth. $2n = 28$. Fl. March–April.

Hab.: Batha. Acco Plain, Sharon Plain, Philistean Plain, Upper and Lower Galilee, Mt. Carmel, Esdraelon Plain, Mt. Gilboa, Samaria, Shefela, Judean Mts., Judean Desert, N. Negev, Dan Valley, Hula Plain, Upper Jordan Valley, Gilead, Ammon, Moav, Edom.

Area : E. Mediterranean.

One of the most common dwarf shrubs of the area; the leading species of various batha communities. Believed to be the סִירִים of the Bible (Is. xxxiv : 13).

Widely used for fuel, broom manufacture and hedging.

7. ROSA L.

Shrubs, erect, scandent or trailing, usually prickly. Leaves alternate, imparipinnate, with stipules adnate to the petiole. Flowers large, hermaphrodite, terminal, solitary or in corymbose cymes. Calyx tube urceolate or ventricose, constricted at throat by a glandular ring; lobes (4–)5(–6), caducous or persistent, foliaceous, spreading or reflexed, entire or pinnatifid. Petals (4–)5(–6), spreading, white, red, pink or yellow. Stamens numerous, inserted at throat of calyx tube; filaments free, thread-like. Carpels numerous, free, sessile at base of hypanthium (calyx tube), often pubescent; ovules 1–2 in each carpel, pendulous; styles persistent, free or connate, elongated. Achenes numerous, included in persistent, fleshy, coloured hypanthium.

Over 100 species in north-temperate and tropical regions.

1. Inflorescences many-flowered. Styles partly united to a conspicuous column. Flowers white. Fruit about 1 cm. long, brick-red.   **2. R. phoenicia**
- Inflorescences few-flowered. Styles free. Flowers pink (rarely white). Fruit 1–2 cm. long, scarlet, turning blackish-crimson.   **1. R. canina**

1. Rosa canina L., Sp. Pl. 491 (1753); Boiss., Fl. 2 : 685 (1872). [Plate 24]

Shrub, 1–2(–3) m. Stems numerous, arcuate. Prickles subequal or unequal, stout, usually curved or falcate. Leaves 5–15 cm.; stipules of upper leaves broad and more or less glandular-ciliate; leaflets 2–3(–4) pairs, 1.5–4 × 1–2.5 cm., ovate, obovate or elliptical, obtuse or acute-acuminate, acutely serrate with the upper teeth connivent, glabrous or pubescent on both sides or pubescent only beneath, eglandular or with few caducous glands. Inflorescences corymbose. Bracts broad and more or less glandular-ciliate. Pedicels 0.5–2.5(–3.5) cm., with or without stipitate glands. Flowers fragrant. Calyx tube (hypanthium) mostly glabrous; lobes reflexed, entire or with 2–6 lateral appendages on each side, pubescent or glandular. Petals 2–2.5 cm., pinkish or rarely white, notched. Styles free, glabrous or more or less pilose. Hip (fruiting hypanthium) 1–2 cm., ovoid to urceolate, scarlet, turning blackish-crimson, smooth or glandular-hispid. Fl. May–August.

An extremely variable species.

1. Leaves pubescent or hirsute on the lower surface.   var. **dumetorum**
- Leaves glabrous on both sides   2
2. Pedicel and calyx tube glabrous.   var. **canina**
- Pedicel and calyx tube glandular-hispid.   var. **verticillacantha**

Var. **canina**. "*R. canina* L. var. *vulgaris* Koch" Boiss., l.c. Leaves glabrous on both sides. Petiole glabrous. Pedicels and calyx tube smooth, glabrous. Petals pink.

Hab.: Oak forests on basalt soils. Upper Galilee.

Var. **dumetorum** (Thuill.) Desv., Journ. Bot. Appl. 2 : 115 (1813). *R. dumetorum* Thuill., Fl. Env. Paris ed. 2, 250 (1798–1799). *R. canina* L. var. *collina* (Hall. f.) Godet, Fl. Jura 215 (1853); Boiss., l.c. non *R. collina* Jacq., Fl. Austr. 2 : 58 (1774). Leaves usually more or less pubescent or hirsute beneath; petiole pilose. Pedicels and calyx tube smooth, glabrous. Petals pink to whitish.

Hab.: Among rocks. Judean Mts.

Var. **verticillacantha** (Mérat) Baker, Journ. Linn. Soc. Lond. Bot. 11 : 232 (1869). *R. verticillacantha* Mérat, Nouv. Fl. Env. Paris 190 (1812). Leaves glabrous on both sides. Pedicels and calyx tube glandular-hispid.

Hab.: Mountain slopes. Upper Galilee (Mt. Meiron).
Area of species: Euro-Siberian, Mediterranean and W. Irano-Turanian.

Used as stock for grafting cultivated varieties; hip edible; fresh fruit used as diuretic, antipyretic and mild astringent.

2. Rosa phoenicia Boiss., Diagn. ser. 1, 10:4 (1849) et Fl. 2:688 (1872). [Plate 25]
Shrub 1–3 m., with long, almost glabrous, climbing branches. Prickles stout, scattered, hooked. Leaves 5–15 cm., lower leaves 5–7-foliolate, upper ones 3-foliolate; petiole pilose, prickly, with broad, glandular-ciliate stipules; leaflets 1.5–3.5 × 1–2.5 cm., ovate-elliptical, obtuse or acute-acuminate, coarsely serrate, dark green on upper, light green on lower surface, pubescent, sometimes both sides glabrescent. Inflorescences corymbose-paniculate, long-peduncled, many-flowered. Peduncles and pedicels usually glandular-pubescent. Bracts leaf-like, the upper bracts ovate, pubescent, with glandular margins. Calyx tube (hypanthium) mostly glabrous, narrowly ellipsoidal; lobes reflexed, acuminate-caudate, entire or with a few lateral lobules, glandular-puberulent or glabrescent inside. Petals white, 1.3–2 × 1.5 cm., notched. Styles glabrous, connate into a column. Hip (fruiting hypanthium) about 1 cm., fleshy, ovoid, brick-red. Fl. May–August.
Hab.: River banks and swamp edges. Acco Plain, Sharon Plain, Philistean Plain, Upper Galilee, Mt. Carmel, Samaria, Upper Jordan Valley, Gilead.
Area: E. Mediterranean, with slight eastward extensions.

Subfam. POMOIDEAE. Carpels 2–5, mostly united with one another, at least at base, and with the concave receptacle. Fruiting hypanthium fleshy, forming a pome. Trees and shrubs.

8. Pyrus L.

Mostly deciduous trees or shrubs, sometimes with thorny branches. Leaves alternate or fasciculate, petiolate, simple, dentate or serrate; stipules caducous. Bracts caducous, subulate. Flowers large, hermaphrodite, in umbel-like corymbs. Calyx 5-fid; tube (hypanthium) campanulate or urceolate; lobes short, more or less triangular. Petals 5, white, suborbicular and short-clawed. Stamens 20–30, with pinkish-violet anthers. Ovary inferior, 2–5-celled; carpels usually 5, almost completely united with each other and with the hypanthium; ovules 2 in each cell, rarely numerous; styles terminal, mostly free. Fruit a pome, mostly 5-celled, each cell 2- or by abortion 1-seeded; mesocarp fleshy, more or less studded with stony granules; endocarp with cartilaginous or coriaceous walls.
About 25 species in north-temperate regions of the Old World.

1. Pyrus syriaca Boiss., Diagn. ser. 1, 10:1 (1849) et Fl. 2:655 (1872). [Plate 26]
Tree 2–10 m., with short, often spinescent branches. Cortex grey. Buds 3–4 mm., broadly ovoid, ciliate. Leaves on very short branches, fasciculate; young leaves pubescent beneath, later glabrous; blade 3–7 × 1–2 cm., longer than the 2–3 (–4) cm. long

petiole, ovate-lanceolate to oblong-lanceolate, cuneate or rounded at base, obtuse or
acute, mucronate, dentate-crenate or serrulate with glandular teeth. Racemes corymbose, many-flowered. Pedicels 1–3 (–5) cm., woolly, later glabrescent. Flowers 2–
2.5 cm. across, white. Calyx tube (hypanthium) woolly; lobes 3–5 mm., as long as
or longer than tube, triangular, mucronulate, woolly on both sides. Petals suborbicular
to obovate, abruptly constricted into a narrow claw. Fruit 2–3 × 1–2.5 cm., globular
or obovoid, much shorter than the thickened, club-shaped pedicel. Fl. March–April.

Hab.: Maquis, forests and devastated woodland. Upper Galilee, Mt. Carmel,
Samaria, Judean Mts., Judean Desert, Gilead, Ammon, Edom. Not rare.

Area: E. Mediterranean and W. Irano-Turanian.

Often used as a stock for grafting cultivated varieties.

9. Eriolobus (DC.) M. Roem.

Deciduous trees or shrubs with erect to ascending, white, hairy to glabrescent branches.
Leaves simple or pinnate, mostly tomentose, at least when young; stipules caducous.
Buds puberulent. Flowers hermaphrodite, usually 6–8 in compound or simple corymbs.
Calyx 5-fid, tomentose; lobes more or less triangular, marcescent. Petals 5, usually
white, rarely pink, obovate or orbicular, with or without claw. Stamens 15–30. Ovary
inferior, of 5 carpels united at least to the middle, membranous-crustaceous in fruit,
enclosed in hypanthium; styles 5, free or united below. Fruit a 5-celled, mostly globular
or obovoid pome, variously coloured; mesocarp fleshy. Seeds 1 (–2) in each cell, oblong-triangular in outline.

Six species from S. E. Europe to E. Asia.

1. Eriolobus trilobatus (Labill. ex Poir.) M. Roem., Syn. Rosifl. 3 : 104, 216 (1847).
Crataegus trilobata Labill. ex Poir. in Lam., Encycl. Suppl. 1 : 291 (1810). *Pyrus
trilobata* (Labill.) DC., Prodr. 2 : 636 (1825). *Sorbus trilobata* (Labill.) Heynh., Nom.
1 : 773 (1841); Boiss., Fl. 2 : 657 (1872). [Plate 27]

Unarmed tree or shrub, up to 6 m. or more. Leaves deciduous, on short branches,
leathery, simple, palmately 3-lobed; petiole 3–7 cm., often a little longer than blade,
tomentose, later glabrescent or glabrous; lobes dentate-serrate, lateral lobes spreading,
2-fid or -incised, terminal lobes 2–3-fid or -incised, rarely undivided. Corymbs terminal,
simple. Bracts caducous, subulate, tomentose. Flowers 3–5 cm. across. Calyx lobes
about 1 cm., lanceolate, densely tomentose on both sides. Petals white, with tomentose
claw. Carpels 5; styles 5, close together and barbate below. Fruit 1–1.6 cm., globular,
or obovoid, dark purple, crowned with the spreading calyx lobes. Seeds cartilaginous.
Fl. May.

Hab.: Shady maquis. Upper Galilee (Mt. Meiron). Very rare.

Area: E. Mediterranean (Palestine to S. Turkey).

Fruit edible.

10. CRATAEGUS L.

Small, much-branched trees or shrubs, mostly deciduous, generally thorny. Leaves alternate, petiolate, simple, pinnatilobed or -partite; stipules caducous, lanceolate, often leaf-like; lobes with entire, dentate or lobulate margins. Bracts and bracteoles present, caducous. Flowers hermaphrodite, in small corymbs, rarely solitary. Calyx (hypanthium) campanulate or urceolate, with 5 short, more or less triangular lobes. Petals 5, white, rarely pink, usually orbicular, inserted on calyx throat. Stamens 5–25; filaments thread-like. Ovary inferior, 1–2-, rarely 3–5-carpelled, 1–5-celled, with 2 ovules in each carpel; carpels connate at least at base and wholly or partly adnate to hypanthium; styles free. Fruit a small, red, yellow or black pome, with umbilicate disk and minute, marcescent lobes on top, usually with juicy flesh and 1–3, rarely 5, bony, 1-seeded pyrenes.

About 100 species in northern regions of the Old World and several hundred species in N. America.

Literature: C. Diapulis, Beiträge zur Kenntnis der orientalischen Pomaceen II, *Repert. Sp. Nov.* 34 : 49–66, 68–69 (1933). A. J. Pojarkova, Contribution to the knowledge of the hawthorns of the Old World, *Bot. Zhurn.* 24 : 437–454 (1939).

1. Fruit yellow. Leaves greyish-green, more or less pubescent on both sides. Tree or shrub.
   2. C. aronia
 - Fruit red. Leaves green, sparingly hairy above and glabrous beneath or glabrous on
   both sides   2
2. Fruit globular, 1–1.5 cm. in diam.; pyrenes 2(–3).   **1. C. azarolus**
 - Fruit ellipsoidal, 0.8–1 × 4–6 cm.; pyrene 1.   **3. C. monogyna**

1. Crataegus azarolus L., Sp. Pl. 477 (1753) excl. [var.] β *aronia* sensu Pojarkova, Bot. Zhurn. 24 : 442 (1939); Boiss., Fl. 2 : 662 (1872) p.p. [Plate 28]

Tree with thorny, brownish, tomentose twigs, up to 10 m. Leaves 3–6 cm., deciduous, leathery, obovate, long-cuneate and tapering to petiole, 3–5-lobed, green, sparingly hairy above or glabrous on both sides; petiole up to 2 cm. or longer; lobes undivided or lobulate, with entire or coarsely dentate apex. Corymbs branched, 4–10-flowered, more or less sparingly tomentose. Pedicels 0.5–2 cm., slender. Flowers about 1.5 cm. in diam. Calyx tube about 4 mm., campanulate; lobes very short, deflexed, broadly triangular, ciliate. Petals 5–7 mm., white, broadly obovate to orbicular, short-clawed. Styles usually 2. Fruit about 1.3 cm. in diam., globular, usually somewhat tapering at base, red; pyrenes usually 2. Fl. April–May.

Hab.: In the more humid maquis. Upper Galilee (Mt. Meiron), Mt. Carmel, Judean Mts.

Area: E. Mediterranean.

Fruit edible, more palatable than that of *C. aronia,* sold in markets.

2. Crataegus aronia (L.) Bosc. ex DC., Prodr. 2 : 629 (1825). [Plate 29]

Tree or shrub with thorny branches, up to 5 m., rarely taller. Young branchlets tomentose, brownish. Leaves 2–5 cm., deciduous, somewhat leathery, obovate, cuneate,

3–5(–7)-lobed, usually greyish, pubescent on both sides; lobes undivided or incised-serrate, or with entire or dentate lobules. Corymbs 6–15-flowered, densely white-tomentose. Pedicels 0.2–1 cm. Flowers about 1.5 cm. in diam. Calyx tube 3–4 mm., campanulate, tomentose; lobes about 2 mm., deflexed, triangular, acute, mucronulate, tomentose on both sides. Petals white, more or less orbicular. Styles usually 3. Fruit (0.8–)1–1.2(–1.5) cm. in diam., globular, sometimes depressed-globular, yellow, to-mentose when young; pyrenes usually (2–)3. Fl. March–April.

C. aronia varies considerably in size and shape of the leaves, in the degree of their lobing, the density of their indumentum, etc. Accordingly this species has been divided by some into a few varieties. We found continuous grading between the forms in the local populations; nevertheless the following two varieties have been distinguished here :

Var. **aronia**. *C. aronia* (L.) Bosc. ex DC., l.c.; Pojarkova, Bot. Zhurn. 24 : 449 (1939). *C. azarolus* L. β *aronia* L., Sp. Pl. 477 (1753). *Mespilus aronia* (L.) Schlecht. in Willd., Enum. Pl. Hort. Berol. Suppl. 35 (1814). *C. azarolus* auct. et Boiss., Fl. 2 : 662 (1872) p.p. Leaves usually 3–4 cm., densely pubescent. Fruit 0.8–1 cm. in diam., not lobed.

Var. **pontica** (C. Koch) Zoh. et Danin (comb. et stat. nov.). *C. pontica* C. Koch, Crat. Mesp. 49 (1854). Leaves considerably larger and less hairy than in preceding variety. Fruit 1.2–1.5 cm. in diam., usually lobea.

While in Upper Galilee the above varieties are well delimited, elsewhere they are connected by intermediate forms, which probably result from intercrossing.

Hab. of species: Maquis and maquis-steppes. Sharon Plain, Philistean Plain, Upper and Lower Galilee, Mt. Carmel, Esdraelon Plain, Mt. Gilboa, Samaria, Shefe-la, Judean Mts., Judean Desert, Gilead, Ammon, Moav, Edom.

Area of species : E. Mediterranean and W. Irano-Turanian.

Fruit edible; sold in markets.

3. Crataegus monogyna Jacq., Fl. Austr. 3 : 50 (1775); "*C. monogyna* (Willd.)" Boiss., Fl. 2 : 664 (1872). [Plate 30]

Shrub or small tree, 3–6 m. Twigs brownish, glabrous or sparingly hairy when young, with spines 1–2 cm. Leaves 2.5–5 × 1.5–3(–4) cm., deciduous, long-petioled, ovate or obovate in outline, mostly cuneate at base, deeply divided into 3–5 acute, often dentate-incised lobes, glabrous above, glabrous to sparingly hairy below, es-pecially along nerves. Corymbs (3–)4–6 cm. across, branched, many-flowered, loose. Pedicels 0.5–1.5 cm., glabrous or very sparingly hairy. Flowers 1–1.3 cm. in diam. Calyx glabrous; tube 3–5 mm., infundibuliform; lobes 2 mm., persistent, deflexed, triangular, acute. Petals white, clawed; limb 5–6 mm., obovate to almost orbicular. Style 1, shorter than stamens; stigma capitate. Fruit 0.8–1 × 0.5–0.7 cm., obovoid to ellipsoidal, red, glabrous; pyrene 1, about 6 × 4 mm., ovoid. Fl. April.

Hab.: Oak maquis, in shady valleys; terra rossa, about 1000 m. Upper Galilee. Very rare.

Area : Mediterranean and Euro-Siberian, with extensions into W. Irano-Turanian territories.

Subfam. PRUNOIDEAE. Receptacle flat or concave. Carpel usually 1, rarely 2–5, free (not adnate to receptacle), each with terminal style and 2 pendulous ovules. Fruit a drupe. Trees or shrubs.

11. AMYGDALUS L.

Shrubs or trees, with spiny or unarmed branches. Leaves deciduous, conduplicate in bud, alternate or clustered, simple, generally dentate-serrate, often with marginal glands; stipules caducous. Flowers hermaphrodite, sessile or short-pedicelled, solitary or twin, rarely in clusters of 3–5. Calyx tube campanulate to urceolate or obconical; lobes 5, ovate to elliptical, obtuse, tomentose. Petals 5, white or pink. Stamens 10–30, free, inserted on margin of calyx tube. Ovary superior, of 1 carpel; style terminal; stigma peltate or truncate. Drupe mostly ovoid; mesocarp fleshy or leathery, dehiscing into 2 valves; endocarp stony or leathery, smooth, pitted or wrinkled. Seed 1 or rarely 2; endosperm 0.

About 30 species, mainly in temperate Asia.

1. Leaves densely canescent on both sides.   **3. A. orientalis**
– Leaves green, glabrous or glabrescent   2
2. Spartoid shrubs, 1–1.5 m., with green angular stems. Leaves linear-lanceolate. Flowers about 1–1.5 cm. in diam. Drupe up to 1.5 cm., with smooth stone.   **4. A. arabica**
– Plants not as above   3
3. Leaves oblong-lanceolate, 4–8 cm. long. Flowers up to 3 cm. in diam. Calyx tube exposed, not concealed by scales. Drupe usually 3 cm., acutish.   **1. A. communis**
– Leaves oblong-elliptical, most of them 2–3 cm. long. Flowers about 2 cm. in diam. Calyx tube entirely concealed by scales. Drupe 1–2(–3) cm., usually obtuse.
           2. A. korschinskii

1. Amygdalus communis L., Sp. Pl. 473 (1753); Boiss., Fl. 2 : 641 (1872). *Prunus amygdalus* (L.) Batsch, Beitr. Entw. Pragm. Gesch. Naturreiche 30 (1801). [Plate 31]

Tree, rarely shrub, 3–8 m., with unarmed branches. Leaves usually 4–8 × 0.5–2 cm.; petiole 1–2.5 cm.; blade oblong to oblong-lanceolate, tapering at base, glandular-serrate or crenate, glabrous. Flowers usually appearing before leaves. Calyx 1–1.5 cm.; tube campanulate-urceolate, somewhat constricted at throat, partly subtended by roundish, mucronate, woolly scales; lobes about as long as tube, ovate-oblong, obtuse, white-tomentose at margin. Petals 1–2 cm., white or pale pink with darker nerves, obovate to almost orbicular, often notched at apex, short-clawed. Drupe (1.5–)2–4 × (1–)1.5–2 cm., compressed, subovoid, acutish, greyish-green, felty, with leathery, tough mesocarp, dehiscing when ripe; stone very hard, about 2 × 1–1.5 cm., mucronate, keeled, yellowish, irregularly pitted. Seeds flattened, cinnamon-brown. Fl. February–March.

Hab.: Maquis. Upper and Lower Galilee, Mt. Carmel, Judean Mts.

Area: E. Mediterranean and W. Irano-Turanian.

This species, which is widely cultivated in Palestine, is also subspontaneous and occurs sometimes in maquis but its indigeneity in Palestine is still questionable.

The cultivated, sweet-seeded, variety is conspecific with the wild ones on which it is grafted. The latter have bitter seeds, containing the glucoside amygdalin which is used in medicine. It has been grown since ancient times for its highly nutritive seeds which contain up to 50% of oils and are widely used in various food manufactures.

Mentioned in the Bible under the names לוּז (e.g. Gen. xxx : 37) and שָׁקֵד (e.g. Gen. XLIII : 11).

2. Amygdalus korschinskii (Hand.-Mazzetti) Bornm., Beih. Bot. Centralbl. 31, 2 : 212 (1914). *Prunus korschinskyi* Hand.-Mazzetti, Ann. Naturh. Mus. Wien 27 : 71 (1913). *A. communis* L. var. *microphylla* Post, Fl. Syr. Pal. Sin. 302 (1883–1896). [Plate 32]

Tree or high shrub, up to 3–4 m. Stems much branching into an ovoid crown. Ultimate branches somewhat spinescent. Leaves 2–4 × 0.5–1.2 cm., crowded on very short branches (brachyblasts); petiole 1–1.5 cm., oblong-elliptical; blade obtuse, apiculate or mucronate, crenate-dentate with teeth ending with a yellow gland, glabrous to glabrescent. Flowers in clusters of 3–6 on short branches or solitary and scattered along longer branches, appearing before leaves. Calyx 1–1.2 cm.; tube tubular, not constricted at throat, entirely concealed by broadly ovate, mucronate, woolly scales; lobes one and a half times as long as tube, oblong, obtuse, with white-tomentose margin. Petals 1–1.2 cm., pinkish-white, obovate, irregularly notched, short-clawed. Drupe 1–2(–3) × 1–1.5 cm., compressed, ovoid to ellipsoidal, obtuse, greyish-green, felty, with leathery mesocarp, dehiscing when ripe; stone 1–2 × 0.8–1.5 cm., very hard, obtuse to acute, keeled, yellowish, irregularly pitted. Seeds flattened, cinnamon-brown. Fl. February–March.

Hab.: Impoverished maquis and maquis-steppes. Upper Galilee, Mt. Gilboa, Samaria, Judean Mts., Judean Desert, C. Negev, Upper Jordan Valley, Gilead, Moav.

Area: W. Irano-Turanian.

Very close to *A. communis* L., but readily distinguished from it by the considerably smaller and obtuse leaves, smaller flowers and usually smaller drupes which are mostly rounded or obtuse at apex. It seems to cross with *A. communis* in nature. Further studies on the relation between this species and *A. communis,* as well as on its variability, are desirable.

Ecologically this species is well delineated, never occurring in typical maquis but in more dry habitats, within the Mediterranean and Irano-Turanian territories of Palestine. It forms, together with *Pistacia atlantica,* a kind of steppe-forest in the Negev mountains and in E. Upper Galilee.

3. Amygdalus orientalis Mill., Gard. Dict. ed. 8, no. 4 (1768); Boiss., Fl. 2 : 642 (1872). [Plate 33]

Much-branched shrub, densely tomentose, later sometimes glabrescent, 1–2 m. Stems often branching from base into erect or ascending branches with spreading, spinescent twigs. Leaves 1–2.5 × 0.4–1 cm., obovate, ovate-oblong or elliptical, tapering to petiole, obtuse, entire or denticulate, densely canescent on both surfaces. Flowers 1.5 cm. across. Petals white. Drupe (1–)1.5–2.5 × 1–1.5 cm., somewhat compressed, ovoid or oblong, acuminate, appressed-canescent, later glabrescent; stone ovoid, obtuse or acute, keeled, obsoletely reticulate-wrinkled. Fl. March–April.

Hab.: Dry, rocky places. Upper Galilee. Very rare.

Area: Irano-Turanian, extending into adjacent Mediterranean territories.

4. Amygdalus arabica Oliv., Voy. Othoman ed. min., 3 : 460 et Atlas t. 47 (1807); Boiss., Fl. 2 : 640 (1872). *Prunus spartioides* Sp., Ann. Sci. Nat. Bot. ser. 2, 19 : 108 (1843); Boiss., l.c. 641. [Plate 34]

Spartoid shrub, 1–2 m., with green, glabrous, unarmed, angular branches. Leaves 1.5–5 × 0.3–0.8 cm., soon deciduous, oblong-linear, tapering to a very short petiole, acute, crenulate-serrate with minute yellowish gland at tip of each tooth. Flowers solitary, scattered along branches, usually appearing before leaves. Calyx tube 2.5–3 × 2–3 mm., campanulate, usually glabrous, concealed by broadly ovate, apiculate scales; lobes 2–3 × 2 mm., erect, later spreading or reflexed, ovate, acutish, hirsute throughout or at margin. Petals up to 8 × 6–7 mm., obovate to orbicular, entire or notched. Drupe up to 1–1.3 × 1 cm., slightly compressed, ovoid-ellipsoidal, acutish, yellowish-green, hairy or glabrous, with leathery mesocarp splitting when ripe; stone mottled, almost smooth. Seeds brown, smooth, minutely pubescent. Fl. January–February.

Hab.: Stony slopes and wadis. Ammon. Rare.

Area: W. Irano-Turanian.

12. CERASUS Mill.

Unarmed or spinescent trees or shrubs, with deciduous simple leaves conduplicate in bud. Flowers small, hermaphrodite, solitary, in pairs or in umbels of 3–4, coming out with or before leaves. Calyx caducous; tube obconical or cylindrical. Petals 5, inserted at throat of calyx and alternating with calyx lobes, pink or purple. Stamens 15–25. Ovary superior, of 1 carpel, with 2 pendulous ovules. Drupe indehiscent, fleshy, globular, coloured; mesocarp juicy; endocarp (stone) very hard, subglobular to ovoid, smooth or somewhat wrinkled. Seed 1.

About 140 species in temperate regions of the northern hemisphere; many of them cultivated for their edible fruit, some as ornamental trees or shrubs.

1. Cerasus microcarpa (C.A. Mey.) C. Koch, Hort. Dendrol. 145 no. 17 (1853); Boiss., Fl. 2 : 646 (1872). *Prunus microcarpa* C. A. Mey., Verz. Pfl. Cauc. 166 (1831). [Plate 35]

Low shrub, often prostrate or procumbent, with stiff, intricate, divaricate branches, up to 1 m. long. Leaves 0.5–1.2 (–2) cm., clustered, short-petioled, ovate-oblong to suborbicular, acute to obtuse, serrate, glandular at base, upper face glabrous or pilose, lower glabrous, pilose or white-tomentose; stipules about 3 mm., lanceolate, with small glandular teeth, hairy. Flowers axillary, solitary or in pairs, their pedicels about as long as calyx tube or longer. Calyx 3–5 mm., tubular, inflated, 5-fid; lobes oblong, obtuse, tomentose above, half to one third as long as the glabrous calyx tube. Petals about 2.5 mm., pink or red (purple), rounded. Stamens 20–24, exserted. Style longer than filaments. Drupe as large as a pea, ovoid to globular, purple; stone somewhat grooved. Fl. March–April.

Hab.: Rocky ground. High mountains of Edom. Rare.

Area: Mediterranean and W. Irano-Turanian.

Our plant probably belongs to var. *pubescens* Bornm., Oesterr. Bot. Zeitschr. 49 : 16 (1899), which is identical with *C. tortuosa* Boiss. et Hausskn. in Boiss., l.c. 647.

13. PRUNUS L.

Trees or shrubs. Leaves deciduous or persistent, alternate or clustered, simple, generally dentate; stipules caducous. Flowers hermaphrodite, corymbose to solitary. Calyx tube obconical, urceolate or cylindrical, with an adnate glandular disk inside; lobes 5, caducous, imbricated. Petals 5, white or pink. Stamens 15–20 or more, free, inserted with petals on throat of calyx. Ovary superior, of 1 carpel, 1-celled, with 2 pendulous ovules; style terminal; stigma peltate or truncate. Drupe indehiscent, globular, ellipsoidal or subcompressed; mesocarp fleshy-juicy, mostly glabrous, sometimes with bloom; endocarp (stone) very hard, ovoid-globular, wrinkled or smooth. Seed 1.

About 30 species, mostly in the northern hemisphere, some also in Trop. Asia and S. America.

1. Prunus ursina Ky., Verh. Zool.-Bot. Ges. Wien 14 : 435 (1864); Boiss., Fl. 2 : 652 (1872). [Plate 36]

Small tree, 3–6 m., with erect, tortuous, somewhat spinescent branches. Twigs velvety or glabrous. Buds long-conical, rather acute. Leaves 2–5 × 1.5–3 cm., deciduous, ovate-elliptical to oblong, rounded or acute at apex, glandular-crenate, greyish-green, upper surface usually glabrous, lower pubescent; petiole 1–2 cm. Pedicels about 5 mm. Flowers usually in pairs, mostly appearing before leaves. Calyx glabrous, 5-fid, conspicuously veined; tube 5–6 mm.; lobes 4–5 mm., broadly elliptical-oblong, obtuse. Corolla white to cream-coloured; petals 0.8–1 cm., obovate to orbicular. Stamens 30 or more. Drupe 2–3 cm. in diam., globular or nearly so, violet-red or yellow, almost glabrous; stone smooth. Fl. April–May.

Hab. : Maquis. Upper Galilee. Rather rare.

Area : E. Mediterranean (Palestine, Syria and Lebanon).

Varies considerably in size of drupe and pubescence of leaves and twigs. Fruit edible.

52. NEURADACEAE

Procumbent, annual, mostly desert herbs. Leaves alternate, pinnately divided or lobed; stipules mostly 0. Flowers hermaphrodite, actinomorphic, axillary, often solitary. Calyx with 5 lobes, alternating with bracteoles of epicalyx. Petals 5. Stamens 10, in 2 rows. Ovary inferior, 5–10-celled; carpels 5–10, connate at base and adnate to inner wall of calyx tube (hypanthium); ovules 1–2 in each cell; styles 10, persistent, indurated. Fruit an indehiscent, dry, few-seeded nut. Seeds without endosperm, germinating in the hypanthium; cotyledons flat.

Three genera and about 10 species in S. Africa and the Sahara.

1. NEURADA L.

Annual, prostrate, woolly herbs. Leaves petiolate, pinnatilobed, with minute stipules. Flowers minute, solitary or in pairs, scattered all along branches. Calyx persistent, cup-shaped, shallow, later expanded, nearly flat below, depressed-conical above, with constricted throat and short lobes alternating with subulate bracteoles turning into prickles. Petals small, slightly exceeding calyx, inserted together with the 10 short stamens on throat of calyx tube. Carpels 10, connate at base and adnate to calyx tube (hypanthium), tapering into slightly exserted subulate styles, later elongating and becoming spinescent; ovule 1 in each carpel. Fruit dry, flattened, orbicular, spinose-muricate, tomentose, persisting after germination of one or more of its seeds. Seeds curved.

Two species mainly in the Sahara and in Arabian and Indian deserts.

1. Neurada procumbens L., Sp. Pl. 441 (1753). [Plate 37]

Annual, woolly-canescent, 10–20 cm. or more. Stems prostrate, alternately branching. Leaves 1–2.5 cm., ovate-oblong, obtusely sinuate-pinnatifid, with 2 stipules at base; petiole about 1 cm. Flowers small, solitary in axils, short-pedicelled. Epicalyx consisting of 5 subulate bracteoles, turning into prickles. Calyx 5-fid; lobes ovate to lanceolate. Petals whitish-yellow or pink, obovate or oblanceolate. Fruit 1.2–2 cm. across, orbicular, echinate above, smooth below, becoming detached from the plants as a synaptospermic unit. $2n = 14$. Fl. February–April.

Var. **procumbens.** *N. procumbens* L., l.c.; Boiss., Fl. 2:735 (1872). Fruit slightly lobed at margin.

Hab.: Sandy soils. Sharon Plain, Philistean Plain, W., N. and C. Negev, Arava Valley.

Var. **stellata** M. et D. Zoh. in D. Zoh. et J. De Angelis, Palest. Journ. Bot. Jerusalem ser. 5 : 249 (1952). Margin of fruit deeply 5-lobed; lobes with 2 or 3 prickly teeth.

Hab.: Loess soils. W. and S. Negev, Arava Valley, Edom.

Area of species : Saharo-Arabian, with extensions into the Sudanian region.

53. MIMOSACEAE

Trees or shrubs, rarely herbaceous plants or climbers. Leaves alternate, stipulate, mostly compound, 2-pinnate, rarely 1-pinnate or reduced to phyllodes; stipules sometimes reduced to spines. Flowers hermaphrodite, mostly small, actinomorphic, usually in heads or spikes. Sepals 3–6, mostly 5, free or partly united. Petals 3–6, mostly 5, valvate, free or connate below, sometimes 0. Stamens as many or twice as many as petals or indefinite, with long, usually coloured filaments, free or united at base; anthers minute, dehiscing longitudinally; pollen grains often united into packets, rarely distinct. Ovary superior, of 1 carpel (rarely of several free carpels) and a simple style; ovules many to 1, anatropous or campylotropous, usually borne on long funicles, often arillate. Fruit a pod (legume), dehiscing along the dorsal and ventral sutures into 2 valves, rarely fruit indehiscent or disarticulating transversely into 1-seeded segments. Seeds with scanty or no endosperm.

About 40 genera and 2,000 species, mainly in tropical and subtropical regions of both hemispheres.

1. Trees. Stamens more than 10; pollen grains aggregated into pollinia.   **1. Acacia**
   – Shrubs (in ours). Stamens 10; pollen grains not aggregated.   **2. Prosopis**

Trib. ACACIEAE. Filaments free, rarely somewhat connate at base; anthers without apical gland; pollen grains aggregated into pollinia.

1. ACACIA Mill.

Armed or unarmed shrubs or trees with 2-pinnate leaves or with leaves reduced to flat phyllodes. Flowers hermaphrodite, minute, numerous in head-like or spike-like inflorescences. Calyx campanulate or cup-like, 4–5-toothed or -parted. Petals usually 4–5, united or free, usually yellow, sometimes 0. Stamens many, exserted; filaments thread-like, free or connate at base. Ovary mostly slightly stipitate, many- to 1-ovuled. Pod membranous, leathery or woody, flat or turgid, linear to ovate, straight, falcate or twisted, sometimes constricted between seeds, usually dehiscing into 2 valves, rarely indehiscent or disarticulating into transverse segments. Seeds compressed, usually borne on long funicles.

Some 700 to 800 species in tropical and subtropical regions; over half of them in Australia.

All species recorded here are native. The biblical name שִׁטִּים (e.g. Exod. xxv : 10) refers to one or several of the local species. The Arabic name *sunt* or *sant* for some local species of *Acacia* most probably agrees with the Hebrew *shitta*.

The 5 species recorded here are the northernmost outposts of African species in Asia. They are most important sources of fuel in the timberless deserts of the area.

Literature : J. P. M. Brenan, Notes on Mimosoideae III, IV, *Kew Bull.* 1957 : 75–96 (1957); 360–372 (1958). G. Schweinfurth, Aufzählung und Beschreibung der Acacien-Arten des Nilgebiets, *Linnaea* 35 : 309–384, pls. IV–XXIII (1867–1868).

1. Flowers in spikes   2
   – Flowers in globular heads   3
2. Pinnae with 7–20 pairs of leaflets; extrastipular prickles 0. Pod thick, leathery, 6–15 cm.
                                                                                          1. A. albida

   – Pinnae with 3–5 pairs of leaflets; extrastipular prickles many. Pod thin, membranous, 3–6 cm.   **5. A. laeta**
3(1). Pod slightly arcuate to falcate, not twisted, somewhat turgid, hairy.   **2. A. gerrardii**
   – Pod spirally twisted   4
4. Young branches, leaves and pods pubescent. Trees, branching from base, umbrella-shaped.   **4. A. tortilis**

– Young branches, leaves and pods glabrous. Trees with distinct trunk not branching from base and a round irregular crown.   **3. A. raddiana**

Sect. GUMMIFERAE (Benth.) Boiss., Fl. 2:635 (1872). Ser. *Gummiferae* Benth., Hook. Lond. Journ. Bot. 1:321, 389 (1842). Trees or shrubs. Stipules all or part spinescent, somewhat connate at base. Flowers in heads or spikes.

1. Acacia albida Del., Fl. Aeg. Ill. 79 no. 964 (1813) et Fl. Eg. 142, t. 52, f. 3 (1813); Boiss., Fl. 2:637 (1872). *Faidherbia albida* (Del.) A. Chev., Rev. Bot. Appl. 14:876 (1934). [Plate 38]

Large tree, branching irregularly and propagating profusely by suckers; bark whitish or pale grey. Branchlets puberulent or glabrous. Leaves about 6 cm., deciduous, glabrous or hairy, with a sessile gland between each of the (2–)4–6(–8) pairs of pinnae; stipular spines not exceeding 2 cm., often much shorter, spreading, straight; leaflets 7–20 pairs, 2.5–6 mm., oblong, oblique, obtuse or mucronulate. Spikes axillary, solitary or in pairs, as long as leaves or longer, on 2–10 cm. long peduncles. Flowers sessile, fragrant. Calyx cup-like, broadly toothed. Petals 4 times as long as calyx, free nearly from base, whitish. Pod 6–15 × (1–)2–3 cm., about 8-seeded, leathery, oblong, arcuate, sometimes becoming contorted at maturity, often wavy-margined, yellowish-brown to orange, transversely net-veined. 2n = 20. Fl. August–November.

Hab.: Alluvial and sandy soils, banks of wadis and basalt ground. Sharon Plain, Philistean Plain, Lower Galilee, Shefela, Upper Jordan Valley, Beit Shean Valley, Lower Jordan Valley, Dead Sea area.

Stands of considerable size occur in the environs of Ashkelon, Shimron (near Haifa), Nahal Tavor (near Gesher) and Taibe (N. W. Gilead).

Area: Sudanian, extending into the E. African region.

A. albida is a Tertiary relic species, which, although tropical in origin, occurs also outside the hotter zones of Israel. Its leaflets vary from almost glabrous to hirsute and from linear to ovate-oblong.

The timber is used for building in Eritrea; it yields a gum extracted in Africa for industry; the bark is sometimes used in tanning.

2. Acacia gerrardii Benth., Trans. Linn. Soc. Lond. 30:508 (1875); Brenan, Kew Bull. 1957:369 (1958). [Plate 39]

Shrub or tree up to 8(–12) m., branching irregularly along upper part of trunk to a very intricate crown. Older branches grey or reddish-grey, with longitudinally fissured bark; flowering shoots tomentose. Leaves 2.5–6 cm.; stipular spines 5–8 cm. or sometimes shorter and not exceeding 1 cm., usually almost horizontal, stout, straight, white; petiole about 1 cm., tomentose, with ovoid gland below the first pair of pinnae; rhachis and rhachilla tomentose; pinnae 2–7 pairs, 1–2.5 cm.; leaflets 8–20 pairs, 3–6 × 0.8–1 mm., linear to oblong, obtuse, pubescent. Peduncles 3–4 cm., tomentose, with a small involucel in their lowest quarter or third. Heads 0.8–1(–1.2) cm. across, 1–2 in each axil. Calyx campanulate; teeth triangular. Corolla twice or more as long as calyx, yellow. Pod 5–10(–12) × 0.7–0.9 cm., leathery, somewhat inflated, arcuate or falcate, rarely straight, mucronate, brown; valves appressed-puberulent, with longitudinal and anastomosing nerves. Seeds 6–7 × 4–4.5 mm., with long funicles. Fl. July–October.

Subsp. **negevensis** Zoh., Israel Journ. Bot. 13 : 39 (1964). Leaflets attached very eccentrically to petiolule (attachment being almost on the margin); midrib of leaflets obscure or invisible. Bracteoles, composing the involucel, longer and with a much narrower basal part than in the typical subspecies. Calyx about 2–2.5 mm., more than half as long as corolla, deeply lobed. Stipe of pod about 0.7–1 cm.

Hab.: Wadis, sandy and pebbly ground. N., C. and S. Negev, Arava Valley, Edom. Less heat-demanding than the two following species; ascends in the S. Negev up to 800 m. above sea level.

Area of species: Sudanian and E. African. Also known from Sinai, and probably from Iraq and Kuwait.

Fairly common in the Negev. Occurring in stands and often associated with *Anabasis articulata* and *Ochradenus baccatus*.

3. Acacia raddiana Savi, Alc. Acacie Egiz. 1 (1830); Boiss., Fl. 2 : 636 (1872) *pro syn.*
A. tortilis (Forssk.) Hayne ssp. *raddiana* (Savi) Brenan, Kew Bull. 1957 : 87 (1957).
[Plate 40]

Small tree, 4–6 m., with a distinct trunk and a round irregular crown; bark reddish-brown. Young branches glabrous. Leaves 3–4.5 cm., glabrous, with short glabrous petioles; stipular spines varying in length, 0.5–6 cm., longer spines spreading, straight, shorter sometimes slightly recurved; pinnae 2–6 pairs, with a small gland under each pair; leaflets 5–12 pairs, 2–7 mm., linear, obtuse, glabrous. Peduncles 1.4–2.6 cm., hairy, with a small involucel near or below middle. Heads 1–5 in each axil, 0.4–1.2 cm. Calyx teeth short. Corolla twice as long as calyx, pale yellow. Pod 6–13 × 0.6–0.9 cm., leathery, compressed, linear, torulose, spirally twisted in 1 or 2 coils, yellowish, glabrous, prominently longitudinally nerved. Seeds 5–6 × 3.5–4 mm. Fl. October–December (also March–April).

Hab.: Hot desert wadis, depressions and oases. W., N. and C. Negev, Lower Jordan Valley, Dead Sea area, Arava Valley, deserts of Edom.

Area: Sudanian, extending into the E. African region.

Fairly common in the N. Arava Valley. Demands less heat and moisture than the following species.

4. Acacia tortilis (Forssk.) Hayne, Darst. Beschr. Arzneik. Gewächse 10 : t. 31 (1827).
Mimosa tortilis Forssk., Fl. Aeg.-Arab. 176 (1775). *A. tortilis* (Forssk.) Hayne ssp. *tortilis* Brenan, Kew Bull. 1957 : 86 (1957). *A. spirocarpa* Hochst. ex A. Rich. var. *minor* Schweinf., Linnaea 35 : 323 (1867–1868); Boiss., Fl. 2 : 636 (1872) *pro syn.*
[Plate 41]

Small tree, 2–4 m., branching from base, umbrella-shaped with flat-topped crown. Young branches reddish, tomentose or pubescent. Leaves about 1–2 cm., with short, patulous-pubescent petioles; stipular spines varying in length, (0.5–)2.5(–5) cm., spreading, hairy, the longer spines straight, the shorter curved; pinnae (4–)5(–8) pairs, with a small gland under each pair; leaflets (4–)10(–12) pairs, 1–2(–3) mm., linear, obtuse, appressed- or patulous-pubescent. Peduncles 1–4 cm., hirsute or tomentose, with a minute involucel below or near middle. Heads 1 or more in each axil, 4–7 mm. across. Calyx campanulate, with triangular teeth. Corolla pale yellow. Pod 3–9 × 0.5–0.6 cm., leathery, compressed to somewhat inflated, linear, constricted between seeds, spirally twisted in 1–3 coils, pubescent, yellowish-brown. Seeds about 3–4 × 2–3 mm. Fl. Spring and autumn.

Hab. : Hot desert wadis. Dead Sea area, Arava Valley and adjoining wadis.

Area : Sudanian, extending into the E. African region.

Less common and more heat-demanding than preceding species.
Yields resin.

Sect. VULGARES (Benth.) Boiss., Fl. 2 : 637 (1872). Ser. *Vulgares* Benth., Hook. Lond. Journ. Bot. 1 : 322, 506 (1842). Trees or shrubs. Stipules not spinescent, subulate, herbaceous or membranous, often lacking altogether. Branches with or without prickles. Flowers (in ours) spicate.

5. Acacia laeta R. Br. ex Benth., Hook. Lond. Journ. Bot. 1 : 508 (18 *2); R. Br. in Salt, Voy. Abyss. App. 65 (1814) *nom. nud.*; Boiss., Fl. 2 : 638 (1872). [Plate 42]

Small tree, 3–5 m., glaucescent, glabrous. Branches with pairs of short, dark, somewhat recurved extrastipular prickles, rarely unarmed. Leaves up to 8 cm., glaucous; stipular spines mostly 0; petiole 1–2 cm., with a small gland above base; pinnae 2–5 pairs, each with 3–5 pairs of 0.8–1.5 cm., oblong, oblique, cuneate, obtuse to acute leaflets. Spikes axillary, solitary or in pairs, as long as subtending leaves or longer. Calyx half as long as corolla, shortly toothed. Petals united to two thirds their length, white. Stamens persistent. Pod 3–6 (–8) × 1–2.5 cm., stipitate, flat, oblong or elliptical, often (when long) with one or two constrictions betwen seeds, obtuse or acute; valves thin, membranous, glabrous, transversely net-veined. Seeds 2–3 or rarely 5, about 8 mm., flattened, almost orbicular. Fl. March–April.

Hab. : Oases in hot deserts. Arava Valley (Ghor es Safieh; after Hart, 1891).

Area : Sudanian.

All records on *A. seyal Del.* (Fl. Aeg. Ill. 79 no. 965, 1813 et Fl. Eg. 142, 1813) from Palestine are erroneous.

Trib. ADENANTHEREAE. Filaments free; anthers tipped with a caducous gland; pollen grains distinct.

2. PROSOPIS L.

Deciduous shrubs and trees, mostly armed with prickles or spines all along the branches. Leaves 2-pinnate with 1–5 pairs of pinnae and many small entire leaflets; stipules minute or 0. Racemes axillary, spike-like or capitate. Flowers small, sessile, bractless. Calyx campanulate, 5-toothed or -parted. Petals 5, united at base or free, greenish to yellow. Stamens 10, free and slightly exserted; anthers tipped with a caducous gland. Ovary often stipitate, many-ovuled; style filiform, with a terminal stigma. Pod in-

dehiscent, variously shaped, with thin to coriaceous exocarp and thick, spongy or
indurated mesocarp. Seeds numerous, compressed, ovoid, separated by cartilaginous
or membranous partitions.

About 30 species in warm-temperate and tropical regions of both hemispheres.

1. Prosopis farcta (Banks et Sol.) Macbride, Contr. Gray Herb. n.s. 59 : 17 (1919);
Eig, Journ. Bot. Lond. 85 : 189 (1937; orth. err. *"farcata"*). *Mimosa farcta* Banks et
Sol. in Russ., Nat. Hist. Aleppo ed. 2, 2 : 266 (1794). *Lagonychium farctum* (Banks
et Sol.) Bobr., in Fl. URSS 11 : 14 (1945). *P. stephaniana* (M.B.) Kunth ex Spreng.,
Syst. Veg. 2 : 326 (1825); Boiss., Fl. 2 : 633 (1872). *M. stephaniana* M.B., Tabl. Casp.
120 (1798) et Beschr. Casp. 205, App. no. 74 (1800). *Acacia stephaniana* (M.B.) Willd.,
Sp. Pl. 4 : 1088 (1806). *L. stephanianum* (M.B.) M.B., Fl. Taur.-Cauc. 3 : 288 (1819).
[Plate 43]

Shrub or dwarf shrub, 0.4–1 m., usually branching from base and propagating by
suckers. Roots and rhizomes very long, often reaching a depth of 15 m. or more.
Branches slender, prickly all along, the younger hairy. Leaves up to 5 cm., ovate,
2-pinnate with (4–)5–7 pairs of pinnae; stipules caducous, herbaceous, oblong-arcuate;
leaflets 10–15 pairs, 3–7 × 2–3 mm., subsessile, oblong, acute, short-hairy. Spikes up
to 7 cm., axillary, pedunculate, many-flowered, cylindrical. Flowers short-pedicelled.
Calyx 5-toothed, one fifth to one fourth as long as corolla. Corolla 4–5 mm., 5-parted,
pale yellow. Stamens somewhat exserted. Pods 1–2 on each raceme, (1–)2–5 × 1–3
cm., ovoid to ellipsoidal, with spongy mesocarp, dark brown when ripe. Seeds few,
dark brown. $2n = 28$. Fl. (April–) May–August.

Hab.: Alluvial soils, among crops; saline ground and river banks. Coastal Galilee,
Acco Plain, Sharon Plain, Philistean Plain, Upper and Lower Galilee, Esdraelon
Plain, Samaria, Shefela, Coastal and N. Negev, Dan Valley, Hula Plain, Upper
Jordan Valley, Beit Shean Valley, Lower Jordan Valley, Dead Sea area, Moav.

Area: W. Irano-Turanian, with extensions into the Mediterranean and Saharo-
Arabian territories.

One of the most noxious weeds in summer crops of the coastal and interior plains on
heavy soil. Also a component of the saline and riparian vegetation in the Dead Sea area
and on the banks of the Jordan River.

The separation of this species from the genus *Prosopis* is, despite the differences in fruit
shape, not justified.

Pods eaten by cattle; also known in medicine as an astringent and anti-dysenteric.

54. CAESALPINIACEAE

Trees, shrubs or rarely herbs, sometimes climbing. Leaves alternate, often stipulate,
usually 1–2-pinnate, rarely simple. Inflorescences axillary or terminal, sometimes arising from older twigs or stems, racemose, rarely cymose, spike- or umbel-like. Flowers
hermaphrodite, rarely unisexual, zygomorphic, rarely almost actinomorphic. Sepals 5,
imbricated in bud, the upper 2 sometimes connate, rarely all connate. Petals 5 or

fewer by abortion, rarely 0, the upper (posterior) one innermost, the others variously imbricated. Stamens 10 or fewer by abortion (rarely numerous), free or variously connate. Ovary superior, sessile or stipitate, 1-carpelled, 1-celled. Fruit a pod (legume), dehiscent or indehiscent, dry or fleshy, sometimes a loment. Seeds with or without endosperm; funicle sometimes forming an aril; embryo with straight or curved radicle and conduplicate cotyledons.

One hundred and fifty genera and 2,200 species, almost exclusively in tropical regions.

1. Petals 0. Trees with fleshy fruit.   **2. Ceratonia**
– Petals large. Trees or shrubs with leathery fruit   2
2. Corolla yellow. Herbs or small shrubs.   **3. Cassia**
– Corolla lilac to purple. Trees.   **1. Cercis**

Trib. BAUHINIEAE. Leaves mostly undivided. Stamens mostly 10, free.

1. CERCIS L.

Trees or tall shrubs. Leaves undivided, entire or emarginate, with small, caducous stipules. Inflorescences short, racemose, borne mostly on older twigs or stems, subtended by small bracts. Flowers hermaphrodite, zygomorphic, lilac to purple, with or without bracteoles. Calyx campanulate, with 5 short teeth. Petals 5, very unequal, spuriously papilionaceous, standard within the wings. Stamens 10, with curved filaments and dorsifixed anthers. Ovary superior, short-stipitate, 1-celled, many-ovuled; style filiform, with obtuse stigma. Fruit a dehiscent, 2-valved, many-seeded, oblong to linear legume. Seeds compressed, with endosperm.

Seven species in the Mediterranean region, E. Asia, Atlantic N. America to Mexico.

1. Cercis siliquastrum L., Sp. Pl. 374 (1753); Boiss., Fl. 2 : 633 (1872). [Plate 44]

Tree with oblong crown or shrub, 3–5(–10) m. Twigs reddish. Leaves 2–12 × 2.5–12 cm., deciduous, somewhat coriaceous, almost orbicular, cordate at base, obtuse and emarginate at apex, glabrous on both sides; petiole about 3 cm. or longer, somewhat thickened. Flowers 1.5–1.8 cm., long-pedicelled, showy, appearing before or together with the leaves in small racemes along the old branches. Calyx teeth triangular. Petals lilac, the upper and innermost shorter than the others. Pod 7–15 cm., flattened, linear, mucronate, narrowly winged along dorsal suture. Seeds 6–8 × 3–5 mm., dark brown, obovate to oblong, truncate at base. Fl. March (–April).

Hab.: Maquis. Upper and Lower Galilee, Mt. Carmel, Samaria, Judean Mts. Fairly common.

Area : E. and N. Mediterranean, with slight extensions into the W. Irano-Turanian region.

Also grown as an ornamental plant; flower buds eaten when pickled; timber used in carpentry.

Trib. CASSIEAE. Leaves mostly 1-pinnate. Anther-bearing stamens often 5–7.

2. CERATONIA L.

Dioecious (rarely polygamous) evergreen trees. Leaves paripinnate; stipules minute or 0. Inflorescences racemose, solitary or in groups on young or older branches, with small caducous bracts and bracteoles. Flowers inconspicuous, green. Calyx tube short, top-shaped, with 5 minute, tooth-like caducous segments. Petals 0. Disk flat or concave. Stamens 5, episepalous, with filiform filaments and ovoid versatile anthers. Ovary short-stipitate, many-ovuled; style short; stigma peltate. Pod indehiscent, thick, fleshy, linear-oblong, transversely divided by pulpy partitions containing large quantities of sugar. Seeds compressed, obovate, very hard, with endosperm.

One species in the Mediterranean region.

1. Ceratonia siliqua L., Sp. Pl. 1026 (1753); Boiss., Fl. 2 : 632 (1872). [Plate 45]

Evergreen tree, 4–8 m., with curved, somewhat flexuous branches and an almost spherical crown. Leaves short-petioled, coriaceous; leaflets 2–3 (–4) pairs, 3–7 × 3–4 cm., petiolulate, oblong-ovate to obovate, obtuse or emarginate, glabrous, dark green above and somewhat lighter beneath. Racemes axillary, solitary or clustered around an indurating axis, many-flowered. Pistillate flowers with thick deflexed ovary, short style and thick stigma, often also with minute but fertile stamens. Pod (8–)10–30 × 1.5–2.5 cm., about 5 mm. thick, many-seeded, linear, straight or curved, brown-violet, shiny; mesocarp pulpy, sweet. Fl. Mainly August–November, but also in other seasons.

Hab.: Maquis, especially in lower altitudes. Coastal Galilee, Acco Plain, Sharon Plain, Philistean Plain, Upper and Lower Galilee, Mt. Carmel, Mt. Gilboa, Samaria, Shefela, Judean Mts., Gilead. Solitary specimens were also found in wadis of C. Negev and in Edom.

Area : Mediterranean.

One of the most important maquis trees; the leading species of the *Ceratonia-Pistacia* community in the coastal belt and the foot-hills of W. Palestine. The talmudic name of this tree חָרוּב is still preserved in Arabic. Pod edible; ripe fruits are rich in sugars and protein, highly nutritive as forage; also known in medicine as fructus ceratoniae; a molasses named dibs is prepared from the ripe fruits; the seeds are reportedly used as a substitute for coffee.

3. CASSIA L.

Herbs, shrubs or trees, rarely climbers. Leaves paripinnate, sometimes reduced to a phyllode; petiole often with sessile or stalked glands. Inflorescences mostly racemose. Calyx tube short; segments 5, imbricated. Corolla of 5 nearly equal petals, or the anterior ones somewhat larger, imbricated, yellow, rarely white or reddish. Stamens 10, subequal, all with anthers, or the upper (posterior) ones shorter or without anthers, sometimes stamens 5; anthers basifixed, opening by slits or pores at apex, equal in size or those of anterior stamens larger. Ovary sessile or stipitate, many-ovuled; style with small truncate stigma. Pod dehiscing by 2 valves or indehiscent or separating into transverse segments with or without transverse septa. Seeds compressed, with endosperm.

About 500 species, mostly in tropical and subtropical regions, particularly of America.

1. Pod falcate, crested along middle. Leaflets obovate, rarely oblong, obtuse. **1. C. italica**
– Pod straight or slightly curved, smooth, not crested. Leaflets oblong to lanceolate, acute.
2. C. senna

1. Cassia italica (Mill.) Lam. ex F. W. Andrews, Fl. Pl. Angl.-Eg. Sudan 2 : 117, f. 49 (1952); Lam. ex Steud., Nom. 167 (1821) *pro syn. Senna italica* Mill., Gard. Dict. ed. 8, no. 2 (1768). *C. senna* [var.] *β* L., Sp. Pl. 377 (1753). *C. obovata* Collad., Hist. Casses 92, t. 15 A (1816); Boiss., Fl. 2 : 631 (1872). [Plate 46]

Perennial herb, woody at base, 50–70 cm. Stems branching from base, glaucous, appressed-hirtellous or glabrous. Leaves about 10 cm. or more, pinnate; stipules 3– 5 mm., obliquely lanceolate; leaflets (3–)5–6(–7) pairs, 1–3 × 0.7–2 cm., obliquely obovate, rarely oblong, obtuse, rarely short-mucronate. Racemes axillary, single, many-flowered, erect, usually longer than subtending leaves, rather loose. Bracts caducous, orbicular-ovate, apiculate. Pedicels short. Flowers 1.5–2 cm. Corolla yellow, striped with violet veins. Anthers unequal, the 2 anterior ones larger. Pod (3–)4–6 × 1.5–2 cm., stipitate, flat, falcate, broadly rounded at the extremities, transversely septate and tipped with the remains of the style; valves coriaceous, with an undulate crest on each side along midrib. Seeds compressed, obovate, retuse. Fl. September–April.

Hab. : Oases, wadis and moist places in hot deserts. Lower Jordan Valley, Dead Sea area, Arava Valley. Uncommon.

Area : Sudanian, with extensions into the E. African region.

Yields the officinal folia and fructus sennae used as a purgative and stimulant.

2. Cassia senna L., Sp. Pl. 377 (1753) excl. [var.] *β. C. acutifolia* Del., Mém. Eg. 3 : 316 (1808), Fl. Aeg. Ill. 61 no. 419 (1813) et Fl. Eg. 75, t. 27, f. 1 (1813). *C. lan-ceolata* Nect., Voy. Eg. Catar. 19, t. 2 (1808) et Collad., Hist. Casses 93, t. 15 C (1816) non Forssk., Fl. Aeg.-Arab. CXI, no. 270 et 85 (1775) nec Lam., Encycl. 1 : 646 (1785). *C. alexandrina* (Gars.) Thell., Bull. Herb. Boiss. ser. 2, 8 : 783 (1908). *Senna alexandrina* Gars., Fig. 1 : t. 42 B (1764) et Descr. 33 (1767) *nom. illegit. S. alexandrina* Mill., Gard. Dict. ed. 8, no. 1 (1768). [Plate 47]

Shrub, sparingly appressed-hirtellous, up to 1 m. Stems ascending, almost herbaceous. Leaves 8–10 cm., with 3–7 pairs of subsessile, lanceolate-oblong to lanceolate, acute leaflets; stipules persistent, subulate. Racemes axillary, many-flowered, erect, usually longer than subtending leaves. Bracts caducous, membranous, ovate or obovate. Pedicels 4–6 mm., elongating in fruit. Flowers about 1–1.5 cm. Corolla yellow. Pod 3–6 × 2–2.5 cm., obliquely stipitate, flat, oblong to elliptical, minutely mucronate, straight or slightly curved, narrowly winged on both sutures, glabrous or puberulent. Seeds compressed, obovate-cuneate. Fl. March–June.

Hab. : Wadis in hot deserts. Arava Valley (Aqaba; Hart 1891). Very rare.

Area : Sudanian.

Used in medicine similarly to the former species.

Cassia holosericea Fresen., Flora 22, 1 : 54 (1839), recorded by Dinsmore in Post, Fl. Syr. Pal. Sin. ed. 2, 1 : 440 (1932), has not been observed by others.

55. PAPILIONACEAE

Herbaceous or woody plants, rarely creeping or climbing, sometimes spiny. Leaves alternate, rarely opposite, usually pinnate, 3-foliolate or digitate, sometimes terminating in or reduced to a tendril, rarely leaves simple; stipules usually present. Flowers hermaphrodite, in axillary or terminal racemes, panicles, heads or spikes, rarely solitary, zygomorphic. Calyx 5-, rarely 4-merous, with sepals more or less united at base, often 2-lipped. Corolla 5-merous, papilionaceous, consisting of a posterior, outermost petal (the standard), 2 lateral, often horizontal, petals (the wings) and 2 anterior and innermost ones usually united by their margins (the keel). Stamens generally 10, either all united by their filaments (monadelphous) or 1 free and 9 fused (diadelphous), rarely all stamens free; anthers basifixed or dorsifixed. Ovary superior, of 1 carpel and simple style; ovules usually numerous, campylotropous, rarely anatropous. Fruit usually a 1-celled, many-seeded pod (legume), dehiscing by 2 valves along the ventral (upper or posterior) and dorsal (lower or anterior) sutures, rarely pod spuriously nearly 2-celled by inflection of dorsal suture, sometimes fruit a many-celled loment with transverse partitions or indehiscent, nut-like, 1- or few-seeded. Seeds usually fairly large, sometimes arillate; endosperm 0 or little; embryo often with incurved radicle adherent to cotyledons.

About 400 genera and 9,000 species in both temperate and tropical regions.

1. Leaves simple or 0; tendrils 0   2
 − All or part of leaves compound, digitate, palmate, 2–3-foliolate or pinnate, rarely leaves simple but then provided with a tendril   9
2. Shrubs. Calyx teeth shorter than tube   3
 − Annuals or shrubs. Calyx teeth usually as long as or longer than tube   6
3. Thorny plants   4
 − Unarmed plants   5
4. Flowers pink or purple. Calyx campanulate. Pod linear, torulose or jointed. Dwarf shrubs.   **31. Alhagi**
 − Flowers yellow. Calyx 2-lipped. Pod ovoid, neither torulose nor jointed. Tall shrubs.
                                                                                     8. Genista
5(3). Flowers white, with brown or purple calyx. Pod 1–2-seeded.   **10. Retama (Lygos)**
 − Flowers yellow. Pod many-seeded.   **7. Spartium**
6(2). Pod jointed, prickly, muricate or deeply furrowed. Annuals.   **25. Scorpiurus**
 − Pod not jointed, more or less smooth   7
7. Leaves dentate, at least in upper part.   **32. Ononis**
 − Leaves entire   8
8. Herbs. Pod 2–10 cm.   **41. Lathyrus**
 − Shrubs. Pod about 1 cm.   **3. Crotalaria**
9(1). Leaves (at least upper ones) with distinct tendrils, not 3-foliolate; sometimes tendrils reduced to a short or long mucro or to a bristle, rarely tendrils 0 but then seeds 1 cm. or more, leaves paripinnate and pods unarmed   10

– Leaves without tendrils, imparipinnate, rarely paripinnate but then seeds smaller than 1 cm.   14

10. All or part of leaves simple, with tendrils.   **41. Lathyrus**

— Leaves not as above   11

11. Leaves of 1 pair of leaflets; rarely leaves of more than 2 pairs but then pod with 2–4 prominent longitudinal nerves or leaflets digitate; stipules and leaflets always entire, the former not dark-spotted.   **41. Lathyrus**

— Leaves of 2 to many pairs of leaflets, rarely only of 1 pair but then stipules dentate or dark-spotted or both   12

12. Stipules usually longer than leaflets, 1 cm. broad or more, dentate or lobed, never dark-spotted; leaflets 1–3 pairs, dentate or lobed.   **42. Pisum**

— Stipules shorter than leaflets, entire, rarely dentate but then dark-spotted; leaflets mostly in several pairs, entire or only notched at apex, rarely dentate but then pod with ciliate-tuberculate margin   13

13. Pod linear to oblong, at least twice as long as broad. Seeds usually not lenticular. Style hairy all around or only on lower (anterior) side (that facing the keel).   **39. Vicia**

— Pod shorter than above – or if as long then style hairy on upper (posterior) surface and glabrous beneath. Seeds compressed, lenticular.   **40. Lens**

14(9). Leaves digitate, of 5–15, more or less equally shaped leaflets, arising from one point. Unarmed, hairy plants with rather large flowers   15

— Leaves pinnate or 3-foliolate, mostly with a pair of true or false stipules remote from the other leaflets   16

15. Annuals. Leaves large, long-petioled. Racemes many-flowered.   **5. Lupinus**

— Perennials, woody at base. Leaves small, sessile. Racemes few-flowered.   **20. Cytisopsis**

16(14). Pod reniform, compressed, 1–2 cm. across. Leaflets entire.   **19. Hymenocarpos**

— Pod and/or leaflets not as above   17

17. Prostrate annuals. Petiole broad; lateral leaflets 4 or more, entire, the terminal one twice as long as others or more. Fruiting calyx very inflated, 1–2 cm. Corolla persistent.
                                                                           18. Physanthyllis

— Plants not as above   18

18. Leaves 3-foliolate; stipules (if present) usually differing from leaflets in shape and size, rarely of the same shape but then distinctly remote from leaflets; very rarely 2 of the lateral leaflets aborted   19

— All or part of leaves pinnate, very rarely 3-foliolate but then pod a loment   37

19. Stipules (if present) differing markedly from leaflets in size and/or shape   20

— Stipules (lower pair of leaflets) equal or nearly equal to leaflets in shape and/or size but often remote from them   34

20. Each leaflet subtended by 2 minute stipelles. Climbing herbs   21

— Leaflets not as above. Plants not climbing   22

21. Pod 5–10 cm., partitioned between seeds.   **43. Vigna**

— Pod about 2 cm. or less, not partitioned between seeds.   **44. Rhynchosia**

22(20). Pod jointed, i.e. transversely septate, 3–7 × 0.1–0.4 cm. Leaflets entire, glabrous. Annuals.   **27. Coronilla**

— Not as above   23

23. Shrubs 1 m. tall or more. Leaflets entire. Flowers yellow, about 1 cm. or more   24

— Herbs, rarely dwarf shrubs, not as above   26

24. Evil-smelling shrubs, up to 1 m. or more. Flowers large, yellow, 1–3 cm. Standard of corolla much shorter than wings. Seeds about 1 cm., violet.   **1. Anagyris**

— Not as above   25

25. Branches spinescent. Pod 2–4 cm., many-seeded.   **6. Calycotome**
— Branches not spinescent. Pod up to 1.2 cm., 1–2-seeded.   **9. Gonocytisus**
26 (23). Ovary borne on a very long gynophore. Fruit ripening underground. Flowers 1–2,
     minute, yellow.   **34. Factorovskya**
— Not as above   27
27. Pod spirally coiled; turns (coils) many, few or 1; rarely pod falcate or slightly twisted.
                                                                       35. Medicago
                                                                                    28
— Pod not spirally coiled or twisted   28
28. Canescent desert annuals. Calyx 3-lobed, lateral lobes 2-fid, twice as long as the lower
     one. Flowers yellowish-white; keel much longer than standard. Leaflets entire.
                                                                       2. Lotononis
— Not as above   29
29. Flowers 1–2, in axils of leaves, rarely in spike-like, many-bracteate inflorescences. All
     stamens united into a tube (monadelphous)   30
— Flowers usually many, arranged in heads or spikes or clusters; individual flowers not
     subtended by green leaves or larger bracts, rarely flowers solitary. Anthers diadelphous
     (9 + 1)   31
30. Leaflets usually dentate, at least at apex. Plants usually glandular-viscid.   **32. Ononis**
— Leaflets entire. Silvery, appressed-silky dwarf shrubs.   **4. Argyrolobium**
31 (29). Pod minute (never exceeding 5 mm. in length), wholly hidden in calyx tube,
     very rarely slightly projecting from it. Flowers usually in heads or spikes.
                                                                       37. Trifolium
— Plants not as above   32
32. Perennials, woody at base. Flowers 1.5–3 cm. Pod 1–2 cm., indehiscent, with a large
     ensiform beak. Flowers never yellow.   **12. Psoralea**
— Plants not as above   33
33. Pod about 8 mm. or less, lenticular, globular or ovoid, net-veined or tuberculate
     or strongly wrinkled, indehiscent, 1–2-seeded. Flowers in spike-like racemes.
                                                                       36. Melilotus
— Pod much longer, many-seeded, mostly linear or cylindrical, ovate to oblong, some-
     times pod small, 1–2-seeded but then ending in a beak as long as the seed-bearing
     portion.   **33. Trigonella**
34 (19). Leaflets dentate. Plants viscid.   **32. Ononis**
— Leaflets entire   35
35. Pod over 2 cm. long, 4-winged or with marked thickenings on edges. Annuals.
                                                                       22. Tetragonolobus
— Pod without wings or thickened edges   36
36. Flowers in heads. Corolla white or flesh-coloured with purple keel. Pod 1 cm. or so.
     Shrubs or perennial herbs of maquis or moist habitats.   **23. Bonjeanea**
— Flowers never in dense heads. Corolla yellow, rarely whitish, pink or purple, but then
     pod much longer than 1 cm.   **21. Lotus**
37 (18). Pod linear, indehiscent, deeply sinuate-dentate along both sutures.   **16. Biserrula**
— Pod not sinuate-dentate   38
38. Pod a loment, i.e. with transverse, 1-seeded segments. Annuals, glabrous or hairy   39
— Pod not a loment (rarely strongly moniliform)   42
39. Segments horseshoe-shaped. Seeds falcate or semicircular.   **28. Hippocrepis**
— Segments not as above   40
40. Segments spiny or prickly.   **29. Hedysarum**
— Segments not spiny   41

41. Calyx 1–2 mm., with broad teeth. Leaflets 3–5 or more but then with broad, truncate or emarginate apex and cuneate base. **27. Coronilla**
— Calyx 4–5 mm., with narrow teeth. Leaflets more than 5, elliptical, not emarginate. **26. Ornithopus**
42 (38). Pod 0.4–2 cm., 1–2-seeded, indehiscent; pericarp with 1 or more spiny crests or with short or long prickles. Flowers never in dense heads. **30. Onobrychis**
— Pod without spiny crests or prickles, rarely with dense prickles but then swamp plants with dense, many-flowered, head-like inflorescences 43
43. Pod usually with a complete or incomplete longitudinal septum or with an inflection growing inwards from dorsal suture. Annuals or perennials, rarely shrubby, mostly hairy. **15. Astragalus**
— Pod not as above 44
44. Pod 6–9 × 0.3–0.6 cm., strongly compressed. Leaflets obtriangular, glabrous. Annual, yellow-flowered weeds. **24. Securigera**
— Not as above 45
45. Leaflets dentate. Pod 0.6–1 cm. Annuals. **38. Cicer**
— Leaflets entire. Pod longer than above. Shrubs or perennial herbs woody at base 46
46. Pod strongly inflated, parchment-like, 2–3 cm. broad. Flowers bright yellow. **14. Colutea**
— Pod not inflated, up to 1 cm. broad. Flowers pink, bluish, violet or purple 47
47. Leaves viscid or glandular-dotted. Pod glandular or viscid or covered with dense prickles. **17. Glycyrrhiza**
— Leaves and fruit not as above 48
48. Pod strongly torulose or transversely partitioned. **11. Indigofera**
— Pod neither torulose nor transversely partitioned. **13. Tephrosia**

Trib. PODALYRIEAE. Stamens free or almost so. Pod not jointed. Leaves mostly 3-foliolate or digitate, more rarely simple. Herbs or shrubs.

1. ANAGYRIS L.

Heavy-scented shrubs or small trees, green in winter. Leaves alternate, digitately 3-, rarely more-foliolate, rather large; stipules united into a sheath opposite leaf. Racemes axillary, few-flowered, subtended by a stipule-like bract. Flowers ebracteolate, large. Calyx persistent, campanulate, with 5 almost equal teeth. Corolla yellow; wings longer than standard and shorter than the 2-parted keel. Stamens free. Ovary short-stipitate, many-ovuled; style erect, filiform; stigma capitate. Pod stipitate, indehiscent, few- to many-seeded, compressed, broadly linear, often torulose, septate between seeds. Seeds large, compressed.

Two (-3) species in the Mediterranean region and S. W. Asia.

1. Anagyris foetida L., Sp. Pl. 374 (1753); Boiss., Fl. 2 : 24 (1872). [Plate 48]
Shrub, 1–2 m. Stems branching almost from base. Branches erect or ascending, the younger appressed-pubescent or tomentose. Leaves alternate, petiolate, 3-foliolate, with tomentose stipules united up to half their length or more; leaflets 3–8 cm., sessile, usually elliptical or lanceolate, mucronulate or sometimes notched, entire, glabrous

above, pubescent beneath, with prominent midrib. Racemes lateral, short-peduncled. Bracts caducous, lanceolate. Pedicels as long as or shorter than calyx, somewhat elongating in fruit. Flowers about 1.5–3 cm. Calyx sometimes blackish-green, appressed-pubescent; teeth triangular. Corolla yellow, with keel twice as long as calyx or more; standard about half as long as keel, obcordate, often with a blackish spot. Pod (3–)8–14 × 1.2–2 cm., pendulous, broadly linear, straight or arcuate, tapering at base and apex, acuminate, usually undulate at margin, glabrous, brownish. Seeds 2–6, compressed, reniform, violet. Fl. January–April.

Hab.: Primarily in open semisteppe vegetation, e.g. *Hyparrhenia* grassland and steppes; also in sites of devastated Mediterranean vegetation. Never occurring in maquis and garigue. Acco Plain, Sharon Plain, Philistean Plain, Upper and Lower Galilee, Esdraelon Plain, Mt. Gilboa, Judean Mts., N. Negev, Ammon.

Area: Mediterranean and W. Irano-Turanian.

Seeds used as a purgative and emetic.

Trib. GENISTEAE. Shrubs or half-shrubs, rarely herbs with simple or digitate leaves and entire leaflets. Stamens usually 10, mostly monadelphous, connate into a tube; anthers often dimorphic. Wings of corolla frequently folded-wrinkled above. Pod not jointed, 1- to many-seeded, dehiscent or not.

2. LOTONONIS (DC.) Eckl. et Zeyh.

Herbs or shrubs with small, mostly digitately 3-foliolate leaves; stipules 1 or 2, rarely 0. Racemes mostly terminal, opposite leaves, capitate or rarely 1- to few-flowered. Calyx turbinate; limb 3-lobed, lateral lobes 2-fid, much longer and broader than the lower one. Standard suborbicular or ovate to oblong, mostly hairy; keel incurved, obtuse, rarely acute. Stamens all connate into a tube, free above. Ovary sessile or short-stipitate, many-ovuled; style curved, more or less elongated. Pod dehiscent, many-seeded, compressed or cylindrical. Seeds with a long funicle.

About 120 species, most in S. Africa, some in N. Africa and in S. W. Asia.

1. Lotononis platycarpa (Viv.) Pichi-Sermolli, Webbia 7 : 331 (1950). *Lotus platicarpos* Viv., Pl. Aeg. 14 no. 14 (1831). *Lotononis dichotoma* (Del.) Boiss., Fl. 2 : 30 (1872). *Lotus dichotomus* Del., Fl. Aeg. Ill. 71 no. 717 (1813) *nom. nud.*; Del. ex Walp., Repert. Bot. Syst. 2 : 838 (1843). *Amphinomia platycarpa* (Viv.) Cufod., Bull. Jard. Bot. Brux. Suppl. 25 : 227 (1955). [Plate 49]

Annual, appressed-tomentose, 10–20 cm. Stems many, diffuse, prostrate or ascending, branching. Leaves 3-foliolate; leaflets 4–8 mm., obovate-cuneate, obtuse. Flowers 1–6, about 1 cm., subsessile, opposite leaves or between 2 leaves. Calyx 3-lobed; lateral segments 2-fid, twice as long as the lower one. Corolla yellowish-white; keel obtuse, longer than standard and wings, one and a half times as long as calyx. Pod 5–8 mm., 6–10-seeded, oblong, slightly oblique. Seeds reniform, wrinkled. Fl. February–March.

Hab.: Deserts. C. and S. Negev, Lower Jordan Valley, Arava Valley, deserts of Edom.

Area: Sudanian and Saharo-Arabian.

3. CROTALARIA L.

Herbs, dwarf shrubs or shrubs. Leaves alternate, simple or digitately 3–7-foliolate; stipules free or 0. Racemes terminal or opposite leaves, 1- to few-flowered. Calyx lobes 5, free, rarely calyx slightly 2-lipped. Corolla yellow, or more rarely blue or purple; standard orbicular or obovate, somewhat gibbous above claw; wings oblong, shorter than standard; keel mostly strongly bent, beaked. Stamens all connate into a tube split above. Ovary sessile, mostly 2- or many-ovuled; style strongly incurved or rectangularly bent, more or less barbulate above; stigma terminal. Pod dehiscent or not, 1- to many-seeded, turgid or inflated. Seeds with filiform funicle.

About 500 species, mainly in tropical regions.

1. Crotalaria aegyptiaca Benth., Hook. Lond. Journ. Bot. 2:473 (1843); Boiss., Fl. 2:25 (1872). [Plate 50]

Dwarf shrub, mostly appressed-canescent, rarely glabrous, 20–60 cm. or more, often intricately branching. Branches erect, green, stiff, angulate or furrowed, often becoming spinescent. Leaves sparse, 5–8 mm., early deciduous, exstipulate, short-petioled, simple, ovate, canescent. Racemes short-peduncled, usually 1-flowered. Bracteoles shorter than thick pedicels, linear-lanceolate. Flowers about 1 cm. Calyx slightly 2-lipped, appressed-canescent, with short-campanulate tube and 5 persistent, lanceolate teeth 2–3 times as long as tube. Corolla yellow with red-striped standard. Pod about 1 cm., 1–3-seeded, turgid, ovoid, glabrous, slightly wrinkled. Seeds reniform. Fl. February–March.

Hab.: Wadis in hot deserts. E., C. and S. Negev, Lower Jordan Valley, Dead Sea area, Arava Valley, deserts of Edom.

Area: Sudanian.

Browsed by camels.

4. ARGYROLOBIUM Eckl. et Zeyh.

Dwarf shrubs or perennial herbs with woody base. Leaves digitately 3-foliolate with entire leaflets; stipules free. Peduncles short. Inflorescences mostly opposite leaves or terminal, racemose or umbellate or 1-flowered. Bracts and bracteoles small. Flowers small. Calyx distinctly 2-lipped; upper lip 2-toothed or sometimes upper sepals free, lower lip shorter, 3-toothed. Standard longer than keel, suborbicular; wings free; keel slightly curved, not beaked. Stamens usually all united into a closed tube. Ovary sessile, many-ovuled, linear; style curved, with oblique stigma. Pod dehiscent, 2-valved, flattened, linear, more or less constricted between seeds, often silky- or tomentose-hairy.

About 80 species mainly in S. Africa, Trop. Africa, the Mediterranean region and S. W. Asia.

1. Racemes terminal. Pod linear-oblong, 5 (–7) mm. broad, 2–3-seeded.
2. A. crotalarioides
– Flowers solitary, opposite leaves. Pod linear, 2 (–3) mm. broad, mostly 6–10-seeded.
1. A. uniflorum

1. Argyrolobium uniflorum (Decne.) Jaub. et Sp., Ill. Pl. Or. 1 : 115 (1843); Boiss., Fl. 2 : 32 (1872). *Cytisus uniflorus* Decne., Ann. Sci. Nat. Bot. ser. 2, 3 : 265 (1835). [Plate 51]

Dwarf shrub, woody at base, silvery- and appressed-hairy, 10–20 cm. Branches rigid, spreading or erect to ascending. Leaves 1–2 cm.; petiole as long as or shorter than leaflets, much longer than the free, lanceolate stipules; leaflets oblong to oblong-linear, acute, hairy on both sides. Flowers 4–6 mm., opposite leaves, solitary, short-pedicelled. Calyx slightly shorter than the yellow corolla, 2-parted, hairy; lobes of upper lip one third to half as long as tube, those of lower lip much shorter. Pod up to 3 × 0.2–0.3 cm., 5–12-seeded, compressed, linear, distinctly torulose, beaked, silvery-hairy. Seeds about 2 mm., subglobular, yellowish-brown, smooth. Fl. March–April.

Hab.: Batha and steppes; sandy and loess soils. Philistean Plain, Shefela, Judean Desert, W., N. and C. Negev, Lower Jordan Valley, Dead Sea area, Arava Valley, Edom.

Area: Saharo-Arabian, with extensions into some adjacent Sudanian and Mediterranean areas.

2. Argyrolobium crotalarioides Jaub. et Sp., Ann. Sci. Nat. Bot. ser. 2, 19 : 42 (1843) et Ill. Pl. Or. 1 : 114, 116, t. 59 (1843); Boiss., Fl. 2 : 31 (1872). *A. syriacum* Boiss., Diagn. ser. 1, 2 : 13 (1843). *A. gracile* Fenzl, Flora 26 : 394 (1843). [Plate 52]

Dwarf shrub, silvery-silky, 8–20 cm. Stems numerous, erect, somewhat flexuous, rigid, leafy below. Leaves 0.8–1.5 cm., petiolate; stipules minute, lanceolate-subulate; leaflets sessile, folded, oblong-lanceolate, appressed-silky. Racemes terminal, loosely spicate. Bracts longer than bracteoles, mostly longer than pedicels, linear-subulate. Flowers 0.8–1 cm., remote. Calyx 2-parted almost to base into 2 lips; the upper lip 2-fid, the lower lip shortly split into subulate lobes. Corolla somewhat longer than calyx, yellow; standard almost as long as keel and wings, broadly obovate, notched. Pod 1.5–2 × 0.5–0.7 cm., (1–)2–3-seeded, flattened, linear-oblong, silvery-silky. Seeds 2 mm. in diam., lenticular, smooth. Fl. April–June.

Hab.: Hills. Dead Sea area (after Oppenheimer, Bull. Soc. Bot. Genève ser. 2, 22 : 317, 1931), Edom (after Nabelek, Publ. Fac. Sci. Univ. Masaryk 35 : 65, 1923).

Area: W. Irano-Turanian.

5. LUPINUS L.

Annual or perennial herbs or half-shrubs. Leaves alternate, petiolate, usually digitately (3–)5–12-foliolate; stipules adnate to base of petiole; leaflets entire, usually oblong to linear, glabrous or hairy. Racemes mostly terminal, many-flowered, rarely axillary and 1- to few-flowered. Bracts mostly caducous. Flowers mostly conspicuous, bracteolate. Calyx cleft into an upper 2-toothed or 2-parted (or rarely entire) lip and a lower entire or 3-toothed one; the 2 bracteoles appearing on the calyx as small lateral calyx lobes. Corolla variously coloured; standard orbicular or ovate; wings obovate or oblong, often connate at tip and enclosing the incurved, beaked keel. Stamens all connate, forming a closed tube; anthers dimorphic. Ovary sessile or subsessile, 2- to many-ovuled; style glabrous, mostly with bearded, terminal stigma. Pod dehiscent, 2-valved, 2- to many-seeded, more or less compressed, torulose or transversely partitioned, mostly silky-hairy; valves thick, leathery. Seeds large, compressed, rounded or angular, variously coloured or mottled, with short funicle; embryo thick with long radicle.

About 500 species, mainly in N. America; some in S. America and in the Mediterranean region.

1. Flowers yellow, fragrant. Seeds smooth.   **6. L. luteus**
   – Flowers lilac, purplish or blue or 2-coloured   2
2. Leaflets not exceeding 5 mm. in width. Seeds smooth, grey-brown, mottled with white.
                                                                               5. L. angustifolius
   – Leaflets broader   3
3. Leaflets hairy beneath, glabrous above. Flowers usually white to bluish-lilac. Upper lip of calyx entire or 2-dentate.   **3. L. albus**
   – Leaflets hairy on both sides   4
4. Seeds smooth. Racemes overtopped by leaves, obscurely whorled. Flowers 1–1.4 cm.
                                                                               4. L. micranthus
   – Seeds tuberculate. Racemes long, exceeding leaves, distinctly whorled. Flowers 1.5–2.3 cm.   5
5. Flowers usually dark blue. Pedicels about half as long as calyx.   **1. L. varius**
   – Flowers lilac to pale blue, often with cream-coloured wings. Pedicels more or less equalling calyx in length.   **2. L. palaestinus**

1. Lupinus varius L., Sp. Pl. 721 (1753) ssp. **orientalis** Franco et P. Silva (ssp. nov. inedit.). *L. pilosus* Murr., Syst. Veg. ed. 13 : 545 (1774); Boiss., Fl. 2 : 27 (1872; "*L. pilosus* L."). [Plate 53]

Annual, villose with white-rusty and spreading hairs, 40–80 cm. Stems erect, simple or slightly branching, hirsute. Leaves 5–17 cm., with petiole longer than blade; stipules frequently longer than 1.5 cm., adnate at base to petiole, linear-filiform, soft- and white-villose; leaflets 8–11, oblong, cuneate at base, obtuse, apiculate, appressed-pilose. Racemes 5–10 cm., densely or interruptedly whorled, much exceeding foliage. Bracts mostly caducous or partly persistent, lanceolate-subulate. Pedicels almost half as long as calyx. Flowers very showy, 1.5–2.3 cm. Calyx persistent, green to bluish; lower lip entire to 3-denticulate, somewhat longer than the deeply 2-partite upper lip and much longer than bracteoles, half as long as corolla. Corolla deep blue (very rarely whitish); petals more or less equal in length; standard large; wings connate at apex; keel boat-shaped, white-blue. Pod 4–8.5 × 1.5–2.5 cm., 2–5-seeded, rather erect, compressed, oblong, torulose, beaked, hirsute. Seeds mostly over 1 cm. broad, flattened, suborbicular, white or pale brown to brown, mottled with red, scabrous-tuberculate. Fl. February–May.

Hab.: Batha and fallow fields. Coastal, Upper and Lower Galilee, Mt. Carmel, Esdraelon Plain, Samaria, Judean Mts., Dan Valley, Hula Plain, Upper Jordan Valley, Gilead, Ammon.

Area: E. Mediterranean (Greece to Egypt).

Var. *variegatus* Plitm., Israel Journ. Bot. 15 : 25 (1966) has not been separated here from the typical form; it deserves a further experimental study.

One of the most showy legumes; also grown as an ornamental.

2. Lupinus palaestinus Boiss., Diagn. ser. 1, 9 : 9 (1849) et Fl. 2 : 27 (1872). [Plate 54]

Annual, with white-rusty spreading hairs, 15–30 cm. Stems erect to ascending, branched from base. Leaves 5–17 cm.; stipules 1–1.5 cm., narrow, adnate at base to petiole, lanceolate-linear; petiole much longer than blade, hairy; leaflets 6–10(–11), varying in size, oblong, lanceolate to obovate, tapering-cuneate at base, obtuse and apiculate at apex, silky- and appressed-hairy on both sides. Racemes terminal, with remote whorls, erect, exceeding leaves. Bracts small, caducous, lanceolate-subulate, hairy. Pedicels more or less equalling calyx in length. Flowers 1.3–2.3 cm., erect-spreading. Calyx persistent, rather gibbous, hirsute-villose; upper lip 2-partite, about two thirds as long as the almost entire to obsoletely 3-denticulate lower lip; the latter much longer than bracteoles. Corolla twice as long as calyx, lilac or pale blue; wings more or less equalling standard in length, connate at apex, cream-coloured; keel bent at a right obtuse angle, violet at apex. Pod 4–7 × 1–2 cm., 2–4-seeded, erect-spreading, rather compressed, oblong-linear, torulose, hirsute-villose, with short beak. Seeds 0.8–1.2 cm., compressed, subglobular, pale or dark brown, tuberculate. Fl. February–April.

Hab.: Sandy and loamy soils. Coastal Galilee, Sharon Plain, Philistean Plain, Shefela, N. Negev (endemic).

Area: E. Mediterranean.

Rather variable in dimensions.

Var. *caeruleus* Bornm., Verh. Zool.-Bot. Ges. Wien 48 : 573 (1898), recorded from Palestine by Dinsmore in Post, Fl. Syr. Pal. Sin. ed. 2, 1 : 298 (1932), should be included within the variability range of the species.

3. Lupinus albus L., Sp. Pl. 721 (1753) ssp. **albus**. *L. termis* Forssk., Fl. Aeg.-Arab. 131 (1775); Boiss., Fl. 2 : 29 (1872). [Plate 55]

Annual, more or less appressed- and silky-villose, 10–60 cm. Stems erect, branching slightly at base. Leaves 5–20 cm.; stipules usually exceeding 2 cm., adnate at base to petiole, subulate-aristate, more or less hairy; petiole much longer than blade; leaflets 6–9, subsessile, oblong-lanceolate to obovate, cuneate at base, obtuse and apiculate at apex, glabrous above, appressed-pubescent beneath. Racemes many-flowered, erect, oblong, exceeding foliage. Bracts caducous, oblong-lanceolate, hairy. Pedicels shorter than calyx. Flowers about 1.5 cm., generally alternate to remotely whorled. Calyx persistent, somewhat gibbous, green to bluish, hairy; lower lip entire or 3-denticulate, longer than the entire or 2-dentate upper lip, much longer than bracteoles. Corolla about twice as long as calyx; standard white-lilac, bluish around margin, equalling the white wings in length; keel a little shorter than wings, blue at top. Pod usually 4–6 × 0.8–1.3 cm., 2–4-seeded, flattened, linear with a short beak, pilose. Seeds compressed, lenticular, white to pale brown, smooth. Fl. February–April.

Hab.: Cultivated and probably spontaneous on sandy soils. Acco Plain, Sharon Plain, Philistean Plain, W. Negev.

Area: E. Mediterranean.
Cultivated as green manure.

4. Lupinus micranthus Guss., Fl. Sic. Prodr. 2 : 400 (1828). *L. hirsutus* L., Sp. Pl. ed. 2, 1015 (1763) et auct. non L., Sp. Pl. 721 (1753). *L. hirsutus* L. var. *micranthus* (Guss.) Boiss., Fl. 2 : 28 (1872). [Plate 56]

Annual, hirsute with spreading, white-rusty hairs, 10–30 cm. Stems ascending to erect, branching from base. Leaves 5–15 cm.; stipules exceeding 1 cm., adnate to petiole for about half their length, narrowly linear-subulate; petiole much longer than blade; leaflets 5–8, subsessile, oblong-obovate or oblanceolate to spatulate, tapering at base, obtuse and apiculate at apex, hirsute on both sides. Racemes terminal, rather short, obscurely whorled, frequently overtopped by leaves. Bracts persistent, subulate. Flowers 1–1.4 cm., very short-pedicelled. Calyx persistent, hirsute; lower lip 3-fid into narrow lobes, longer than the 2-partite upper lip. Corolla slightly longer than to one and a half times as long as calyx; petals more or less equal, blue or 2-coloured. Fruiting racemes rather thick, overtopped by leaves. Pod 2.5–4.5 × 0.7–1 cm., (2–)3–5-seeded, erect-spreading, compressed, oblong-linear, torulose; beak short, filiform. Seeds somewhat compressed, ovoid, yellowish and mottled with grey-brown or red, smooth. Fl. March–April.

Hab.: Sandy and heavy soils, batha and also among crops. Coastal Galilee, Sharon Plain, Philistean Plain, Upper Galilee, Judean Mts.

Area: Mediterranean.

The above description has been extended here to include also local populations in which the standard of the corolla is blue, the wings white to pink and the seeds mottled with grey-brown.

5. Lupinus angustifolius L., Sp. Pl. 721 (1753). [Plate 57]

Annual, appressed-pilose, 10–60 cm. Stems erect, simple or branching, pale green. Leaves 3.5–12 cm.; stipules about 1 × 0.2–0.5 cm., adnate at base to petiole, narrowly linear; petiole longer than blade; leaflets 5–9, varying from 1 to 5 mm. in width, subsessile, linear to linear-oblong, cuneate, tapering at base, obtuse at apex, subglabrous above, appressed-pilose beneath. Racemes terminal, few- to many-flowered. Bracts caducous, ovate to lanceolate. Pedicels shorter than calyx, hairy. Flowers 1–1.5 cm., rather dense, alternate, erect-spreading. Calyx 6–8 mm., persistent, pilose; lower lip entire or 2–3-denticulate, much longer than the deeply 2-partite upper one. Corolla 2–3 times as long as calyx, blue or blue-white, rarely purplish-violet; petals more or less equal in length; wings connate at apex. Fruiting racemes elongated, rather dense. Pod 3–6 × 0.7–1.2 cm., 4–6-seeded, erect-spreading, somewhat compressed, oblong-linear, torulose, appressed-villose, with filiform style. Seeds 4–7 mm. across, somewhat compressed, oblong-ovoid, grey-brown and mottled with white, smooth. Fl. March–April.

Var. **angustifolius.** *L. angustifolius* L., l.c.; Boiss., Fl. 2 : 28 (1872). *L. reticulatus* Desv. var. *philistaeus* (Boiss.) Boiss., Fl. 2 : 29 (1872); Post, Fl. Syr. Pal. Sin. 212 (1883–1896). *L. linifolius* Roth var. *philisteus* (Boiss.) Dinsmore in Post, Fl. Syr. Pal. Sin.

ed. 2, 1 : 298 (1932). Leaflets narrow, 1–4 mm. broad; stipules 2–3 mm. broad. Corolla about 1 cm., blue or blue and white. Upper lip of calyx 3 mm., lower lip 6 mm. Pod 0.7–1.1 cm. broad.

Hab.: Fallow fields and batha; sandy soils. Coastal Galilee, Acco Plain, Sharon Plain, Philistean Plain.

Var. **basalticus** Zoh. et Plitm. in Plitm., Israel Journ. Bot. 15 : 26 (1966). Leaflets 2–5 mm. broad; stipules 4–5 mm. broad. Corolla about 1.3 cm. long, bluish or sometimes purplish-violet. Upper lip of calyx 4 mm., lower lip 7 mm. Pod about 1 cm. broad.

Hab.: Fallow fields and batha; heavy basalt soils. Upper and Lower Galilee, Dan Valley, Hula Plain, Upper Jordan Valley.

Area of species : Mediterranean.

6. Lupinus luteus L., Sp. Pl. 722 (1753); Boiss., Fl. Suppl. 158 (1888). [Plate 58]

Annual, with white-rusty, more or less appressed hairs, 10–45 cm. Stems ascending to erect, simple or branching from lower part. Leaves 4–15 cm.; stipules 1–2 cm., adnate at base to petiole, linear; petiole much longer than blade; leaflets 6–11, subsessile, variable in size, oblanceolate to narrowly obovate, tapering-cuneate at base, obtuse to acute and apiculate at apex, silky- and appressed-hairy, mainly on lower surface. Racemes terminal, whorled, exceeding foliage. Bracts small, mostly caducous, lanceolate-subulate. Pedicels shorter than calyx, hairy. Flowers 1.3–1.7 cm., erect-spreading, fragrant. Calyx persistent, pubescent; lower lip 3-denticulate, much longer than the bracteoles and the 2-partite upper lip. Corolla twice as long as calyx, yellow; petals more or less equal in length; wings connate at apex; keel somewhat purple at apex. Pod 3.5–6 × 1–1.4 cm., 2–4-seeded, erect-spreading, flat, oblong-linear, torulose, densely appressed-silky; beak short. Seeds about 7 mm., compressed–subglobular, pinkish and mottled with white-brown, smooth. Fl. March–May.

Hab.: Batha and grassy places; sandy soils (not cultivated). Coastal Galilee, Acco Plain, Sharon Plain, Philistean Plain, Arava Valley.

Area : Mediterranean.

6. CALYCOTOME Link

Spiny shrubs. Stems divaricately branching. Leaves deciduous, alternate, borne on short spinescent twigs, digitately 3-foliolate; stipules minute or 0. Bracts entire or 3-fid. Flowers conspicuous, solitary or in small clusters among leaves. Calyx spreading, transversely cut at anthesis into a caducous conical hood and a truncate tube. Petals free, yellow; standard obovate to ovate, longer than keel; wings oblong-obovate. Stamens all connate into a closed tube. Ovary sessile or subsessile, many-ovuled; style incurved; stigma capitate or oblique. Pod dehiscing by 2 valves, somewhat 4-angled, not flattened, slightly septate inside; dorsal suture narrower than the widely broadened, thickened or 2-winged ventral suture. Seeds without caruncle.

Three species in the Mediterranean region.

Literature : W. Rothmaler, Revision der Genisteen II. Die Gattungen *Erinacea, Spartium* und *Calycotome, Bot. Jahrb.* 74 : 276–287 (1949).

1. Calycotome villosa (Poir.) Link in Schrad., Neues Journ. Bot. 2, 2 : 51 (1808); Boiss., Fl. 2 : 36 (1872). *Spartium villosum* Poir., Voy. Barb. 2 : 207 (1789). [Plate 59]

Shrub, divaricately branched, with short, spinescent twigs, hairy or glabrous, 0.5–1.5 m. Stems and branches evergreen, grooved. Leaves deciduous, on spinescent twigs, long-petioled, 3-foliolate; leaflets 0.4–1 × 0.2–0.5 cm., petiolulate, obovate to oblong, glabrous above, somewhat silky-hairy beneath. Peduncles very short, later elongating. Racemes 1- to few-flowered. Bracts much shorter than calyx, broadly ovate. Flowers 1–1.5 cm., sweet-scented. Calyx prior to anthesis 5–7 mm., densely appressed-villose. Corolla yellow; standard with obovate notched limb. Pod 2–4 × 0.5–0.7 cm., dehiscent, somewhat 4-angled, short-beaked, woolly-hirsute. Seeds 2–3 mm. across, almost globular, yellow. Fl. January–March.

Hab.: Maquis, batha and garigue. Coastal Galilee, Acco Plain, Sharon Plain, Philistean Plain, Upper and Lower Galilee, Mt. Carmel, Mt. Gilboa, Samaria, Shefela, Judean Mts., W. Judean Desert, Upper Jordan Valley, Gilead,' Ammon. Very common.

Area : Mediterranean.

One of the most common shrubs in Mediterranean Palestine; covers vast extents in areas of devastated forest and maquis; plays an important part in the successional stages leading to arboreal climax communities; also occurs in the eastern and southern semisteppe zones as a dominant species in certain climax communities.

7. Spartium L.

Erect, broom-like shrubs or small trees. Stems simple, terete, usually green. Leaves short-lived, exstipulate, alternate or almost opposite, simple, usually on sterile branches. Racemes terminal, 1- to few-flowered, with caducous bracts and bracteoles. Flowers large, copious. Calyx membranous, almost sheath-like, split above, with 5 minute teeth forming a 2-toothed upper and a slightly 3-toothed lower lip. Corolla yellow; standard obovate to orbicular, shorter than the curved, acute keel; wings lanceolate, obtuse, with claws adnate to staminal tube; petals of keel separate. Stamens all connate into a closed tube; filaments capillary; anthers minute. Ovary sessile, many-ovuled; style elongated, filiform and curved above; stigma oblique, linear. Pod dehiscing by 2 twisting valves, flattened. Seeds linear.

One species in the Mediterranean region.

1. Spartium junceum L., Sp. Pl. 708 (1753); Boiss., Fl. 2 : 36 (1872). [Plate 60]

Evergreen shrub or small tree, glabrous, 1–3 m. Stems grey. Twigs green, furrowed. Leaves 1–4 × 0.5–1.7 cm., early deciduous, lanceolate-linear, tapering at base, glabrous or slightly hairy; petiole broadened and sheath-like at base. Flowers about 2 cm., sweet-scented, short-pedicelled, in loose terminal racemes. Standard broadly obovate to orbicular. Pod 6–9 × 0.6–0.8 cm., 6- to many-seeded, linear, glabrous or hairy, becoming dark brown; valves twisting at dehiscence. Seeds compressed, reddish-brown, shiny, without caruncle. Fl. April–June.

Hab.: Maquis. Upper and Lower Galilee, Mt. Carmel, Samaria, Judean Mts., Dan Valley.

Area: Mediterranean.

One of the frequent components of the maquis.

Formerly officinal (herba and semen genistae hispanicae or genistae junceae and also cortex genistae); used in wicker-work and also as a fibre plant in some W. Mediterranean countries; essential oil of the flowers sometimes used in cosmetics; widely grown as an ornamental plant.

8. GENISTA L.

Small to rather large shrubs, spinescent or unarmed. Leaves exstipulate, simple or digitately 3-foliolate, rarely with minute stipules. Racemes axillary, many- to 1-flowered. Bracts and bracteoles various. Calyx shortly 2-lipped, upper lip deeply 2-fid, lower lip shortly 3-toothed; teeth much shorter than tube. Corolla mostly yellow; standard ovate; wings oblong, deflexed after opening; keel slightly bent or straight, often deflexed, obtuse, with a protuberance at either side; claws of lower petals often adnate to staminal tube. Stamens all connate into a closed tube; anthers unequally long. Ovary sessile, mostly many-ovuled; style curved; stigma capitate or oblique. Pod dehiscing by 2 valves or indehiscent, globular, rhomboidal or ovoid – or flattened and linear. Seeds few to many.

About 90 species in Mediterranean region, in Europe and W. Asia.

Literature: P. B. Gibbs, A revision of the genus *Genista* L., *Notes Roy. Bot. Gard. Edinb.* 27 : 11–99 (1966).

1. Genista fasselata Decne., Ann. Sci. Nat. Bot. ser. 2, 4 : 360 (1835); Sp., Ann. Sci. Nat. Bot. ser. 3, 2 : 250 (1844; *"sphacelata"*); Boiss., Fl. 2 : 39 (1872; *"sphacelata"*). [Plate 61]

Spiny shrub, hirsute, 1–2 m. Branches and twigs alternate, intricate, mostly spreading, curved, terete, distinctly striate-grooved; flowering branches spinescent. Leaves 5–8 mm., early deciduous, simple, linear-lanceolate to oblong-spatulate, the upper reduced to minute, black scales. Flowers 0.8–1.2 cm., solitary or loosely racemose along branches, on pedicels shorter than calyx. Calyx glabrescent; teeth short, triangular. Corolla yellow; standard and keel silvery-hairy outside. Pod 0.8–1 cm., 2-seeded, ovoid, obliquely beaked, wrinkled. Fl. May–June.

Hab.: Mainly in maquis and pine forests. Mt. Carmel and adjacent coastal hills.

Area: E. Mediterranean.

9. GONOCYTISUS Sp.

Erect shrubs with slender, green, unarmed, wand-shaped branches. Leaves exstipulate, digitately 3-foliolate, except for the upper ones which are simple; leaflets entire. Racemes terminal, few- to many-flowered. Calyx short, top-shaped, obliquely truncate, obsoletely 2-lipped; upper lip short, with 2 remote, triangular teeth, lower lip minutely 3-toothed. Corolla yellow; standard obovate; claws of lower petals adnate to staminal tube. Stamens all connate into a closed tube; anthers bearded at base and apex. Pod small, tardily dehiscent, 2-valved, 1–2-seeded, slightly flattened, obliquely rhomboidal or oblong.

Two species in the eastern part of the Mediterranean region.

1. Gonocytisus pterocladus (Boiss.) Sp., Ann. Sci. Nat. Bot. ser. 3, 3:154 (1845); Boiss., Fl. 2:47 (1872). *Cytisus pterocladus* Boiss., Diagn. ser. 1, 2:10 (1843). [Plate 62]

Shrub, appressed-hairy or glabrescent, about 1 m. (sometimes more). Stems erect, branched, distinctly ribbed, the young branches triquetrous, almost winged, green. Leaves 1–3 × 0.4–1 cm., sessile, digitately 3-foliolate; leaflets oblong to linear, acute. Racemes elongated, loose. Flowers 0.8–1 cm. Calyx green or yellowish. Standard nearly as long as to somewhat longer than wings and keel. Pod 1–1.2 cm., 1–2-seeded, somewhat compressed, narrowly oblong-rhomboidal, attenuate at base, with a thick margin and a short, persistent beak. Fl. April–May.

Hab.: Maquis and garigue. Upper Galilee.

Area: E. Mediterranean.

10. RETAMA Boiss. (*Lygos* Adans.)*

Spartoid shrubs or small trees. Branches erect or ascending, silky-hairy or glabrous, with green, grooved twigs. Leaves early deciduous, exstipulate, simple, small, narrow. Racemes lateral, few- to many-flowered. Calyx spathe-like with hemispherical tube and 5 teeth. Corolla much longer than calyx; claws of petals adnate to staminal tube; standard plicate, oblong to obovate-orbicular; wings longer than keel. Stamens all connate into a closed tube; anthers muticous to apiculate. Ovary sessile or short-stipitate, 2- to few-ovuled; style filiform, glabrous; stigma papillose. Pod mostly indehiscent, 1–2-seeded; pericarp leathery or fleshy. Seeds without caruncle, globular, yellow or brown; radicle thick, less than half as long as cotyledons.

Some 5 species mainly in S. Mediterranean and Sahara.

Literature: E. Spach, Monographia generis *Spartium*, *Ann. Sci. Nat. Bot.* Ser. 2, 19 : 285–297 (1843). M. Zohary, A revision of the genus *Retama* Boiss., *Bull. Res. Counc. Israel* D, 7 : 1–12 (1959).

1. Retama raetam (Forssk.) Webb in Webb et Berth., Phyt. Canar. 2:56 (1842). [Plate 63]

Spartoid shrub, appressed- and silky-hairy, 1–3 m. Roots thick, poorly branching, mainly vertical, up to 20 m. long. Stems thick, furrowed. Branches upright or spreading, the younger ones sometimes recurved or deflexed, grooved. Leaves 0.5–2 × 0.3–

---

* Although the generic name *Lygos* is, from the point of view of priority, the valid name, the name *Retama* should be conserved, being widespread in taxonomical and geobotanical literature. It is also an old name derived from the biblical "rotem" and the Arabic "retam".

0.8 cm., very short-lived, linear-oblong. Racemes 1–5-flowered, along twigs. Flowers 1–1.5 cm. Calyx purplish; upper lip with 2 broadly triangular teeth, lower with 3 short teeth. Corolla white; petals with purple tips; standard about as long as or longer than wings, purple-veined, mostly obovate-orbicular; keel somewhat shorter than wings, acute or obtuse. Pod 0.7–2 × 0.5–0.9 cm., indehiscent or tardily dehiscent, ovoid to oblong or ellipsoidal, with a short, erect mucro or an erect or curved beak; pericarp leathery or fleshy, smooth or wrinkled. Seeds yellow or brown. 2n = 48. Fl. February–April.

Var. **raetam**. *R. raetam* (Forssk.) Webb, l.c.; Boiss., Fl. 2:37 (1872; "*roetam*"). *Genista raetam* Forssk., Fl. Aeg.-Arab. 214 (1775). "*R. duriaei* (Sp.) Webb" Boiss., Fl. Suppl. 159 (1888) quoad spec. palaest. Mostly strictly branching, yellowish-green. Pod tapering into a beak or abruptly mucronate; pericarp indehiscent, thin, leathery. Seeds brown, rarely yellow.

Hab.: Mainly in deserts; sandy, rocky and gravelly ground. Judean Desert, E., C. and S. Negev, Upper and Lower Jordan Valley, Arava Valley, deserts east of Ammon, Moav, Edom.

Var. **sarcocarpa** Zoh., Bull. Res. Counc. Israel D, 7:8 (1959). Diffusely branching, with silky-silvery indumentum. Upper branches deflexed. Pod tardily dehiscent, fleshy, shortly ellipsoidal or ovoid, with more or less abrupt, short, straight or recurved mucro or beak, strongly wrinkled when dry. Seeds lemon-yellow, rarely green.

Hab.: Sands and sandy soils. Acco Plain, Sharon Plain, Philistean Plain, W. Negev. A dominant component in the vegetation of stabilized dunes of the Mediterranean coastal plain.

Area of species: Saharo-Arabian, with extensions into local Irano-Turanian territories and sandy soil belt of the Mediterranean coast.

One of the most common desert and littoral shrubs. Very striking in its spartoid habit and white flowers. This is the רֹתֶם of the Bible (e.g. I Kings xix:5).

Branches used in preparing a wash for the eyes; used in home industry for coarse cords.

Trib. ASTRAGALEAE (Galegeae). Herbs or shrubs. Leaves mostly imparipinnate, rarely digitate or simple, without tendrils. Stamens 10, diadelphous (9 connate and 1 free).

11. INDIGOFERA L.

Herbs or shrubs, mostly silky-hairy. Leaves imparipinnate or digitate, rarely simple; stipules mostly present, small, adnate at base to petiole, bristle-like. Flowers in axillary racemes. Calyx small, oblique, campanulate or tubular, teeth equal or the lowest teeth longer. Corolla pink or red; standard obovate or orbicular; wings oblong, slightly adhering to keel; keel gibbous or spurred on both sides, straight or slightly incurved, obtuse or acuminate. Stamens diadelphous (9+1); connective of anthers ending in a gland or mucro. Ovary sessile or nearly so, many- or 1–2-ovuled; style glabrous; stigma capitate, often hairy. Pod dehiscent or not, 2-valved, linear or oblong, straight or curved, terete, tetragonous or compressed, rarely globular, strongly torulose or septate between seeds. Seeds ovoid, globular or cubic, without caruncle.

About 500 species, mainly in tropical regions.

1. Pod 2–2.5 cm. Racemes much longer than leaf.	**1. I. oblongifolia**
– Pod 1–1.4 cm. Racemes much shorter than leaf.	**2. I. articulata**

1. Indigofera oblongifolia Forssk., Fl. Aeg.-Arab. 137 (1775). *I. paucifolia* Del., Fl. Aeg. Ill. 70 no. 686 (1813) et Fl. Eg. 107, t. 37, f. 2, 2' (1813); Boiss., Fl. 2 : 190 (1872). [Plate 64]

Half-shrub, grey- and appressed-pubescent, 30–50 cm. Stems erect, branching. Leaves simple or composed of 2–5, usually alternate, petiolulate, oblong-lanceolate, somewhat folded, entire leaflets, with somewhat recurved, mucronate apex; stipules minute, triangular. Racemes much longer than leaves, many-flowered, elongated. Pedicels as long as calyx. Calyx teeth as long as tube, lanceolate. Corolla twice as long as calyx, red. Pod 2–2.5 × 0.2–0.3 cm., 6–8-seeded, deflexed, cylindrical, torulose, curved, obtuse and mucronate, appressed-hirsute. Seeds somewhat flattened, ovoid, smooth. Fl. March–April.

Hab. : Sandy places. Dead Sea area (Ghor es Safieh, after Hart 1891).

Area : Sudanian.

2. Indigofera articulata Gouan, Ill. Obs. Bot. 49 (1773). *I. argentea* L., Mant. Alt. 273 (1771) non Burm. f., Fl. Ind. 171 (1768); Boiss., Fl. 2 : 190 (1872). *I. tinctoria* Forssk., Fl. Aeg.-Arab. 138 (1775) non L., Sp. Pl. 751 (1753). [Plate 65]

Shrub, silvery-hairy, 1–2 m. Stems erect, much branched. Branches furrowed. Leaves 4–6 cm.; stipules small, setaceous; leaflets 4-paired, 1–2 cm., opposite, petiolulate, obovate, obtuse, entire, silvery-hairy on both sides, turning blackish when dry. Racemes 2–2.5 cm., sessile or almost so, 12–20-flowered, elongating in fruit. Pedicels about as long as calyx. Flowers small, 3–4 mm. Calyx small, silvery-hairy, with 5 teeth about as long as tube. Corolla about 4 times as long as calyx, reddish-yellow, canescent. Pod 1–1.5 × 0.3 cm., 3–4-seeded, terete, necklace-shaped, hairy. Seeds globular, smooth. Fl. February–March.

Hab. : Oases. Upper Jordan Valley, Dead Sea area.

Area : Tropical regions.

Formerly grown as a most important dye plant (a source of indigo).

12. PSORALEA L.

Shrubs, half-shrubs or perennial herbs, hairy or glandular-dotted. Leaves digitate (with 3 or more leaflets), pinnate or simple; broad base of stipules clasping the stem, scarcely adnate to petiole. Racemes axillary or terminal, capitate or spike-like, pedunculate or sessile, rarely flowers in fascicles. Calyx campanulate, equally 5-toothed or upper teeth shorter and partly connate. Corolla blue, pink, violet or white; petals nearly equal in length; standard ovate to orbicular, frequently auriculate at base of limb; wings oblong; keel obtuse, incurved. Stamens diadelphous. Ovary sessile or short-stalked, 1-ovuled; style filiform or dilated at base; stigma capitate. Pod indehiscent, 1-seeded, relatively small, beaked or not. Seeds usually adherent to pericarp.

About 150 species in temperate and tropical regions, mostly in S. Africa, Australia, N. W. America, some in the Mediterranean region.

1. Heads 5–8-flowered. Calyx teeth usually as long as tube. Terminal leaflets of lower leaves about 0.6–1 (–1.5) cm.   **2. P. flaccida**
– Heads 10–30-flowered. Calyx teeth usually longer than tube. Terminal leaflets of lower leaves usually much longer than above.   **1. P. bituminosa**

1. Psoralea bituminosa L., Sp. Pl. 763 (1753). [Plate 66]

Perennial herb, appressed-hirsute, 0.5–1 (–2) m. Stems mostly erect, sometimes prostrate, rather thick, more or less striate to sulcate. Leaves long-petioled, digitately 3-foliolate; stipules lanceolate to subulate; leaflets of lower leaves usually 2–5 cm., ovate to elliptical or orbicular, rarely obcordate, obtuse, truncate or acute, those of upper leaves 5–8 cm., oblong, elliptical, lanceolate or linear-lanceolate, acute, the terminal leaflets longer than the lateral, petiolulate. Peduncles longer than subtending leaves. Racemes capitate or spicate in flower, (10–)15–30-flowered, slightly elongating in fruit. Bracts shorter than or as long as calyx, 2–3-toothed. Flowers about 1.5–3 cm. Calyx hirsute, rarely glabrous; teeth usually subulate, longer or very rarely as long as or shorter than tube, unequal, lower teeth longer. Corolla longer than calyx, pink, blue to violet, sometimes cream-coloured or white; standard somewhat longer than wings and keel. Pod 1.3–2.8 cm. (incl. beak), ovoid; beak usually longer than pod, sometimes black, hairy, rarely glabrous. Fl. March–July.

1. Prostrate plants, up to 40 cm. Leaflets of lower leaves ovate to orbicular, truncate at apex. Beak very long.   var. **prostrata**
– Erect plants, 0.6–1.5 (–2) m. Leaflets of lower leaves ovate to elliptical or oblong, acute   2
2. Flowers in more or less spicate racemes. Pod small, glabrous or slightly hairy. Leaflets of lower leaves broadly ovate. Plants growing in humid sites.   var. **hulensis**
– Plants not as above   3
3. Calyx 1.6–2.1 cm. Pod large; beak curved.   var. **bituminosa**
– Calyx shorter than above. Pod small, black; beak short, broad and straight.
                                                                                        var. **brachycarpa**

Var. **bituminosa**. *P. bituminosa* L., l.c.; Boiss., Fl. 2 : 187 (1872). *P. bituminosa* L. var. *genuina* Rouy in Rouy et Fouc., Fl. Fr. 5 : 131 (1899). *P. palaestina* Gouan, Ill. Obs. Bot. 51 (1773). *P. bituminosa* L. var. *palaestina* (Gouan) Hal., Consp. Fl. Gr. 1 : 426 (1900). *P. plumosa* Reichb., Fl. Germ. Exc. 869 (1832). Erect plant, 0.6–1.5 m. Stems thick. Leaflets large, those of lower leaves 4–7 × 2–3.5 cm., ovate to elliptical, those of upper leaves 6–8 × 1.5 cm., lanceolate. Heads (12–)15–24-flowered. Corolla pink to blue, rarely cream-coloured. Pod 1.6–2 cm. (incl. beak); beak 1–1.5 cm., curved.

Hab.: Batha and fallow fields. Acco Plain, Sharon Plain, Philistean Plain, Upper and Lower Galilee, Esdraelon Plain, Samaria, Shefela, Judean Mts., Hula Plain, Upper Jordan Valley.

Var. **prostrata** Zoh.* *P. bituminosa* L. var. *plumosa* Feldm. in herb. non (Reichb.) Reichb. f. in Reichb., Ic. Fl. Germ. 22 : 91 (1903) nec Nyarady in Savul., Fl. Reip. Rom. 5 : 238 (1957). Prostrate, up to 40 cm. Stems slender. Leaflets small, those of lower leaves up to 4 cm. in diam., orbicular to ovate, obtuse at apex and truncate; those of upper leaves up to 7 × 3 cm., elliptical to lanceolate, acute. Heads 20–30-flowered. Corolla white to cream-coloured or pink, rarely violet. Pod 1.7–2.8 cm. (incl. beak); beak 1.3–2 cm.

Hab. : As above. Upper and Lower Galilee, Mt. Carmel, Judean Mts., Ammon.

Var. **brachycarpa** Feldm.* Erect plant with thick stems. Leaflets of lower leaves longer than broad, ovate to elliptical, those of upper leaves 5–11 × 1.2–2 cm., lanceolate to linear-lanceolate. Racemes head-like, 15–18-flowered, somewhat elongating in fruit. Calyx small, up to 1.3 cm. Pod up to 1.4 cm., black, usually almost hidden in calyx; beak about 8 mm., broad at base, straight, yellow.

Hab. : As above. Lower Jordan Valley, Dead Sea area.

Var. **hulensis** Feldm.* Erect shrub, 1.5–2 m. Stems thick, sulcate. Leaflets of lower leaves 4–6 × 3–5 cm., obcordate; those of upper leaves lanceolate to elliptical. Racemes spicate, 18–24-flowered. Calyx glabrous, 1–2.1 cm. Corolla blue. Pod small, 1.3–1.4 cm. (incl. beak); beak 7–8 mm., straight.

Hab. : By water. Dan Valley, Hula Plain.

Area of species : Mediterranean, with extensions into W. Irano-Turanian territories.

One of the most common hemicryptophytes of the country; a dominant of the *Psoralea-Echinops* community. Not palatable except for a certain strain which is worth studying.

Popularly considered to be a tonic and emmenagogue.

2. Psoralea flaccida Nab., Publ. Fac. Sci. Univ. Masaryk 35 : 74 (1923); Post, Fl. Syr. Pal. Sin. ed. 2, 1 : 368 (1932). [Plate 67]

Perennial herb, woody at base, appressed- and white-bristly, 25–40 cm. Stems ascending or procumbent, slender, weak, flexuous. Leaves long-petioled; leaflets 0.8–1.5 (–2) cm., those of the lower leaves minute, nearly orbicular, with long-petiolulate terminal leaflet and almost sessile lateral leaflets; leaflets of upper leaves lanceolate-linear, acute. Peduncles much longer than leaves. Racemes head-like, 5–6 (–8)-flowered. Bracts small, dilated at base, 2–3-toothed; teeth triangular, abruptly subulate, the middle tooth much longer than the lateral. Flowers about 1.8 cm. Calyx about 1 cm., white-hairy with a few black hairs; teeth as long as tube, equal, long-subulate. Corolla almost twice as long as calyx, pink. Pod 5 mm. (not incl. beak), hirsute; beak twice as long as seed-bearing part of pod, appressed-setulose. Fl. March–April.

Hab. : Rocky sites. Edom.

Area : E. Mediterranean.

This species still deserves further study to confirm its separation from *P. bituminosa*.

* See Appendix at end of this volume.

13. Tephrosia Pers.

Herbs, half-shrubs or shrubs. Leaves stipulate, imparipinnate; leaflets many, rarely 1–3 pairs, entire. Racemes opposite leaves or terminal, loose. Calyx campanulate, with 5 almost equal teeth, the upper 2 connate at base. Corolla mostly red to purple, with clawed petals; standard broad, almost orbicular, silky-hairy or tomentose outside; wings oblong to obovate, adherent to incurved keel. Stamens diadelphous, the upper one free only at base, later becoming entirely free. Ovary sessile, 2- to many-ovuled; style incurved, often flattened; stigma glabrous or bearded. Pod 2-valved, compressed, linear, rarely ovoid or ellipsoidal, not septate between seeds or only slightly so. Seeds flattened.

About 250 species mainly in tropical regions, especially in Africa.

1. Pod 3–5 cm., linear to linear-oblong, many-seeded. ·   **1. T. apollinea**
 – Pod 1–1.5 cm., ovoid, 1-seeded.   **2. T. nubica**

1. Tephrosia apollinea (Del.) Link, Enum. Hort. Berol. Alt. 2 : 252 (1822); Boiss., Fl. 2 : 192 (1872). *Galega apollinea* Del., Fl. Aeg. Ill. 70 no. 688 (1813) et Fl. Eg. 144, t. 53, f. 5 (1813). [Plate 68]

Shrub, appressed- and silvery-hairy, 30–60 cm. Stems much branched. Branches erect to ascending, flexuous, grooved-angular. Leaves up to 10 cm. or more; stipules 3–4 mm., linear-lanceolate; leaflets 2–5-paired, 1.5–3 × 0.4–1 cm., petiolulate, oblong, retuse, silky-canescent on both sides. Peduncles at first shorter than subtending leaves, later elongating. Racemes axillary or opposite leaves, few- to many-flowered, loose. Bracts much shorter than deflexed pedicels. Flowers about 1 cm. Calyx minutely appressed-hairy; teeth somewhat longer than tube, triangular-lanceolate. Corolla purple. Pod 3–5 × 0.4–0.6 cm., many-seeded, spreading to deflexed, compressed, linear, slightly torulose, obliquely short-beaked, appressed-hairy to glabrescent. Seeds 2 mm., oblong-ellipsoidal, mottled with brown. 2n = 22. Fl. Spring, late summer.

Hab.: Wadis and among rocks in hot deserts. S. Negev, Dead Sea area, Arava Valley, deserts of Edom.

Area: Mainly Sudanian and E. African regions.

Contains a blue dye.

2. Tephrosia nubica (Boiss.) Baker in Oliver, Fl. Trop. Afr. 2 : 125 (1871) var. **abyssinica** (Jaub. et Sp.) Schweinf., Bull. Herb. Boiss. 4 (App. 2) : 247 (1896). *Pogonostigma nubicum* Boiss., Diagn. ser. 1, 2 : 40 (1843). *P. abyssinicum* Jaub. et Sp., Ill. Pl. Or. 5 : 88, t. 477 (1856). [Plate 69]

Perennial herb with woody stock, densely appressed-canescent, 30–60 cm. Branches erect, grooved. Leaves 5–10 cm.; stipules minute, subulate; leaflets 1.2–5 × 0.8–1 cm., oblong to lanceolate, acute, those of lower leaves 2–4-paired, those of upper leaves 1–2-paired. Racemes terminal or opposite leaves, loose, much elongating in fruit. Flowers about 1 cm., with bracts and pedicels shorter than calyx. Calyx densely hirsute; teeth subulate, broadened at base, longer than tube. Corolla light pink; standard silky-hairy at back. Pod about (1–)1.5 cm., short-stipitate, 1-seeded, ovoid, obliquely mucronate-beaked, densely subpatulous-hirsute, with curved, bearded stigma. Seeds ellipsoidal-reniform, mottled with brown. Fl. Spring, late summer.

Hab. : Hot deserts in wadis and among rocks. Arava Valley.

Area : E. Sudanian.

14. COLUTEA L.

Shrubs, much branching. Leaves imparipinnate with minute, free, membranous stipules and opposite or alternate, entire leaflets. Racemes axillary, few- to many-flowered. Flowers showy, long-pedicelled. Calyx campanulate to tubular, white- or black- and appressed-hairy; calyx teeth equal or the upper shorter. Corolla yellow or purple; standard nearly orbicular, limb erect, base with a fold or protuberance on either side; wings oblong, falcate; keel obtuse, curved. Stamens diadelphous. Ovary stipitate, 3- to many-ovuled; style incurved, bearded along its upper (inner) side, hooked above, with an ovate stigma hidden among hairs. Pod stipitate, indehiscent or gaping at apex, membranous, much inflated. Seeds kidney-shaped.

About 15 species, mainly in the temperate and tropical regions of the Old World.

Literature : K. Browicz, The genus *Colutea* L., *Monogr. Bot. Warszawa* 14 : 1–134 (1963).

1. Ovary densely hairy. Leaflets 0.5–1.5 × 0.3–0.7 cm. Standard with folds united above claw into a horseshoe-shaped protuberance. **2. C. istria**
- Ovary glabrous. Leaflets 2–3 × 1–2 cm. Folds of standard not horseshoe-shaped but parallel and almost obsolete. **1. C. cilicica**

1. Colutea cilicica Boiss. et Bal. in Boiss., Diagn. ser. 2, 5 : 83 (1856) et Fl. 2 : 195 (1872). [Plate 70]

Shrub, brownish-grey, sparingly appressed-hairy or glabrous, 2–3 m. Leaves 6–10 cm., sparingly hairy beneath to glabrous; stipules up to 3 mm., scarious, ovate; leaflets (3–)4–5-paired, 2–3 × 1–2 cm., thin, elliptical to somewhat obovate or sometimes suborbicular, rounded and short-mucronate or shallowly retuse at apex, often glaucescent, sparingly hairy beneath or glabrous. Peduncles shorter than subtending leaves. Racemes usually 3–5-flowered. Bracts up to 2 mm., narrowly ovate. Pedicels considerably shorter than flowers. Flowers mostly 2–2.2 cm., sometimes smaller. Calyx 7–9 mm., broadly campanulate, sparingly white- or black-hairy or glabrous; teeth about 2 mm., acute. Corolla yellow; wings longer than keel, spurred, usually convolute at margins. Ovary glabrous. Pod 5–7 × 2.5–3 cm., long-stipitate, indehiscent, parchment-like, glabrous. Seeds about 4 mm. across. Fl. May–June.

Hab. : Recorded by Browicz (Monogr. Bot. 14 : 47, 1963), from Mt. Carmel on the basis of a specimen deposited in Herb. Firenze. It has not been observed in Palestine by anybody else, but its prior occurrence here is not improbable, as it has been met with recently at the foot of Mt. Hermon, near Majdal Shams and Wadi el Abal.

Area : E. Mediterranean.

2. Colutea istria Mill., Gard. Dict. ed. 8, no. 2 (1768). *C. halepica* Lam., Encycl. 1 : 353 (1785); Boiss., Fl. 2 : 195 (1872; "*haleppica*"). [Plate 71]

Shrub, glaucous, sparingly white-, appressed- and setulose-hairy or glabrescent, (0.5–)1–2 m. Branches very slender, spreading, often with white, scaly bark. Leaves (2–)5–15 cm.; leaflets 4–6-paired, remote, 0.5–1.5 × 0.3–0.7 cm., petiolulate, obovate to elliptical, rarely orbicular, obtuse, retuse, hairy on both sides. Peduncles mostly longer than subtending leaves. Racemes few-flowered. Bracts minute. Pedicels shorter to longer than flowers. Flowers 1.5–2 cm. Calyx 5–7 mm., broadly campanulate; teeth one fifth as long as tube or less, unequal, broadly triangular, appressed-hirtellous. Corolla yellow; standard folds united above claw into a horseshoe-shaped protuberance; wings convolute, much shorter than the truncate keel. Ovary oblong, densely hairy. Pod (3–)4–6 × 2–3 cm., long-stipitate, on long, deflexed pedicel, parchment-like, split at tip, glabrous or sparingly hairy. Seeds 4–5 mm. across. Fl. March–April.

Hab.: On rocks or walls and in desert wadis. Lower Galilee, Samaria, Judean Mts., Judean Desert, C. Negev, Edom. Rare.

Area: W. Irano-Turanian, extending into some adjacent tropical territories.

Spontaneous in the Negev, Edom and Lower Galilee, but probably cultivated in some of the other localities mentioned.

15. ASTRAGALUS L.

Shrubs, half-shrubs or perennial and annual herbs. Leaves all imparipinnate or paripinnate and then petiole with a spinescent or unarmed elongation; stipules free or adnate to petiole or connate. Inflorescences simple of 1- to many-flowered racemes or compound of many racemes crowded together. Flowers usually conspicuous. Calyx campanulate, turbinate or tubular, unchanged, torn or inflated in fruit; teeth 5, equal or unequal. Corolla variously coloured; standard various, mostly notched; claws of wings and keel free or nearly so or more or less adnate to staminal tube; keel obtuse, rarely acute. Stamens diadelphous. Ovary sessile or stipitate, many-ovuled; style usually becoming indurated in fruit. Pod varying greatly in shape and size, sessile or stipitate (with gynophore), dehiscent or not, usually 2-valved, with dorsal suture growing inwards so as to form a complete or partial false septum dividing the pod lengthwise into 2 cells, each of which is 1- or many-seeded; sometimes pod not septate, 1-celled; ventral suture mostly keeled, sometimes inflexed; valves mostly diverging at maturity, without becoming separated. Seeds mostly compressed, globular or ovoid, without caruncle.

About 2,000 species, grouped in over 100 sections, mainly holarctic with the largest centres of distribution in S. W. Asia.

Literature: A. Bunge, Generis Astragali species gerontogeae, *Mém. Acad. Sci. Pétersb.* Ser. 7, 11, 16: 1–140 (1868); ibid., 15, 1: 1–254 (1869). P. E. Boissier, *Flora Orientalis* 2: 205–498 & *Suppl.* 174–189, Geneva & Basel, 1872, 1888. A. Eig, *Systematic Studies on Astragali of the Near East (especially Palestine, Syria, Iraq)*, Israel Sci. Press, Jerusalem 1955, 1–187. K. H. Rechinger, H. Dulfer & A. Patzak, Sirjaevii fragmenta astragalogica, I–III, *Oesterr. Akad. Wiss. Anz. Math.-Naturw. Kl.* 5: 51–93 (1958); IV, *Sitz. Oesterr. Akad. Wiss. Math.-Naturw. Kl.* Abt. 1, 167: 321–361 (1958); V–VIII, ibid., 168: 95–182 (1959); IX–XI, ibid., 168: 693–718 (1959); XII, ibid., 168: 719–787 (1959); XIII–XVII, ibid., 170: 9–68 (1961).

1. Spiny shrubs or herbs; spines consisting of persistent, indurated leaf petioles   2
- Plants not spiny   7
2. Calyx bladdery-inflated, membranous, about 1–1.5 cm. across.   **43. A. spinosus**
- Calyx not as above   3
3. Pod 3–5 cm., exserted from calyx.   **36. A. sieberi**
- Pod very small, hidden within calyx   4
4. Leaflets glabrous or almost so, 1–3 cm. Spines (5–)7–15 cm. Flower heads 5–10 cm.
                                                                     42. A. deinacanthus
- Leaflets hairy, 0.3–1 cm. Spines and heads shorter than above   5
5. Flowers 1–1.5 cm., in dense heads. Calyx 6–7 mm., with teeth as long as tube. Standard
   limb 3–4 times as long as claw.   **39. A. echinus**
- Plants not as above   6
6. Leaflets 6–7-paired, 3–4 mm., without terminal spine. Calyx teeth twice as long as tube.
                                                                     40. A. cruentiflorus
- Leaflets 4–5(–8)-paired, 4–8 mm., with terminal spine. Calyx teeth 3 times as long as
   tube.   **41. A. bethlehemiticus**
7(1). Flowers yellow, arranged in globular or ovoid heads, 4–6 cm. or more across. Pod
   hidden in calyx.   **44. A. oocephalus**
- Not as above   8
8. Calyx bladdery-inflated in fruit, 1.5–3 cm. Corolla yellow, up to 3(–4) cm. Perennial
   prostrate herbs.   **45. A. kahiricus**
- Calyx not as above   9
9. Flowers yellow or yellowish-white, rarely white, 2–4 cm., in small, axillary racemes,
   scattered along the leafy and strongly developed erect stems. Pod ovoid, ovoid-oblong or
   globular, 1.5–6 × 1–3(–4) cm. Leaves with 10–35 pairs of leaflets. Perennials   10
- Flowers and/or pod not as above or plants stemless   14
10. Pod about 3–6 cm. long, 2.5–4 cm. broad   11
— Pod smaller   13
11. Leaflets 10–15(–22) pairs.   **25. A. macrocarpus**
— Leaflets 20–30 pairs   12
12. Stipules 1–1.8 cm. Pod about 4 cm. (not including beak).   **26. A. gileadensis**
— Stipules much longer. Pod smaller.   **27. A. postii**
13(10). Flowers cream-coloured or yellow. Pod hirsute.   **29. A. feinbruniae**
— Flowers white. Pod glabrous.   **28. A. galilaeus**
14(9). Pod shortly ovoid, 0.8–1(–1.5) cm., covered with a white fleece almost as thick
   as diameter of fruit. Flowers violet with paler petal margins. Low perennial herbs,
   woody at base.   **50. A. amalecitanus**
— Not as above   15
15. Stemless herbaceous perennials. Leaves woolly, white or yellowish, all radical, rosulate,
   with 20 or more very crowded pairs of leaflets. Flowers red, purple or violet in a dense
   terminal head or spike borne on a 10–20 cm. long peduncle (scape)   16
— Plants not as above   17
16. Beak as long as or longer than the seed-bearing portion.   **24. A. oxytropifolius**
— Beak much shorter.   **23. A. cretaceus**
17(15). Stemless plants, with many rather large radical leaves. Flowers yellow or yellowish-
   white, large. Racemes short, arising from leaf axils and much shorter than leaves.
   Pod 1–8 × 0.5–1.5 cm.   18
— Plants not as above   23
18. Pod 5–8 cm., indehiscent, with spongy or woody, prominently net-nerved valves and

    a stout, sharp-pointed (spiny) beak.   **35. A. acinaciferus**
— Not as above   19
19. Pod acutely 3-keeled, glabrous, rarely with only a few scattered hairs; gynophore
    (stipe) very short; beak very short, curved.   **30. A. platyraphis**
— Pod hairy or villose, not as above   20
20. Pod keeled along both sutures. Gynophore (stipe) 2–3 mm.   **34. A. aaronii**
— Pod keeled along ventral suture only, dorsal suture depressed-grooved   21
21. Gynophore 3–6 mm. Flowers 2.3–3 cm. Pod 1.6–3 cm. (not incl. gynophore and beak).
                                                                       31. A. beershabensis
— Gynophore 0 or inconspicuous   22
22. Leaflets obovate to orbicular, 0.3–1 × 0.2–0.7 cm., hairy on both sides. Flowers 1.8–
    2.2 cm. Pod 2–2.2 cm.   **33. A. aaronsohnianus**
— Leaflets obovate to oblong, 0.7–1 × 0.3–0.5 cm., glabrous above, hairy beneath.
    Flowers 2.5–3 cm. Pod 1–2.5 cm.   **32. A. alexandrinus**
23 (17). Pod triangular to heart-shaped in cross section, 5–8 mm. long and 5–8 mm. broad
    at base, with deflexed tip. Racemes 6–12-flowered, in dense axillary heads.
                                                                          1. A. epiglottis
— Not as above   24
24. Fruiting racemes umbellate, of 1–2 whorls; pods with two kinds of hairs, or with one
    kind but then hairs not tuberculate at base. Annuals   25
— Not as above   27
25. Pods linear to oblong, nearly terete, densely hispid with spreading hairs, erect or
    slightly spreading.   **5. A. schimperi**
— Pods triangular in cross section, 2-gibbous at base, stellately spreading   26
26. Pods 0.5–1.2 cm., 2–3 (–6) in each head.   **2. A. tribuloides**
— Pods 1.3–2 cm., (3–)4–6 (–10) in each head.   **3. A. cruciatus**
27 (24). Caulescent perennials. Flowers yellow, 2–3.5 cm. Pod 3–8 × 0.7–1.5 cm., cylindrical
    or somewhat flattened, straight or very slightly falcate, tapering into a stout point
    or beak   28
— Not as above   30
28. Pod up to 8 cm., dagger-shaped, i.e. tapering into a spinescent tip; valves crustaceous
    or spongy, prominently and obliquely nerved. Calyx teeth one fifth as long as tube.
    Leaflets glabrous above, strigulose beneath.   **35. A. acinaciferus**
— Not as above   29
29. Leaflets 20–30 pairs, broadly ovate to orbicular-obcordate, deeply notched. Pod up
    to 1 cm. thick. Calyx teeth as long as tube.   **38. A. fruticosus**
— Leaflets 10–15 pairs, ovate-oblong. Pod much thinner. Calyx teeth much shorter.
                                                                          37. A. sparsus
30 (27). Pod strongly net-wrinkled transversely. Calyx teeth shorter than tube. Leaves
    with few cuneate leaflets. Flowers small, white. Annuals.   **6. A. corrugatus**
— Not as above   31
31. Pod circular or semicircular, sometimes unevenly circular (fishhook-shaped)   32
— Pod straight or arcuate   40
32. Perennials with woody base. Leaflets linear to elliptical, 4–7-paired. Racemes 6–16-
    flowered. Calyx 1–1.5 cm. Pod (2.5–)6–7 cm.   **48. A. sanctus**
— Annuals. Calyx and / or pod usually shorter   33
33. Pod mottled with red, ending in a short stiff beak, curved inwards. Leaflets 1–4 pairs.
                                                                        14. A. annularis
— Pod and leaves not as above   34

34. Pod deflexed-pendulous. Leaflets 8–12 pairs   35
— Pod erect or spreading. Leaflets generally fewer in number   36
35. Pod fishhook-shaped, cylindrical or semicylindrical (i.e. more or less orbicular or semiorbicular in cross section).   **17. A. hamosus**
— Pod unequally semicircular, or almost fishhook-shaped but triquetrous (i.e. more or less triangular in cross section).   **8. A. trimestris**
36(34). Pod 2–3 × 0.3–0.4 cm., cylindrical or very slightly flattened, with two kinds of hairs : short appressed and longer tuberculate and spreading ones. Leaflets 2–4 pairs. Flowers white.   **9. A. gyzensis**
— Not as above   37
37. Calyx teeth as long as tube. Racemes 4–6-flowered.   **13. A. moabiticus**
— Calyx teeth much shorter than tube   38
38. Racemes 5–8(–15)-flowered, rhachis appressed-bristly. Valves not separating at maturity. Leaflets linear or elliptical, acute.   **11. A. callichrous**
— Racemes 1–3(–5)-flowered   39
39. Pod 1.5–2 mm. broad, semicircular or almost circular; style caducous. **12. A. hispidulus**
— Pod about 3 mm. broad, semicircular, very deeply furrowed at back; style persistent.   **10. A. intercedens**
40(31). Perennials with woody stock and many branches arising from older aerial short stems. Leaflets mostly 5–7 pairs   41
— Annuals, sometimes perennating, with no woody stock   43
41. Flowers about 1 cm. Pod about 3–4 times as long as broad.   **46. A. zemeraniensis**
— Flowers 1.6–3 cm. Pod longer than above   42
42. Leaflets 1 cm. or more, oblong, acute. Pod about 6–8 cm.   **49. A. trachoniticus**
— Leaflets shorter, obovate, obtuse or retuse. Pod shorter.   **47. A. adpressiusculus**
43(40). Pod 3.5–5(–6) × 0.3 cm., straight, with a sharp-pointed hook-shaped beak. Leaflets 3–7-paired   44
— Not as above   45
44. Racemes 3–6-flowered. Fruiting peduncle longer than subtending leaves. Pod almost straight, sparingly hairy.   **7. A. negevensis**
— Flowers solitary, sessile. Pod falcate, densely hairy.   **18. A. scorpioides**
45(43). Pod glabrous, mottled with brown. Peduncles awned at tip. Flowers about 1 cm. or less, white.   **16. A. guttatus**
— Not as above   46
46. Pod 5 mm. or more thick, oblong-prismatic, glabrescent or finely appressed-hairy. Flowers 1–1.2 cm., cream-coloured. Plants usually erect. Leaflets 7–11 pairs, glabrous above, up to 3 cm.   **15. A. boeticus**
— Not as above   47
47. Racemes umbellate, 2–4-flowered. Pod about 2 cm., with patulous bristles tuberculate at base. Flowers less than 1 cm.   **4. A. transjordanicus**
— Racemes racemose. Plants prostrate. Flowers longer than above   48
48. Pod at least 6–10 times as long as broad   49
— Pod at the most 3–4(–5) times as long as broad   50
49. Pod 6–7 mm. thick. Racemes 3–5-flowered. Style not persistent.   **22. A. peregrinus**
— Pod 4–5 mm. thick. Racemes 5–10-flowered. Style persistent.   **21. A. berytheus**
50(48). Pod mostly whitish-grey, fleecy or with white long hairs, rarely glabrous. Calyx white-woolly.   **20. A. bombycinus**
— Pod blackish, not fleecy, sometimes glabrescent. Calyx white- and black-villose.
                                                                         19. A. palaestinus

Sect. EPIGLOTTIS Bge., Mém. Acad. Sci. Pétersb. ser. 7, 11, 16:8 (1868). Flowers whorled-capitate. Pod 2-celled, few-seeded, trigonous, compressed, rigid; dorsal suture with a broad furrow. Keel almost as long as wings.

1. Astragalus epiglottis L., Sp. Pl. 759 (1753) emend. L., Mant. Alt. 274 (1771); Boiss., Fl. 2:223 (1872); Eig, Astrag. Near East 6 (1955). [Plate 72]

Annual, appressed-pubescent, 10–25 cm. Stems numerous or few, erect or ascending. Leaves 3–8 cm.; stipules connate in lower portion and adnate to petiole, lanceolate-subulate; petiole appressed-pubescent; leaflets 4–7 pairs, about 1–1.2 × 0.5 cm., oblong-linear, mucronate, hairy on either side. Peduncles much shorter than subtending leaves. Heads axillary, 6–12-flowered. Flowers 5–6 mm. Calyx campanulate, white- and black-hairy; teeth nearly as long as tube, subulate. Corolla yellowish or bluish-yellow; standard broadly obovate, mucronate. Pod about 5 mm. long and up to 8 mm. broad at base, deflexed, trigonous to ovoid, with margins almost folded back, subcordate in cross section, appressed-hirsute; beak small, curved. Seeds 1–3(–4) in each pod. Fl. March–April.

Hab.: Batha. Philistean Plain, Upper Galilee, Esdraelon Plain, Mt. Gilboa, Samaria, Judean Mts., Judean Desert, Upper Jordan Valley, Gilead, Moav.

Area: Mediterranean.

Sect. OXYGLOTTIS Bge., Mém. Acad. Sci. Pétersb. ser. 7, 11, 16:10 (1868). Flowers arranged in 1 or 2–3 whorls, crowded together in a head or umbel. Pod 2-celled, mostly few-seeded, lanceolate, oblong or ovoid-trigonous, with furrowed back. Wings longer than keel.

2. Astragalus tribuloides Del., Fl. Aeg. Ill. 70 no. 696 (1813); Boiss., Fl. 2:224 (1872); Eig, Astrag. Near East 6 (1955). [Plate 73]

Small prostrate annual, (3–)5–15 cm. Branches leafy, greyish, appressed-pubescent, arising from base. Leaves 5–10 cm.; stipules free nearly to base, hyaline, lanceolate-subulate, hirsute; petiole appressed-silky; leaflets 6–15 pairs, 0.6–1 × 0.1–0.2 cm., oblong-elliptical to linear, upper leaflets crowded. Heads sessile or pedunculate, 3–6-flowered. Flowers about 0.5–1.4 cm. Calyx tubular; teeth half as long to as long as tube, subulate. Corolla pink or whitish. Pods 0.5–1.2 cm., mostly stellately diverging, triquetrous, oblong-lanceolate, 2-gibbous at base, slightly curved, often acute, appressed-hairy (with long and short hairs) or glabrous. Fl. February–March.

The following varieties have been distinguished:

1. Peduncles 0.5–1.5 cm.	var. **subpedunculatus** Eig, l.c.
– Peduncles much shorter or 0	2
2. Pod 0.8–1.2 cm.	3
– Pod 5–7 mm.	4
3. Pod hairy. Flowers 1.2–1.4 cm.	var. **tribuloides**
– Pod glabrous. Flowers about 1 cm.	var. **elarishensis** Eig, Bull. Inst. Agr. Nat. Hist. 6:29 (1927; "*el-arishensis*")
4(2). Pod hairy, somewhat longer than calyx. Flowers about 5 mm.	var. **minutus** (Boiss.) Boiss., l.c. 225
– Pod glabrous	var. **leiocarpus** Boiss., l.c. 225

All these varieties occur in Palestine, sometimes side by side. They call for a more critical study.

Hab. of species: Steppes and deserts. Samaria, Shefela, Judean Desert, N., E., C. and S. Negev, Lower Jordan Valley, Dead Sea area, Arava Valley, Gilead, Ammon, Moav, Edom. Fairly common.

Area of species: Saharo-Arabian and Irano-Turanian.

3. Astragalus cruciatus Link, Enum. Hort. Berol. Alt. 2 : 256 (1822). [Plate 74]

Annual, grey, appressed-hairy, 5–20(–25) cm. Stems few, erect or prostrate, leafy. Leaves 5–8 cm.; stipules connate below and adnate to petiole, hyaline, triangular to lanceolate, hairy; petiole appressed- to patulous-hairy; leaflets 6–12 pairs, about 1 cm., flat, oblong-lanceolate, obtuse, appressed-bristly. Peduncles shorter or longer than subtending leaves, spreading or erect. Heads 4–6(–10)-flowered. Flowers 5–8 mm., sessile, bluish-white. Calyx densely black- and white-hairy; teeth almost as long as tube, lanceolate-subulate. Pods (1–)1.3–2 cm., in groups of (3–)4–6(–10), stellately spreading in 1 or 2 rows, triquetrous, linear-lanceolate, arcuate, 2-gibbous at base, tapering-acute, with minute recurved beak, appressed-pubescent; valves slightly diverging but not separating at maturity. Fl. March–April.

1. Pod 0.8–1 cm.	var. **radiatus**
– Pod 1.7–2 cm.	2
2. Pods arranged in 1 row.	var. **cruciatus**
– Pods in 2 rows.	var. **biserialis**

Var. **cruciatus.** *A. cruciatus* Link, l.c.; Boiss., Fl. 2 : 225 (1872); Eig, Astrag. Near East 10 (1955). Pods 1.7–2 cm., 4–6 per head, all in 1 row.

Hab.: Batha and steppes. Philistean Plain, Mt. Carmel, Judean Mts., Judean Desert, Negev, Upper and Lower Jordan Valley, Gilead, Ammon, Moav, Edom.

Var. **biserialis** Zoh.* Pods as in above, 6–10 per head, arranged in 2 rows.

Hab.: As above. Philistean Plain, Samaria.

Var. **radiatus** Schweinf. fide V. Täckh., Stud. Fl. Eg. 305 (1956) excl. syn. [*A. pseudostella* Del.]. *A. radiatus* Ehrenb. ex Bge., Mém. Acad. Sci. Pétersb. ser. 7, 11, 16 : 11 (1868) et 15, 1 : 8 (1869) non Stev., Bull. Soc. Nat. Mosc. 4 : 267 (1832); Boiss., Fl. 2 : 226 (1872). Pods about 1 cm., 5–9 per head.

Hab.: As above. Philistean Plain (recorded by Dinsmore in Post, Fl. Syr. Pal. Sin. ed. 2, 1 : 378, 1932, under *A. pseudostella* Del., Fl. Eg. Suppl. t. 64, f. 15, 1813), Ammon, Edom.

Area of species: Mediterranean and Saharo-Arabian (extending into Irano-Turanian territories).

Markedly polymorphic; the above division is tentative only.

4. Astragalus transjordanicus Sam. ex Rech. f., Ark. Bot. ser. 2, 1, 5 : 307 (1949); Eig, Astrag. Near East 12 (1955). [Plate 75]

---

* See Appendix at end of this volume.

Annual, patulous-hirsute, 10–30 cm. Stems few, ascending or erect, branching. Leaves mostly 2–4 cm., linear-oblong, with patulous-hirsute petioles; stipules obliquely triangular-lanceolate; leaflets (5–)7–9 pairs, crowded, 2–8 × 1.5–5 mm., short-petiolulate, elliptical, truncate, somewhat notched, densely hairy on either side. Peduncles 1.5–3.5 cm., spreading or ascending, white- and black-hairy. Heads 2–4(–5)-flowered, more or less erect. Bracts longer than pedicels, membranous, lanceolate, ciliate. Flowers about 1 cm. Calyx 4–6 mm., campanulate; teeth as long as or somewhat shorter than tube, linear-subulate, with white and black patulous hairs. Corolla violet; standard shorter than wings, oblong to obovate. Pods 2–2.5 cm. long and 5–6 mm. thick near base, divergent or erect, lanceolate, slightly falcate, with convex, sulcate back, covered with long, stiff, patulous bristles tuberculate at base; beak short, recurved. Fl. April.

Hab.: Steppes. Ammon (endemic).

Area: W. Irano-Turanian.

5. Astragalus schimperi Boiss., Diagn. ser. 1, 2 : 53 (1843). [Plate 76]

Annual, appressed-hairy or villose, (5–)10–30 cm. Stems procumbent or ascending, furrowed, with long internodes. Leaves 3–7 cm., with hairy petioles; stipules almost free, triangular-lanceolate, setulose; leaflets 4–8 pairs, 0.5–1 cm., petiolulate, flat, oblong-elliptical, hairy on both sides. Peduncels often longer than leaves. Heads (2–)4–8-flowered. Bracts linear-subulate, with hyaline, ciliate margins. Flowers 1–1.5 cm., subsessile. Calyx tubular, densely white- (or also black-) hairy; teeth one third to one half as long as tube, linear-lanceolate. Corolla bluish-white or violet. Pods 1.5–2.5 × 0.25–0.4 cm., stellately spreading or erect in umbellate heads, nearly terete, linear to oblong, curved, with both long, patulous hairs with tuberculate base, and also short, appressed hairs, rarely patulous bristles only; beak short, recurved. Fl. February–April.

1. Pods very loosely covered with uniform bristles, glabrous in the interspaces.
                                                                                                var. **aradensis**
   – Pods more or less continuously covered with 2 kinds of hairs   2
2. Pods erect, 5–8 in a head.   var. **aravensis**
   – Pods spreading, 2–6 in a head.   var. **schimperi**

Var. **schimperi**. *A. schimperi* Boiss., l.c. et Fl. 2 : 226 (1872); Eig, Astrag. Near East 13 (1955). *A. schimperi* Boiss. ssp. *eu-schimperi* Eig, l.c. et var. *typicus* Eig, l.c. Heads 2–6-flowered. Pods stellately spreading.

Hab.: Sands. S. Edom.

Var. **aravensis** Zoh.* Heads 5–8-flowered. Pods erect.

Hab.: Sandy soils. Arava Valley. Ammon.

Var. **aradensis** Zoh.* Pods erect, with long, very scattered, patulous bristles, glabrous between bristles.

Hab.: Rocky ground. E. Negev.

* See Appendix at end of this volume.

This is obviously an intermediate form between *A. schimperi* and *A. transjordanicus*, readily distinguished from the latter by its many-flowered head and its more delicate pod. A more intensive study may raise var. *aradensis* to the rank of a species.

Area of species : E. Saharo-Arabian.

Sect. HARPILOBUS Bge., Mém. Acad. Sci. Pétersb. ser. 7, 11, 16 : 13 (1868). Flowers racemose on axillary peduncles, purple or white. Pod 2-celled, many-seeded, linear, usually semicircular or arcuate, curved at apex; dorsal suture convex, furrowed. Calyx campanulate, rarely subcylindrical. Standard not appendiculate; keel shorter than wings.

6. Astragalus corrugatus Bertol., Rar. Ital. Pl. Dec. 3 : 33 no. 1 (1810) et Amoen. Ital. 38 (1819); Eig, Astrag. Near East 16 (1955). [Plate 77]

Annual, sparingly appressed-hairy, branching from base, 10–30 cm. Branches diffuse, ascending or procumbent. Leaves 3–5 cm.; stipules hyaline, lanceolate; petiole glabrous or sparingly hairy; leaflets 5–8 pairs, 0.5–1.2 cm., linear-cuneate, retuse, pubescent on both sides. Peduncles shorter or longer than subtending leaves. Racemes 1–4 (–7)-flowered. Bracts 2 mm., lanceolate, ciliate. Flowers 5–8 mm. Calyx campanulate, appressed- and white-hairy; teeth about half as long as tube, lanceolate or subulate. Corolla white. Pod 3–4 × 0.2–0.3 cm., erect, almost cylindrical, semicircular or arcuate, hooked or with a short mucro at tip, glabrous, transversely or net-wrinkled all along; dorsal suture convex, ventral suture flat of furrowed. Seeds 10–20. Fl. March–April.

Subsp. **corrugatus**. *A. corrugatus* Bertol., l.c. et in DC., Prodr. 2 : 289 (1825); Boiss., Fl. 2 : 232 (1872). Pod mostly semicircular, hooked at tip, transversely wrinkled throughout.

Hab. : Steppes. Arava Valley, Moav, Edom.

Subsp. **tenuirugis** (Boiss.) Eig, l.c. *A. tenuirugis* Boiss., Diagn. ser 1, 9 : 61 (1849). Pod arcuate, ending in a short curved mucro, net-wrinkled on ventral surface only.

Hab. : Steppes. Edom.

This subspecies is still to be tested as to constancy.

Area of species : W. Irano-Turanian and Saharo-Arabian.

7. Astragalus negevensis Zoh. et Fertig (nom. nov.). *A. damascenus* Boiss. et Gaill. in Boiss., Diagn. ser. 2, 6 : 56 (1859) non DC., Prodr. 2 : 298 (1825); Boiss., Fl. 2 : 233 (1872); Eig, Astrag. Near East 17 (1955). [Plate 78]

Annual, glabrous or sparingly pubescent, 10–15 cm. Stems erect, branched, leafy. Leaves 8–10 cm.; stipules free, almost hyaline, lanceolate, acuminate, ciliate; leaflets (3–)6–7 pairs, remote, 1–1.5 cm., oblong or linear, retuse, glabrous or sparingly hirsute. Peduncles as long as or longer than subtending leaves, rigid. Racemes 2–4 (–6)-flowered. Bracts longer than pedicels, hyaline, lanceolate. Flowers about 1 cm., remote. Calyx tubular; teeth nearly half as long as tube. Corolla white. Pod erect, 3.5–5 (–6) × 0.3–0.4 cm., compressed, rather straight, tapering into a rigid hook, appressed-hairy or glabrous; dorsal suture deeply furrowed, ventral keeled; valves dehiscing and separating at maturity. Fl. March–April.

Var. **glabratus** (Eig) Zoh. et Fertig (comb. nov.). *A. damascenus* Boiss. et Gaill. var. *glabratus* Eig, l.c. Stems and leaves glabrescent. Pod glabrous or almost so.

Hab.: Steppes. Judean Desert, N. Negev, Moav, Edom.

Area of species: W. Irano-Turanian.

8. Astragalus trimestris L., Sp. Pl. 761 (1753); Boiss., Fl. 2 : 234 (1872); Eig, Astrag. Near East 17 (1955). [Plate 79]

Annual, greyish-green, pubescent, 10–30 cm. Stems few, prostrate or ascending, branching all along. Leaves 3–10 cm.; stipules minute, free or slightly connate at base, membranous, upper part triangular-lanceolate, acuminate, ciliate; leaflets 8–10 pairs, 1–1.5 cm., oblong to elliptical, retuse, glabrescent above, hairy beneath. Racemes 2–6-flowered, on peduncles as long as or longer than subtending leaves. Bracts about 2 mm., lanceolate-subulate. Flowers 1–1.3 cm. Calyx tubular-campanulate, white- or white- and black-hairy; teeth as long as or shorter than tube. Corolla white; standard slightly longer than wings. Pod 3–5(–6) × 0.3(–0.4) cm., deflexed, triquetrous, hook-shaped or unevenly semicircular, broadly canaliculate and 2-keeled at back, inconspicuously keeled at ventral suture, appressed-hairy, tapering at apex into a short, slightly recurved beak. Fl. February–March.

Hab.: Sandy deserts. Philistean Plain, W. and C. Negev, Arava Valley, Edom.

Area: Saharo-Arabian, with extensions into the Mediterranean coastal plain.

9. Astragalus gyzensis Del., Fl. Aeg. Ill. 70 no. 690 et Fl. Eg. Suppl. t. 64, f. 14 (1813); Bge., Mém. Acad. Sci. Pétersb. ser. 7, 11, 16 : 14 (1868) et 15, 1 : 16 (1869) p.p.; Boiss., Fl. 2 : 234 (1872) p.p. non *A. gyzensis* auct. Fl. Ross. *A. hauarensis* Boiss., Diagn. ser. 1, 9 : 63 (1849). [Plate 80]

Annual, greyish-canescent, 10–25 cm. Stems few or solitary, diffuse, prostrate or ascending, densely hirsute. Leaves 4–10 cm.; stipules triangular, acute; leaflets 2–4 pairs, remote, 0.8–1.2 cm., terminal leaflet often longer, flat, elliptical-oblong to broadly elliptical, retuse, appressed-pubescent on either side. Peduncles shorter than the very long-petioled subtending leaves. Racemes loose, 3–5-flowered. Bracts minute, hyaline, triangular. Flowers 1–1.3 cm. Calyx 5–9 mm., tubular, white- and appressed-hirsute; teeth shorter than tube, lanceolate. Corolla almost twice as long as calyx, white; standard oblong, longer than keel. Pod 2–3.5 × 0.3–0.4 cm., cylindrical or somewhat compressed, semicircular, tapering at both ends, ending in a short mucro and covered with both short, appressed hairs and also larger, spreading hairs with tuberculate base; dorsal suture furrowed, ventral keeled; valves separating at maturity. Fl. February–March.

Hab.: Deserts. Arava Valley.

Area: Saharo-Arabian.

Astragalus aslujensis Eig, Astrag. Near East 18 (1955) (from Northern Negev) was hesitatingly published because of the inadequate material. No other specimens have been found since.

Sect. ANKYLOBUS (Stev.) Bge., Mém. Acad. Sci. Pétersb. ser. 7, 11, 16 : 15 (1868; orth. err. *"Ankylotus"*). Gen. *Ankylobus* Stev., Bull. Soc. Nat. Mosc. 29, 2 : 148 (1856). Flowers racemose on axillary peduncles. Calyx tubular. Standard lingulate-appendiculate at apex. Pod many-seeded, linear, arcuate to semicircular; dorsal suture convex, furrowed.

10. Astragalus intercedens Sam. ex Rech. f., Ark. Bot. ser. 2, 1, 5 : 308 (1949). *A. maris-mortui* Eig, Astrag. Near East 21 (1955). [Plate 81]

Annual, 10–20 cm., covered with appressed and patulous white hairs. Stems few to many, ascending, branching. Leaves 1–3 cm.; stipules 2–5 mm., triangular-lanceolate, ciliate; leaflets 4–6(–8) pairs, inserted all along the somewhat dilated petiole, 0.5–0.8(–1) cm., subpetiolulate, obovate or oblong, cuneate at base, obtuse or slightly retuse at apex, hairy on both sides. Peduncles mostly longer than subtending leaves. Racemes 1–3(–4)-flowered. Bracts 1.5–2 mm., longer than pedicels, triangular-subulate to lanceolate, hairy and ciliate. Flowers 1–1.5 cm., purple (yellowish when dried). Calyx about 8 mm., tubular, black- and white-hirsute; teeth about 1.5 mm., lanceolate-subulate. Pod 2.5–4 × 0.25–0.35 cm., erect, dorsally compressed, linear, falcate, strigulose, very deeply grooved-canaliculate at back, separating at maturity into 2 valves, each closed by a septal lamella. Fl. March–April.

Hab. : Steppes. Judean Desert, Dead Sea area, Moav, Edom.

Area : E. Saharo-Arabian.

11. Astragalus callichrous Boiss., Diagn. ser. 1, 9 : 62 (1849) et Fl. 2 : 235 (1872); Eig, Astrag. Near East 19 (1955). [Plate 82]

Annual, green, patulous-tomentellous, 10–20 cm. Stems erect or ascending, branching from base, leafy. Leaves (3–)6–10 cm.; stipules free almost to base, lanceolate; leaflets 7–10 pairs, 0.8–2 cm., elliptical to linear, obtuse, hairy on both sides. Peduncles slender, as long as or longer than subtending leaves. Racemes 5–8(–15)-flowered. Bracts minute, about 2 mm., subulate, black- and white-hairy. Flowers showy, 1.6–2.2(–2.4) cm. Calyx 7–9 mm., tubular, black- and white-hairy; teeth about one third as long as tube, linear-lanceolate. Corolla violet; limb of standard oblong, gradually tapering. Pod 3–5 × 0.2 cm., erect, somewhat compressed, cylindrical, circular or semicircular, with both short, dense and appressed bristles, and longer, scattered and patulous bristles with tuberculate base; dorsal suture convex, grooved; beak minute or obsolete; valves not separating at maturity. Fl. January–April.

Hab. : Coastal batha and deserts. Acco Plain, Sharon Plain, Philistean Plain, Lower Galilee, Esdraelon Plain, Samaria, Judean Mts., Judean Desert, Negev, Upper and Lower Jordan Valley, Dead Sea area, Gilead, Ammon, Moav, Edom.

Area : E. Saharo-Arabian, slightly extending into the Mediterranean territory.

12. Astragalus hispidulus DC., Astragalogia 132, t. 13 (1802); Boiss., Fl. 2 : 235 (1872); Eig, Astrag. Near East 18 (1955). [Plate 83]

Annual, patulous-hispid, 5–25 cm. Stems erect, ascending or prostrate, sparingly branching. Leaves 3–5 cm.; stipules membranous, lanceolate, ciliate; leaflets 4–7 pairs, 0.5–1 cm., linear to oblong-elliptical, obtuse. Peduncles as long as or longer than subtending leaves. Racemes (1–)2–3(–5)-flowered. Bracts 2–4 mm., longer than pedicels. Flowers 1.2–1.4 cm. Calyx tubular, with soft, patulous, white and black hairs; teeth one third to one half as long as tube, subulate. Corolla pink to pale purple. Pod 3–4 × 0.15–0.2 cm., somewhat flattened, circular or semicircular, acute, with two types of short bristles: appressed or patulous, the latter tuberculate at base. Fl. March–April.

Hab.: Sandy and gravelly steppes and deserts. Judean Desert, C. Negev, Lower Jordan Valley, Dead Sea area, Arava Valley, Moav, Edom.

Area: E. Saharo-Arabian.

Differs from *A. callichrous* mainly in its more hairy vesture, few-flowered racemes and smaller flowers with their brighter colour. There are, however, intermediate forms between this species and *A. callichrous*.

13. Astragalus moabiticus Post, Fl. Syr. Pal. Sin. Add. 11 (1883–1896) et ed. 2, 1 : 380 (1932); Eig, Astrag. Near East 22 (1955).

Annual, sparingly hairy, 5–10 cm.; leaflets 5–8 pairs, 6 × 2 mm., elliptical, obtuse. Peduncles as long as leaves or shorter. Racemes small, 4–6-flowered. Calyx white- and black-hairy; teeth as long as tube, linear, setaceous. Corolla purple to violet; limb of standard obovate-retuse. Pod not known. Fl. April.

Hab.: Moav (endemic).

Area: W. Irano-Turanian.

The above description is taken from Post, l.c.; no authentic specimen of this species has, so far, been examined.

Sect. HAEMATODES Bge., Mém. Acad. Sci. Pétersb. ser. 7, 11, 16 : 15 (1868). Flowers loosely racemose, pink. Calyx campanulate. Standard not appendiculate; keel shorter than wings. Pod 2-celled, many-seeded, angulate, linear, semicircular or circular; dorsal suture concave, furrowed.

14. Astragalus annularis Forssk., Fl. Aeg.-Arab. 139 (1775); Boiss., Fl. 2 : 236 (1872); Eig, Astrag. Near East 23 (1955). [Plate 84]

Annual, more or less patulous-hairy, 10–20 cm. Stems solitary or few, diffuse. Leaves 2–6 cm.; stipules 1–2 mm., free almost to base, triangular-lanceolate; leaflets (1–)2–4 pairs, 0.5–1.7 × 0.2–0.4 cm., obovate to oblong, obtuse, hairy on either side. Peduncles almost as long as subtending leaves. Racemes (1–)2–5-flowered. Bracts longer than pedicels, subulate, bristly. Flowers 0.6–0.8(–1) cm. Calyx campanulate, black- and white-hairy; teeth almost as long as tube, subulate. Corolla pink to pale purple. Pod 3–5(–6) × 0.25–0.4 cm., spreading, semicircular to mostly circular, laterally compressed, ending in a short incurved mucro, appressed-bristly, glabrescent at maturity and mottled with red; dorsal suture deeply furrowed, ventral obtuse. Fl. March–April.

Hab.: Deserts, mainly sandy soils. Sharon Plain, Philistean Plain, Samaria, W., N. and C. Negev.

Area: E. Saharo-Arabian, with limited extensions into E. Mediterranean coastal territories.

Sect. CYAMODES Bge., Mém. Acad. Sci. Pétersb. ser. 7, 11, 16 : 16 (1868). Flowers racemose, cream-coloured. Keel shorter than wings. Pod 2-celled, many-seeded, sub-membranous, thick, prismatic-oblong, straight; dorsal suture subconcave, deeply furrowed.

15. Astragalus boeticus L., Sp. Pl. 758 (1753); Boiss., Fl. 2 : 236 (1872). [Plate 85]

Annual, leafy, green, sparingly hairy, 10–50 cm. Stems erect, much branched from base, grooved. Leaves 8–15 cm.; stipules membranous, glabrous, ciliate, free portion triangular; leaflets 7–11 pairs, up to 3 cm., oblong to linear, retuse, glabrous above, appressed-hairy beneath. Peduncles shorter than subtending leaves, erect or spreading, somewhat thickened. Racemes 2–15-flowered. Bracts almost as long as calyx tube, hyaline, lanceolate, black- and white-hairy. Flowers 1–1.2 cm. Calyx tubular, black- and white-hairy; teeth as long as or somewhat shorter than tube, subulate. Corolla cream-coloured. Pod (2–)3–4 × 0.5 cm., erect, oblong-prismatic, straight, appressed-hairy to glabrescent, with broadly furrowed dorsal suture and prominently keeled ventral one; beak hook-shaped. Fl. February–April.

Hab.: Fields and roadsides. Acco Plain, Sharon Plain, Philistean Plain, Upper Galilee, Esdraelon Plain, Samaria, Shefela, Judean Mts., Negev, Hula Plain, Edom.

Area: Mediterranean.

In the Coastal Negev a short-fruited form occurs which may perhaps be considered a separate variety.

Young pods edible.

Sect. AULACOLOBUS Bge., Mém. Acad. Sci. Pétersb. ser. 7, 11, 16 : 18 (1868). Flowers racemose, pale violet. Calyx campanulate. Standard obcordate; keel broad, much longer than wings, almost equal to standard.

16. Astragalus guttatus Banks et Sol. in Russ., Nat. Hist. Aleppo, ed. 2, 2 : 260 (1794); Eig, Astrag. Near East 24 (1955). *A. conduplicatus* Bertol., Misc. Bot. 2 : 17, t. 3, f. 2 (1843) et Nov. Comment. Bonon. 6 : 231 (1844); Boiss., Fl. 2 : 237 (1872). [Plate 86]

Annual, green, nearly glabrous, 10–20 cm. Stems few, mostly prostrate, grooved or angular. Leaves 5–8 cm.; stipules free almost to base, hyaline, triangular-ovate; leaflets 5–8 pairs, 0.6–1 cm., oblong to linear, cuneate, retuse. Peduncles generally as long as or shorter than subtending leaves, aristate at apex. Racemes loosely 1–2(–3–4)-flowered. Bracts as long as or longer than calyx tube, hyaline, linear. Flowers up to about 1 cm. Calyx about 0.6 cm., campanulate, black-hairy; teeth as long as tube, linear-lanceolate. Corolla white. Pod 2–2.5 × 0.5–0.7 cm., spreading or deflexed on a somewhat indurated pedicel, oblong, arcuate, mottled with brown; dorsal suture obtusely 2-keeled, ventral slightly keeled. Fl. March–April.

Hab.: Fields. Judean Mts., N. and C. Negev, Ammon, Moav, Edom.

Area: W. Irano-Turanian.

Sect. BUCERAS Bge., Mém. Acad. Sci. Pétersb. ser. 7, 11, 16 : 12 (1868). Flowers racemose, small, cream-coloured. Standard oblong; keel shorter than wings. Pod 2-celled, many-seeded, indurated, leathery, almost cylindrical, falcate or hook-shaped; dorsal suture obsoletely furrowed.

17. Astragalus hamosus L., Sp. Pl. 758 (1753). [Plate 87]

Annual, appressed-pubescent, 10–30(–50) cm. Stems few or many, erect or procumbent, usually much branched. Leaves 4–15 cm.; stipules triangular, acuminate; leaflets in many pairs, up to 1–2 cm., obovate to oblong, retuse, glabrous above, appressed-hairy beneath. Peduncles shorter than subtending leaves. Racemes axillary, many-flowered. Flowers 0.8–1 cm. Calyx tubular; teeth as long as or slightly longer than tube, subulate. Corolla much longer than calyx, yellowish-white; standard oblong-elliptical; wings slightly longer than keel. Pod (2–3–)4–6(–7) × 0.2–0.3 cm., deflexed, cylindrical-terete to semicylindrical, fishhook-shaped with tip slightly curved outwards, sparingly appressed-hairy. Fl. March–May.

Var. **hamosus.** *A. hamosus* L., l.c.; Boiss., Fl. 2 : 238 (1872). *A. hamosus* L. var. *subsessilis* Eig ex Rech. f., Ark. Bot. ser. 2, 2, 5 : 370 (1952) *nom. nud.* Pod 4–7 cm.

Hab. : Fields and roadsides. Acco Plain, Sharon Plain, Philistean Plain, Upper and Lower Galilee, Mt. Carmel, Esdraelon Plain, Samaria, Shefela, Judean Mts., W. and N. Negev, Hula Plain, Upper and Lower Jordan Valley, Dead Sea area, Gilead, Ammon, Moav, Edom.

Var. **microcarpus** Zoh.* Pod 2–3 cm. or less. Differs from *A. brachyceras* Ledeb., Cat. Hort. Dorpat. 3 (1822), in its fishhook-shaped (and not arcuate) pod. The records of *A. brachyceras* from Palestine are doubtful.

Hab. : As above. Upper Galilee, Judean Mts., Ammon, Moav.

Area of species : Mediterranean, penetrating deeply into Irano-Turanian territories.

18. Astragalus scorpioides Pourr. in Willd., Sp. Pl. 3 : 1280 (1802). *A. canaliculatus* Schlecht. in Willd., Enum. Pl. Hort. Berol. Suppl. 52 (1814); Post, Fl. Syr. Pal. Sin. ed. 2, 1 : 382 (1932). [Plate 88]

Annual, greenish, appressed-bristly, 10–15 cm. Stems many, ascending to decumbent, sparingly branching, leafy. Leaves up to 7 cm.; stipules 3–4 mm., membranous, ovate-oblong, acute to acuminate; leaflets 0.6–1 cm., 6–8 pairs, somewhat remote, petiolulate, oblong-elliptical, retuse, almost glabrous above, appressed-hirsute beneath. Bracts about 2 mm., membranous, ovate-oblong, long-ciliate. Flowers axillary, solitary, rarely twin, sessile or subsessile. Calyx about 8 mm., tubular, appressed-hairy with white bristles below and black ones above; teeth subulate, shorter than to as long as tube. Corolla one and a half times as long as calyx, pale pink. Pod 3.5–4.5 × 2.5–3 mm., compressed-cylindrical, falcate-arcuate, tapering, with incurved, hooked tip, appressed-hirsute; dorsal suture deeply grooved. Seeds many. Fl. April.

Hab. : Semisteppe batha, grey-brown soil. S. Judean Mts.

Area : Mediterranean and W. Irano-Turanian (known so far from the Syrian Desert, Algeria and Spain).

* See Appendix at end of this volume.

Sect. PLATYGLOTTIS Bge., Mém. Acad. Sci. Pétersb. ser. 7, 11, 16:16 (1868). Flowers racemose. Calyx tubular-campanulate. Corolla brown or purple, violet or flesh-coloured; standard broadened at base, acuminate; keel shorter than wings. Pod 2- or incompletely 2-celled, many-seeded, linear, oblong, lanceolate to ovoid, straight or arcuate, deeply furrowed on back.

19. Astragalus palaestinus Eig, Journ. Bot. Lond. 72 : 124 (1934). [Plate 89]

Annual, biennial or perennial herb with patulous white and black hairs, 10–50 cm. Stems many, prostrate, branching from base. Leaves 5–15 cm.; stipules long-acuminate, blackish; leaflets 8–12 pairs, remote or crowded, 0.4–1.2 cm., petiolulate, obovate-obcordate or oblong-elliptical, retuse, often mucronulate, hairy on both sides. Peduncles longer than subtending leaves. Racemes many, (5–)8–17-flowered. Bracts shorter than calyx, lanceolate. Flowers 1.8–2 cm., short-pedicelled. Calyx 1–1.2 cm., densely black-and white-villose; teeth shorter than or as long as tube, lanceolate. Corolla lurid violet; standard oblong-rhombic. Pod (1.4–)1.8–3(–3.5) × 0.4–0.8(–1) cm., oblong or lanceolate to ovoid-oblong, more or less curved, often hairy, more or less reticulate-wrinkled or tuberculate; both sutures usually grooved; valves not or hardly separating at maturity. Seeds 12–20, about 2 mm., globular. Fl. March–April.

Subsp. **palaestinus**. *A. palaestinus* Eig ssp. *eu-palaestinus* Eig, l.c. Pod about 1.5–2 cm., thick, oblong; both sutures furrowed.

Hab.: Batha and fallow fields. Sharon Plain, Upper and Lower Galilee, Esdraelon Plain, Samaria, Judean Mts., Judean Desert, Negev, Hula Plain, Upper and Lower Jordan Valley, Gilead, Ammon, Moav, Edom.

Subsp. **jordanensis** Eig, l.c. Pod ovoid-oblong, 1.4–1.6 × 0.9–1 cm.; both sutures furrowed; all parts densely villose.

Hab.: Steppes. Judean Desert, Lower Jordan Valley, Dead Sea area.

Subsp. **hierosolymitanus** Eig, l.c. Pod lanceolate, 2.8–3.5 × 0.5–0.6 cm.; dorsal suture narrowly grooved, ventral keeled or slightly grooved.

Hab.: Batha. Esdraelon Plain, Mt. Gilboa, Judean Mts.

Area of species: E. Mediterranean and W. Irano-Turanian.

The above subspecies should be reexamined both as to their constancy and their relation to *A. bombycinus* Boiss.

The relationship between *A. palaestinus* Eig and *A. tuberculosus* DC., Astragalogia 33 (1802), is, despite the revision by Eig, l.c., still not quite clear, as has been pointed out by Rechinger f., Ark. Bot. ser. 2, 2, 5 : 370 (1952).

20. Astragalus bombycinus Boiss., Diagn. ser. 1, 2 : 50 (1843). [Plate 90]

Annual, rarely perennial herb, white-woolly, 5–20(–30) cm. Stems prostrate, rarely ascending, branching from base. Leaves 3–6 cm.; stipules free almost to base, ovate-oblong, acuminate; leaflets 5–8(–10) pairs, often crowded, 2–6 mm., obovate, retuse, appressed-hairy on both sides. Peduncles about as long as or longer than leaves, the lower peduncles shorter. Racemes 2–8-flowered. Flowers 1.2–1.4 cm., short-pedicelled. Calyx white-woolly; teeth slightly shorter than tube. Corolla white with darker spot on keel, sometimes flesh-coloured; standard oblong, tapering. Pod 1–1.8(–2.5) × 0.6–0.8 cm., oblong to ovoid, curved, ending in a short sharp point, densely villose to almost glabrous, transversely wrinkled; dorsal suture broadly grooved, ventral suture keeled; valves not separating at maturity. Seeds 8–10, about 2 mm. across, irregularly angular. Fl. March–April.

Var. **bombycinus.** *A. bombycinus* Boiss., l.c. et Fl. 2 : 240 (1872); Eig, Astrag. Near East 30 (1955). Pod whitish-grey, villose-fleecy throughout.
    Hab. : Deserts. C. Negev, Arava Valley, Ammon Desert.

Var. **aravensis** Zoh.* Pod blackish, glabrous or glabrescent.
    Hab. : As above. Arava Valley.
    Area of species : E. Saharo-Arabian, with extensions into adjacent Irano-Turanian areas.

21. Astragalus berytheus Boiss. et Bl. in Boiss., Diagn. ser. 2, 2 : 33 (1856) et Fl. 2 : 240 (1872). [Plate 91]
    Annual, crisp-pubescent or -villose, especially above, 10–60 cm. Stems prostrate, branching from base. Leaves 5–15 cm., linear in outline; stipules triangular, acuminate; leaflets 7–11 pairs, 0.3–1 cm., linear, oblong-cuneate, rarely ovate, retuse, hairy. Peduncles rather thick, about as long as subtending leaves. Racemes 5–10-flowered. Flowers about 2 cm., on pedicels shorter than bracts. Calyx about 1 cm., black-pilose; teeth about half as long as tube. Corolla purplish to white with purple spots; standard gradually tapering, slightly notched at apex. Pod 3–5 × 0.3–0.4 cm., many-seeded, cylindrical-triquetrous, arcuate, with long bristles tuberculate at base, net-wrinkled; dorsal suture deeply grooved, ventral suture keeled; valves not separating at maturity; style persistent. Seeds about 1 mm. across, reniform. Fl. March–April.
    Hab. : Consolidated dunes and sandy clay soils. Acco Plain, Sharon Plain, Philistean Plain, Shefela.
    Area : E Mediterranean.

22. Astragalus peregrinus Vahl, Symb. Bot. 1 : 57 (1790); Boiss., Fl. 2 : 241 (1872). [Plate 92]
    Annual, white-villose, 20–40 cm. long. Stems prostrate, much branching from base. Leaves 5–12 cm.; stipules acuminate; leaflets 8–12 pairs, 0.8–1.5 cm., petiolulate, obovate-oblong, retuse, hairy beneath, glabrescent or glabrous above. Peduncles 3–8 cm., shorter than subtending leaves, even in fruit. Racemes (2–)3–5-flowered, rather loose. Flowers 1.6–2 cm. Calyx with white and black hairs; teeth somewhat unequal, the longest almost as long as tube. Corolla white to pink, with purple spot on keel; standard tapering, acute to acuminate. Pod 5–6 × 0.5–0.7 cm., triquetrous, with narrow dorsal groove and sharp ventral serrulate keel, straight or slightly arcuate, tapering at top, densely covered with long bristles tuberculate at base. Seeds many, about 2 mm. across, tetragonous when ripe. Fl. March–April.
    Hab. : Sandy deserts and loess soils. W., N. and C. Negev.
    Area : E. Saharo-Arabian.

* See Appendix at end of this volume.

Sect. DASYPHYLLIUM Bge., Mém. Acad. Sci. Pétersb. ser. 7, 11, 16 : 48 (1868). Stemless or almost stemless perennials with rosulate leaves and imbricately crowded leaflets. Peduncles scape-like; racemes spicate or head-like. Calyx tubular or funnel-shaped. Standard very long. Pod 2-celled, few-seeded, oblong to ovoid-triquetrous, keeled along both sutures, long-villose.

23. Astragalus cretaceus Boiss. et Ky. in Boiss., Diagn. ser. 2, 5 : 84 (1856) et Fl. 2 : 246 (1872) non Pall., Nov. Acta Petrop. 10 : 56 (1776) *nom. nud.* [Plate 93]

Perennial, stemless, yellowish-grey, woolly. Roots vertical, fusiform. Leaves 8–30 cm., ascending or prostrate, forming a dense rosette, linear; stipules shortly connate, membranous, triangular-lanceolate, densely soft-hairy; leaflets 20–30 pairs, densely crowded, 0.6–0.8(–1) × 0.3–0.4 cm., flat, linear-oblong, lower leaflets obovate, all retuse, villose-woolly on both surfaces. Inflorescences 3–6 cm., head- to spike-like, many-flowered, dense, ovoid or oblong, borne on a villose scape as long as leaves or longer. Bracts about 1 cm., subulate, feathery. Flowers 1.5–2 cm. Calyx about 1 cm., tubular, soft-hairy; teeth one third as long as tube. Standard purple, ovate, nearly entire, much longer than the red keel. Pod 1–1.2 × 0.8–0.9 cm., compressed, ovoid-oblong, densely covered with long bristles; beak 3–4 mm., slightly curved. Fl. February–April.

Hab. : Semisteppe batha and steppes. Judean Mts., Judean Desert, N. Negev, Gilead, Ammon, Moav.

Area : W. Irano-Turanian.

24. Astragalus oxytropifolius Boiss., Diagn. ser. 1, 9 : 37 (1849) et Fl. 2 : 246 (1872); Post, Fl. Syr. Pal. Sin. 263 (1883–1896) et ed. 2, 1 : 385 (1932); Opphr., Bull. Soc. Bot. Genève ser. 2, 22 : 330 (1931).

Stemless perennial, greyish- or yellowish-woolly, 20–30 cm. Leaves 10–20 cm.; stipules connate at base, free portion lanceolate, acuminate; leaflets 20–25 pairs, crowded to more or less distant, about 1 cm., oblong to linear-oblong, retuse. Scapes thick, longer than subtending leaves, black- and white-hairy. Heads ovoid, elongating in fruit to an oblong-cylindrical, 5–8 cm. long spike. Bracts as long as tube of calyx, linear, black-hispid. Calyx rusty-hirsute; teeth about half as long as tube. Corolla one and a half times as long as calyx, violet. Pod 6–9 mm., compressed-triquetrous, oblong, densely hirsute, tapering into a somewhat incurved beak longer than or as long as the seed-bearing portion. Fl. April–May.

Hab. : Stony places. Gilead.

Area : E. Mediterranean.

According to Oppenheimer, l.c., there are transitions between this species and *A. cretaceus.*

Sect. ASTRAGALUS. Sect. *Christiani* DC., Prodr. 2 : 295 (1825) p.p. Sect. *Phacodes* et *Christiana* Bge., Mém. Acad. Sci. Pétersb. ser. 7, 11, 16 : 29, 30 (1868). Caulescent, tall perennials. Petiole persistent. Racemes axillary along the stem. Flowers large, white or yellow. Calyx tubular, rarely campanulate. Corolla glabrous. Pod subsessile, 2-celled, few-seeded, almost indehiscent; valves thick, corky.

25. Astragalus macrocarpus DC., Astragalogia 143 no. 73, t. 28 (1802) non Pall., Nov. Acta Petrop. 10 : 56 (1776) *nom. nud.* [Plate 94]

Perennial herb, villose-hairy, 30–60 cm. Stems erect, furrowed, mostly hollow, leafy. Leaves 10–25 cm., arcuate-spreading; petiole furrowed, hirsute; stipules 1.2–3 cm., free nearly to base, membranous, linear-subulate, hairy; leaflets 10–22 pairs, 1–2 × 0.6–1 cm., petiolulate, folded or flat, ovate to oblong-elliptical, retuse. Peduncles much shorter than subtending leaves. Racemes cauline, mainly on lower half of stem, 5–12-flowered. Bracts 2–3 times as long as pedicels, subulate, hairy. Flowers up to 3.5 cm. Calyx half as long as corolla, sparingly white-villose; teeth about half as long as tube or shorter, lanceolate-linear. Corolla yellow; standard oblong, spatulate, retuse. Pod 5–6 × 3 (–4) cm., woody-corky, obovoid, inflated, with rounded or concave sutures and a sharp, straight beak 1 cm. Fl. April–May.

Var. **macrocarpus**. *A. macrocarpus* DC., l.c.; Boiss., Fl. 2 : 273 (1872). *A. macrocarpus* DC. var. *typicus* Eig, Astrag. Near East 41 (1955). *A. huninensis* Freyn et Bornm. in Freyn, Bull. Herb. Boiss. 6 : 980 (1898). Pod hairy.

Hab.: Fields. Acco Plain, Philistean Plain, Mt. Carmel, Esdraelon Plain, Upper and Lower Galilee, Samaria, Shefela, Judean Mts., Judean Desert, N. and C. Negev, Upper Jordan Valley, Gilead, Edom.

Var. **leiocarpus** Eig, l.c. 42. Ovary and pod glabrous or almost so.

Hab.: Fields. Esdraelon Plain, Upper Jordan Valley.

Area of species: E. Mediterranean.

Specimens collected by the present author at the *locus classicus* of *A. huninensis* Freyn et Bornm. do not differ from *A. macrocarpus* DC. Also Eig, l.c., examining the type specimen of *A. huninensis,* found that the ovary is hairy and not glabrous as claimed by the authors of this binomial.

26. Astragalus gileadensis Eig, Astrag. Near East 42 (1955). [Plate 95]

Green perennial herb, 40–70 cm. Stems many, erect, thick, leafy, furrowed, villose. Leaves (15–)20–25(–30) cm., remote, spreading-arcuate; stipules 1–1.8 cm., membranous, lanceolate-subulate, long-ciliate; petiole patulous-hairy; leaflets (10–)20–25 pairs, about 1–1.5 × 0.4–0.8 cm., often folded, oblong to oblong-obovate, often slightly retuse, glabrous above, hairy beneath. Peduncles very short. Racemes 1–3-flowered. Calyx 1.7–2 cm., densely patulous- and white-hairy; teeth somewhat shorter than tube, lanceolate-subulate. Corolla unknown. Pod about 4 × 1.7–2 cm. (not fully mature), covered with sparse long hairs and dense short hairs, irregularly (mostly longitudinally) reticulate-wrinkled; beak straight or somewhat curved, 1–1.2 cm. Fl. April.

Hab.: Batha. Gilead (endemic).

Area: E. Mediterranean.

From the same locality Eig, l.c. 43, has also described *A. gileadensis* ssp. *macrocarpoides* which approaches *A. macrocarpus* DC. in the shape of its fruits, with the remark that this may be a hybrid form between *A. gileadensis* and the latter.

27. Astragalus postii Eig, Astrag. Near East 44 (1955). [Plate 96]

Green perennial herb, 40–60 cm. Stems many, erect, striate, densely patulous-hairy. Leaves 25–30 cm., crowded, with patulous-hairy petioles; stipules membranous, 2–3 cm., lanceolate-linear, ciliate; leaflets about 25–30 pairs, 1–1.3 × 0.7–0.8 cm., oblong to ovate or orbicular, slightly retuse, glabrous above, appressed-hirsute beneath. Peduncles decreasing in length from base upwards. Lower racemes 2–4-flowered, upper racemes 1-flowered. Bracts much longer than pedicels, hyaline, linear-setaceous, ciliate. Flowers 3–3.5 cm. Calyx 1.8–2.2 cm., white-hirsute; teeth almost as long as tube, linear-setaceous. Corolla cream-coloured (when dried), standard about 3 cm., with oblong-obovate, slightly retuse limb. Ovary densely villose; style very long (up to 2.5 cm.). Pod (young) 3–3.2 × 1.7–1.8 cm. (without beak), oblong-ellipsoidal, densely hirsute; beak 1.3–1.5 cm. Fl. April–May.

Hab.: Batha and rocky places. Gilead (endemic, recorded by Post, Fl. Syr. Pal. Sin. 265, 1883–1896 et ed. 2, 1 : 388, 1932, under *A. graecus* Boiss. et Sprun. in Boiss., Diagn. ser. 1, 2 : 57, 1843), Moav.

Area : Probably E. Mediterranean.

According to Eig, l.c., this species is distinguished from *A. gileadensis* by its dense indumentum, the very long stipules, the more numerous leaflets, the longer calyx teeth and the stouter beak of the pod.

28. Astragalus galilaeus Freyn et Bornm. in Freyn, Bull. Herb. Boiss. 6 : 978 (1898); Eig, Astrag. Near East 54 (1955). [Plate 96a]

Green perennial herb, 40–50 cm. Stems thick, erect, leafy, furrowed, villose. Leaves spreading, linear, with villose petioles; lower leaves 5–7 cm., upper leaves 15–20 cm.; stipules free, not adnate to petiole, hyaline, triangular-lanceolate, villose; leaflets 15–20 pairs, 0.6–1 × 0.6–0.7 cm., orbicular to obovate, obtuse to retuse, glabrous above, patulous-hirsute beneath. Peduncles short. Racemes (2–)4–5-flowered. Bracts much longer than pedicels, hyaline, setaceous, acute, ciliate. Flowers 3–3.9 cm. Calyx villose; teeth as long as or somewhat shorter than tube, setaceous, broader at base. Corolla white; standard rhombic-elliptical, retuse. Pod (immature) 2.5 × 1 cm., somewhat compressed, oblong, glabrous, longitudinally wrinkled; dorsal suture ribbed, ventral suture broad and slightly furrowed; beak 1 cm. Fl. April–May.

Hab.: Batha. Upper Galilee (endemic).

Area : E. Mediterranean.

The description of this species was completed by Eig, l.c., who discussed its relations to some allied species.

The whole cluster of species around *A. macrocarpus* requires further taxonomical study as to both delimitation and subdivision of the species.

29. Astragalus feinbruniae Eig ex Rech. f., Ark. Bot. ser. 2, 1, 5 : 309, t. 7 (1949); Eig, Astrag. Near East 47 (1955; "*feinbrunii*"). [Plate 97]

Green, caulescent perennial herb, 30–60 cm. Stems thick, simple or sparingly branched, leafy. Branches spreading, dense, long- and white-pilose. Leaves up to 25 cm. or more; stipules 0.7–1.5 cm., membranous, almost acute, glabrous, ciliate, prominently nerved; petiole hirsute; leaflets often 20–35 pairs, 0.5–1 cm., often folded,

mostly ovate to orbicular, retuse, glabrous above, appressed-pilose beneath. Peduncles
1–4 cm. Racemes mostly confined to the lower half of stem, 2–4(–5)-flowered. Bracts
2–3 times as long as pedicels, hyaline, linear-subulate. Flowers 2–3(–3.5) cm. Calyx
1.3–1.6 cm., tubular, white-hirsute; teeth one third to one half as long as tube,
lanceolate-subulate. Corolla cream-coloured to white; limb of standard obovate-oblong
to almost orbicular, slightly notched. Pod 1.8–2.7 × 1–1.7 cm. (not incl. beak), compressed, oblong and coarsely reticulate-wrinkled, almost globular to ovoid, with strongly
convex back and more or less straight ventral suture, keeled on both sides; beak stout,
up to 0.8–1.4 cm. Fl. March–April.

Subsp. **feinbruniae**. *A. feinbrunii* Eig in Opphr. et Evenari, Bull. Soc. Bot. Genève ser.
2, 31 : 271 (1941) *nom. nud.* Pod 1.8–2.2 cm., compressed, unilaterally inflated,
strongly reticulate-wrinkled; beak almost straight.

Hab.: Fields and semisteppe batha. Philistean Plain, Shefela, Judean Mts., Judean
Desert, N. Negev, Lower Jordan Valley.

Subsp. **judaicus** Eig ex Eig, Astrag. Near East 48 (1955); Eig in Rech. f., Ark. Bot. ser.
2, 2, 5 : 369 in adn. et 370 (1952) *nom. nud.* (incl. var. *macrocarpus* Eig in Rech. f.,
l.c. *nom. nud.*). Pod 2.5–2.7 cm., ovoid-globular, more or less equally inflated on both
sides; beak more or less curved.

Hab.: As above. Judean Desert, N. Negev, Beit Shean Valley.

Area of species: W. Irano-Turanian.

Sect. MYOBROMA (Stev.) Bge., Mém. Acad. Sci. Pétersb. ser. 7, 11, 16 : 33 (1868).
Gen. *Myobroma* Stev., Bull. Soc. Nat. Mosc. 4 : 268 (1832). Stemless or almost stemless perennials. Flowers yellow or cream-coloured, in racemes crowded mostly among
the basal leaves. Calyx tubular with gibbous base. Pod mostly incompletely or wholly
2-celled, papery or leathery, turgid.

30. Astragalus platyraphis Fisch. ex Bge., Mém. Acad. Sci. Pétersb. ser. 7, 11, 16 : 37
(1868) et 15, 1 : 48 (1869); Eig, Astrag. Near East 60 (1955). [Plate 98]

Green, stemless perennial herb, slightly woody at base, hirsute to villose. Leaves
10–20 cm., erect or ascending, rarely procumbent; stipules up to 2 m. or more, free
to near base, membranous, lanceolate, glabrous, ciliate at margin; petiole patulous-
hirsute; leaflets 10–15 pairs, 0.6–1.2 × 0.3–0.7 cm., petiolulate, often folded, obovate
to oblong or lanceolate. Racemes 3–7-flowered, on short, somewhat thickened peduncles
crowded between leaves. Bracts much longer than the 3 mm. long pedicels, lanceolate-
subulate. Flowers 2.5–2.8 cm. Calyx 1.4–1.8 cm.; tube hirsute to glabrescent; teeth
2–5 mm., linear-lanceolate, ciliate. Corolla yellow; standard obovate, deeply notched.
Pod 1.2–4 × 0.6–1 cm., leathery, triquetrous, oblong; beak stout, 2–3 mm.; gynophore
1–3 mm.; valves separating at maturity. Seeds 6–8, 2–3 × 3–4 mm., obliquely reniform. Fl. March–April.

Var. **platyraphis**. *A. platyraphis* Fisch. ex Bge., l.c.; Boiss., Fl. 2 : 284 (1872). *A. platy-*
raphis Fisch. ex Bge. var. *typicus* Eig, l.c. Racemes and leaves short; leaflets often
0.7–1 cm. Pod (2.8–)3–3.3 cm.

Hab. : Steppes and field edges. Gilead, Ammon, Edom.

Var. **microcarpus** Eig, l.c. Differs from the preceding variety by the small pod, 1.2–
1.5 cm.

Hab. : As above. Ammon, Moav, Edom.

Area of species : W. Irano-Turanian.

31. Astragalus beershabensis Eig et Sam. ex Rech. f., Ark. Bot. ser. 2, 1, 5 : 309, t. 8
(1949); Eig et Sam. in Eig, Astrag. Near East 62 (1955; *"bersabeensis"*). [Plates
99, 100]

Stemless, green, herbaceous perennial herb, abundantly branching at base, villose or
sparingly patulous-hairy. Leaves 10–30 cm., ascending or erect, patulous-hairy; stipules
1–1.5 cm., with lower part adnate to petiole, membranous, oblong-ovate to lanceolate;
leaflets 1–2 × 0.4–0.7 cm., petiolulate, folded or flat, oblong to obovate, obtuse or
retuse, hirsute on both sides or only on lower side. Racemes (2–)3–4(–5)-flowered, on
short or somewhat elongated peduncles. Bracts much longer than pedicels, membranous,
lanceolate-subulate to linear, long-ciliate. Flowers 2.3–3 cm. Calyx 1.5–1.7 cm., tubular, white-hairy; teeth one third to one half as long as tube, narrowly lanceolate. Corolla
yellow or yellowish-brown; standard obovate, notched. Pod 1.6–3 cm., almost trigonous,
ellipsoidal to oblong, patulous-hairy, keeled along ventral suture only, borne on a
gynophore 3–6 mm.; beak short, curved; valves dehiscing but not separating. Seeds
3 mm., irregularly reniform. Fl. February–April.

Var. **beershabensis.** *A. beershabensis* Eig et Sam. ex Rech. f., l.c. *A. bersabeensis* Eig
et Sam. var. *typicus* Eig, Astrag. Near East 63 (1955). [Plate 99]. Leaves 10–20 cm.
Peduncles 1–4 cm. Pod 1.6–2.5 cm. (rarely larger).

Hab. : Sand and loess soils. N., E. and C. Negev. Fairly common.

Var. **elongatus** (Barb.) Eig, Astrag. Near East 63 (1955). *A. alexandrinus* Boiss. var.
elongata Barb., Herbor. Levant 131 (1882). [Plate 100]. Leaves 20–30 cm. Peduncles
5–18 cm. Flowers 3 cm. Corolla brownish.

Hab. : As above. Judean Desert, N. Negev (endemic).

Area of species : W. Saharo-Arabian.

Future studies may raise var. *elongatus* to the rank of a species.

32. Astragalus alexandrinus Boiss., Diagn. ser. 1, 9 : 75 (1849) et Fl. 2 : 284 (1872);
Eig, Astrag. Near East 63 (1955). [Plate 101]

Perennial, stemless, green herb, slightly woody at base, patulous-villose. Leaves
10–25 cm., ascending; stipules 1.2–1.5 cm., connate and adnate to petiole in lowest
quarter, membranous, oblong-lanceolate, acuminate, glabrous, long-ciliate; petiole
patulous-hairy; leaflets 12–18 pairs, 0.7–1 × 0.3–0.5 cm., flat or folded, oblong to
obovate, rounded or slightly retuse at apex, glabrous above, hairy beneath, long-ciliate;
terminal leaflets crowded. Racemes 3–5-flowered, on slender peduncles one half to
one fourth as long as subtending leaves or less. Bracts 1 cm. or longer, almost twice
as long as pedicels, lanceolate-subulate, long-hairy. Flowers 2.5–3 cm. Calyx 1.3–
1.5 cm., sparsely hirsute; teeth 3–5 mm., linear-lanceolate. Corolla yellow; standard

obovate, notched. Pod 1–2.5 × 0.7–1 cm., ovoid, hirsute, minutely tuberculate and wrinkled, with obtuse or depressed and grooved dorsal suture and keeled ventral one; beak short, 2–4 mm., slightly incurved; gynophore 0; valves dehiscing but not separating. Seeds 4–8, flattened, obliquely reniform. Fl. March–April.

Hab.: Sand and loess soils. W., N. and C. Negev.

Area: E. Saharo-Arabian (Palestine-Egypt).

There are all transitions between var. *typicus* Eig, l.c., with smaller fruit, and var. *sublaxus* Eig, l.c. 64, with longer fruit and more elongated peduncles.

33. Astragalus aaronsohnianus Eig, Astrag. Near East 67 (1955) excl. ssp. *aaronii*. *A. aaronsohnii* Eig ex Rech. f., Ark. Bot. ser. 2, 2, 5 : 367 (1952) *nom. nud.* [Plate 102]

Perennial, almost stemless, grey herb, patulous-hairy, with forked woody base. Leaves 5–12 cm., with short, rather persistent, striate, patulous-hirsute petioles; stipules with base adnate to petiole, membranous, white, oblong, hirsute and short-ciliate, later glabrous, those of upper leaves up to 1.3–1.4 × 0.5 cm.; leaflets 14–20 pairs, rather crowded, 0.3–1 × 0.2–0.7 cm., flat, obovate to orbicular, hirsute on both sides. Peduncles much shorter than subtending leaves, 2–3-flowered, villose. Bracts almost as long as or longer than pedicels, membranous, linear, hirsute. Flowers 1.8–2.2 cm. Calyx 1.1–1.3 cm., tubular, densely patulous- and white-hirsute; teeth one third to one half as long as tube, linear-lanceolate. Corolla yellow; standard obovate, notched. Pod 2–2.2 × 0.5–0.6 cm., depressed, oblong, white-hirsute, grooved at back and keeled at ventral side, with beak about 6 mm. Fl. March–April.

Hab.: Sandstone hills. Edom (endemic).

Area: E. Saharo-Arabian.

34. Astragalus aaronii (Eig) Zoh. (comb. et stat. nov.). *A. aaronsohnianus* Eig ssp. *aaronii* Eig, Astrag. Near East 68 (1955). [Plate 103]

Perennial, stemless, greenish, hirsute herb, with a somewhat woody stock. Leaves 15–25 cm., ascending to almost erect, with grooved, patulous-hairy petiole; stipules free nearly to base, membranous, oblong, hairy all over; leaflets 9–10 pairs, very scattered, 0.8–1 × 0.4–0.8 cm., minutely petiolulate, flat, obovate to obovate-cuneate, rounded or notched at apex, appressed-hairy on both sides. Peduncles about 2 cm., 3–4-flowered. Pedicels long, recurved in fruit, longer than bracts. Flowers about 2.5 cm. Calyx about 1.2 cm., villose; teeth 2–4 mm., lanceolate-linear. Corolla yellow; standard obovate, notched. Pod 1.5–2 × 0.5–0.7 cm., dorsally compressed, ellipsoidal, hairy, keeled along both sutures, with a short, slightly curved beak and gynophore 2–3 mm. Fl. March–April.

Hab.: Sandy rocks. Edom (endemic).

Area: W. Irano-Turanian.

Sect. CHRONOPUS Bge., Mém. Acad. Sci. Pétersb. ser. 7, 11, 16 : 41 (1868). Perennial, stemless or caulescent, white-pilose herbs or dwarf shrubs, with persistent, often spinescent petioles. Racemes few-flowered, axillary. Flowers yellow. Calyx mostly tubular. Pod 2-celled, many-seeded, more or less elongated, ligneous or fleshy.

35. Astragalus acinaciferus Boiss., Diagn. ser. 1, 9 : 72 (1849); Eig, Astrag. Near East 70 (1955). [Plate 104]

Perennial, woody at base, appressed- and strigulose-canescent, 20–30 cm. Stems very short to conspicuous. Leaves up to 20 cm. or more; petiole slightly indurated, not becoming spiny but persistent; stipules crowded, membranous, triangular, acuminate, strigulose; leaflets 15–25 pairs, somewhat crowded in upper part of leaf, 0.3–1 cm., mostly folded, ovate to oblong, obtuse or retuse. Racemes axillary, 1–5-flowered, on a more or less conspicuous peduncle. Flowers about 2.5–3.2 cm. Calyx about half as long as corolla, tubular, patulous-hairy; teeth one fifth as long as tube. Corolla yellow. Pod 5–8 × 1–1.5 cm., pedicellate, ligneous or spongy, slightly dorsally compressed, dagger-shaped, slightly arcuate, tapering to an acute, stout beak, appressed-strigulose to glabrescent, prominently net-veined longitudinally, becoming blackish except for the white sutures and beak; valves tardily dehiscent in upper part, but not separating. Seeds 15–20, 6–8 mm. across, flat, more or less 4-angled. 2n = 16. Fl. February–March.

Var. **acinaciferus**. *A. acinaciferus* Boiss., l.c. et Fl. 2 : 300 (1872). *A. acinaciferus* Boiss. var. *typicus* Eig, l.c. Peduncles short. Racemes 1–3-flowered.

Hab. : Steppes and gravelly wadi beds in deserts. Judean Desert, Lower Jordan Valley, Dead Sea area, Gilead, Ammon, Edom.

Var. **racemosus** (Opphr.) Eig, l.c. *A. sieberi* DC. var. *racemosus* Opphr., Bull. Soc. Bot. Genève ser. 2, 22 : 330 (1931). Peduncles 3–5 cm. Racemes 3–5-flowered. Flowers 3–3.2 cm.

Hab. : Deserts; mostly in wadis. Arava Valley, Dead Sea area, Edom.

Area of species : E. Saharo-Arabian.

36. Astragalus sieberi DC., Prodr. 2 : 295 (1825); Boiss., Fl. 2 : 301 (1872). [Plate 105]

Dwarf shrub, branching from base, 15–25 cm. Stems and branches short, appressed- and woolly-canescent with white antrorse hairs. Leaves 7–15 cm.; stipules triangular, long-acuminate, ciliate; petiole becoming spinescent; leaflets 20–25 pairs, crowded, 2–5 (–7) mm., ovate or orbicular, glabrous above, appressed-strigose beneath or white-hairy throughout. Racemes few-flowered, crowded at base of short branches. Flowers about 2.5 cm., short-pedicelled. Calyx tube hairy or glabrescent, one fifth to one quarter as long as tube, white-ciliate. Corolla yellow. Pod 3–4 (–5) × 0.5–0.8 cm. (incl. beak), somewhat compressed, triquetrous, oblong, straight or slightly curved; dorsal suture obtuse, ventral narrowly keeled; valves woody, net-veined, sparsely appressed-strigulose or glabrescent; beak stout, 0.7–0.8 (–1) cm. Seeds many, 5 mm. across, angular. Fl. February–April.

Hab. : Wadis in deserts. Dead Sea area, Arava Valley.

Area : E. Saharo-Arabian.

37. Astragalus sparsus Del. ex Decne., Ann. Sci. Nat. Bot. ser. 2, 3 : 267 (1835); Boiss., Fl. 2 : 299 (1872); *A. sparsus* Del., Nouv. Fragm. Arab. Petr. (inedit.). [Plate 106]

Caulescent, perennial herb, patulous-hairy to white-woolly, 30–60 cm. Stems elongated, prostrate, branching. Leaves 6–15 cm.; stipules 1.2–1.5 cm., rather leaf-like, lanceolate-subulate; petiole patulous-hairy; leaflets 10–15 pairs, 1–2 cm., petiolulate, often folded, ovate-oblong to elliptical, obtuse to retuse, mucronulate, hairy or glabrous above, densely hairy beneath. Racemes axillary, all along the stem, nearly sessile, 4–7-flowered. Bracts half as long as calyx, filiform, hairy. Flowers 2.5–3.5 cm. Calyx 1.2–1.4 cm., tubular, sparsely long-hirsute; teeth one third to one half as long as tube, lanceolate-linear. Corolla yellow; standard oblong, tapering, somewhat longer than wings. Pods 3–4 × 0.7–0.8 cm., stellately spreading, crustaceous, linear-lanceolate, terete, almost straight, soft-hairy, tapering into a beak 5–8 mm.; dorsal suture convex, slightly grooved, ventral suture concave, keeled; valves dehiscing but not separating. Seeds about 3 mm., compressed, lentiform. Fl. March–April.

Hab.: Hot deserts; sand and granite ground. Arava Valley.

Area: E. Saharo-Arabian.

38. Astragalus fruticosus Forssk., Fl. Aeg.-Arab. 139 (1775); Eig, Astrag. Near East 73 (1955). *A. tomentosus* Lam., Encycl. 1:312 (1783); Boiss., Fl. 2:302 (1872). [Plate 107]

Perennial, white-tomentose, little-branching herb, 30–50 cm. Stems erect or procumbent, up to 1 cm. thick in lower part, with remains of older petioles. Leaves 15–30 cm., ascending; stipules 0.8–1 cm., free almost to base, triangular-lanceolate, acuminate; leaflets 20–30 pairs, 1–1.5 × 0.6–1 cm., mostly folded, orbicular or broadly ovate, notched, green above, canescent beneath; younger leaflets crowded. Flowers 2.2–2.4 cm., axillary, in fascicles of 3–4, sessile or very short-pedicelled. Calyx campanulate, villose; teeth as long as tube, lanceolate. Corolla yellow; standard oblong, obtuse, notched, somewhat longer than keel. Pod 4.5–6(–7) × 1–1.2 cm., erect, terete or somewhat compressed, straight or somewhat arcuate, with strong, straight, spiny beak about 1 cm.; dorsal suture convex, ventral suture concave, keeled; valves partially dehiscing but not separating, woody-spongy, longitudinally nerved, tomentose-hairy. Seeds many, 2–4 mm., reniform. Fl. March–April.

Hab.: Desert sandy soils and wadis. Philistean Plain, Negev.

Area: Saharo-Arabian.

Sect. STENONYCHIUM Bge., Mém. Acad. Sci. Pétersb. ser. 7, 11, 16:79 (1868). Shrubs or half-shrubs with spinescent petioles. Flowers in congested racemes subtended by large caducous bracts. Bracteoles 0. Calyx tube glabrous at base. Standard stenonychious, i.e. having an auriculate, lyrate limb borne on a narrow claw. Pod 1-seeded, minute, globular, included in calyx.

39. Astragalus echinus DC., Astragalogia 197, t. 34 (1802); Boiss., Fl. 2:338 (1872). [Plate 108]

Spiny dwarf shrub, 25–50 cm. Branches intricate, with erect-patulous spines (older, persistent, blackish leaf petioles) 2–3 cm. Leaves 1.5–3 cm.; stipules up to 7 mm., triangular, glabrous, not striate; leaflets 5–7 pairs, 4–9 × 1–2 mm., shorter than terminal spine of petiole, oblanceolate, mucronate to spinulose, appressed-canescent. Racemes congested into a globular head 2 cm. Calyx with densely villose teeth as long as tube. Flowers about 1.5 cm. Corolla twice as long as calyx; limb of standard 3 times as long as claw, lyrate, retuse, slightly auriculate at base. Pod 6 mm., 1-seeded, hidden in calyx, densely villose. Fl. March–April.

Hab.: Mountains. Edom (El Khanzirah, E. of Dead Sea, after Dinsmore in Post, Fl. Syr. Pal. Sin. ed. 2, 1 : 393, 1932).

Area: W. Irano-Turanian.

Sect. RHACOPHORUS Bge. sensu Boiss., Fl. 2 : 213 (1872). As in Sect. *Stenonychium*, but calyx tube hirsute down to its base. Claws of lower petals long-adnate to staminal tube.

40. Astragalus cruentiflorus Boiss., Diagn. ser. 1, 9 : 82 (1849) et Fl. 2 : 354 (1872). [Plate 109]

Spiny dwarf shrub, 15–50 cm. Branches intricate, with spreading spines (leaf petioles) 2–4 cm., turning blackish with age. Leaves 2–4 cm., at the ends of branches, densely canescent-tomentose; stipules white, thin, linear-lanceolate, acute, ciliate; petiole brownish-tawny, ending in a glabrous spine; leaflets 6–7 pairs, 3–4 mm., plicate, ovate-oblong, mucronate, with appressed silvery-silky hairs. Racemes 4–5-flowered, crowded together into globular heads. Bracts 6–7 × 2–3 mm., about half as long as calyx, membranous, ovate, concave, acute, tomentose on back. Calyx 1.2–1.5 cm., a little shorter than corolla, white-hispid; teeth twice as long as tube, linear-setaceous. Corolla purple; standard 1.8–2 cm.; limb acutely auriculate, slightly longer than claw. Ovary densely villose. Pod about 4 mm., oblong, white-hairy, with a straight beak 2 mm. Fl. July–August.

Hab.: Mountains. Edom.

Area: W. Irano-Turanian.

41. Astragalus bethlehemiticus Boiss., Diagn. ser. 1, 9 : 85 (1849) et Fl. 2 : 358 (1872; "*bethlemiticus*") emend. Eig, Astrag. Near East 99 (1955). [Plate 110]

Spiny dwarf shrub, 15–40 cm. Branches many, erect to spreading, with old persistent leafless spines in lower part. Spines (leaf petioles) 4–6(–8) cm., stout. Leaves with canescent, spiny-tipped petioles; stipules ovate, with free portion triangular; leaflets 4–5(–8) pairs, 4–8 mm., oblong, keeled, acute, spiny-mucronate, densely appressed- and silvery-canescent. Bracts longer than calyx tube, membranous, concave, ovate to almost orbicular, acute or mucronate, woolly on back. Flowers 1.5–1.8 cm., in 4–6 axillary fascicles crowded together into heads or spikes. Calyx 1–1.5 cm., very densely white-hispid; teeth 3 times as long as tube, setaceous and densely plumose. Corolla considerably longer than calyx, purple; limb of standard almost acute, auriculate. Pod 2–3 mm., indehiscent, white-woolly, hidden within calyx tube. Fl. May–July.

Hab.: Batha and semisteppes. Judean Mts., Judean Desert, N. and C. Negev, Gilead, Ammon, Moav.

Area: W. Irano-Turanian.

The local specimens correspond to the form called by Eig, l.c., ssp. *eu-bethlehemiticus* var. *typicus*.

This species and the former one supply tragacanth, a gum collected by the desert inhabitants, who incise the roots.

Sect. MACROPHYLLIUM Boiss., Fl. 2 : 214 (1872). Spiny half-shrubs, with long leaves and long spines. Racemes crowded into large heads. Bracts narrow, persistent. Bracteoles 0. Calyx tube villose to base. Standard as in Sect. *Stenonychium*. Pod small, hidden in calyx.

42. Astragalus deinacanthus Boiss., Diagn. ser. 1, 9 : 76 (1849) et Fl. 2 : 374 (1872). [Plate 111]

Spiny dwarf shrub, 25–35 cm. Stems branching into numerous, erect, dense branches covered with long, dry, spiny petioles in lower part. Spines (leaf petioles) 5–10(–15) cm., stout. Leaves 8–15 cm.; stipules membranous, triangular-ovate with free portion lanceolate, glabrous, ciliate, nerved; petiole 15–30 cm., stout, tapering into a strong spine; leaflets (4–)5–7 pairs, remote, 1–3 × 0.5–1 cm., petiolulate, rigid, oblong-lanceolate, tapering on both ends, glabrous or very sparingly hirsute, nerved, ending with a yellowish spine 1–2(–3) mm. Bracts as long as or shorter than calyx, membranous, linear, tapering on both ends, hirsute-plumose. Flowers 2–2.5 cm., in dense fascicles, crowded together into ovoid or globular heads 5–10 × 4–8 cm. Calyx 1–1.8 cm., densely white-hirsute; teeth half as long as tube or more, almost glabrous at apex. Corolla 2–2.5 cm., pale purple; limb as long as claw. Pod small, 8 mm., oblong, densely appressed-silky, hidden in fleecy calyx tube. Fl. April–June.

Hab.: Semisteppe batha. Upper Galilee, Judean Mts., Judean Desert, Upper Jordan Valley, Moav.

Area: W. Irano-Turanian.

Sect. POTERIUM Bge., Mém. Acad. Sci. Pétersb. ser. 7, 11, 16 : 74 (1868; "*Poterion*"). Spiny half-shrubs. Stipules free or almost free from petiole. Peduncles axillary, 1- to few-flowered. Flowers 2-bracteolate. Calyx tubular, later inflated. Pod 1 (–2–4)-seeded, hidden in calyx.

43. Astragalus spinosus (Forssk.) Muschl., Verh. Bot. Ver. Prov. Brandenb. 49 : 98 (1907); Eig, Astrag. Near East 112 (1955). *Colutea spinosa* Forssk., Fl. Aeg.-Arab. 131 (1775). *A. forskahlei* Boiss., Diagn. ser. 1, 9 : 101 (1849) et Fl. 2 : 392 (1872). [Plate 112]

Very spiny dwarf shrub, appressed-canescent, 30–60 cm. Branches intricate, with long, stout, erect-patulous, whitish spines (persistent petioles). Leaves crowded, first short, then elongating, becoming spiny; stipules woolly, almost entirely adnate to petiole, ending in 2 short, free, hyaline, triangular lobes; petiole 5–12 cm.; leaflets 4–5 pairs, 0.4–1 cm., oblong-elliptical to linear, tapering at base, obtuse, hairy on both sides. Peduncles about 1 cm. Racemes axillary, scattered along the branches, 1–2-flowered. Bracteoles 2–3 mm., subulate, hirsute. Flowers 2–2.5 cm. Calyx 1–1.5 cm., soft- and white-hairy, first tubular, then inflated, up to 1.5–2 × 1–1.5 cm. in fruit, membranous, 30–40-nerved; teeth 2–3(–4) mm., subulate. Corolla white. Pod 0.6–1 cm., stipitate, oblong, appressed-hairy, hidden in the calyx; ventral and dorsal sutures slightly keeled; beak subulate, about 2 mm. 2n = 16. Fl. March–April.

Hab.: Steppes and deserts. Philistean Plain, Judean Desert, Negev, Lower Jordan Valley, Dead Sea area, Arava Valley, deserts of Ammon, Moav and Edom. Fairly common.

Area: W. Irano-Turanian, extending into adjacent Saharo-Arabian territories.

Sect. ALOPECIAS (Stev.) Bge., Mém. Acad. Sci. Pétersb. ser. 7, 11, 16 : 58 (1868). Gen. *Alopecias* Stev., Bull. Soc. Nat. Mosc. 4 : 266 (1832). Tall and caulescent perennial herbs. Leaves large, not spinescent; stipules large, free. Flowers in dense heads or spikes, yellow or cream-coloured. Calyx tubular or campanulate, growing slightly in fruit. Pod sessile, 2-celled, 2- to few-seeded, included in calyx.

44. Astragalus oocephalus Boiss., Diagn. ser. 1, 2 : 56 (1843) et Fl. 2 : 410 (1872). [Plate 113]

Perennial herb, sparingly hirsute or glabrescent, up to 1 m. or more. Stems erect, sparingly branched, somewhat flexuous, striate. Leaves about 20–30 cm., erect or spreading; stipules linear-setaceous with a broader base; leaflets 12–20 pairs, 1.5–3 × 1–1.4 cm., ovate-oblong, obtuse to retuse, glabrous. Flower heads 4–6 × 3–4 cm., sessile in the axils of upper leaves, very compact, globular or ovoid. Bracts shorter than calyx, membranous, subulate. Flowers 2–2.5 cm. Calyx 1.5–1.8 cm., campanulate, densely patulous-hirsute; teeth about as long as tube, linear-subulate. Corolla yellow; standard with lanceolate entire limb somewhat longer than wings. Pod 5–7 mm., ovoid to globular, appressed-hairy, hidden in the slightly inflated and closed calyx; beak short, somewhat recurved. Seeds 2, rather large. Fl. March–June.

Hab.: Fields. Sharon Plain, Lower Galilee, Esdraelon Plain, Upper and Lower Jordan Valley. Rare.

Area: W. Irano-Turanian.

44a*. Astragalus azraqensis C. C. Townsend, Kew Bull. 21 : 53, 54, f. 1 (1967)

Perennial herb, 12–20 cm. Stems simple, white-woolly with long hairs. Leaves imparipinnate, mostly radical; cauline leaves 1–3; stipules 1.2–1.5 cm., almost free, lanceolate-subulate; leaflets 17–21-paired, 0.7–1.7 × 0.4–1.4 cm., ovate, obtuse, almost glabrous above (except for long hairs at margin), long-hairy beneath. Racemes mostly shorter than leaves and elongating only slightly, ovoid, later becoming short-cylindrical. Bracts longer than pedicels. Calyx about 1.5 cm., long- and white-villose; tube inflated in fruit; teeth almost as long as tube, filiform, later diverging. Standard 2.5–3 × 1–1.2 cm., dirty greenish-pink, oblong, constricted at middle, notched at apex, longer than the greenish-yellow wings and keel. Ovary 12–14-ovuled, sparsely long-pilose; style glabrous. Pod (immature) included in the inflated calyx, compressed, ovoid, glabrescent.

* This species was published when the manuscript was in press, and therefore could not be included in the key or numbered appropriately.

Hab.: Desert; loose sand in a wadi. E. Ammon (E. of Azraq ed Druz; endemic).
Area: W. Irano-Turanian.

Sect. EREMOPHYSA Bge., Mém. Acad. Sci. Pétersb. ser. 7, 11, 16:62 (1868). Caulescent perennial herbs, often with large leaves and leaflets and large free stipules. Racemes axillary, spike-like, short-peduncled, rather loose. Flowers 2-bracteolate. Calyx first tubular, later becoming bladdery-inflated. Pod stipitate, 2-celled, included in calyx.

45. Astragalus kahiricus DC., Prodr. 2:292 (1825); Boiss., Fl. 2:420 (1872). [Plate 114]

Perennial leafy herb, woolly-canescent, 30–80 cm. Stems procumbent, branching, thick, flexuous, hollow, furrowed. Leaves 20–30 cm., erect; stipules about 8 mm., herbaceous, broadly triangular, acuminate, ciliate; petiole furrowed, hirsute; leaflets 5–9 pairs, 1.8–3 × 1.4–2.4 cm., petiolulate, orbicular to broadly obovate, often retuse, glabrous above, hairy beneath. Racemes 10–25 cm., axillary, short-peduncled, many-flowered, cylindrical, loose, later elongating. Bracts much longer than pedicels, subulate. Flowers 3–4 cm. Flowering calyx 1.5–2 cm., tubular, patulous-hairy; teeth one fourth to one third as long as tube, lanceolate-subulate. Corolla yellow; standard with oblong limb as long as or shorter than wings, somewhat notched. Pod 1.2 cm., stipitate, 2-celled, somewhat compressed, obliquely ovoid, glabrous, transversely ribbed, hidden in the bladdery-inflated calyx up to 2–3 cm.; dorsal suture convex, ventral suture deeply grooved; beak 2–3 mm. Seeds 2–4 mm., reniform. Fl. January–April.

Hab.: Deserts; sand and loess soil. Negev. Not rare.
Area: E. Saharo-Arabian.

Sect. ONOBRYCHIUM Bge., Mém. Acad. Sci. Pétersb. ser. 7, 11, 16:100 (1868). Caulescent perennial herbs. Stipules more or less connate. Calyx campanulate or tubular. Flowers capitate, rarely in loose racemes. Bracteoles 0. Pod oblong, often 2-celled, often many-seeded.

46. Astragalus zemeraniensis Eig, Astrag. Near East 117 (1955). [Plate 115]

Perennial herb, woody at base, appressed-setulose, 20–30 cm. Stems many, erect, ascending or prostrate. Leaves 1.5–4 (–5) cm., densely appressed-bristly; stipules connate, free portion 1–2 mm., lanceolate; leaflets 5–8 pairs, 4–8 mm., folded or flat, linear to elliptical. Peduncles 2–3 times as long as leaves. Racemes capitate to spike-like, 12–15-flowered. Bracts longer than the very short pedicels, lanceolate. Flowers 1–1.5 cm. Calyx about half as long as corolla, tubular to campanulate, appressed-, white- and black-hairy; teeth 1–2 mm., linear-lanceolate. Corolla purple; standard with ovate-oblong limb shorter than wings. Pod about 1.2 × 0.2 cm., oblong, appressed-setulose, tapering to an incurved beak 2–2.5 mm. Fl. March–April.

Hab.: Steppes. Edom.
Area: W. Irano-Turanian.

The local populations of this species belong to ssp. **petraensis** Eig, l.c. 118, which differs from the typical form in its slightly smaller calyx, longer and narrower nerveless pod and narrower standard and wings. According to Eig this subspecies may represent an independent species. Mouterde (in litt.) synonymizes the species with *A. kotschyanus* Boiss., Diagn. ser. 1, 2 : 44 (1843) et Fl. 2 : 437 (1872).

Sect. PROSELIUS (Stev.) Bge., Mém. Acad. Sci. Pétersb. ser. 7, 11, 16 : 116 (1868). Gen. *Proselias* Stev., Bull. Soc. Nat. Mosc. 4 : 268 (1832). Perennial, stemless or very short-stemmed herbs, sometimes woody at base. Stipules adnate to petiole in their lower part. Flowers 2-bracteolate, in dense or loose, spike-like, often long-peduncled racemes. Calyx tubular, often gibbous at base, not inflated in fruit. Standard with folded margins, often recurved. Pod mostly 2-celled, many-seeded.

47. Astragalus adpressiusculus Eig, Astrag. Near East 126 (1955). [Plate 116]

Perennial herb, woody at base, appressed- and setulose-hairy, 20–30 cm. Older woody stems numerous, short, 2–6 cm., erect or ascending, covered with scaly petiole bases. Leaves 2–6 cm., silvery-canescent; stipules 0.6–1 cm., adnate to petiole, white-setulose, upper part free, 3–6 mm., lanceolate, acute, very short-mucronate; rhachis canaliculate; leaflets (5–)6–7 (–8) pairs, (3–)4–6 (–9) × 2–5 mm., oblong and obovate-oblong. Peduncles 2–3 times as long as subtending leaves. Racemes (5–)7–12 (–16)-flowered, ovoid, later spike-like. Bracts longer than pedicels, scarious, lanceolate, more or less setulose. Flowers 1.6–2 cm. Calyx 7–8 mm., tubular, black- and white-pilose; teeth 1–2 mm., triangular-linear. Corolla purple. Pod (very young) 1–1.5 × 0.2 cm., cylindrical, appressed- and white-hirsute, tapering; beak 4–5 mm. Fl. March–April.

Hab. : Steppes. Edom (endemic).

Area : W. Irano-Turanian.

Sect. XIPHIDIUM Bge., Mém. Acad. Sci. Pétersb. ser. 7, 11, 16 : 123 (1868). Shrubs, half-shrubs or perennial herbs. Stipules free or only shortly adnate to petiole. Flowers in loose or compact, long-peduncled heads or racemes. Bracteoles 0. Calyx tubular, not becoming inflated. Standard with folded margins, often recurved. Pod 2-celled, linear or oblong, many-seeded.

48. Astragalus sanctus Boiss., Diagn. ser. 1, 9 : 47 (1849) et Fl. 2 : 483 (1872). *A. sanctus* Boiss. var. *stenophyllus* Bornm., Mitt. Thür. Bot. Ver. N. F. 30 : 76 (1913); var. *typicus* Eig, Astrag. Near East 129 (1955); var. *albohirtus* Eig, l.c. 130; var. *nigrohirtus* Eig, l.c. 130; var. *marcocarpus* Eig, l.c. 130; var. *microcarpus* Eig, l.c. 130. [Plate 117]

Perennial, somewhat woody at base, appressed-, silky-canescent herb, 20–30 cm. Stems many, erect or ascending, diffuse. Leaves 5–10 cm.; stipules 2–4 mm., herbaceous, triangular-lanceolate, hirsute-ciliate; leaflets 4–7 pairs, 0.8–1.6 × 0.2–0.4 cm., petiolulate, elliptical or linear, obtuse, mucronate, hairy on both sides. Peduncles stout, as long as or longer than subtending leaves. Racemes elongated, loosely 6–16-flowered. Bracts as long as or a little longer than pedicels, triangular-subulate, white- and black-hairy. Flowers about 2.5 cm. Calyx tubular, black- or white-hirsute; teeth one fifth to one quarter as long as tube, lanceolate-linear. Corolla violet, pink or purple; standard with ovate, abruptly narrowing limb notched at apex, much longer than keel and wings. Pod 2.5–7.5 × 0.3–0.4 cm., erect-spreading, somewhat compressed, cy-lindrical, semicircular, tapering into a straight beak, covered with white or black or mixed hairs, keeled along both sutures. Fl. February–May.

Hab.: Steppes; stony and calcareous ground. Judean Mts., Judean Desert, Negev, Upper and Lower Jordan Valley, Dead Sea area, Arava Valley, Gilead, Ammon, Moav, Edom.

Area: W. Irano-Turanian.

Extremely variable in fruit size and hair colour.

49. Astragalus trachoniticus Post, Journ. Linn. Soc. Lond. 24:426 (1888); Eig, Astrag. Near East 131 (1955). [Plate 118]

Perennial herb, somewhat woody at base, grey-canescent, 10–25 cm. Stems many, diffuse. Leaves 3–12 cm.; stipules herbaceous, connate at base, the free portion deflexed, lanceolate, acuminate, black- and white- or only white-hairy; leaflets (3–)4–7 pairs, 0.7–1.2 cm., oblong to linear, acute, sometimes ovate to orbicular, appressed-canescent on both sides. Peduncles usually shorter (rarely longer) than subtending leaves. Racemes 2–5-flowered. Bracts longer than pedicels, lanceolate. Flowers 2.5–3 cm. Calyx about 1.5 mm., tubular, somewhat gibbous at base; teeth 2–3 mm., triangular-lanceolate. Corolla pink; standard a little longer than keel, ovate, almost entire. Pod 6–8 × 0.3 cm., somewhat compressed, more or less cylindrical, straight or slightly curved, ap-pressed- and white-hirsute, tapering to a straight beak 0.6–1 cm.; dorsal suture fur-rowed, ventral suture keeled; valves dehiscing and separating. Fl. March–April.

Var. **trachoniticus**. Leaflets generally linear or oblong.

Var. **latifolius** Eig, l.c. Leaflets broadly oblong or ovate to orbicular.

Hab. of species: Steppes. Ammon, Moav, Edom.

Area of species: W. Irano-Turanian.

Sect. AMMODENDRON Bge., Mém. Acad. Sci. Pétersb. ser. 7, 11, 16:128 (1868). Shrubs or half-shrubs. Stipules connate, not adnate to petiole. Flowers racemose. Calyx campanulate. Bracteoles 0. Standard with or without recurved limb, folded along margins. Pod 2-celled, few-seeded, small, turgid, ovoid or oblong.

50. Astragalus amalecitanus Boiss., Diagn. ser. 1, 9:46 (1849) et Fl. 2:485 (1872); Eig, Astrag. Near East 131 (1955). [Plate 119]

Dwarf perennial, tufted, somewhat shrubby, silky-hairy, 10–20 cm. Stems many, each divided into a group of secondary branches bearing leaves and flowers. Leaves 3–6 cm., silky-hairy; stipules hyaline, adnate to petiole in lower part, ending in 2 triangular, ciliate teeth; leaflets (3–)4–10 pairs, somewhat crowded, 3–8 × 2–3 mm., oblong, acute. Peduncles much longer than subtending leaves. Racemes 5–15-flowered. Bracts twice as long as pedicels, hyaline, oblong, ciliate. Flowers 2–2.5 cm. Calyx about 1.3 cm., tubular, later inflated and split, white- and black-hairy; teeth about one fourth as long as tube, lanceolate-linear. Corolla violet with white petal margins; standard much longer than wings, oblong, obtuse. Pod 0.8–1.5 cm., oblong, with a dense cover of white fleece as thick as diameter of pod; dorsal suture furrowed, ventral suture keeled; beak 2–3 mm., somewhat curved. Fl. March–April.

Hab. : Steppes and deserts; stony hillsides. W., N. and C. Negev.

Area : W. Irano-Turanian.

Astragalus leucophaeus Sm., Trans. Linn. Soc. Lond. 1 : 252 (1791), *A. aleppicus* Boiss., Diagn. ser. 1, 2 : 58 (1843), *A. angulosus* DC., Astragalogia 234 (1802) as well as a few other species recorded for Palestine by Lowne (in Boiss., 1872), Paine (1875), Tristram (1884), Dinsmore in Post (1932) and others, have not been found by us; they are, most probably, based on misidentifications and, therefore, have been excluded from Flora Palaestina.

16. BISERRULA L.

Annuals. Leaves stipulate, imparipinnate, with small leaflets. Racemes 3–10-flowered. Calyx campanulate, almost equally 5-toothed. Standard ovate; wings free; keel obtuse, somewhat shorter than wings. Stamens diadelphous; upper stamen free; filaments thread-like above. Ovary sessile, many-ovuled; style short, thick, incurved; stigma capitate. Pod indehiscent, many-seeded, dorsally strongly compressed, 2-celled, with a very narrow median partition connecting the sutures lengthwise; valves with pinnately serrate-dentate keel. Seeds many, flattened, reniform.

One species in the Mediterranean region.

1. Biserrula pelecinus L., Sp. Pl. 762 (1753). [Plate 120]

Annual, appressed- to slightly patulous-hairy or glabrous, 10–40 cm. Stems few to many, procumbent to ascending, sparingly branching, furrowed. Leaves 5–15 cm.; stipules membranous, ovate to oblong, patulous-hairy or ciliate; leaflets 6–15 pairs, 0.3–1.5 × 0.2–0.7 cm., emarginate, hairy on both sides. Peduncles mostly shorter than subtending leaves. Racemes short, somewhat crowded at top of peduncles. Bracts shorter than calyces and longer than pedicels, membranous, hairy. Flowers 5–8(–9) mm. Calyx blackish, appressed-hairy; tube campanulate, shorter than subulate teeth. Corolla much longer than calyx, sky-blue. Pod 2–5 × 0.5–0.8 cm., linear, flat, sinuate-dentate with denticulate lobes, hairy or glabrous, with 2 rows of lenticular seeds. 2n = 16. Fl. March–April.

Var. **pelecinus.** *B. pelecinus* L., l.c.; Boiss., Fl. 2 : 204 (1872). All parts of plant hairy.

Var. **glabra** Eig, Bull. Inst. Agr. Nat. Hist. 6 : 28 (1927). All parts of plant glabrous.

Hab. of species : Fallow fields, roadsides and batha. Coastal Galilee, Acco Plain, Sharon Plain, Philistean Plain, Upper and Lower Galilee, Mt. Carmel. Esdraelon Plain, Mt. Gilboa, Shefela, Judean Mts., Judean Desert, W. Negev, Hula Plain, Upper and Lower Jordan Valley, Dead Sea area, Ammon, Edom.

Area of species : Mediterranean.

17. GLYCYRRHIZA L.

Perennial herbs or half-shrubs, glabrous, scabrous or glandular, with a thick, sweet root. Leaves imparipinnate, stipulate; leaflets mostly entire, generally glabrous above, viscid or glandular-hairy beneath. Racemes axillary, spike-like or capitate, subtended by caducous, membranous bracts. Flowers ebracteolate. Calyx somewhat 2-lipped; upper teeth connate and shorter than lower. Corolla white, yellowish, blue or violet; standard erect, oblong to narrowly ovate; wings and keel acute. Stamens diadelphous. Ovary sessile, 2- to many-ovuled, glabrous or glandular; style incurved at apex, glabrous; stigma terminal, capitate. Pod indehiscent or tardily dehiscent, leathery, turgid or flattened, ovoid, oblong to linear, usually covered with bristles, glands or prickles, sometimes glabrous. Seeds reniform to globular.

About 15 species, mainly in warm-temperate regions of the northern hemisphere, also in S. America and Australia.

- 1. Pod glabrous or glandular-hairy. Racemes loose, spike-like.   **1. G. glabra**
- – Pod covered with prickles. Racemes dense, head-like, globular or ovoid (rarely oblong).
                                                                                   2. G. echinata

1. Glycyrrhiza glabra L., Sp. Pl. 742 (1753); Boiss., Fl. 2 : 202 (1872). [Plate 121]
Erect perennial herb, viscid, 50–100 cm. Stems many, sparingly branching. Leaves 5–15 cm.; stipules oblong, hairy, mostly inconspicuous or 0; leaflets 4–8 pairs, 3–5 × 1–2 cm., oblong to oblong-elliptical, acute or obtuse, viscid beneath. Racemes shorter than or as long as subtending leaves, loose, cylindrical. Flowers 1 cm. Calyx teeth often longer than tube, equal, linear- or triangular-lanceolate. Corolla blue or violet with whitish standard. Ovary glabrous or glandular-hairy. Pod (1–)2–3 × 0.4–0.7 cm., flattened, oblong to linear, glabrous or sparsely or densely glandular, (1–)2- to many-seeded. Fl. May–October.

Var. **glabra**. *G. glabra* L. var. *typica* Reg. et Herd., Pl. Semen. 2 : 38 (1864). *G. glabra* L. var. *violacea* (Boiss. et Noë) Boiss., l.c. *G. violacea* Boiss. et Noë in Boiss., Diagn. ser. 2, 2 : 23 (1856). Nearly glabrous. Leaflets viscid beneath. Pod glabrous, oblong, 1–7-seeded.

Hab.: Swamps and river banks. Philistean Plain, Upper Jordan Valley, Beit Shean Valley, Lower Jordan Valley.

Var. **glandulifera** (Waldst. et Kit.) Reg. et Herd., l.c. 39; Boiss., Fl. 2 : 202 (1872). *G. glandulifera* Waldst. et Kit., Pl. Rar. Hung. 1 : 20, t. 21 (1800). Stems more or less pubescent or roughly glandular. Leaflets usually glandular beneath. Pod sparsely or densely glandular, many- or 2–3-seeded.

Hab.: As above. Acco Plain, Sharon Plain, Philistean Plain, Upper and Lower Galilee, Esdraelon Plain, Shefela, Upper Jordan Valley.

Area of species : Mediterranean, Euro-Siberian and Irano-Turanian.

The dried rhizomes and roots are the liquorice (sweet wood) of commerce, used in the tobacco industries; also used in pharmacy; a refreshing drink named "sus" is prepared from the roots and sold in the Orient.

2. Glycyrrhiza echinata L., Sp. Pl. 741 (1753); Boiss., Fl. 2 : 203 (1872). [Plate 122]
Perennial glabrescent herb, 20–50 cm. Stems erect. Leaves 4–16 cm.; stipules lanceolate-subulate; leaflets 5–6 pairs, 0.6–3 × 1–1.4 cm., oblong to elliptical, obtuse or acute, sometimes mucronulate, glandular-punctate beneath or on both sides. Peduncles up to 7 cm., shorter than subtending leaves. Flowers 2–4 mm., in dense spherical to oblong heads 1–4 cm. across. Calyx teeth triangular. Corolla bluish. Ovary glandular. Fruiting heads 3–7 cm., spherical to ellipsoidal. Pod 1–1.5 × 0.5 cm., 2–3-seeded, flattened, obovate-oblong or elliptical, with long, dense or loose prickles. Fl. May–October.

Var. **echinata.** Flowering heads 1–1.5 (–2) cm. in diam., spherical. Peduncles about 2 cm. Fruiting heads 3–4 cm. in diam., spherical to ovoid. Pod armed with dense prickles mostly on upper face only.
Hab.: Swamps and by water. Sharon Plain, Philistean Plain, Upper Galilee, Hula Plain, Gilead.

Var. **frearitis** (Orph. ex Nym.) Boiss., l.c. *G. frearitis* Orph. ex Nym., Consp. 188 (1878). Flowering heads 2–4 cm., oblong, loosely flowered. Peduncles 3–7 cm. Fruiting heads 4–7 cm., oblong-ellipsoidal. Pod less densely echinate, usually 3-seeded.
Hab.: As above. Sharon Plain, Hula Plain.
Area of species: E. Mediterranean, with extensions into Irano-Turanian and Euro-Siberian territories.

Trib. LOTEAE. Herbs, rarely shrubs. Leaves pinnate, many-foliolate, but usually (1–)3–5-foliolate and spuriously digitate; leaflets entire. Inflorescences head- or umbel-like, rarely flowers solitary. Stamens diadelphous, rarely monadelphous; all the filaments, or the alternate ones only, dilated at apex; anthers uniform. Ovary 2- or many-ovuled. Pod dehiscent or not, 2-valved, not jointed. Cotyledons leaf-like.

18. PHYSANTHYLLIS Boiss.

Annual herbs with imparipinnate leaves. Inflorescences axillary, head-like. Calyx tubular, equally 5-toothed; tube much inflated in fruit. Corolla persistent; petals long-clawed. Stamens diadelphous. Ovary 2-ovuled. Pod indehiscent, 2-seeded, parchment-like, hidden in calyx, tapering into a stalk, transversely partitioned and constricted between the seeds.
One species in the Mediterranean region.

1. Physanthyllis tetraphylla (L.) Boiss., Voy. Bot. Midi Esp. 2 : 162 (1839) et Fl. 2 : 159 (1872). *Anthyllis tetraphylla* L., Sp. Pl. 719 (1753). [Plate 123]
Annual, appressed- or patulous-villose, 10–40 cm. Stems prostrate, nearly simple. Leaves with broadened petiole; lower leaves with 1 leaflet, ovate, obovate or oblong; uppermost leaves with 1–2 lateral pairs of entire leaflets and an obovate terminal leaflet 2–4 cm. Heads axillary, nearly sessile, few-flowered. Flowers 2 cm., subsessile.

Calyx hairy; teeth 3 mm., equal, triangular. Standard bright yellow with pinkish veins; wings and keel cream-coloured. Fruiting calyx 2 × 1 cm., inflated, sometimes violet-veined. Pod 1 × 0.4 cm., stipitate, 2-seeded, constricted between seeds; beak 1 mm. Seeds tuberculate, brownish-black. Fl. February–April.

Hab.: Batha. Coastal Galilee, Sharon Plain, Philistean Plain, Upper and Lower Galilee, Mt. Carmel, Esdraelon Plain, Samaria, Shefela, Judean Mts., Judean Desert, Dan Valley, Upper Jordan Valley, Gilead, Ammon, Moav.

Area: Mediterranean.

19. HYMENOCARPOS Savi

Annuals, usually villose. Lower leaves stipulate, 1–3-foliolate, upper exstipulate, imparipinnate, with 2–4 pairs of leaflets, the terminal leaflet the largest; all leaflets entire. Racemes axillary, umbellate, long-peduncled, 2–4-flowered, subtended by a bract. Flowers rather conspicuous. Calyx tubular, deeply and equally 5-toothed. Petals free, short-clawed, yellow; standard almost orbicular; wings obovate; keel beaked, incurved. Stamens diadelphous; 5 of the filaments dilated at apex. Ovary short-stipitate, 2-ovuled; style incurved, with terminal stigma. Pod indehiscent, 2-celled by means of a transverse partition, flat, strongly curved, orbicular, circinate, with outer margin broadly winged, aculeate-denticulate or entire. Seeds 2.

One (or 2) species in the Mediterranean region.

1. Hymenocarpos circinnatus (L.) Savi, Fl. Pis. 2 : 205 (1798). [Plate 124]

Annual, more or less villose, 30–60 cm. Stems ascending or procumbent. Lower leaves 4–6 cm., simple, oblong-spatulate, entire; upper leaves with 2–4 pairs of leaflets, each 1–3 × 0.4–0.6 cm., the terminal leaflet larger. Racemes 2–4-flowered, on peduncles mostly shorter than subtending leaves. Flowers about 7 mm. Calyx teeth longer than tube, linear. Pod 1.4–1.8 cm. across, orbicular or kidney-shaped, appressed-hairy or glabrous; wings broader than pod proper, prickly-crenate at margin, reticulate. Seeds 2, germinating in consecutive years. 2n = 16. Fl. February–May.

Var. **circinnatus.** *H. circinnatus* (L.) Savi, l.c.; Boiss., Fl. 2 : 159 (1872). *Medicago circinnata* L., Sp. Pl. 778 (1753). *Cornicina circinnata* (L.) Boiss., Voy. Bot. Midi Esp. 2 : 163 (1839). Pod appressed-hairy.

Hab.: Batha and fallow fields. Coastal Galilee, Acco Plain, Sharon Plain, Philistean Plain, Upper and Lower Galilee, Mt. Carmel, Esdraelon Plain, Mt. Gilboa, Shefela, Judean Mts., Judean Desert, W. and N. Negev, Hula Plain, Upper and Lower Jordan Valley, Dead Sea area, Gilead, Ammon, Edom.

Var. **leiocarpus** Eig, Bull. Inst. Agr. Nat. Hist. 6 : 26 (1927). Pod glabrous throughout.

Hab.: As above. Sharon Plain, Mt. Carmel, Esdraelon Plain, Judean Desert.

Area of species: Mediterranean.

H. nummularius (DC.) G. Don, Gen. Syst. 2 : 173 (1832), seems to be a slight variation of *H. circinnatus,* differing from it in the wing of the pod, which is entire.

20. CYTISOPSIS Jaub. et Sp.

Half-shrubs with silky-silvery indumentum. Leaves sessile, digitate, of 5–7 leaflets. Racemes 1–3-flowered, borne on small indurated branches. Flowers large. Calyx tubular, 2-lipped, upper lip 2-fid, a little longer than the 3-parted lower lip. Petals long-clawed, the lower 4 adnate to staminal tube; standard ovate-oblong; keel slightly incurved. Stamens diadelphous. Ovary sessile, many-ovuled; style slightly incurved, thickened in upper part; stigma truncate. Pod 2-valved and incompletely partitioned between seeds, woody, cylindrical, straight.

One or 2 species in the E. Mediterranean countries.

1. Cytisopsis pseudocytisus (Boiss.) Fertig (comb. nov.). *Cornicina pseudocytisus* Boiss., Diagn. ser. 1, 2 : 15 (1843). *Cytisopsis dorycniifolia* Jaub. et Sp., Ill. Pl. Or. 1 : 155, t. 84 (1844); Boiss., Fl. 2 : 160 (1872). *Anthyllis argentea* Desv., Ann. Sci. Nat. Bot. 9 : 408 (1826) non Salisb., Prodr. Stirp. 332 (1796). [Plate 125]

Half-shrub with thick woody stock, appressed- and silvery-silky, 15–60 cm. Stems many, ascending or procumbent, diffuse, branched. Leaves sessile on a short sheath-like cushion (stipule); leaflets 5–7, 1–1.5 × 0.2–0.3 cm., linear-spatulate, tapering, mucronate, with revolute margin; the older leaflets prominently nerved beneath. Flowers 1–3 in racemes borne on short branches, short-pedicelled, with 2 bracteoles at base. Calyx tube 1–1.5 cm.; teeth much shorter than tube. Corolla yellow; petals long-exserted, very long-clawed. Pod up to 2 × 0.4 cm., many-seeded, densely silky-hairy; valves tardily dehiscent, woody. Seeds globular, brown, smooth. Fl. February–April.

Hab.: Batha and pine forest on soft rendzina soil. Sharon Plain, Mt. Carmel and adjacent coastal hills.

Area: E. Mediterranean.

21. LOTUS L.

Annual or perennial herbs, rarely half-shrubs. Leaves pinnate, mostly 5-foliolate; stipules minute, mostly setaceous or reduced to tubercles or 0; leaflets entire, lower pair of leaflets remote from the 3 proximate upper leaflets. Peduncles long, rarely short, often with 3 leaf-like bracts beneath the flowers. Racemes axillary, capitate or umbellate, rarely 1-flowered. Bracteoles mostly 0. Calyx 5-toothed or 5-fid; teeth equal or the lowest teeth longer, rarely calyx 2-lipped. Corolla yellow, pink, red to purple, rarely white, with obovate to orbicular standard, obovate wings and a beaked, 2-gibbous keel abruptly or gradually incurved. Stamens diadelphous. Ovary sessile, many-ovuled; style tapering or thickened above, incurved, glabrous, provided with a tooth or appendix at inner margin; stigma terminal or lateral. Pod dehiscent, many-seeded, linear to oblong, straight or curved, rarely with transverse partitions. Seeds globular to lenticular.

Over 100 species, mainly in the Mediterranean region, temperate Eurasia, N. America, S. Africa and Australia.

Literature : A. Brand, Monographie der Gattung *Lotus, Bot. Jahrb.* 25 : 166–232 (1898). J. B. Gillett, *Lotus* in Africa south of the Sahara, etc., *Kew Bull.* 13 : 361–381 (1958). K. Larsen, Cytotaxonomical studies in *Lotus* IV. Some cases of polyploidy, *Bot. Tidskr.* 54 : 44–56 (1958). C. C. Heyn, A study in the *Lotus peregrinus* group, *Israel Journ. Bot.* 15 : 37–47 (1966). C. C. Heyn & I. Herrnstadt, The *Lotus creticus* group, *Kew Bull.* 21 : 299–309 (1967).

1. Flowers usually white. Pod hook-shaped, 4–7 × 0.1–0.2 cm.　　　**13. L. conimbricensis**
 – Flowers yellow, pink or red. Pod not hook-shaped　　　**2**
2. Flowers pink to red　　　**3**
 – Flowers yellow　　　**5**
3. Annuals. Flowers usually 1–2 on peduncles shorter than leaves. Keel of corolla with beak bent to about 90°.　　　**11. L. glinoides**
 – Perennials. Flowers in racemes of 2–6 on peduncles much longer than leaves. Keel of corolla with beak less strongly bent, or keel straight　　　**4**
4. Flowers intensely purple. Standard oblong. Plants densely woolly.　　　**12. L. lanuginosus**
 – Flowers pink. Standard obovate. Plants glabrous or sparingly hairy, not woolly.　　　**10. L. gebelia**
5 (2). Pod thick, fleshy, 5 mm. broad or more, not torulose, ending in a short, incurved beak. Seeds wrinkled.　　　**14. L. edulis**
 – Pod not fleshy and less than 5 mm. broad. Seeds smooth　　　**6**
6. Calyx campanulate; teeth equal. Plants of swampy habitats　　　**7**
 – Calyx 2-lipped; teeth unequal. Plants of coastal sandy soils or of heavy inland soils　　　**9**
7. Small, villose annuals. Calyx teeth lanceolate-subulate. Pod thin, about 1.5 mm. broad.　　　**6. L. angustissimus**
 – Perennials, up to 1 m. long, glabrous to slightly hirsute or soft-hairy. Pod at least 2 mm. broad　　　**8**
8. Plants glabrous to slightly hirsute. Leaflets linear-obovate to linear. Peduncles many times longer than leaves.　　　**4. L. tenuis**
 – Plants soft-hairy (except for first branches and leaves). Leaflets ovate. Peduncles about twice as long as leaves.　　　**5. L. palustris**
9 (6). Pod linear-compressed, strongly torulose to almost moniliform. Seeds lenticular, smooth and shiny.　　　**9. L. ornithopodioides**
 — Pod cylindrical, not or very slightly torulose　　　**10**
10. Annuals. Flowers usually about 1 cm. or less. Calyx distinctly 2-lipped; some of the calyx teeth much shorter than tube. Stems hairy throughout but not appressed-silky　　　**11**
 — Perennials. Flowers usually 1.5 cm. long or more (rarely 1.2 cm.). Calyx campanulate or only slightly 2-lipped. Stems and leaves appressed- and silky-hairy or very sparingly hairy or glabrous　　　**12**
11. Peduncles 0 to as long as subtending leaves (very rarely longer). Mature pod terete, at least 2 mm. broad, mostly about 4 cm. long.　　　**7. L. peregrinus**
 — Peduncles at least twice as long as subtending leaves. Mature pod compressed, 1–1.5 mm. broad, 2–4 cm. long.　　　**8. L. halophilus**
12 (10). Grey-silvery plants, densely appressed- and silky-hairy. Leaflets (at least upper ones) oblong to lanceolate, most of them about twice as long as broad. Keel of corolla with long, straight beak.　　　**1. L. creticus**
 — Green plants, glabrous or hairy, very rarely slightly silky-hairy. Leaflets obovate, most of them less than twice as long as broad　　　**13**

13. Inland plants of batha and maquis. Keel ending abruptly in a claw; beak almost as
    long as keel.   **3. L. collinus**
— Littoral plants, exposed to sea spray. Keel gradually tapering into a claw; beak much
    shorter than above.   **2. L. cytisoides**

Sect. LOTUS. Sect. *Xantholotus* Brand, Bot. Jahrb. 25 : 204 (1898). Young pod not
fleshy; suture not impressed or only slightly so. Flowers yellow, rarely yellowish-white
or white.

1. Lotus creticus L., Sp. Pl. 775 (1753); Boiss., Fl. 2 : 164 (1872) p.p. *L. commutatus*
Guss., Fl. Sic. Prodr. 2 : 545 (1828) et auct. *L. salzmanni* Boiss. et Reut., Pugill. Pl.
Nov. 37 (1852). [Plate 126]
   Perennial with woody base, appressed- and silky-hairy, 30–60 cm. Stems many,
erect or procumbent, rigid. Leaves 1–3 cm.; leaflets usually 0.8–1.5 cm., thick and
often fleshy, the upper leaflets obovate to oblong-cuneate, lower pair smaller, apiculate. Peduncles thick, 2–5 times as long as subtending leaves. Racemes (2–)3–6(–8)-
flowered. Bracts 3, shorter than calyx. Flowers about 1.5 cm. Calyx about half as long
as corolla, campanulate or slightly 2-lipped; lateral teeth shorter than others. Corolla
bright yellow; keel about equal in length to standard and slightly exceeding the wings,
with a long, straight and dark-tipped beak. Pod up to 4 × 0.2 cm., cylindrical. Seeds
about 1.5 mm. in diam., globular, sometimes irregularly compressed, light to dark
brown, often with dark spots, smooth. 2n = 28. Fl. March–June (–August).
   Hab. : Sandy sea shore. Coastal Galilee, Acco Plain, Coast of Carmel, Sharon Plain,
Philistean Plain.
   Area : Mediterranean.

2. Lotus cytisoides L., Sp. Pl. 776 (1753). *L. creticus* sensu Brand, Bot. Jahrb. 25 : 207
(1898) et auct. alt. non L., Sp. Pl. 775 (1753). [Plate 127]
   Perennial, green, mostly glabrescent, rarely pubescent, 20–30 cm. Stems many,
ascending or procumbent, branching, slender. Leaves up to 2 cm., often thick and
fleshy; upper leaflets lanceolate or ovate to obovate, sometimes truncate, apiculate,
lower pair conspicuously smaller. Peduncles 2–4 times as long as subtending leaves.
Racemes 3–5-flowered. Bracts 3, usually shorter than calyx. Flowers 1–1.2(–1.5) cm.
Calyx indistinctly 2-lipped; teeth unequal, the lateral ones shortest. Corolla yellow;
standard nearly as long as wings; keel distinctly shorter than wings, short-beaked,
strongly curved, sometimes dark-tipped. Pod varying in length, usually about 3(–4) ×
0.2 cm., terete to linear, straight. Seeds about 1.5 mm. in diam., globular to irregularly
compressed, light to dark brown, smooth. 2n = 28. Fl. March–June.
   Hab. : Sea shore spray zone; mostly on rocks. Coastal Galilee, Acco Plain, Sharon
Plain, Mt. Carmel.
   Area : Mediterranean region.

Throughout its area of distribution this species varies in its indumentum. In addition
to the sericeous-hairy and the glabrous forms, usually cited in the literature, there are also
others with various degrees of hair density. In Palestine the sericeous-hairy form has not yet
been found, except for a single herbarium specimen from Natanya (Sharon Plain), while

the non-sericeous form, of which the chromosome number is cited here, is met with in a
number of localities.

3. Lotus collinus (Boiss.) Heldr., Herb. Gr. Norm. 1320 (1896 vel 1897). *L. creticus*
L. var. *collinus* Boiss., Fl. 2 : 165 (1872). *L. cytisoides* sensu Boiss., Fl. Suppl. 170
(1888) p.p. non L., Sp. Pl. 776 (1753). *L. cytisoides* L. ssp. *collinus* (Boiss.) Murb.,
Acta Univ. Lund 33, 12 : 68 (1897). *L. commutatus* Guss. var. *collinus* (Boiss.) Brand,
Bot. Jahrb. 25 : 208 (1898). *L. judaicus* Boiss. ex Bornm., Verh. Zool.-Bot. Ges. Wien
48 : 583 (1898). [Plate 128]

Perennial, pubescent to glabrescent, 15–25 cm. Stems erect, diffusely much branching from the base, slender. Leaves 1–3 cm.; upper leaflets 1–1.5 × 0.4–0.8 cm., obovate
to cuneate, apiculate, lower pair smaller. Peduncles (2–)3–5(–7) times as long as
subtending leaves. Racemes (1–)2–4(–5)-flowered. Bracts 3, longer or shorter than
calyx, usually unequal. Flowers 1.2–1.5 cm. Calyx about half as long as corolla, indistinctly 2-lipped; lateral teeth shorter than others. Corolla bright yellow; keel about
as long as wings and shorter than standard, curved, with a fairly long beak. Pod
3–3.5 × 0.2–0.3 cm., terete, straight. Seeds about 1.5 mm. across, globular, dark
brown, smooth. $2n = 14$. Fl. March–May.

Hab.: Calcareous soils of foothills and mountains, batha and maquis. Upper and
Lower Galilee, Mt. Carmel, Samaria, Shefela, Judean Mts., Ammon, Moav.

Area : Mediterranean.

The record of *L. arabicus* L., Mant. 104 (1767) from Palestine (after Dinsmore in Post,
Fl. Syr. Pal. Sin. ed. 2, 1 : 358, 1932) has not been confirmed.

4. Lotus tenuis Waldst. et Kit. ex Willd., Enum. Pl. Hort. Berol. 797 (1809). *L. corniculata* L. var. *tenuifolia* L., Sp. Pl. 776 (1753); Poll., Fl. Palat. 2 : 349 no. 711 (1777).
L. tenuifolius C. Presl in J. et C. Presl, Deliciae Prag. 46 (1822) non Burm. f., Prodr.
Fl. Cap. 22 (1768). *L. tenuifolius* (Poll.) Reichb., Fl. Germ. Exc. 506 (1832). *L. tenuifolius* (L.) Reichb. var. *uniflorus* Boiss., Fl. 2 : 166 (1872). [Plate 129]

Perennial herb, glabrous, rarely slightly hirsute, up to 1 m. Branches slender, often
twining or prostrate. Leaflets 1.4–2.5 × 0.2–0.4 cm., linear to oblong-linear, apiculate, all more or less equal. Peduncles long, many times longer than subtending leaves.
Racemes 1–3(–5)-flowered. Bracts usually 3, varying in size. Flowers 0.8–1.3 cm.
Calyx more or less campanulate; teeth slender, about as long as tube. Corolla yellow;
standard often red-veined, longer than keel and wings; keel longer than wings, strongly
curved, with fairly long beak. Pod 2–4 × about 0.2 cm., terete, straight. Seeds about
1 mm. in diam., globular, greenish-brown, smooth. $2n = 12$. Fl. May–August.

Hab.: Damp soils, river banks and swamps. Acco Plain, Sharon Plain, Philistean
Plain, Mt. Carmel, Esdraelon Plain, Shefela, Judean Mts., Coastal, W. and N. Negev,
Hula Plain, Upper Jordan Valley, Dead Sea area, Arava Valley, Gilead, Moav.

Area : Mainly W. Euro-Siberian, Mediterranean and Irano-Turanian.

Largely variable. Plants from southern, arid parts have larger leaflets and pods than
those from northern parts. Linnaeus's distinction between the typical *L. corniculatus* and
var. *tenuifolius* is not clear-cut and a thorough study of these forms will probably include
L. tenuis within the *L. corniculatus* complex.

5. Lotus palustris Willd., Sp. Pl. 3 : 1394 (1802). *L. lamprocarpus* Boiss., Diagn. ser. 1, 9 : 33 (1849) et Fl. 2 : 166 (1872). [Plates 130, 131]

Perennial, greyish and hispid. Stems with long, erect or slightly trailing branches, up to 1 m. Leaflets 1.4–2 × 0.6–1.2 cm., lanceolate-ovate to obovate, apiculate, lower pair larger. Peduncles 2–4 times as long as subtending leaves. Racemes 2–3 (–4)-flowered. Flowers 0.8–1 cm. Calyx campanulate; teeth about twice as long as tube. Corolla somewhat longer than calyx, yellow; keel about as long as standard and wings, curved, with a short, slightly bent tip. Pod 1.8–2.4 × 0.2 cm., linear, straight. Seeds about 1 mm. in diam., globular, greenish-yellow, smooth. 2n = 12. Fl. March–September.

Hab.: Swampy soils, sometimes saline; often along river beds, ditches and ponds. Acco Plain, Sharon Plain, Philistean Plain, Upper and Lower Galilee, Esdraelon Plain, Samaria, Shefela, Dan Valley, Hula Plain, Upper Jordan Valley, Beit Shean Valley, Lower Jordan Valley, Dead Sea area, Gilead.

Area: S. and E. Mediterranean.

In *L. palustris* a considerable seasonal polymorphism may be discerned; whereas branches in spring and early summer have long internodes and bear large flowers and long fruit [Plate 130], those of the late summer or autumn have short internodes and fruit and small leaflets [Plate 131]. There is also much variation in the indumentum according to season: the first stems appearing after germination have short internodes and are glabrous, later they elongate strongly and become densely hairy. It seems that the shorter, densely hairy, late summer branches were taken by some authors for *L. hispidus* Desf.

6. Lotus angustissimus L., Sp. Pl. 774 (1753); Boiss., Fl. 2 : 171 (1872) excl. syn. [*L. palustris* Willd.]. [Plate 132]

Slender annual, patulous-hairy, (15–)20–30(–50) cm. Stems usually erect, rarely procumbent, branched. Leaflets obovate to oblong, apiculate, lower pair usually smaller. Peduncles slender, as long as to 3 times as long as subtending leaves. Racemes 1–3-flowered. Bracts 1–3, shorter or longer than calyx, unequal. Flowers small, 5–7 (–8) mm. Calyx campanulate; teeth longer than tube, lanceolate-subulate, acuminate, patulous-hairy. Corolla distinctly longer than calyx, yellow; keel narrow, usually longer than wings and about as long as standard, bent from the middle. Pod 0.8–1.5 (–2) × 0.1 cm., terete, straight. Seeds less than 1 mm. in diam., dark, smooth. 2n = 24. Fl. March–May.

Hab.: Damp sandy soils. Sharon Plain, Philistean Plain.

Area: Mediterranean, with extensions into the S. W. provinces of the Euro-Siberian region.

Two forms can be distinguished: one with large leaflets (up to 1.5 cm.) and flowers (up to 8 mm.), and long peduncles (up to 2 cm.); the other with small leaflets (up to 8 mm.) and flowers, and shorter peduncles (about 7 mm.); there are rare intermediates between the two. The large form often resembles current-year shoots of *L. palustris*, but is readily distinguished from the latter by the indumentum, the narrower calyx teeth and the keel.

7. Lotus peregrinus L., Sp. Pl. 774 (1753). [Plates 133, 133a]

Annual, appressed-hairy, 10–40 (–50) cm. Stems procumbent or erect, usually branching. Leaflets 1–1.4 × 0.6–0.8 cm., obovate to oblong, obtuse, rarely acute, lower pair usually smaller, ovate. Peduncles usually thick, shorter than subtending leaves, very rarely longer. Racemes (1–)2–3(–4)-flowered. Bracts 3, longer than calyx. Flowers 0.8–1.2 cm. Calyx about two thirds as long as corolla, distinctly 2-lipped; lateral teeth of lower lip triangular, much shorter than the linear lower tooth. Corolla yellow; standard longer than wings and keel; keel strongly curved, very shortly beaked. Pod 2.5–4(–5) × (0.1–)0.25 (–0.4) cm., terete, straight, sometimes torulose. Seeds (1–)1.5–3 mm. in diam., globular, usually yellow to green, smooth. 2n = 28. Fl. March–May.

Very polymorphic.

Var. **peregrinus**. *L. peregrinus* L., l.c.; Boiss., Fl. 2 : 172 (1872). [Plate 133]. Peduncles usually short and thick. Racemes (1–)2–4-flowered. Pod 1–1.5 mm. thick. Seeds yellow, often 1–1.5 mm. across.

Hab.: Mainly on heavy, rarely on sandy soils; batha and maquis, roadsides and fallow fields. Common throughout the area except in the southernmost parts.

Var. **carmeli** (Boiss.) Post, Fl. Syr. Pal. Sin. 250 (1883–1896). *L. carmeli* Boiss., Diagn. ser. 1, 9 : 34 (1849) et Fl. 2 : 172 (1872). [Plate 133a]. Peduncles usually slenderer and longer. Racemes 1 (–2)-flowered. Pod 2–4 mm. thick. Seeds 2–3 mm., usually dark.

Hab.: Batha and maquis. Lower Galilee, Mt. Carmel, Judean Mts., Gilead (endemic).

Area of species : E. Mediterranean.

8. Lotus halophilus Boiss. et Sprun. in Boiss., Diagn. ser. 1, 2 : 37 (1843). [Plates 134, 134a]

Annual, tomentellous, (5–)10–30(–40) cm. Stems prostrate or ascending, much branching. Leaflets 3–8 × 2–4 mm., ovate, obovate or rhombic, sometimes apiculate, lower pair a little shorter than others. Peduncles slender, 2–3(–4) times as long as subtending leaves. Racemes 1–4(–5)-flowered. Bracts 3, usually of the same size as leaflets. Flowers 0.5–1(–1.4) cm. Calyx distinctly 2-lipped; teeth shorter than tube, unequal. Corolla one and a half to two times as long as calyx, pale yellow; standard longer than wings and keel; the latter curved, short-beaked. Pod 2–4 × 0.1–0.15 cm., cylindrical, slightly flattened and torulose, somewhat arcuate, obliquely mucronate-beaked. Seeds minute, globular, yellow to light brown, smooth. 2n = 14 (28?). Fl. February–March.

Var. **halophilus**. *L. villosa* Forssk., Fl. Aeg.-Arab. LXXI (1775) non Burm. f., Prodr. Fl. Cap. 23 (1768). *L. pusillus* Viv., Fl. Lib. Spec. 47, t. 17, f. 3 (1824) non Medik., Beobacht. 1783 : 226 (1784). *L. pusillus* Viv. var. *major* Boiss., Fl. 2 : 173 (1872). *L. aucheri* Boiss., Diagn. ser. 1, 2 : 38 (1843). [Plate 134]. Plant 5–12 (–15) cm. Flowers 1–2 (–3) in a raceme, 6–9 mm. long. Pod up to 2 × 0.1–0.12 cm.

Hab.: Sandy soils. Coastal Galilee, Acco Plain, Coast of Carmel, Sharon Plain, Philistean Plain, Mt. Carmel, Shefela, Coastal, W., N. and C. Negev, Edom.

Var. **macranthus** (Boiss.) Heyn (comb. nov.). *L. pusillus* Viv. var. *macranthus* Boiss.,

Fl. 2:173 (1872). [Plate 134a]. Plant 15–30 cm. Flowers 3–5 in a raceme, 1–1.4 cm. Pod usually longer and broader than in var. *halophilus*.

Hab.: As in preceding variety but generally in less arid sites.

Area of species: Mediterranean, with extensions into the adjacent Saharo-Arabian territory.

9. Lotus ornithopodioides L., Sp. Pl. 775 (1753); Boiss., Fl. 2:173 (1872). [Plate 135]

Annual, appressed-hairy, 15–50 cm. Stems few or many, erect, sparingly branched. Leaflets 0.8–1.8 × 0.4–1 cm., obovate to rhombic, lower pair ovate, usually much smaller than others. Peduncles slender, up to one and a half times as long as subtending leaves. Racemes (2–)3–5-flowered. Bracts 3, longer than calyx, resembling leaflets. Flowers about 1 cm. Calyx distinctly 2-lipped; teeth unequal, the longest longer than tube. Corolla distinctly longer than calyx, yellow; standard as long as wings; keel slightly shorter and strongly curved. Pod (1–)2.5–4.5 × 0.2–0.3 cm., flat, linear, slightly arcuate, strongly torulose. Seeds 2 mm. in diam., dark brown, smooth. 2n = 14. Fl. April–May.

Hab.: Heavy soils; batha and field borders. Coastal Galilee, Acco Plain, Sharon Plain, Upper Galilee, Mt. Carmel, Judean Mts., Dan Valley, Hula Plain.

Area: Mediterranean, with extensions into adjacent Euro-Siberian provinces.

10. Lotus gebelia Vent., Descr. Pl. Jard. Cels t. 57 (1801); Boiss., Fl. 2:168 (1872). [Plate 136]

Perennial, glaucescent, glabrous to sparsely hirsute, about 50 cm. Stems erect, branching. Leaflets 1–1.5 × 0.4–0.7 cm., obliquely obovate to cuneate, lower pair ovate, smaller than the others. Peduncles 2–4 times as long as subtending leaves. Racemes 2–5 (–6)-flowered. Bracts 1–3, shorter or longer than calyx, unequal. Flowers 1.5–1.8 cm. Calyx campanulate; teeth usually as long as tube or slightly shorter. Corolla about twice as long as calyx, pink; standard much longer than wings and keel, obovate; keel with long, straight beak. Pod usually 3–4 × 0.3 cm., terete, often torulose. Seeds about 1.5 mm. in diam., dark. 2n=14. Fl. April–May.

Hab.: Batha. Gilead.

Area: W. Irano-Turanian, with extensions into E. Mediterranean territories.

Only the typical form has, as yet, been found in Palestine.

11. Lotus glinoides Del., Ann. Sci. Nat. Bot. ser. 2, 7:286 (1837); Boiss., Fl. 2:170 (1872). [Plate 137]

Annual, appressed-hairy, 10–30(–50) cm. Stems ascending, profusely branching. Leaves small; upper leaflets obovate to oblong, cuneate. Peduncles shorter than subtending leaves, sometimes absent. Racemes 1–2(–3)-flowered. Bracts 1–3, longer than calyx. Flowers 5–7 mm. Calyx more or less campanulate; teeth as long as tube. Corolla one and a half times as long as calyx; standard longer than wings and keel, pink; wings pink; keel purple, with beak bent to nearly 90°. Pod about 2 × 0.2 cm., terete; distal end arcuate. Seeds 1 mm. across, globular, brown-yellow with dark spots, smooth. Fl. March–May.

Hab.: Hot deserts. Arava Valley.

Area: E. Sudanian.

12. Lotus lanuginosus Vent., Jard. Malm. 1:92 (1803); Boiss., Fl. 2:169 (1872). [Plate 138]

Perennial, greyish, woolly, up to 50 cm. Stems procumbent or ascending, profusely branching. Leaves with very short petioles; leaflets minute, up to 1.2 × 0.5 cm., obovate-cuneate, obtuse, apiculate, lower pair equal to other leaflets. Peduncles 2–4 times as long as subtending leaves. Racemes 1–3(–4)-flowered. Bracts 3, shorter than calyx. Flowers 1–1.5 cm. Calyx nearly campanulate; teeth about as long as or somewhat shorter than tube. Corolla about one and a half times as long as calyx, purple; standard longer than wings, oblong; wings longer than short-beaked keel. Pod 2–3 × 0.2 cm., cylindrical, straight, usually torulose, long-beaked. Seeds 1.5–2 mm. in diam., globular, dark brown with darker spots, smooth. 2n = 14. Fl. March–May.

Hab.: Deserts. N., C. and S. Negev, Arava Valley, Ammon, Moav, Edom.

Area: E. Saharo-Arabian.

13. Lotus conimbricensis Brot., Phyt. Lusit. 1 : no. 28 (1801); Boiss., Fl. 2 : 171 (1872). *L. coimbrensis* Willd., Sp. Pl. 3 : 1390 (1802). [Plate 139]

Annual, glabrous or sparingly hirsute, 10–20(–30) cm. Stems procumbent or ascending, usually branching. Leaflets ciliate, the upper leaflets up to 1.2–0.7 cm., obovate-cuneate to rhombic, apiculate, the lower pair ovate and usually larger. Peduncles shorter than subtending leaves. Racemes 1(–2)-flowered. Bracts usually 3, as long as calyx or slightly longer. Flowers 0.8–1 cm. Calyx distinctly shorter than corolla, rarely as long, campanulate, ciliate; teeth almost as long as tube, lanceolate-subulate. Corolla white, very rarely yellow; standard ovate, with pink veins; keel curved, with a long, straight, purple beak. Pod 4–7 × 0.1–0.2 cm., terete, semicircular to fishhook-shaped. Seeds minute, globular, brownish-yellow, smooth. 2n = 12. Fl. March–May.

Hab.: Heavy soils and sandy loams. Sharon Plain, Upper Galilee, Shefela, Hula Plain.

Area: Mediterranean.

Sect. KROKERIA (Moench) Brand, Bot. Jahrb. 25 : 204 (1898). Gen. *Krokeria* Moench, Meth. 143 (1794). Young pod fleshy; ventral suture deeply impressed. Flowers yellow.

14. Lotus edulis L., Sp. Pl. 774 (1753); Boiss., Fl. 2 : 173 (1872). *Krokeria edulis* Moench ex Willk. et Lange, Prodr. Fl. Hisp. 3 : 340 (1877) *pro syn*. [Plate 140]

Annual, pubescent, 20–30 cm. Stems usually erect, branching. Leaves about 2 cm.; upper leaflets up to 1.5 × 1 cm., usually more or less obovate, often truncate, emarginate, lower pair of leaflets smaller and apiculate. Peduncles 2–4 times as long as subtending leaves. Racemes 1–3-flowered. Bracts 3, slightly shorter or longer than calyx. Flowers up to 1.5 cm. Calyx up to 1 cm., campanulate; teeth much longer than tube, linear-lanceolate. Corolla distinctly longer than calyx, golden-yellow; standard longer than wings and keel, red-veined; keel only slightly curved, with dark-tipped beak.

Pod 3.5 × 0.7 cm., fleshy, arcuate, hooked at apex; ventral suture deeply impressed. Seeds 3 mm., somewhat compressed, globular to oblong, dark, minutely tuberculate. 2n = 14. Fl. March–May.

Hab.: Batha and garigue on light and heavy soils. Coastal Galilee, Acco Plain, Sharon Plain, Upper and Lower Galilee, Mt. Carmel, Judean Mts., Upper and Lower Jordan Valley.

Area: Mediterranean.

22. TETRAGONOLOBUS Scop.

Herbs with the aspect of *Lotus*. Leaves pinnate, of 5 leaflets; the upper 3 leaflets remote from the 2 stipule-like lower ones. Flowers solitary or 2–4 on an axillary peduncle. Calyx almost equally 5-toothed. Corolla red or yellow; keel curved, long-beaked. Stamens diadelphous. Ovary sessile; style thickened towards top; stigma lateral. Pod many-seeded, cylindrical, partitioned inside, the nerves on the sutures dilated into wings or strongly thickened ribs. Hardly separable from *Lotus*.

About 12 species in Eurasia and the Mediterranean region.

1. Pod 5–8 mm. broad, wings of pod about 2–4 mm. broad, undulate. Flowers usually red, usually solitary. **2. T. palaestinus**
- Pod slender, about 2–3 mm. broad, wingless, with thick margins along sutures. Flowers yellow, usually in pairs. **1. T. requienii**

1. Tetragonolobus requienii (Mauri ex Sanguinetti) Daveau, Bull. Soc. Bot. Fr. 43:365 (1896); *T. requieni* (Mauri?) Fisch. et Mey., Ind. Sem. Hort. Petrop. 2:23 (1836) *comb. illegit. Lotus requieni* Mauri in Ten., Rel. Viagg. Abruz. 81 no. 707 (1830) *nom. nud.*; Mauri ex Sanguinetti, Cent. Prodr. Fl. Rom. Add. 106 (1837). "*T. conjugatus* (L.) Ser. in DC., Prodr." sensu Boiss., Fl. 2:175 (1872) excl. var. (in observ.). *L. conjugatus* L., Sp. Pl. ed. 2, 1089 (1763) *nom. confus.* [Plate 141]

Annual, patulous-pilose, 10–25 cm. Stems procumbent to ascending. Leaves 1–3 cm.; stipules (lower pair of leaflets) about 8 mm., adnate at base to petiole; petiole as long as or shorter than blade; leaflets 1–2 × 0.7–1 cm., spatulate, deltoid or oblong-obovate, tapering at base, mucronulate at apex. Peduncles longer than subtending leaves. Racemes axillary, usually 2-flowered. Flowers 1–1.3 cm. Calyx about 8 mm.; teeth as long as tube or somewhat longer, lanceolate, acute. Corolla exceeding calyx, yellow (probably also purple); standard longer than keel. Pod 2.5–5 × 0.3 cm., slender, wingless, but with 2 thick ribs along each suture. Seeds many, about 2 mm., globular, brown. Fl. March–May.

Hab.: Fields. Sharon Plain, Philiṣtean Plain, Upper and Lower Galilee, Mt. Carmel, Esdraelon Plain, Samaria, Shefela, Judean Mts., Hula Plain.

Area: Mainly W. Mediterranean.

2. Tetragonolobus palaestinus Boiss. et Bl. in Boiss., Diagn. ser. 2, 2:20 (1856) et Fl. 2:175 (1872). *T. purpureus* Moench var. *palaestinus* (Boiss.) Post, Fl. Syr. Pal. Sin. 251 (1883–1896). [Plate 142]

Annual, patulous-hirsute, 10–50 cm. Stems procumbent to ascending, sometimes erect, simple or branching from base, striate. Leaves 2–5 cm.; stipules (lower pair of leaflets) about 1 cm., shorter than petiole and adnate to it at base, ovate, acute; petiole shorter than blade; leaflets 1–3 cm., obovate to spatulate or deltoid, cuneate at base, obtuse, usually apiculate, terminal leaflet, and sometimes all the leaflets, oblong to oblong-obovate. Peduncles usually shorter than subtending leaves. Flowers 1.4–1.5 cm., usually solitary, rarely 2 on a peduncle. Calyx about 1 cm.; teeth longer than tube, linear, tapering. Corolla exceeding calyx, purple, rarely yellow; standard longer than wings and keel; keel as long as wings. Pod (2–)2.5–6(–7) × 0.5–0.8 cm.; wings of pod 2–4 mm. wide, mostly wavy. Seeds many, 2–3 mm., globular, brown. Fl. March–June.

Hab.: Batha and fields. Coastal Galilee, Acco Plain, Coast of Carmel, Sharon Plain, Philistean Plain, Mt. Gilboa, Upper and Lower Galilee, Mt. Carmel, Esdraelon Plain, Samaria, Shefela, Judean Mts., Dan Valley, Hula Plain, Upper Jordan Valley, Gilead, Moav.

Area: E. Mediterranean.

Very polymorphic in the dimensions of the plants, leaves and pods. Some specimens from Gilead and Sharon Plain are distinguished by their oblong or oblong-ovate, acute leaflets.

One of the most promising local forage plants, recently taken into cultivation.

23. BONJEANEA Reichb.

Perennial herbs or shrubs. Leaves digitate, 3–5-foliolate; stipules minute or 0; leaflets entire, the 1 or 2 lowest pairs of leaflets stipule-like, somewhat remote from the others. Flowers mostly in capitate or umbellate racemes. Calyx almost campanulate, 5-toothed or sometimes slightly 2-lipped. Corolla white or pink, keel often with darker tip; standard broadly ovate to oblong, often lyrate; wings connivent or coalescent above, with a longitudinal fold or with a transversely inflated projection; keel obtuse to slightly curved. Stamens diadelphous; filaments of 5 stamens dilated at apex. Ovary sessile, 1–4-ovuled; style gradually tapering at apex, with capitate stigma. Pod dehiscent, 2-valved, 1–4-seeded, ovoid, short-linear, more or less transversely septate inside; valves straight or twisting at dehiscence.

Four species, mostly in the Mediterranean region.

Literature: M. Rikli, Die Gattung *Dorycnium* Vill., *Bot. Jahrb.* 31 : 314–404 (1901).

1. Flowers 1 cm. or more, 5–10 in a head. Pod ovoid or oblong, slightly exserted from calyx.
2. B. hirsuta

– Flowers 5 mm., 20–40 in a dense head. Pod cylindrical, 3 times as long as calyx.
1. B. recta

1. Bonjeanea recta (L.) Reichb., Fl. Germ. Exc. 507 (1832). *Lotus recta* L., Sp. Pl. 775 (1753). *Dorycnium rectum* (L.) Ser. in DC., Prodr. 2 : 208 (1825); Boiss., Fl. 2 : 161 (1872). [Plate 143]

Shrub, much branched, appressed- to patulous-pubescent, 0.5–2 m. Stems and branches striate to angular. Leaves about 3–4 cm., petiolate; leaflets 1.2 (–3) × 0.5–1.5

cm., obtuse, mucronulate, hairy on both sides, upper leaflets obovate-cuneate, stipular leaflets longer than petiole, ovate. Racemes head-like, many-flowered, borne on peduncles twice as long as subtending leaves. Pedicels as long as or somewhat longer than calyx. Flowers about 4–5 mm. Calyx campanulate; teeth much longer than tube, equal, subulate. Corolla considerably longer than calyx, white to pink; standard a little longer than wings and keel. Pod about 1 × 0.15–0.2 cm., much longer than calyx, slender, cylindrical, straight, acute, glabrous, blackish, shiny. Seeds globular, brown. Fl. April–September.

Hab.: Elevated river banks and swamps. Acco Plain, Sharon Plain, Upper Galilee, Esdraelon Plain, Samaria, Dan Valley, Hula Plain, Upper Jordan Valley.

Area: Mediterranean.

2. Bonjeanea hirsuta (L.) Reichb., Fl. Germ. Exc. 507 (1832). *Lotus hirsuta* L., Sp. Pl. 775 (1753). *Dorycnium hirsutum* (L.) Ser. in DC., Prodr. 2 : 208 (1825); Boiss., Fl. 2 : 161 (1872). [Plate 144]

Perennial herb or half-shrub, hirsute-villose, rarely glabrous, 20–50 cm. Stems erect or procumbent, terete. Leaves 1.5–3 cm., nearly sessile; leaflets oblong, rarely obovate-cuneate, acute to obtuse, mucronate; stipular leaflets much longer than petiole, ovate to lanceolate. Peduncles longer than subtending leaves. Involucre of 3–4 leaflets. Flowers 1–1.5 cm., (4–)5–10 in a head. Calyx campanulate; teeth longer than tube, lanceolate-subulate. Corolla almost twice as long as calyx; standard oblong-spatulate, white, longer than white wings and purplish keel. Pod 0.7–1.4 × 0.4 cm., slightly exserted from calyx, turgid, ovoid or oblong, acute, glabrous, blackish. Seeds globular, brown. Fl. April–June.

Hab.: Maquis. Upper Galilee, Mt. Carmel, Samaria. Rare.

Area: Mediterranean.

Trib. CORONILLEAE. Herbs or half-shrubs. Leaves mostly pinnate, rarely simple; leaflets entire. Inflorescences axillary, umbellate and many-flowered, rarely flowers solitary or few. Stamens diadelphous; all the filaments, or the alternate filaments only, dilated at apex; anthers uniform. Pod usually jointed, separating or not into 1-seeded segments.

24. SECURIGERA DC.

Annual herbs with the aspect of *Coronilla*. Leaves all imparipinnate; stipules small, membranous; leaflets entire, broadened at apex, mucronate, usually glabrous. Racemes head-like, pedunculate. Bracts small; bracteoles 0. Flowers later deflexed. Calyx short-campanulate, more or less 2-lipped with upper teeth long-connate. Corolla yellow; standard almost orbicular; keel tapering-beaked. Stamens diadelphous; alternate filaments somewhat dilated at apex. Ovary sessile, many-ovuled; style incurved, glabrous; stigma capitate. Pod flattened, elongated-linear, beaked, somewhat constricted between seeds, not separating into segments, margins thickened on both sides. Seeds flat, quadrangular.

One species in the Mediterranean region.

1. Securigera securidaca (L.) Deg. et Doerfl., Denkschr. Akad. Wiss. Wien 64 : 718 (1897). *Coronilla securidaca* L., Sp. Pl. 743 (1753). *S. coronilla* DC. in Lam. et DC., Fl. Fr. ed. 3, 4 : 609 (1805); Boiss., Fl. 2 : 176 (1872). [Plate 145]

Annual, glabrous or sparingly hairy, 40–60 cm. Stems few, diffuse or erect, furrowed. Leaves up to 15 cm.; stipules small, free, lanceolate; leaflets 0.8–2 × 0.5–1 cm., oblong, cuneate at base, truncate or retuse at apex. Peduncles axillary, longer than leaves, elongating in fruit. Racemes 4–8-flowered. Bracts minute, membranous, deflexed. Flowers about 1 cm. Calyx very short, about 2 mm., with teeth as long as tube. Corolla yellow; standard with reddish veins. Pod up to 8.5 × 0.5–0.6 cm., 6–12-seeded, with reflexed, hook-shaped beak. Seeds compressed, axe-shaped, brown to brownish-green. Fl. April–May.

Hab.: Weed among winter crops. Acco Plain, Sharon Plain, Philistean Plain, Upper and Lower Galilee, Mt. Carmel, Esdraelon Plain, Samaria, Shefela, Judean Mts., Dan Valley, Hula Plain, Upper Jordan Valley.

Area: E. Mediterranean, slightly extending into W. Irano-Turanian territories.

25. SCORPIURUS L.

Annuals. Leaves undivided, entire; stipules adnate to petiole. Racemes axillary, pedunculate, 1- or few-flowered, bracteate. Flowers ebracteolate. Calyx short-campanulate; teeth somewhat unequal, the upper teeth long-connate. Petals yellow, sometimes reddish, long-clawed; standard almost orbicular; wings obliquely oblong to obovate; keel with curved beak. Stamens diadelphous; alternate stamens dilated at apex. Ovary sessile, many-ovuled; style incurved, dilated at the middle, attenuate at apex; stigma terminal, capitate. Pod indehiscent, subcylindrical, coiled in 1 to several turns, more or less constricted between segments, grooved or crested lengthwise or covered with warts, protuberances or prickles along crests. Seeds reniform to ovoid-oblong.

Two species and a few varieties mainly in the Mediterranean region.

Literature: C. C. Heyn & V. Raviv, Experimental taxonomic studies in the genus *Scorpiurus* (Papilionaceae), *Bull. Torrey Bot. Cl.* 93 : 259–267 (1966).

1. Scorpiurus muricatus L., Sp. Pl. 745 (1753). [Plate 146]

Annual, hirtellous, 10–30 cm. Stems few to many, procumbent, angular to furrowed. Leaves 3–8 cm., petiolate, lanceolate to lanceolate-spatulate to oblong-spatulate, 3–5-nerved; stipules linear-lanceolate, acuminate, membranous at margin. Peduncles shorter than leaves, elongating in fruit. Racemes (1–)2–4-flowered. Flowers 1–1.5 cm., short-pedicelled. Calyx about 5 mm., campanulate, cleft almost to middle into 5 more or less equal teeth; teeth longer than tube, lanceolate, acute. Corolla yellow; standard 1 × 0.8 cm., longer than wings; wings oblong; keel with strongly curved, acute beak. Ovary prickly or scabrous. Pod 3–6 cm., irregularly twisted, constricted between seeds, glabrous or hairy, longitudinally ridged, ridges more or less smooth or tuberculate or covered with simple or hooked or 2-fid prickles. Seeds short, reniform to semilunate, brown to yellowish; hilum black. 2n = 28. Fl. March–April.

Var. **muricatus.** *S. muricata* L., l.c.; Boiss., Fl. 2 : 178 (1872), incl. var. *laevigata* (Sm.) Boiss., l.c. *S. sulcata* L., l.c. p.p.; Boiss., l.c. 179 p.p. Pod with smooth or tuberculate ribs, usually coiled in one plane only.

Var. **subvillosus** (L.) Fiori et Bég. in Fiori et Paol., Fl. Anal. Ital. 2 : 89 (1900). *S. subvillosa* L., l.c.; Boiss., l.c. 179. *S. sulcata* L., l.c. p.p.; Boiss., l.c. 179 p.p. Pod prickly, usually coiled in two planes.

Hab. of species : Batha, fields and roadsides. Coastal Galilee, Acco Plain, Coast of Carmel, Sharon Plain, Philistean Plain, Upper and Lower Galilee, Mt. Carmel, Esdraelon Plain, Mt. Gilboa, Samaria, Shefela, Judean Mts., W., N. and C. Negev, Dan Valley, Hula Plain, Upper Jordan Valley, Beit Shean Valley, Lower Jordan Valley, Dead Sea area, Gilead, Ammon, Moav.

Area of species : Mainly Mediterranean, with extensions into the Irano-Turanian region.

26. ORNITHOPUS L.

Annual slender herbs. Leaves minutely stipulate, imparipinnate; leaflets many. Flowers small, in axillary, long-peduncled umbels, naked or bracteate. Calyx tubular-campanulate, 5-toothed; teeth equal, or the upper teeth connate at base and less deeply separated than the lower. Standard almost orbicular to obovate; wings oblong; keel obtuse, shorter than wings. Stamens diadelphous; alternate filaments dilated towards the top; anthers all similar. Ovary sessile, many-ovuled. Pod a loment, flat or terete, curved, usually separating at maturity into 1-seeded segments. Seeds oblong, ovoid to globular.

Nine species in the Mediterranean region, S. and C. Europe and W. Asia; one species in Uruguay.

1. Peduncles with a pinnate leaf (bract) at apex. Pod flattened, ending in a hooked, sharp-pointed beak.   **2. O. compressus**
- Peduncles naked at apex. Pod cylindrical, ending in a somewhat incurved beak.
                                                                            1. O. pinnatus

1. Ornithopus pinnatus (Mill.) Druce, Journ. Bot. Lond. 45 : 420 (1907). *Scorpiurus pinnata* Mill., Gard. Dict. ed. 8, no. 5 (1768). *O. ebracteatus* Brot., Fl. Lusit. 2 : 159 (1804); Boiss., Fl. 2 : 177 (1872). [Plate 147]

Annual, nearly glabrous, 10–30 cm. Stems slender, ascending or procumbent, often branched. Leaves 4–8 cm., all petiolate; stipules minute, adnate to base of petiole, ovate; leaflets 3–6-paired, 0.6–1.5 × 0.2–0.4 cm., linear-lanceolate to narrowly obovate, cuneate at base, mucronulate, entire; lower pair distant from base of petiole. Peduncles filiform, as long as subtending leaves. Inflorescences umbellate, 2–4(–5)-flowered, ebracteate. Flowers 6–8 mm., with very short bracteoles and pedicels. Calyx about 5 mm., tubular; teeth one sixth to one quarter as long as tube, lanceolate, acute. Corolla yellow, veined with red. Pod about 3 × 0.1–0.2 cm., erect, cylindrical, falcate to semicircular, glabrous, ending in a conical, incurved beak; segments longitudinally ribbed, cylindrical or slightly angular. Seeds oblong, yellow. Fl. February–May.

Hab.: Fields and batha; sands and sandy clay, rarely calcareous soils. Sharon Plain, Philistean Plain, Samaria.

Area: Mediterranean.

2. Ornithopus compressus L., Sp. Pl. 744 (1753). [Plate 148]

Annual, villose, 10–40 cm. Stems slender, procumbent to ascending, branching from base. Leaves, except the lower ones, sessile, up to 7 cm.; stipules minute, lanceolate or 0; leaflets 8–16-paired, 0.5–1 cm., oblong to elliptical, mucronulate. Inflorescences umbellate, 2–5-flowered, with a pinnate leaf (bract) at apex of peduncle overtopping the flowers. Flowers 5–6 mm., minutely pedicellate. Calyx tubular or funnel-shaped; teeth half as long as to as long as tube, linear-lanceolate. Pod 4 × 0.2–0.25 cm., deflexed, flat, linear, falcate, slightly constricted between seeds, hairy or glabrous, ending in a hooked, sharp-pointed beak. Seeds ovoid, compressed, reddish to brown. Fl. February–April.

Var. **compressus**. *O. compressus* L., l.c.; Boiss., Fl. 2 : 178 (1872). Pod villose.

Hab.: Fields, sandy and sandy-loamy soils. Acco Plain, Coastal Galilee, Sharon Plain, Philistean Plain, Judean Mts.

Var. **leiocarpus** Eig, Bull. Inst. Agr. Nat. Hist. 6 : 26 (1927). Pod glabrous.

Hab.: As above. Together with the preceding variety.

Area of species: Mediterranean; also recorded from some S. W. provinces of the Euro-Siberian region.

27. CORONILLA L.

Annual or perennial herbs or shrubs with stipulate, imparipinnate, very rarely 3-foliolate leaves. Racemes axillary, mostly umbellate, long-peduncled. Flowers deflexed. Calyx short-campanulate; teeth short, often equal, the upper teeth partly connate, forming an upper lip. Petals yellow, purple or white, clawed; standard almost orbicular; wings oblique, obovate; keel acutely beaked. Stamens diadelphous. Ovary sessile, many-ovuled; style glabrous; stigma minutely capitate. Pod a loment, teretetetragonous or flattened, elongated, straight or curved; segments 1-seeded, elongated-linear. Seeds elongated to square.

About 25 species, mainly in the Mediterranean region and Central Europe.

Literature: A. Uhrova, Revision der Gattung *Coronilla* L., *Beih. Bot. Centralbl.* 53, 2 : 1–174 (1935).

1. Leaflets 1–5 (–7)   2
 – Leaflets 9–17   3
2. Leaflets 1–3; terminal leaflet many times longer than others.   **4. C. scorpioides**
 – Leaflets mostly 3–7; terminal leaflet longer than the rest or not.   **3. C. repanda**
3 (1). Pod straight, not flattened, with a cylindrical to filiform beak. Leaflets 5–7 (–8)-paired.   **1. C. cretica**
 – Pod arcuate or semicircular, flattened, with a broad, triangular beak. Leaflets (6–) 7–13-paired.   **2. C. rostrata**

1. Coronilla cretica L., Sp. Pl. 743 (1753). [Plate 149]

Annual, subglabrous to somewhat pubescent, 10–40 cm. Stems ascending to erect, slightly branching from base. Leaves 4–10 cm., glabrous; stipules very small, caducous, oblong-lanceolate; leaflets 5–7(–8)-paired, 0.6–1.8 × 0.4–0.8 cm., truncate to retuse and often mucronulate at apex. Peduncles mostly longer than subtending leaves, elongating in fruit. Racemes umbellate, 3–9-flowered. Bracts small, caducous. Pedicels slightly longer than calyx. Flowers 0.5–0.7 cm. Calyx minute, puberulent; teeth short, broad. Corolla 4–5 times as long as calyx, pink to white; standard purple-veined; keel purple at apex. Pod (2.5–)3–8 × 0.1 cm., erect, slightly recurved at apex, with angular segments. Seeds angular, oblong-linear, brown, smooth. Fl. March–June.

Var. **cretica**. *C. cretica* L., l.c.; Boiss., Fl. 2 : 182 (1872). Racemes 3–6-flowered. Pod 2.5–7 cm. Stems few.

Hab. : Fields and moist places. Sharon Plain, Upper and Lower Galilee, Mt. Carmel, Esdraelon Plain, Mt. Gilboa, Samaria, Dan Valley, Hula Plain, Upper Jordan Valley.

Var. **multiflora** Plitm., Israel Journ. Bot. 15 : 29 (1966). Racemes 4–9-flowered. Pod 6–8 cm. Stems many. 2n = 12.

Hab. : River banks. Dan Valley.

Area of species : Mediterranean, extending into S. Euro-Siberian territories.

2. Coronilla rostrata Boiss. et Sprun. in Boiss., Diagn. ser. 1, 2 : 100 (1843). [Plate 150]

Annual, subglabrous or hairy, 10–40 cm. Stems erect to procumbent, branching from base. Leaves 3–12(–14) cm.; stipules very small, caducous, ovate-lanceolate; leaflets 7–13 pairs, 0.5–1.5 × 0.4–0.8 cm., petiolulate, oblong-obovate, cuneate, truncate to retuse and mucronulate at apex. Peduncles longer than subtending leaves, hairy at base. Racemes (1–3–)4–7(–9)-flowered. Bracts minute, scarious, lanceolate. Pedicels slightly longer than calyx. Flowers 0.7–1 cm. Calyx minute, glabrous to puberulent, with short and broad, triangular teeth. Corolla 3–4 times as long as calyx, white to pink, sometimes yellow; standard purple-veined. Pod (2–)4–7 × 0.25 cm., spreading, compressed, narrowly linear, semicircular, narrowly margined, thickened at joints, flat and beaked at apex. Seeds compressed, oblong, brown, smooth. Fl. March–April.

Var. **rostrata**. *C. rostrata* Boiss. et Sprun., l.c. *C. parviflora* Willd., Sp. Pl. 3 : 1155 (1802) non Moench, Meth. 121 (1794); Boiss., Fl. 2 : 183 (1872). Racemes 4–7(–9)-flowered. Stems almost simple, 10–40 cm.

Hab. : Batha. Coastal Galilee, Sharon Plain, Philistean Plain, Upper and Lower Galilee, Mt. Carmel, Esdraelon Plain, Mt. Gilboa, Samaria, Judean Mts., Hula Plain, Upper Jordan Valley.

Var. **pauciflora** (Plitm.) Fertig (comb. nov.). *C. parviflora* Willd. var *pauciflora* Plitm., Israel Journ. Bot. 15 : 29 (1966). Racemes 1–3-flowered. Caespitose herbs up to 10 cm.

Hab. : Batha and maquis. Upper Galilee.

Area of species : Mainly E. Mediterranean.

3. Coronilla repanda (Poir.) Guss., Fl. Sic. Syn. 2 : 302 (1844?). *Ornithopus repandus* Poir., Voy. Barb. 2 : 215 (1789) et in Lam., Encycl. 4 : 620 (1798). [Plate 151]

Annual, glaucous, glabrous, 5–30 cm. Stems 1 to many, procumbent to erect, simple or branching. Leaves 0.8–4 cm., short-petioled, somewhat fleshy, the lower leaves simple or 3-foliolate, the upper leaves of 2–3 pairs of leaflets; stipules scarious, connate and sheathing; leaflets usually 0.8–2 × 0.3–0.6 cm.; the lowermost leaflets small, suborbicular, the rest larger, cuneate-obovate to oblong-elliptical. Peduncles slightly longer than leaves, rarely shorter. Racemes umbellate, (1–)2–4-flowered. Bracts rudimentary, caducous. Pedicels a little shorter than calyx. Flowers 5–7 mm. Calyx small, glabrous, with 5 short, triangular teeth. Corolla 2–3 times as long as calyx, yellow; standard purple-veined; keel curved. Pod 2–5 cm., on deflexed pedicel, narrowly linear, angular, arcuate to circular. Seeds oblong, brown, smooth. Fl. March–May.

Hab.: Sandy soils. Sharon Plain, Philistean Plain, Coastal, W. and N. Negev.

Area: S. Mediterranean.

4. Coronilla scorpioides (L.) Koch, Syn. Fl. Germ. Helv. 188 (1835); Boiss., Fl. 2 : 183 (1872). *Ornithopus scorpioides* L., Sp. Pl. 744 (1753). [Plate 152]

Annual, glaucous, glabrous, (5–)10–40 cm. Stems ascending to erect, simple or branching, especially from base. Leaves 1–5 cm., subsessile, mostly ternate, rarely simple, rather thick; stipules connate, often sheathing at base, somewhat scarious; lateral leaflets 1–3, small, 3–8 mm., sometimes soon deciduous, sessile, suborbicular, the terminal leaflets much larger, 1–4 cm., short-petiolulate, ovate to elliptical, sometimes mucronulate. Peduncles glabrous, rarely longer than leaves. Racemes (1–)2–4-flowered. Bracts rudimentary, caducous. Pedicels about as long as calyx. Flowers 4–6 mm. Calyx small, glabrous, with 5 short, triangular teeth. Corolla 2–3 times as long as calyx, yellow; standard purple-veined; keel rather curved. Pod 3–7 × 0.2 cm., spreading or deflexed, tetragonous, linear, arcuate to coiled-circular, slightly constricted between seeds, with beak 2–3 mm. Seeds oblong, dark brown, smooth. Fl. February–June.

Hab.: Fields and batha. Coastal Galilee, Sharon Plain, Philistean Plain, Upper and Lower Galilee, Mt. Carmel, Esdraelon Plain, Mt. Gilboa, Samaria, Shefela, Judean Mts., Judean Desert, W. and N. Negev, Dead Sea area, Dan Valley, Hula Plain, Upper and Lower Jordan Valley, Ammon, Moav, Edom.

Area: Mediterranean, extending into the adjacent Irano-Turanian territories.

28. HIPPOCREPIS L.

Annual or perennial herbs or shrubs. Leaves imparipinnate, with many entire leaflets; stipules small or 0. Racemes axillary, umbellate, many-, few- or 1-flowered, bracteate. Flowers deflexed. Calyx campanulate, 5-toothed with 2 upper teeth more or less connate. Petals yellow or white, sometimes with violet or purple stripes, long-clawed; standard almost orbicular; wings oblong to obovate; keel tapering, beaked. Stamens diadelphous; alternate filaments slightly dilated at top; anthers all equal. Ovary sessile, many-ovuled; style incurved, subulate; stigma small. Pod a loment, flattened, straight or curved, the margin excavated opposite each seed; segments horseshoe-shaped, usually separating at maturity. Seeds curved.

About 20 species in the Mediterranean region and Europe.

Literature: J. Bornmüller, Kritische Bemerkungen über annuelle *Hippocrepis* Arten, *Notizbl. Bot. Gart. Mus. Berlin* 10 (95) : 421–451 (1928).

1. Pod circular or spirally coiled; segments very narrow, ring-like, horned. **3. H. bicontorta**
- Pod straight to circular; segments excavated, but neither ring-like nor horned   2
2. Racemes 1–2-flowered, rarely up to 4-flowered, but then the opening of sinus of each pod segment facing the concave margin of the pod; pod straight or arcuate. Peduncles 0 or very short, rarely long.   **1. H. unisiliquosa**
- Racemes (2–)3–6(–8)-flowered. Opening of sinus of pod segment facing the convex margin of the pod.   **2. H. multisiliquosa**

1. Hippocrepis unisiliquosa L., Sp. Pl. 744 (1753). [Plate 153]

Annual, 5–40 cm., glabrous to sparingly puberulent. Stems procumbent to erect, simple or branching, especially at base, slightly striate. Leaves 2–7 (–10) cm., petiolate; stipules small, scarious, lanceolate, greenish-purplish, ciliate at apex, sometimes with a dark, prominent gland at base; leaflets 3–7 pairs, 0.9–1.5 × 0.2–0.4 cm., subsessile, linear-oblong to obovate, cuneate at base, retuse or truncate and mostly mucronulate at apex. Racemes subsessile, rarely pedunculate, 1–2 (very rarely 4)-flowered. Flowers 4–7 mm., on very short, rather hairy pedicels. Calyx persistent, glabrous, with 5 lanceolate teeth almost as long as tube, the upper teeth connate at base. Corolla twice as long as calyx, yellow; standard sometimes pink-veined; keel incurved. Pod 2–5.5 × 0.2–0.6 cm., erect to sometimes deflexed, compressed, linear, of 4–12 flattened segments, straight to arcuate; sinus of each segment open or almost closed, opening of sinus facing the concave margin of pod, segments glabrous but papillose-hairy above seeds. Seeds cylindrical, arcuate to almost circular, brown, smooth. Fl. February–June.

1. Racemes usually 1-flowered (rarely 2- or more-flowered). Pod 4–6 (rarely 3) mm. broad, almost straight to slightly arcuate   (subsp. **unisiliquosa**) 2
- Racemes usually 2-3-flowered, rarely 1-flowered. Pod 2–3 (rarely 4) mm. broad, strongly curved   (subsp. **bisiliqua**) 3
2. Racemes 1 (–2)-flowered.   var. **unisiliquosa**
- Racemes 1–4-flowered.   var. **multisiliqua**
3 (1). Pod sessile.   var. **bisiliqua**
- Pod on peduncle up to 2 cm.   var. **pedunculata**

Subsp. **unisiliquosa.** Flowers 1, rarely 2 or up to 4 in each raceme. Pod 2–5 × (0.3–)0.4–0.6 cm., almost straight to slightly arcuate, mostly with less than 10 segments; sinus of segment open to closed.

Var. **unisiliquosa.** *H. unisiliquosa* L., l.c.; Boiss., Fl. 2 : 184 (1872). Pods 1 (–2) in each raceme, slightly arcuate. 2n = 14.

Hab.: Fields, batha and steppes. Coastal Galilee, Sharon Plain, Philistean Plain, Upper and Lower Galilee, Mt. Carmel, Esdraelon Plain, Samaria, Shefela, Judean Mts., Judean Desert, W., N. and C. Negev, Hula Plain, Upper Jordan Valley, Ammon, Moav, Edom.

Var. **multisiliqua** Eig (in herb.) ex Plitm., Israel Journ. Bot. 15 : 28 (1966). Pods 1–4 in each raceme, about 4–6 mm. broad, short-pedicelled. Stems long, somewhat divaricately branching, rigid. Leaves up to 5 cm.; leaflets about 3 mm. broad. Flowers 6 mm. 2n = 14.

   Hab. : Fields and steppes. Dan Valley, Upper and Lower Jordan Valley.

Subsp. **bisiliqua** (Forssk.) Bornm., Notizbl. 10 : 438 (1928). Flowers and pods 2–3, rarely 1 in each raceme. Pod 2–3(–4) mm. broad, more strongly curved than in ssp. *unisiliquosa*, with up to 10 segments; sinus often completely closed, with overlapping edges.

Var. **bisiliqua**. *H. bisiliqua* Forssk., Fl. Aeg.-Arab. LXXI (1775). *H. unisiliquosa* L. var. *biflora* (Spreng.) Post, Fl. Syr. Pal. Sin. 280 (1883–1896). *H. biflora* Spreng., Pl. Min. Cog. Pugill. 2 : 73 (1815); Boiss., l.c. 185. Leaves 1–5 cm. Racemes subsessile. Pods (1–)2–3 in raceme, papillose-hairy around sinuses. 2n = 14.

   Hab. : Fields, batha, steppes and deserts. Sharon Plain, Philistean Plain, Judean Mts., Judean Desert, Coastal, W., N. and C. Negev, Upper and Lower Jordan Valley, Dead Sea area, Edom.

Var. **pedunculata** (Eig) Plitm., Israel Journ. Bot. 15 : 28 (1966). *H. biflora* Spreng. var. *pedunculata* Eig, Bull. Inst. Agr. Nat. Hist. 6 : 27 (1927). Some of the leaves 5–10 cm. Racemes on peduncles up to 2 cm. long. Pods 1–3 in each raceme, almost glabrous.

   Hab. : Fields. Esdraelon Plain.

   Area of species : Mediterranean, with extensions into Irano-Turanian provinces.

2. Hippocrepis multisiliquosa L., Sp. Pl. 744 (1753). [Plates 154, 155]

   Annual, glabrous to sparingly appressed-puberulent, 10–50 cm. Stems procumbent to erect, simple or branching, especially at base, sometimes tufted, slightly striate. Leaves (2–)4–9 cm., petiolate; leaflets (2–)3–8 pairs, 0.6–1.4 × 0.2–0.5 cm., linear or oblong to more or less obovate and cuneate at base, obtuse and truncate or retuse and mucronulate at apex, glabrous to sparingly pubescent. Racemes 3–8-flowered, on peduncles as long as or longer or much shorter than subtending leaves. Bracts minute, sometimes caducous, more or less scarious, mostly 2-fid, with prominent dark glands at base. Flowers 5–7 mm., short-pedicelled. Calyx glabrous, with 5 lanceolate, tapering teeth, one to one and a half times as long as tube, the upper teeth mostly connate at base. Corolla up to twice as long as calyx, yellow or white, with pink or purple veins; keel curved. Pods (2–)3–6 in a raceme, about 5 × 0.3–0.4 cm., mostly compressed-linear, semicircular to circular, glabrous to scabrous or hairy, sometimes with glandular cilia along margins; segments flattened, sinus almost completely closed, opening of sinus facing the convex margin of pod. Seeds cylindrical, arcuate-subcircular, brown, smooth. 2n = 14.

Subsp. **multisiliquosa**. [Plate 154]. Leaves 4–9 cm.; stipules lanceolate-subulate, ciliate, with 2 prominent dark glands at base; leaflets 3–8-paired. Peduncles longer to much shorter than subtending leaves. Racemes 3–8-flowered. Calyx teeth as long as or longer than tube, lanceolate, tapering. Corolla yellow; standard pink-veined. Pod glabrous to scabrous or papillose-hairy. Fl. March–May.

Var. **multisiliquosa**. *H. multisiliquosa* L., l.c.; Boiss., Fl. 2 : 185 (1872). Peduncles longer than or about as long as subtending leaves.

Hab. : Batha and fields. Coastal Galilee, Acco Plain, Sharon Plain, Philistean Plain, Upper and Lower Galilee, Mt. Carmel, Esdraelon Plain, Judean Mts., C. Negev, Upper and Lower Jordan Valley, Moav.

Var. **brachypoda** Aarons. ex Evenari in Opphr. et Evenari, Bull. Soc. Bot. Genève, ser. 2, 31 : 275 (1941). Peduncles much shorter than subtending leaves.

Hab. : As above. Sharon Plain.

Area of subspecies : Mediterranean.

Subsp. **eilatensis** Zoh.* [Plate 155]. Leaves 2–6 cm.; stipules minute, almost free, ovate-triangular; leaflets in 2–4 pairs, 0.8–1 × 0.2–0.3 cm., obovate to oblong, cuneate at base, obtuse and slightly retuse at apex. Peduncles as long as or longer than subtending leaves. Racemes 3–4-flowered. Flowers 5–6 mm., on pedicels much shorter than calyx. Calyx campanulate, with broadly triangular teeth somewhat shorter than the tube, the upper teeth the shortest. Corolla white with dense purple veins; standard somewhat longer than wings and keel, almost orbicular, apiculate. Pod about 8-jointed, hairy all over, with glandular cilia along margins. Fl. March–April.

Hab. : Sandy deserts. Arava Valley.

Area of subspecies : Sudanian.

Differs from *H. constricta* Kunze, Pugill. Pl. Prim. 42 (1838), in several respects, e.g., colour of corolla, position of the segment sinuses, indumentum, and smaller number of leaflet pairs.

3. **Hippocrepis bicontorta** Loisel., Nouv. Not. 32 (1827). *H. cornigera* Boiss., Diagn. ser. 1, 2 : 102 (1843) et Fl. 2 : 185 (1872). [Plate 156]

Annual, sparingly appressed-pubescent, 10–40 cm. Stems procumbent to ascending, with short branches, sometimes tufted, slender. Leaves 1–5 cm., petiolate; stipules small, subulate-lanceolate, ciliate; leaflets in 2–6 pairs, 0.5–1.2 × 0.1–0.3 cm., narrowly oblong to linear, obtuse to truncate at apex, appressed-puberulent. Peduncles usually longer than subtending leaves. Racemes 2–5-flowered. Bracts rudimentary, scarious, triangular, 2-fid. Flowers 4–7 mm., short-pedicelled. Calyx almost glabrous, with 5 lanceolate-triangular teeth less than half as long as tube. Corolla twice as long as calyx, yellow; standard purple-veined; keel incurved. Pod up to about 4 cm., spreading to deflexed, compressed, circular to spirally twisted, almost glabrous to papillose-hairy; segments very narrow, flattened, ring-like, horned, opening of sinus facing the convex margin of pod. Seeds cylindrical, arcuate, brown, smooth. 2n = 14. Fl. March–May.

Hab. : Sandy steppes. Philistean Plain, Coastal, W., N. and C. Negev, Edom.

Area : Saharo-Arabian.

* See Appendix at end of this volume.

29. Hedysarum L.

Annual or perennial herbs, half-shrubs or shrubs, glabrous or silky-hairy to villose. Leaves stipulate, imparipinnate with 3–7 pairs of leaflets. Racemes axillary, pedunculate, bracteate. Flowers bracteolate. Calyx campanulate, subequally 5-toothed. Corolla pink or white or rarely yellowish; standard narrow at base, with obovate to obcordate limb; wings short or elongated, auriculate; keel obliquely truncate at apex, slightly curved, mostly longer than wings. Stamens diadelphous; anthers all equal. Ovary subsessile, 4- to many-ovuled; style bent in upper part. Pod a flattened loment; segments usually several, rarely 1, indehiscent, separating readily, nearly rounded or square, glabrous or prickly. Seeds compressed, reniform.

About 160 species in temperate regions of the northern hemisphere.

1. Hedysarum spinosissimum L., Sp. Pl. 750 (1753); Sm. in Sibth. et Sm., Fl. Gr. 8 : 16, t. 721 (1832); Boiss., Fl. 2 : 513 (1872). *H. pallens* (Moris) Hal., Consp. Fl. Gr. 1 : 453 (1900). *H. spinosissimum* L. var. *pallens* (Moris) Rouy in Rouy et Fouc., Fl. Fr. 5 : 291 (1899). [Plate 157]

Annual, pubescent, 10–40 cm. Stems many, procumbent to ascending, often sparingly branched. Leaves 3–8 cm., imparipinnate, glabrous, the lower rosulate; stipules coriaceous, triangular, with lower part adnate to petiole; leaflets 4–7 pairs, 0.5–1.2 cm., oblong-elliptical, obtuse to retuse, almost glabrous above, hairy beneath. Racemes (1–)2–7(–8)-flowered, on 2–10 cm. long peduncles. Pedicels short, bracteolate. Flowers 0.8–1 cm. Calyx half as long as corolla; teeth often longer than tube, linear. Corolla pale pink; standard oblong-cuneate, notched and mucronulate at apex. Pod 2–4 cm., compressed; segments (1–)2–4, ovoid-discoid, prickly and hairy, readily separating; beak short. Fl. March–April.

Hab.: Batha and steppes on sandy or loessy ground. Sharon Plain, Philistean Plain, Mt. Carmel, W., N. and C. Negev.

Area: Mediterranean.

Two ecotypes connected by intergrading forms are met with in Palestine: (1) In the southern type (Negev) the racemes are 3–8-flowered, pods 2–4-jointed, segments 5–7 mm., with short prickles [var. *pallens* (Moris) Rouy, l.c.; Heyn, Israel Journ. Bot. 12 : 188 (1963)]. (2) In the northern type the racemes are 1–4-flowered, pods 1–3-jointed, segments 0.7–1 cm., with long hooked prickles (var. *spinosissimum*; Heyn, l.c.).

30. Onobrychis Mill.

Herbs, rarely shrubs. Leaves usually imparipinnate; stipules scarious; leaflets numerous, entire. Flowers in axillary racemes. Bracts often coloured. Calyx campanulate; lobes 5, nearly equal. Corolla variously coloured; standard obcordate to obovate; wings short; keel obliquely truncate, usually shorter than or exceeding standard. Stamens diadelphous, the upper stamen free at base and connate with the others at middle; filaments not dilated; anthers all equal. Ovary sessile, 1–2-ovuled; style filiform; stigma terminal. Pod indehiscent, sessile or stipitate, exserted from calyx, leathery, not jointed, flattened, more or less semiglobular or orbicular-circinate, with pitted disk and spiny crests or margins. Seeds 1 (–2–3), broad, kidney-shaped to oblong.

About 170 species, mainly in S. W. Asia, the Mediterranean region and in temperate Europe and Asia.

Literature : G. Sirjaev, *Onobrychis* generis revisio critica, *Publ. Fac. Sci. Univ. Masaryk* 56 : 1–195 (1925), 76 : 1–165 (1926); Supplementum ad monographiam *"Onobrychis* generis revisio critica", *Bull. Soc. Bot. Bulgarie* 4 : 7–24 (1931); Supplementum II ad *Onobrychis* generis revisio critica, *Publ. Fac. Sci. Univ. Masaryk* 242 : 1–14 (1937).

1. Pod glabrous or hairy (but never white-woolly), thick, semiglobular, ellipsoidal or irregularly angled, not flattened or circinate, usually pitted and provided with crests of prickles on disk and sometimes also along margin. Corolla glabrous, pink or flesh-coloured   2
– Pod woolly, flattened, circinate, discoid, orbicular or obovate. Corolla hairy, white, yellow or yellowish   7
2. Annuals. Pod usually about 1 cm. long or more. Racemes few-, rarely up to 10-flowered   3
– Perennials. Pod 3–7 mm. long. Racemes many-flowered, spike-like, elongated   5
3. Racemes loose, (3–)4–8(–15)-flowered. Pod 0.9–1.2 cm., 1-seeded; disk densely covered with prickles; crest divided into numerous, narrow, triangular-subulate, simple prickles.   **6. O. caput-galli**
– Not as above   4
4. Leaflets 7–11-paired. Flowers 0.9–1 cm. Wings shorter than keel. Pod with only 3 crests of spines and no accessory crest; lobes of main crest obtuse, dentate at apex. Germination pits 2.   **8. O. squarrosa**
– Leaflets 5–8-paired. Flowers 7–8 mm. Wings longer than keel. Pod with 3 marginal crests of spines and 1 or more accessory crests on disk of pod; lobes of main crest sharp-pointed, dentate along margin. Germination pits 3 (2).   **7. O. crista-galli**
5(2). Flowers 5–7 mm. Standard much longer than keel.   **1. O. supina**
– Flowers about 1 cm. long or more. Standard shorter than keel   6
6. Pod obovoid or obconical, truncate at apex.   **3. O. kotschyana**
– Pod semiglobular, apex rounded in outline.   **2. O. cadmea**
7(1). Pod about 1.5 cm., suborbicular-circinate. Leaflets orbicular-obovate, obtuse, the terminal one much larger.   **5. O. wettsteinii**
– Pod 0.6–1 cm., orbicular. Leaflets oblong-elliptical.   **4. O. ptolemaica**

Sect. ONOBRYCHIS. Sect. *Eubrychis* DC., Prodr. 2 : 344 (1825) et Mém. Légum. 7 : 347 (1826) p.p. Sect. *Eubrychis* DC. emend. Sirj., Publ. Fac. Sci. Univ. Masaryk 56 : 58 (1925). Perennials. Ovary usually 1-ovuled. Pod semiglobular or obovoid, crested.

1. Onobrychis supina (Chaix) DC. in Lam. et DC., Fl. Fr. ed. 3, 4 : 612 (1805). *Hedysarum supinum* Chaix in Vill., Prosp. Pl. Dauph. 41 (1779) et Hist. Pl. Dauph. 1 : 342 (1786). *O. gracilis* sensu Boiss., Fl. 2 : 535 (1872) non Bess., Enum. Pl. Volh. 74 (1822).

Perennial, appressed-canescent herb, 20–60 cm. Stems ascending to prostrate, slender.

Leaflets 5–9 pairs, 0.7–1 × 0.15–0.3 cm., elliptical, those of the upper leaves narrowly linear-lanceolate. Peduncles slender, becoming much longer than leaves. Racemes many-flowered, loose, elongated. Flowers 5–7 mm. Calyx half as long as corolla; teeth twice as long as tube, lanceolate-subulate, ciliate. Corolla pink; standard much longer than keel. Pod small, 4–5 mm., somewhat longer than calyx, semiglobular or obovoid, appressed-hirtellous; disk unequally and deeply pitted, almost unarmed; crest narrow with 5–6 teeth. Fl. May–June.

Hab.: Dry hills. Gilead (recorded by Dinsmore in Post, Fl. Syr. Pal. Sin. ed. 2, 1 : 412, 1932), not observed by us.

Area: Mainly N. Mediterranean.

2. Onobrychis cadmea Boiss., Diagn. ser. 1, 2 : 96 (1843) et Fl. 2 : 536 (1872). [Plate 158]

Perennial, appressed- and silky-canescent, 30–50 cm. Stems ascending, woody at base. Leaves 5–10 cm.; leaflets 6–12-paired, about 1 cm., oblong to linear-elliptical, mucronate. Peduncles much longer than subtending leaves. Racemes many-flowered, loose, oblong, elongating in fruit. Bracts shorter than pedicels, triangular. Flowers 1.2–1.8 cm. Calyx considerably shorter than corolla; teeth up to twice as long as tube, subulate, ciliate. Corolla pink; standard as long as keel. Pod 5–7 mm., semiglobular, appressed-tomentellous, somewhat shorter than calyx; disk with deep unequal pits, often with 4–5 prickles on either side; crest narrower than disk, deeply divided into 3–5 triangular prickles. Fl. May–June.

Hab.: Dry hills. Gilead, Ammon, Moav (recorded by Post, Fl. Syr. Pal. Sin. 282, 1883–1896 et ed. 2, 1 : 412, 1932), Edom.

Area: W. Irano-Turanian.

3. Onobrychis kotschyana Fenzl, Pugill. 3 (1842); Boiss., Fl. 2 : 537 (1872). *Hedysarum onobrychis* Banks et Sol. in Russ., Nat. Hist. Aleppo ed. 2, 2 : 260, t. 11 (1794) non L., Sp. Pl. 751 (1753). [Plate 159]

Perennial, appressed-hirsute, 10–30 cm. Stems erect or procumbent, striate. Leaves 3–7 cm.; stipules shorter than petiole, connate, coriaceous, ovate, acute; leaflets 3–7 pairs, 0.4–1.8 cm., oblong, those of upper leaves lanceolate, acute or sometimes obtuse, mucronate, glabrous above, silky-hairy beneath. Peduncles somewhat forked. Racemes long, many-flowered, loose. Bracts shorter than calyx, ovate, acute. Flowers 0.7–1 (–1.5) cm., subsessile. Calyx 3–7 (–9) mm.; teeth twice as long as tube, equal, lanceolate-subulate, hirsute. Corolla pale pink, glabrous; standard much shorter than keel; wings shorter than calyx. Pod 4–6 mm., shorter or somewhat longer than calyx, obovoid or obconical, truncate at apex, pubescent, with a deeply and unequally pitted disk, unarmed or with 2–3 prickles; crest with 2–3 triangular-subulate prickles. Fl. May–June.

Hab.: Steppes. Gilead, Ammon, Edom.

Area: W. Irano-Turanian.

Our plants belong to var. *genuina* Sirj., Publ. Fac. Sci. Univ. Masaryk 56 : 99 (1925). Stems subglabrous or sparingly appressed-pilose. Calyx about 9 mm. long. Corolla 1–1.5 cm.

Bornmüller distinguished a small-flowered form (f. *parviflora* Bornm. ex Sirj., l.c.; f. *parviflora* Bornm., Beih. Bot. Centralbl. 31, 2 : 210, 1914 *nom. nud.*), in which the calyx is 6–7.5 and corolla 0.7–1 (–1.1) cm. long.

Sect. HYMENOBRYCHIS DC., Prodr. 2 : 346 (1825) et Mém. Légum. 7 : 347 (1826). Perennials. Ovary usually 2-ovuled. Pod crested, with dorsal prickles; margin denticulate, rarely entire.

4. Onobrychis ptolemaica (Del.) DC., Prodr. 2 : 347 (1825). [Plate 160]
Perennial, villose, 20–40 cm. Stems many, erect or ascending, branching from neck, striate. Leaves 7–10 (–15) cm.; stipules lanceolate, acute; leaflets 4–8-paired, 1–2 × 0.2–0.8 cm., oblong to elliptical or lanceolate to linear or ovate to oblong, acute or obtuse at apex, upper surface glabrous, lower sparingly hirsute. Peduncles longer than subtending leaves. Racemes long, many-flowered. Pedicels much shorter than calyx, deflexed in fruit. Flowers 1–1.8 cm. Calyx about half as long as corolla; teeth longer than tube, lanceolate, the 2 lower teeth elongating in fruit. Corolla yellowish, brown-striped, hairy; wings as long as calyx, horseshoe-shaped; keel as long as or somewhat longer than standard. Pod 0.6–1 cm. across, flattened, orbicular, yellowish-woolly, pitted; disk and margin with minute prickles. 2n = 16. Fl. March–May.

Var. **ptolemaica**. *O. ptolemaïca* (Del.) DC., l.c.; Boiss., Fl. 2 : 547 (1872). *Hedysarum ptolemaïcum* Del., Fl. Aeg. Ill. 70 no. 684 (1813) et Fl. Eg. 111, t. 39, f. 1 (1813). Leaflets 1–2 × 0.3–0.8 cm., oblong to elliptical, acute. Pod 0.8–1 cm. in diam.
Hab.: Steppes. N. and C. Negev, Arava Valley.

Var. **stenophylla** Zoh. et Plitm. in Plitm., Israel Journ. Bot. 15 : 30 (1966). Leaflets 1–2 × 0.2 cm., lanceolate to linear. Pod 6–8 mm. in diam.
Hab.: As above. Arava Valley, Ammon, Edom.
Area of species: W. Irano-Turanian and Saharo-Arabian.

5. Onobrychis wettsteinii Nab., Publ. Fac. Sci. Univ. Masaryk 35 : 91, f. 9 (1923); Post, Fl. Syr. Pal. Sin. ed. 2, 1 : 414 (1932). [Plate 161]
Perennial, glabrescent to pilose, 20–50 cm. Stems almost woody at base. Leaves 5–16 cm.; stipules connate, sheathing, adnate to the petiole, those of upper leaves 3-nerved, white- to yellowish-silky, with triangular-lanceolate, acute, free portions; leaflets 3–5-paired, 0.7–1.2 × 0.4–0.8 cm., short-petiolulate, orbicular-obovate, obtuse, mucronulate, almost glabrous above, white-villose beneath. Peduncles longer than leaves. Racemes long, very loose. Bracts 2 mm., lanceolate. Flowers up to 1.5 cm., short-pedicelled. Calyx about 7 mm., campanulate, spreading-villose, 10-nerved; teeth somewhat longer than tube, lanceolate. Corolla yellowish-white, hairy; standard with tawny lines and spots, obcordate, appressed-hirsute; wings shorter than or as long as calyx, pubescent. Pod 1.3–1.5 cm., flattened, suborbicular-circinate, rather woolly, pitted and slightly prickly at disk; crest broad, toothed at margin. Fl. June.
Hab.: Rocky places. Edom.
Area: W. Irano-Turanian.

Sect. LOPHOBRYCHIS Hand.-Mazzetti, Oesterr. Bot. Zeitschr. 59 : 373 (1909). Annuals. Ovary 1–3-ovuled. Pod semiorbicular in outline, cristate. Stipules connate, opposite leaves.

6. Onobrychis caput-galli (L.) Lam., Fl. Fr. 2 : 651 (1778); Boiss., Fl. 2 : 529 (1872). *Hedysarum caput-galli* L., Sp. Pl. 751 (1753). [Plate 162]

Annual, hairy, 10–30 cm. Stems procumbent to erect, mostly branching, especially at base, striate. Leaves 5–15 cm.; stipules shorter than petiole, connate at base, white-scarious with a median green nerve, ovate-lanceolate, aristate; leaflets 5–9 pairs, 0.5–2.5 × (0.2–)0.3–0.7(–0.9) cm., subsessile, oblong to oblong-linear, often cuneate at base, mucronulate, hairy beneath. Peduncles as long as subtending leaves, somewhat elongating in fruit, erect. Racemes (3–)4–8(–15)-flowered. Bracts small, longer than pedicels, white-scarious, lanceolate. Flowers 5–7 mm., short-pedicelled. Calyx with narrow, subulate-linear, pilose-ciliate teeth, 2–3 times as long as the glabrous tube. Corolla not or only very slightly exceeding the calyx, purple-pink; standard slightly emarginate; wings shorter than keel; keel about as long as standard. Pod 0.9–1.2 cm., somewhat compressed, semiglobular; disk pitted, appressed-pubescent, densely covered with prickles; crest with numerous, narrow, triangular-subulate, simple prickles 2–6 mm. Seed 1, about 3 mm., subreniform, brown to black, smooth. 2n = 28. Fl. March–April.

Hab.: Batha and fields. Sharon Plain, Philistean Plain, Upper and Lower Galilee, Esdraelon Plain, Mt. Gilboa, Samaria, Judean Mts., Dan Valley, Upper Jordan Valley, Gilead, Ammon, Edom.

Area : Mainly Mediterranean.

7. Onobrychis crista-galli (L.) Lam., Fl. Fr. 2 : 652 (1778). [Plate 163]

Annual, appressed-hairy, 10–30 cm. Stems erect, ascending or procumbent, branching from base. Leaves 5–20 cm.; stipules connate at base, ovate-oblong, mucronate; leaflets (5–)7–8(–9–12) pairs, 1–1.5 × 0.2–0.5 cm., petiolulate, oblong to linear, acute or obtuse-truncate and mucronate, hairy beneath. Peduncles shorter than subtending leaves, erect. Racemes 2–3(–5)-flowered. Bracts longer than pedicels. Flowers 7–8 mm. Calyx hirsute; teeth 4–5 times as long as tube, lanceolate-subulate, almost equal to or exceeding pink to white corolla. Pod about 1 × 0.8–1 cm., semiglobular, hairy; disk usually with 1 row of pits; the 3 main crests with 3–4 flat, dentate, acute prickles; accessory crest of disk with much shorter spiny lobes. Seeds (2–)3 in each pod, 2–3 mm. across, yellowish to brown. 2n = 16. Fl. March–May.

Subsp. **crista-galli.** Leaflets usually 8–11-paired, 1–3 mm. broad. Corolla pink to pinkish-white; wings longer than keel. Crests indurated; spines about as long as pod or shorter.

Var. **crista-galli.** *O. crista-galli* (L.) Lam., l.c.; Boiss., Fl. 2 : 528 (1872); Sirj., Publ. Fac. Sci. Univ. Masaryk 56 : 46 (1925). *Hedysarum caput-galli* L. var. *crista-galli* L., Mant. Alt. 448 (1771) in observ. *O. crista-galli* (L.) Lam. var. *lenticularia* Post, Fl. Syr. Pal. Sin. 282 (1883–1896). Leaflets usually 9–11-paired. Corolla pink. Accessory crests with spines 0.5–3 mm.

Var. **subinermis** Heyn, Bull. Res. Counc. Israel D, 11 : 179 (1962). Leaflets usually 8-paired. Corolla pinkish-white. Main crest with very short spines; accessory crests with conical spines.

Subsp. **eigii** Sirj., Bull. Soc. Bot. Bulg. 4 : 8 (1931). Leaflets usually less than 8 pairs, 1–2 mm. broad. Corolla nearly white; wings shorter than keel. Crests leaf-like; spines 2–3 times longer than diameter of pod, soft, linear-subulate, green, strongly toothed along margins.

Hab. of species: Mainly steppes and deserts; mostly primary habitats. Sharon Plain, Philistean Plain, Mt. Carmel, Samaria, N. and S. Negev, Lower and Upper Jordan Valley, steppes and deserts of Ammon, Moav and Edom.

Area of species: Mainly Saharo-Arabian, with extensions into the Irano-Turanian region.

8. Onobrychis squarrosa Viv., Pl. Aeg. 14, t. 2, f. 8 (1831); Sirj., Publ. Fac. Sci. Univ. Masaryk 56 : 49 (1925). *O. gaertneriana* Boiss., Diagn. ser. 1, 9 : 108 (1849) et Fl. 2 : 528 (1872). *O. crista-galli* L. var. *gaertneriana* (Boiss.) Post, Fl. Syr. Pal. Sin. 281 (1883–1896). [Plate 164]

Annual, hairy, 10–30 cm. Stems ascending or procumbent, branching from base, very leafy. Leaves 8–25 cm.; stipules connate at base, ovate, acute; leaflets 7–12-paired, 0.7–1.5 × 0.3–0.7 cm., ovate-oblong to obovate, obtuse or retuse, mucronate, hairy beneath. Peduncles shorter than subtending leaves. Racemes 1–2(–3)-flowered. Flowers 0.9–1 cm. Calyx appressed-hirsute; teeth 3–4 times as long as tube, lanceolate-subulate. Corolla pink-violet; wings slightly shorter than keel. Pod (0.8–)1–1.4 × 0.6–1 cm., semiglobular, sparsely hairy or setulose, with 2 rows of pits at the base of disk; the main crests each with a row of 3–4 flattened, unbranched, obtuse or truncate, denticulate prickles; accessory crest 0 or rarely with 2–3 very short, spiny-tipped protuberances. Seeds 2 in each pod, 3–4(–5) mm. 2n = 32. Fl. March–May.

Hab.: Fields, roadsides and batha. Very common. Acco Plain, Sharon Plain, Philistean Plain, Upper and Lower Galilee, Mt. Carmel, Mt. Gilboa, Samaria, Judean Mts., Judean Desert, N. Negev, Hula Plain, Upper and Lower Jordan Valley, Gilead, Ammon, Moav.

Area: Mainly E. Mediterranean, with extensions into the W. Irano-Turanian territories.

O. aequidentata (Sm.) Urv., Mém. Soc. Linn. Paris 1 : 346 no. 669 (1822), reported for Palestine by Dinsmore in Post, Fl. Syr. Pal. Sin. ed. 2, 1 : 411 (1932) has not been found by us.

31. ALHAGI Gagnebin

Half-shrubs or perennial herbs. Stems much branched, rigid. Branches spinescent, bearing leaves and flowers. Leaves simple, entire, with minute, persistent, subulate stipules. Flowers solitary, pedicellate. Calyx campanulate, 5-toothed. Corolla purple or pink; standard reflexed, obovate, often notched; wings oblong-falcate, somewhat shorter than the gradually incurved, obtuse keel. Stamens diadelphous; filaments filiform; anthers uniform. Ovary subsessile, with many ovules; style filiform, curved; stigma short, terminal. Pod a many-seeded, subterete to compressed, irregularly necklace-shaped loment, often constricted and septate between the seeds; segments usually tardy in separating. Seeds reniform to almost square.

Some 3 or 5 species, mainly in S. W. Asia and S. E. Europe.

1. Alhagi maurorum Medik., Vorl. Churpf. Phys.-Oken. Ges. 2 : 397 (1787) p.p. *Hedysarum alhagi* L., Sp. Pl. 745 (1753) p.p. *A. maurorum* DC., Prodr. 2 : 352 (1825); Boiss., Fl. 2 : 558 (1872). *A. mannifera* Desv., Journ. Bot. Appl. 1 : 120, t. 4, f. 4 (1813) *sine descr. et f. spec., nom. illegit.*; DC., Prodr. 2 : 352 (1825) *pro syn.*; Keller et Shap., Sov. Bot. 1933, 3–4 : 157 (1933). *Manna hebraica* D. Don, Prodr. Fl. Nepal. 247 (1825). [Plate 165]

Shrubby perennial, glabrous or with spreading or appressed hairs, 0.4–1 m. Stems erect to ascending, much branched, striate, with short, spreading, hirtellous, spinescent twigs. Leaves 1–2 cm. (rarely longer), oblong to obovate, obtuse or acute, apiculate; stipules small, subulate; petiole short. Pedicels as long as or somewhat longer than calyx. Flowers about 1–1.2 cm., axillary, on spiny twigs. Calyx 3–4 mm., campanulate; teeth short, triangular-ovate. Corolla 3 times as long as calyx. Ovary silky-hairy. Pod 1.2–2.5(–3) × 0.3–0.4 cm., 2–8-seeded, spongy, linear-cylindrical, often constricted between seeds, sparingly hairy or glabrous. Seeds about 2 mm., reniform, brown, smooth. Fl. April–September.

Hab.: Fields and salines. Coastal Galilee, Acco Plain, Sharon Plain, Philistean Plain, Upper and Lower Galilee, Mt. Carmel, Esdraelon Plain, Shefela, Judean Mts., Negev, Hula Plain, Upper Jordan Valley, Beit Shean Valley, Lower Jordan Valley, Dead Sea area, Arava Valley, Moav.

Area: Mainly Irano-Turanian, with extensions into Mediterranean, Sudanian and Saharo-Arabian territories.

Although fairly variable in indumentum, leaves and calyx, no varieties could be distinguished in the local populations of this species. The species has been excessively split on the basis of a few very inconsistent characteristics. Thus *A. graecorum* Boiss., Diagn. ser. 1, 9 : 114 (1849) and other taxa should be included within this species.

A noxious weed in deep alluvial soils; tolerates saline and wet soils; requires warmer winters, hence limited mainly to the plains and valleys of the area. Roots vertical and extremely deep.

Eaten by camels; known in folk medicine as a remedy for a variety of diseases.

Trib. ONONIDEAE. Herbs, rarely shrubs. Leaves stipulate, mostly 3-foliolate, rarely almost simple; leaflets dentate-serrate. Inflorescences racemose, 1- to few-flowered, leafy, often crowded into spikes or panicles. Stamens monadelphous; filaments connate; anthers dimorphic. Pod dehiscent, 2-valved.

32. ONONIS L.

Shrubs, half-shrubs and herbs, sometimes spiny, often glandular-pubescent. Leaves mostly short-petioled or sessile, mostly of 3 dentate-serrate leaflets, sometimes reduced to 1 leaflet only; stipules large, leaf-like. Flowers axillary, solitary or 2–3 together, often crowded into terminal racemes, spikes, panicles or heads. Bracts leaf-like or 0. Calyx campanulate or tubular, often with 5 equal teeth. Corolla pink, purple, yellow or white; standard almost orbicular, with short claw; wings oblong to obovate; keel curved, beaked. Stamens monadelphous. Ovary more or less stipitate, 2- to many-ovuled; style mostly flat, curved or geniculate, glabrous; stigma oblique or capitate. Pod dehiscent, 2-valved, oblong, lenticular, cylindrical or linear, exserted from or enclosed in calyx. Seeds smooth or finely granulate.

About 75 species in Eurasia and especially in the Mediterranean region.

Literature: G. Sirjaev, Generis *Ononis* L. revisio critica, *Beih. Bot. Centralbl.* 49, 2: 381–665 (1932).

1. Flowers yellow or white (sometimes with pink veins)   2
  – Flowers pink to purple   9
2. Stems woolly-canescent, densely covered with imbricated, sheathing stipules (without leaflets). Pod 1–1.8 cm. Standard up to 7 mm. broad. Rare shrubby perennials.   **3. O. vaginalis**
  – Not as above   3
3. Pod 0.3–1 cm. (very rarely slightly longer)   4
  – Pod longer than 1 cm.   5
4. Flowers 7–9 mm. Leaves all or almost all simple. Littoral annuals.   **10. O. variegata**
  – Flowers 1.3–2 cm. Leaves all or almost all 3-foliolate. Mostly inland plants.   **9. O. pubescens**
5(3). Pod linear, strongly compressed, torulose, up to 2.5 cm. long.   **4. O. ornithopodioides**
  – Pod cylindrical or slightly compressed, not torulose   6
6. Corolla much longer than calyx (up to about twice as long)   7
  – Corolla about as long as or shorter than calyx   8
7. Flowers yellow. Standard often striped with red. Mature pod up to 3 mm. broad. Leaflets acute or rounded at apex. Evergreen shrubs or dwarf shrubs.   **2. O. natrix**
  – Flowers often white. Standard not striped, sometimes pink at apex. Mature pod usually 4–7 mm. broad. Leaflets mostly truncate. Annuals.   **7. O. biflora**
8(6). Leaflets oblong-elliptical to obovate, often retuse. Standard about 1 cm. Pod up to 4 mm. broad. Seeds about 2 mm.   **6. O. viscosa**
  – Leaflets oblong-lanceolate to linear, sometimes truncate. Standard 6–7 mm. Pod up to 2.5 mm. broad. Seeds about 1 mm.   **5. O. sicula**
9(1). Branches spiny. Perennial herbs with large rosulate winter leaves and small cauline summer leaves.   **1. O. antiquorum**
  – Plants not spiny. Annuals   10
10. Pod cylindrical, deflexed, 9–16-seeded. Seeds tuberculate, hardly 1 mm. Flowers 6–8 mm.   **8. O. reclinata**
  – Pod oblong-ovoid. Seeds usually less than 6 in a pod   11
11. Leaves simple, the lower leaves 3–10 cm. Flowers 1.5–1.8 cm., arranged in dense, leafy spike-like inflorescences. Pod much shorter than calyx, 1–3-seeded.   **15. O. alopecuroides**

— Leaves predominantly 3-foliolate, usually smaller than above   12
12. Calyx tube glabrous, with ovate-lanceolate, ciliate teeth a little shorter than or as long as whitish tube. Flowers arranged in dense terminal spike-like inflorescences, each flower subtended by a bract-like, imbricated, white-scarious, inflated stipules concealing the calyx tube.   **14. O. mitissima**
— Not as above   13
13. Hirsute plants. Flowering branches dense, spike- or head-like, with imbricated, usually simple floral leaves (bracts), concealing the calyx tube. Corolla much shorter than calyx. Pod 1–2-seeded.   **13. O. phyllocephala**
— Viscid-pubescent plants. Corolla as long as calyx or longer. Pod 2–5-seeded. Flowering branches not as above   14
14. Calyx 0.9–1.4 cm. Pod shorter than calyx. Seeds rather smooth.   **11. O. hirta**
— Calyx 5–8 mm. Pod about as long as calyx. Seeds tuberculate.   **12. O. serrata**

Sect. ACANTHONONIS Willk. in Willk. et Lange, Prodr. Fl. Hisp. 3 : 392 (1877). Perennials. Lateral branches mostly spinescent. Leaves ternate, lower leaves simple. Flowers solitary or in racemes, purple to pink.

1. Ononis antiquorum L., Sp. Pl. ed. 2, 1006 (1763). [Plate 166]

Perennial, shrubby, subglabrous to patulous-hairy, with subsessile glands, 20–75 cm. Stems many, ascending to erect, rigid, somewhat slender, flexuous, with spiny twigs often in pairs. Leaves 3-foliolate, the lowest leaves sometimes simple, subglabrous to glandular-pubescent; stipules large, adnate to petiole for nearly all their length; winter leaves 4–8 cm., radical, almost rosulate, with large, long-petiolulate, oblong to elliptical, serrate-dentate leaflets; summer leaves smaller, 0.7–2 cm., cauline, short-petioled, with subsessile, oblong-obovate, obtuse, serrulate-denticulate leaflets. Flowers about 1.5 cm., solitary, on peduncles shorter than calyx. Calyx teeth about twice as long as tube, lanceolate, glabrous to sparingly pilose. Corolla almost twice as long as calyx, pink, sometimes reddish; standard longer than keel; keel longer than wings. Pod slightly shorter than calyx, 1–2-seeded, rhomboidal-ovoid to elliptical-lenticular, glandular-pubescent. Seeds 1–2 mm., compressed-subglobular, tuberculate or smooth, brown-black. Fl. April–October.

Var. **leiosperma** (Boiss.) Post, Fl. Syr. Pal. Sin. 217 (1883–1896). *O. leiosperma* Boiss., Fl. 2 : 57 (1872) excl. var. β. *O. spinosa* L. ssp. *leiosperma* (Boiss.) Sirj., Beih. Bot. Centralbl. 49, 2 : 590 (1932) var. *genuina* Sirj., l.c. 591. Seeds smooth. Plants covered with sessile glands, sparingly patulous-villose to glabrescent.

Hab.: Fields and somewhat moist places, also along wadis. Acco Plain, Sharon Plain, Philistean Plain, Upper and Lower Galilee, Mt. Carmel, Esdraelon Plain, Mt. Gilboa, Shefela, Judean Mts., Judean Desert, W. and N. Negev, Dan Valley, Upper and Lower Jordan Valley, Gilead, Ammon, Moav.

Var. **tomentosa** (Boiss.) Dinsmore in Post, Fl. Syr. Pal. Sin. ed. 2, 1 : 305 (1932). *O. leiosperma* Boiss. var. *tomentosa* Boiss., l.c. Plants patulous-tomentose.

Hab.: As above. Grows together with preceding variety, but much rarer.

Area of species: N. and E. Mediterranean and W. Irano-Turanian, slightly extending into S. W. Euro-Siberian territories.

One of the most common shrubby hemicryptophytes. A leading species of the segetal *Ononis leiosperma–Carthamus tenuis* association in the mountain winter crops. It is a deep-rooting, seasonally heterophyllous plant in which the large winter leaves are replaced by small summer leaves, confined to the spiny flowering shoots.

The records of var. *longispina* Post, l.c. from Gilead are not documented and are doubtful.

Sect. NATRIX Griseb., Spicil. Fl. Rumel. 1 : 12 (1843) emend. Sirj., Beih. Bot. Centralbl. 49, 2 : 433 (1932). Annual or perennial herbs, rarely shrubs, not spiny. Peduncles 1–2-flowered, mostly terminating in an awn. Floral leaves often of 1 leaflet. Corolla yellow to pink. Pod deflexed, linear-oblong, rarely ovoid-oblong.

2. Ononis natrix L., Sp. Pl. 717 (1753); Boiss., Fl. 2 : 58 (1872); Sirj., Beih. Bot. Centralbl. 49, 2 : 452 (1932). [Plate 167]

Half-shrub, glandular-hairy, viscid, 10–70 cm. Stems many, ascending to erect, profusely branched with spreading to erect branches, rigid, leafy. Leaves 1–6 cm., the upper leaves sometimes simple, the rest 3-foliolate, rarely of 5–7 leaflets; stipules almost as long as petiole and adnate to it for about half their length, oblong-lanceolate; petiole somewhat shorter than blade, hairy; leaflets oblanceolate-linear to oblong, obovate or almost orbicular, acute to obtuse, serrate or denticulate, rarely almost entire. Flowers (0.6–)1–1.8(–2) cm., in terminal, loose and leafy raceme-like inflorescences, on usually awned, hairy, 1-flowered peduncles longer or shorter than subtending leaves. Calyx (0.4–)0.6–1.1 cm.; teeth 1–4 times as long as tube, linear to lanceolate. Corolla about twice as long as calyx, yellow; standard large, red- or purple-veined, obovate to orbicular; wings shorter than standard, a little longer than keel. Pod (0.9–)1.2–2 × 0.2–0.3 cm., 2–3 times as long as calyx, deflexed, cylindrical, beaked, hirsute. Seeds about 2 mm., compressed-subglobular, brown, tuberculate. $2n = 32$. Fl. March–October (–December).

1. Leaves almost all 3 (sometimes 5–7)-foliolate, very short-petioled to sessile; leaflets very narrow, 0.5–3 mm.   ssp. **stenophylla** 2
– Leaves and leaflets not as above
2. Leaflets up to 1 cm., mostly ovate to obovate.   ssp. **hispanica**
– Leaflets up to 2 cm., mostly elliptical to oblong-lanceolate.   ssp. **natrix**

Subsp. **natrix.** *O. natrix* L. ssp. *eunatrix* Aschers. et Graebn., Syn. Mitteleur. Fl. 6, 2 : 363 (1907); Sirj., l.c. 454. Stems erect, 10–70 cm., densely glandular-hairy. Leaflets usually 1–2 × 0.5–1 cm., elliptical to oblong-lanceolate. Flowers (0.7–)1.2–1.8(–2) cm.

Var. **natrix.** *O. natrix* L. var. *major* Boiss., Voy. Bot. Midi Esp. 2 : 149 (1839). Flowers 1.3–2 cm.

Hab.: Batha. Upper and Lower Galilee, Mt. Carmel, Esdraelon Plain, Mt. Gilboa, Samaria, Judean Mts., Judean Desert, Dan Valley, Hula Plain, Lower Jordan Valley, Gilead, Ammon, Moav, Edom.

Var. **euphrasiifolia** Opphr., Bull. Soc. Bot. Genève ser. 2, 22 : 318 (1931; "*euphrasiaefolia*"). Leaflets ovate-elliptical, with 8 narrowly lanceolate teeth. Fruiting peduncles up to 3.5 cm.

Hab.: Crevices of calcareous rocks. Gilead.

This very doubtful variety was considered by Sirjaev (in herb.) as a subvariety of the former variety.

Subsp. **hispanica** (L.f.) Cout., Fl. Port. 331 (1913); Sirj., l.c. 466. *O. hispanica* L.f., Suppl. 324 (1781). *O. natrix* L. var. *hispanica* (L.f.) Webb in Webb et Berth., Phyt. Canar. 2:23 (1842). *O. natrix* L. var. *microphylla* Boiss., Voy. Bot. Midi Esp. 2:149 (1839) et Fl. 2:59 (1872). *O. microphylla* C. Presl, Bot. Bemerk. 50 (1844). Stems ascending. Leaflets small, up to 0.8(–1) cm., ovate or obovate, sometimes almost orbicular or oblong. Flowers (0.6–)0.8–1.5(–1.7) cm. Pod (0.9–)1.1–1.5(–1.7) cm., generally smaller than in the former subspecies.

Hab.: Batha. Judean Mts., Judean Desert, Dead Sea area, Arava Valley, Edom.

Subsp. **stenophylla** (Boiss.) Sirj., l.c. 470. *O. natrix* L. var. *stenophylla* Boiss., Fl. 2:59 (1872). Half-shrub. Stipules and leaves mostly crowded on short branches; leaves sessile to short-petioled, usually 3-foliolate but some compound of 5–7 leaflets; leaflets (0.5–)1–2(–3) mm. broad, narrowly oblanceolate to narrowly linear. Flowers (0.9–)1.1–1.5(–1.8) cm. Calyx 4–8 mm. Standard purple-veined. Pod 1–1.9 cm. Seeds a little smaller than in ssp. *natrix*.

Hab.: Batha; calcareous-sandy soils. Sharon Plain, Philistean Plain, Coastal Negev.

Area of species: Mediterranean, with extensions into adjacent territories of the Saharo-Arabian region.

O. natrix L. ssp. *ramosissima* (Desf.) Briq., Prodr. Fl. Corse 2:254 (1913) and its var. *boissieri* Sirj., l.c. 466 ("*boissierii*"), var. *macrophylla* Post, Fl. Syr. Pal. Sin. 217 (1883–1896) et ed. 2, 1:306 (1932) with its larger truncate leaflets, var. *laxiuscula* Post, l.c. with its loose slender branches and var. *tomentosa* Boiss., Fl. 2:59 (1872) are all doubtful taxa and probably only habitat forms of this very polymorphic species which calls for a thorough study of its infraspecific taxa.

3. Ononis vaginalis Vahl, Symb. Bot. 1:53 (1790); Boiss., Fl. 2:59 (1872). *O. cherleri* Forssk., Fl. Aeg.-Arab. 130 (1775) non L., Sp. Pl. ed. 2, 1007 (1763). [Plate 168]

Dwarf shrub, woolly-canescent, glandular-viscid, 20–50 cm. Stems erect, rigid, with short, ascending branches, densely covered with imbricated, sheathing stipules and often also with few small, subsessile leaves consisting of 1, rarely 3, thick, obovate-cuneate, denticulate leaflets. Peduncles longer than leaves, 1-flowered. Flowers 0.8–1.5 cm., short-pedicelled. Calyx teeth one and a half to twice as long as the top-shaped and glandular tube, lanceolate-linear, acute. Corolla up to 1.5 cm., glabrous; standard longer than keel and wings, yellowish, purple-striped. Pod 1–1.8 × 0.25–0.3 mm., 2–3 times as long as calyx, 5–10-seeded, linear, mucronate. Seeds about 2 mm. in diam., minutely tuberculate. Fl. July–August.

Hab.: Sandy soils. Edom (after Dinsmore in Post, Fl. Syr. Pal. Sin. ed. 2, 1:306, 1932). Very rare.

Area: W. Irano-Turanian, with extensions into the Saharo-Arabian region.

4. Ononis ornithopodioides L., Sp. Pl. 718 (1753); Boiss., Fl. 2:59 (1872). [Plate 169]

Annual, patulous- and glandular-pubescent, 17–25 cm. Stems erect to ascending, with slender branches. Leaves 1.5–4 cm., the lower leaves sometimes simple or of 2 elliptical or ovate, serrulate leaflets, the rest 3-foliolate, with oblong-elliptical, cuneate, serrate leaflets; stipules adnate to petiole for about half their length, ovate-lanceolate, acute, almost entire; petiole shorter than blade; lateral leaflets sessile, the terminal one petiolulate. Peduncles longer than petiole, mostly 2-flowered, aristate. Flowers 6–9 mm., subsessile or short-pedicelled, erect to deflexed. Calyx persistent, pilose; teeth subulate-filiform, 4–5 times as long as tube. Corolla almost equalling calyx in length or usually a little shorter, yellow; standard somewhat longer than keel; keel somewhat longer than wings. Pod usually 2–2.5 × 0.2–0.25 cm., 2–3 times as long as calyx, (3–)6–10-seeded, pendulous, strongly flattened, linear, torulose, short-beaked, glandular-hairy. Seeds about 2 mm., subglobular to slightly reniform, brown to red, tuberculate. 2n = 32. Fl. February–May.

Hab.: Batha and fields. Upper and Lower Galilee, Mt. Carmel, Esdraelon Plain, Mt. Gilboa, Samaria, Shefela, Judean Mts., Judean Desert, Upper Jordan Valley, Dead Sea area, Gilead, Ammon, Moav.

Area: Mediterranean.

5. Ononis sicula Guss., Cat. Pl. Boccadifalci Adn. 78 (1821); Boiss., Fl. 2 : 60 (1872); Sirj., Beih. Bot. Centralbl. 49, 2 : 496 (1932). *O. viscosa* L. var. *sicula* (Guss.) Fiori in Fiori et Paol., Fl. Anal. Ital. 2 : 30 (1900). [Plate 170]

Annual, hispid-pilose, glandular, 5–25 cm. Stems erect-ascending, often profusely branching from base. Leaves 1–5 cm., glandular-pubescent, the lowest leaves, and sometimes the uppermost, simple, the rest 3-foliolate, rarely all simple; stipules almost as long as petiole or longer, adnate to it for about half their length, lanceolate, acute, nearly entire; petiole much shorter than blade; leaflets mostly oblong-lanceolate to linear, rarely elliptical, sometimes truncate, serrate towards apex. Peduncles about as long as subtending leaves, with an awn about 1 cm. or less, 1 (–2)-flowered. Flowers 0.7–1 cm., short-pedicelled. Calyx persistent, hispid; teeth 3–4 times as long as tube, subulate-linear. Corolla distinctly shorter than calyx, pale yellow; standard 6–7 mm., longer than keel and wings, sometimes purple-veined. Pod 1–1.8(–2) × 0.15–0.25 cm., almost twice as long as calyx, 8–25-seeded, pendulous, cylindrical-inflated, short-beaked, patulous-hirsute. Seeds about 1–1.5 mm., subglobular to slightly reniform, tuberculate-scabrous. Fl. February–May.

Hab.: Fields, batha and steppes. Philistean Plain, Esdraelon Plain, Samaria, Shefela, Judean Mts., Judean Desert, W., N. and C. Negev, Upper and Lower Jordan Valley, Dead Sea area, Gilead, Ammon, Moav.

Area: S. Mediterranean, Saharo-Arabian and Irano-Turanian.

O. sicula is rather polymorphic. It probably intercrosses with *O. viscosa* and also with *O. biflora*; some intermediate forms between these species have been found in the Shefela, the Judean Mts., and in the N. Negev.

The following forms are particularly worth mentioning : (a) Peduncles 2-flowered (Lower Jordan Valley). (b) Petioles and fruiting peduncles 2 cm. or more long (N. Negev). (c) All leaves simple; stipules adnate to petiole for more than half their length (Transjordan). (d) Plants less densely leafy, with truncate leaflets (Judean Desert). (e) Awn of peduncle about 1 cm.; some of the pods about 2 cm.; stems more or less rigid (Judean Mts.)

6. Ononis viscosa breviflora L. ssp. (DC.) Nym., Syll. 285 (1854–1855) et Consp. 161 (1878); Rouy in Rouy et Fouc., Fl. Fr. 4 : 261 (1897); Sirj., Beih. Bot. Centralbl. 49, 2 : 524 (1932). *O. breviflora* DC., Prodr. 2 : 160 (1825); Boiss., Fl. 2 : 60 (1872). *O. viscosa* L. var. *breviflora* (DC.) Fiori in Fiori et Paol., Fl. Anal. Ital. 2 : 29 (1900). [Plate 171]

Annual, glandular-hispid, 10–40 cm. Stems ascending to erect, mostly branching, more or less rigid. Leaves 1.5–8 cm., the lowest and the uppermost frequently simple, the rest 3-foliolate, subglabrous to sparingly hispid; stipules almost as long as petiole, generally adnate to it for about half their length, lanceolate, acute, mostly serrulate, sparingly pilose; upper stipules entire; petiole much shorter than blade; leaflets 1–5 × 0.3–2 cm., oblong-elliptical to obovate, obtuse to truncate, usually slightly retuse at apex, serrulate-denticulate. Peduncles as long as subtending leaves or a little shorter, 1-flowered, patulous-hirsute, with a long awn (about 1 cm. or more). Pedicels one third to one half as long as calyx. Flowers 0.8–1.4 cm., erect to deflexed. Calyx persistent, hispid; teeth 4–6 times as long as tube, rather erect in flower but divaricate in fruit, subulate-lanceolate. Corolla as long as or shorter than calyx, pale yellow; standard somewhat longer than wings and keel. Pod 1–2(–2.5) × 0.3–0.4 cm., 5–14-seeded, pendulous, cylindrical, short-beaked. Seeds about 2 mm., subglobular to reniform, yellow to brown, scabrous to tuberculate. Fl. February–May (–June).

Hab.: Fields and batha. Acco Plain, Sharon Plain, Philistean Plain, Upper and Lower Galilee, Mt. Carmel, Esdraelon Plain, Samaria, Shefela, Judean Mts., Judean Desert, Hula Plain, Upper Jordan Valley, Beit Shean Valley, Dead Sea area, Gilead.

Area: Mediterranean, with extensions into W. Irano-Turanian territories.

7. Ononis biflora Desf., Fl. Atl. 2 : 143 (1798); Boiss., Fl. 2 : 60 (1872). [Plate 172]

Annual, glandular-pubescent, 6–50 cm. Stems erect or ascending, branching, slender, rigid, somewhat angular. Leaves 1–5 cm., 3-foliolate, the lower leaves sometimes simple; stipules rather large, adnate to petiole for more than half their length, acute, often entire, hairy; petiole shorter than blade; leaflets oblong-obovate to oblong-elliptical, obtuse or truncate, serrate-dentate towards apex. Peduncles about as long as or a little longer, rarely a little shorter than subtending leaves, mostly 2-flowered, erect, hairy, sometimes shortly aristate. Pedicels as long as calyx tube. Flowers 1–1.5 cm., erect to deflexed. Calyx persistent; teeth up to twice as long as tube, subulate-lanceolate, hairy. Corolla almost twice as long as calyx, white (rarely yellow); standard longer than wings, sometimes pink at apex; wings as long as pink-tipped keel. Pod 1.5–2.5 × (0.3–)0.4–0.7(–0.8) cm., short-stipitate, 16–24-seeded, pendulous, cylindrical or dorsally compressed, short-beaked, hairy. Seeds about 2–3.5 mm., globular or reniform, dark brown, granular-tuberculate. Fl. March–April.

Hab.: Fields. Acco Plain, Philistean Plain, Mt. Carmel, Esdraelon Plain, Mt. Gilboa, Samaria, Judean Mts., Judean Desert, Lower Jordan Valley, Gilead, Ammon, Moav.

Area: E. and S. Mediterranean, with extensions towards W. Irano-Turanian territories.

8. Ononis reclinata L., Sp. Pl. ed. 2, 1011 (1763); Boiss., Fl. 2 : 61 (1872). [Plate 173]

Annual, villose-hirsute, glandular-viscid, 5–25 cm. Stems erect to ascending, diffusely branching or almost simple, slender. Leaves 0.8–2.5 cm.; lowest and uppermost leaves simple, suborbicular to oblong, obtuse, the rest 3-foliolate; stipules small, shorter than petiole, acute; petiole shorter than blade; leaflets 0.7–1 (–1.5) × 0.2–0.5 cm., oblong to linear, rarely obovate, mostly cuneate at base, truncate, serrate-denticulate at apex. Peduncles as long as or shorter than subtending leaves, 1-flowered, stiff, not awned. Flowers 6–8 mm., pendulous, forming terminal, leafy, short, spike-like inflorescences. Calyx hirsute or villose; teeth 3–5 times as long as tube, narrowly linear, acute. Corolla as long as calyx or shorter, pink; standard somewhat violet, a little longer than the white, pinkish or cream-coloured wings and keel. Pod 7–9 mm., as long as calyx or longer, 9–16-seeded, pendulous, cylindrical, mucronate, hirsute. Seeds many, less than 1 mm., subglobular-reniform, brown, tuberculate. Fl. March–April.

Var. **minor** Moris, Fl. Sard. 1 : 422 (1837); Boiss., l.c. *O. mollis* Savi, Mem. Soc. Ital. Mod. 9 : 351, t. 8 (1802). *O. reclinata* L. var. *mollis* (Savi) Hal., Oesterr. Bot. Zeitschr. 47 : 62 (1897). *O. reclinata* L. var. *fontanesii* Webb et Berth., Phyt. Canar. 2 : 28 (1842). Flowers small. Peduncles longer than calyx. Calyx longer than corolla. Pod not or almost not exceeding calyx.

Hab.: Fields, batha and steppes. Coastal Galilee, Acco Plain, Sharon Plain, Philistean Plain, Upper and Lower Galilee, Mt. Carmel, Esdraelon Plain, Mt. Gilboa, Samaria, Shefela, Judean Mts., Judean Desert, Negev, Hula Plain, Upper and Lower Jordan Valley, Gilead, Ammon, Moav.

Area: S. Mediterranean and W. Irano-Turanian, with extensions into the Saharo-Arabian and Sudanian regions.

9. Ononis pubescens L., Mant. Alt. 267 (1771); Boiss., Fl. 2 : 62 (1872). [Plate 174]

Annual, patulous-hirsute, glandular-viscid, 10–50 cm. Stems erect, corymbosely branching. Leaves 2–7 cm.; lowermost and uppermost leaves sometimes simple, the rest 3-foliolate; stipules adnate to petiole for about half their length, ovate-lanceolate, acute; petiole almost as long as blade; leaflets large, oblong-elliptical or obovate to oblong-linear, obtuse, entire to serrulate. Flowering branches up to 10 (–20) cm., arranged in a corymbose inflorescence. Flowers 1.3–1.8 cm., solitary, short-pedicelled, on short peduncles shorter to longer than calyx. Calyx persistent, hirsute; teeth 4–5 times as long as tube, oblong-lanceolate, acute. Corolla a little longer than calyx, yellow; standard large, suborbicular, yellowish-white with pink-violet veins. Pod about 1 (–1.3) cm., a little shorter than calyx, 1–3-seeded, deflexed, flattened, ovoid-rhomboidal, mucronate or beaked, hairy. Seeds 2–4 mm., subglobular, brown, sometimes black-spotted, smooth. Fl. March–May (–June).

Hab.: Batha and roadsides. Sharon Plain, Upper and Lower Galilee, Mt. Carmel, Esdraelon Plain, Samaria, Shefela, Judean Mts., Hula Plain, Upper and Lower Jordan Valley, Golan, Gilead, Ammon.

Area: Mediterranean.

10. Ononis variegata L., Sp. Pl. 717 (1753); Boiss., Fl. 2 : 62 (1872). [Plate 175]

Annual, patulous- and glandular-pubescent, 3–15 cm. Stems procumbent to ascending, rather caespitose, short-branching. Leaves 0.5–1.5 cm., subsessile, the lowest leaves rarely 3-foliolate, the rest mostly simple, obovate, obtuse, sometimes truncate, plicate, sharply dentate-serrate, glabrous to sparingly pilose, prominently nerved; stipules 3–5 mm., adnate to the short petiole for most of their length, sheathing, ovate, serrate-dentate, subglabrous. Flowers about 1 cm., solitary on hairy peduncles much shorter than calyx, arranged in terminal, leafy, loose, raceme-like inflorescences. Calyx 5–7 mm.; teeth about as long as tube, lanceolate, acute, hairy. Corolla up to twice as long as calyx, dark yellow or yellowish-white; standard sometimes pink-veined, puberulent outside; wings much shorter than keel and standard. Pod 7–9 mm., exserted from calyx, 7–13-seeded, oblong-ovoid, short-beaked, puberulent. Seeds 2 mm., subglobular-reniform, brown, smooth. Fl. March–May.

Hab. : Sandy soil. Acco Plain, Coast of Carmel, Sharon Plain, Philistean Plain, Coastal Negev.

Area : Mediterranean.

11. Ononis hirta Desf. ex Poir. in Lam., Encycl. Suppl. 1 : 741 (1811); Boiss., Fl. 2 : 63 (1872). *O. hirta* Desf., Tabl. 187 (1804) *nom. nud.* [Plate 176]

Annual, crisp-hirsute, glandular, somewhat viscid, (6–)10–40 cm. Stems decumbent to ascending, branching, especially from base. Leaves 1–5 cm.; lowermost and uppermost leaves frequently simple, the rest 3-foliolate, sparingly hirsute; stipules rather small, shorter than petiole and adnate to it for almost half their length, oblong-ovate, dentate, subglabrous; petiole shorter than blade; leaflets obovate to oblong-elliptical, dentate-serrate at margin, those of the uppermost leaves incised-dentate at apex, obtuse. Flowers 0.9–1.5 cm., longer than floral leaves, solitary, short-peduncled, erect to deflexed, arranged in terminal, raceme-like inflorescences dense towards apex, glandular-hairy. Calyx persistent, usually glandular-hairy; teeth twice as long as tube or more, lanceolate. Corolla pink to pale blue; standard a little longer than keel; keel a little longer than wings. Pod (4–)5–7 mm., distinctly shorter than calyx, 2–4-seeded, oblong-ovoid, mostly glandular-hairy. Seeds about 2 mm., subglobular, reddish-brown to almost black, rather smooth. Fl. March–May.

Hab. : Fields; heavy, calcareous soils. Coastal Galilee, E. Sharon Plain, Philistean Plain, Upper and Lower Galilee, Esdraelon Plain, Mt. Gilboa, Samaria, Shefela, Judean Mts., Hula Plain, Upper Jordan Valley, Gilead, Ammon.

Area : S. Mediterranean.

Var. *glandulosa* Bornm., Verh. Zool.-Bot. Ges. Wien 48 : 576 (1898), recorded by Dinsmore in Post, Fl. Syr. Pal. Sin. ed. 2, 1 : 309 (1932), is, according to Sirjaev, l.c., only a more glandular form that occurs exclusively in Palestine.

12. Ononis serrata Forssk., Fl. Aeg.-Arab. 130 (1775); Boiss., Fl. 2 : 63 (1872). [Plate 177]

Annual, viscid-pubescent, 10–50 cm. Stems decumbent to erect, with slender branches, arising especially from the indurated base. Leaves 1–3.5 cm., floral leaves simple, the rest 3-foliolate, sparingly pubescent; stipules rather small, adnate to petiole for more than half their length, ovate-lanceolate, acute, serrulate to entire, subglabrous; petiole shorter than blade; leaflets obovate to oblong-linear, sometimes suborbicular, cuneate, obtuse to truncate at apex, sharply serrate-denticulate. Flowers 0.7–1.2 cm., mostly shorter than floral leaves, solitary, short-peduncled to sessile, erect, arranged in terminal, leafy, loose, raceme-like inflorescences denser towards apex. Calyx 5–8 mm., persistent, pubescent; teeth (1–)2–3 times as long as the pale green tube, lanceolate-linear or lanceolate-subulate. Corolla somewhat longer than calyx, pinkish; standard bluish-purple; keel and wings whitish. Pod 4–9 mm., about as long as calyx, 2–5-seeded, erect, compressed, ovoid, beaked or hardly so, pubescent. Seeds 1–2(–3) mm. in diam., ovoid-subglobular, brown to red, tuberculate. Fl. March–April.

Var. **serrata.** Stems usually decumbent. Branches slender. Leaflets oblong to linear, infrequently obovate, sparsely and acutely serrate-dentate. Flowers 7–9 mm., pinkish-white. Calyx teeth 2–3 times as long as tube, lanceolate-linear. Corolla scarcely longer than calyx. Pod 4–6 mm., 3–5-seeded, short-beaked or not. Seeds 1–2 mm.

Hab.: Sandy soil. Acco Plain, Sharon Plain, Philistean Plain, Judean Desert, Coastal, W., N. and C. Negev, Edom.

Var. **major** Lange, Pugill. Pl. Hisp. 351 (1860–1865); Boiss., l.c. *O. serrata* Forssk. ssp. *diffusa* (Ten.) Rouy in Rouy et Fouc., Fl. Fr. 4 : 268 (1897). *O. diffusa* Ten., Prodr. Fl. Nap. 1 : XLI (1811). Stems ascending-erect, diffusely branching, rigid, 10–50 cm. Leaflets suborbicular or obovate to rather oblong-cuneate, densely serrate-denticulate. Flowers about 1 cm., pink. Calyx teeth 1–2 times as long as tube, lanceolate-subulate. Corolla longer than calyx. Pod 7–9 mm., 2–3(–5)-seeded, mostly beaked. Seeds 2–3 mm.

Hab.: As above. Acco Plain, Sharon Plain, Philistean Plain, Upper Jordan Valley. Area of species : Mediterranean and Saharo-Arabian.

Sect. BUGRANA Griseb., Spicil. Fl. Rumel. 1 : 12 (1843) emend. Sirj., Beih. Bot. Centralbl. 49, 2 : 533 (1932). Annuals, rarely perennials. Peduncles 0 or reduced to a more or less conspicuous swelling. Flowers axillary, solitary, arranged in terminal, head- or spike-like inflorescences. Pod not deflexed, 2–4-seeded, ovoid or rhomboidal.

13. Ononis phyllocephala Boiss., Fl. 2 : 63 (1872). [Plate 178]

Annual, patulous-hirsute, 10–30 cm. Stems ascending to erect, rather branching, slender. Leaves 1–2.5 cm., mostly 3-foliolate; stipules adnate to the hairy petiole for more than half their length, ovate, acute, serrulate; petiole shorter than blade; leaflets subsessile, obovate to oblong-linear, obtuse, acutely serrate, prominently nerved; floral leaves often simple, oblong-linear, with imbricated, scarious, bract-like stipules covering the calyx tube. Flowers about 1.3 cm., solitary, subsessile, arranged in terminal, capitate or spicate inflorescences. Calyx persistent, hirsute; teeth 3 times as long as tube, narrowly lanceolate, acute or incised at apex. Corolla much shorter than calyx, pink; standard longer than keel and wings. Pod about 6 mm., 1–2-seeded, somewhat inflated, ovoid, sparingly hirsute. Seeds about 2 mm., subglobular, dark brown, granular-tuberculate. Fl. March–May.

Hab.: Batha. Sharon Plain, Upper Galilee, Mt. Carmel, Esdraelon Plain, Judean Mts. Rare.

Area: E. Mediterranean (Palestine and Syria).

14. Ononis mitissima L., Sp. Pl. 717 (1753); Boiss., Fl. 2:64 (1872). [Plate 179]

Annual, crisp-puberulent to villose, 15–80 cm. Stems erect to ascending, branching, especially at the indurated base. Leaves 1.5–6 cm., sparsely glandular-pubescent, the uppermost leaves often simple, the rest 3-foliolate; stipules adnate to the petiole for more than half their length, acute, entire or obscurely serrulate, subglabrous, striate; petiole much shorter than blade, hairy; leaflets oblong, elliptical or obovate, obtuse, mucronulate, densely serrate-denticulate; floral leaves often simple, with large, imbricated, scarious, white or pink, bract-like stipules concealing the calyx tube. Flowers about 1 cm., on short peduncles in erect, densely spicate inflorescences, 2–5 (–7) cm. Calyx persistent; tube white, glabrous, striate; teeth a little shorter than tube, ovate-lanceolate, spiny-tipped, glandular-ciliate at margin. Corolla a little longer than calyx, pink, later bluish; standard purplish, longer than the somewhat white keel and wings. Pod about 7 mm., 2–3-seeded, more or less equalling calyx in length, flattened, ovoid, short-beaked, sparingly pubescent. Seeds 1–2 mm., compressed, subglobular, brown, tuberculate. Fl. March–May.

Hab.: Batha and fallow fields; mostly on heavy soils. Coastal Galilee, Sharon Plain, Philistean Plain, Upper and Lower Galilee, Mt. Carmel, Esdraelon Plain, Mt. Gilboa, Shefela, Judean Mts., Dan Valley, Hula Plain, Upper Jordan Valley. Uncommon.

Area: Mediterranean.

15. Ononis alopecuroides L., Sp. Pl. 717 (1753); Boiss., Fl. 2:64 (1872). [Plate 180]

Annual, sparingly hairy, 15–75 cm. Stems ascending to erect, branching, rigid, somewhat woody at base. Leaves 1.2–10 cm., simple, oblong to obovate or elliptical, mostly obtuse, serrulate, subglabrous; stipules large, adnate to petiole, forming an auriculate sheath, entire or serrulate; petiole shorter than blade; floral leaves strongly reduced in size, as long as or longer than calyx, often simple, oblong to linear, acutish, dentate above, sparingly hirsute, ciliate at margin, with scarious, bract-like stipules. Flowers 1.5–1.8 cm., solitary, subsessile, forming terminal, erect, dense, spike-like inflorescences 2–15 cm., later elongating. Calyx hirsute; teeth about twice as long as tube, subulate. Corolla somewhat shorter to somewhat longer than calyx, pink to purple; standard longer than wings; wings about as long as keel. Pod much shorter than calyx, 1–3-seeded, inflated, ovoid, hairy, with a short, hooked beak. Seeds 2–3 mm., reniform, shiny, sometimes slightly pitted. Fl. April–May.

Hab.: Fallow fields; damp soils. Acco Plain, Sharon Plain, Philistean Plain, Upper and Lower Galilee, Mt. Carmel, Esdraelon Plain, Samaria, Shefela, Dan Valley, Hula Plain, Upper Jordan Valley.

Area: Mediterranean.

Trib. TRIFOLIEAE. Annual or perennial herbs, rarely shrubs. Leaves stipulate, 3-foliolate; leaflets mostly dentate. Inflorescences few- or many-flowered, capitate, spicate, racemose or paniculate. Pod mostly indehiscent, many- to few- or 1-seeded, exserted from or included in calyx tube.

33. Trigonella L.

Annual or perennial herbs or shrubs. Stems branched, leafy. Leaves 3-foliolate, with entire, dentate or incised stipules adnate to petiole. Racemes axillary, many-, rarely 1-flowered, sometimes umbellate or spicate. Calyx mostly campanulate, 5-toothed. Corolla yellow, white, lilac or rarely bluish; petals free or wings adhering to keel by means of a tooth; keel obtuse. Stamens diadelphous; filaments not dilated at apex. Pod dehiscing along one or both sutures or indehiscent, 1- to many-seeded, terete, linear, lanceolate or ovate, sometimes flat and wing-like, often beaked. Seeds smooth or tuberculate; embryo jointed betwen radicle and cotyledons.

About 130 species, mainly in the Mediterranean region, S. W. Asia and C. Asia.

Literature: G. Sirjaev, Generis *Trigonella* L. revisio critica, *Publ. Fac. Sci. Univ. Masaryk* 102 : 1–57 (1928); 110 : 1–37 (1929); 192 : 1–15 (1934); 128 : 1–31 (1930); 136 : 1–33 (1931); 148 : 1–43 (1932); 170 : 1–38 (1933). N. Feinbrun, Über die Variabilität von *Trigonella monspeliaca* L. und die pflanzengeographischen Verhältnisse ihrer Formen, *Beih. Bot. Centralbl.* 51, 2 : 389–396 (1933). I. T. Vassilchenko, Review of the species of genus *Trigonella* L., *Acta Inst. Bot. Acad. Sci. URSS* Ser. 1, 10 : 124–269 (1953).

1. Pod flattish, sword-shaped, 5–15 × 0.4–0.5 cm., with a very long beak. Flowers 1–2 in each leaf axil. Corolla 1–1.8 cm., white, cream-coloured or pale blue   2
 − Pod and flowers not as above   3
2. Flowers white or cream-coloured. Pod with remote, longitudinal and anastomosing nerves. Leaflets oblong to obovate-oblong.   **19. T. foenum-graecum**
 − Flowers pale blue (rarely cream-coloured or whitish). Pod with dense longitudinal nerves. Leaflets mostly obovate-cuneate.   **20. T. berythea**
3(1). Pod flat; valves membranous or parchment-like, ciliate or dentate at margin, 0.5–1.2 cm. broad   4
 − Pod cylindrical or slightly flattened; valves neither membranous nor ciliate   5
4. Pod broadly semiovate, 1–2 × (0.7–)0.8–1.2 cm.; margin dentate. Corolla about 6 mm.   **1. T. schlumbergeri**
 − Pod oblong, 1.5–3 × 0.5–0.8 cm.; margin spiny-ciliate. Corolla 0.8–1 cm.   **2. T. arabica**
5(3). Flowers lilac.   **13. T. lilacina**
 − Flowers yellow or whitish   6
6. Pod 1–2-seeded, ending in a curved seedless beak almost as long as seed-bearing portion   7
 − Pod 4- to many-seeded, not beaked as above   8
7. Leaflets oblong-lanceolate, 2–4 times as long as broad. Fruiting racemes about 1 cm. across.   **18. T. spicata**
 − Leaflets obovate to oblong-cuneate, scarcely one and a half times to twice as long as broad. Fruiting racemes up to 2.5 cm. across.   **12. T. filipes**
8(6). Racemes 5–12(–18)-flowered. Flowers about (0.8–)1(–1.5) cm. Pod (2.5–)3–5 cm., glabrous, very slightly falcate or circular.   **9. T. caelesyriaca**
 − Not as above   9

9. Racemes 1–2 (very rarely 3)-flowered. Pod (4–)5–8 cm., falcate or with a hook-shaped
    tip   10
– Racemes usually many-flowered. Pod not as above   11
10. Pod falcate, net-veined with transversely oblique areoles; tip of pod not hook-shaped.
                                                                                      16. T. noaeana
— Pod straight or slightly arcuate, net-veined with longitudinally oblique areoles; tip
    of pod hook-shaped.   **15. T. monantha**
11 (9). Pod with transverse, or obliquely transverse nerves or wrinkles or furrows, rarely
    with both thick transverse and thin longitudinal nerves   12
— Pod with longitudinal nerves or wrinkles or furrows, rarely pod smooth   19
12. Pod erect or spreading, not deflexed, straight or very slightly arcuate, 1.3–2.5 cm.;
    ventral suture entire, dorsal sinuate.   **14. T. astroites**
— Pod not as above   13
13. Flowering and fruiting racemes usually sessile or almost so   14
— Flowering and fruiting racemes pedunculate   16
14. Pod semicircular or almost circular, 2–6 cm.   **8. T. spinosa**
— Pod falcate or only slightly curved   15
15. Longer calyx teeth shorter than or as long as calyx tube. Pod 0.4–0.8(–1) cm.
                                                                                     6. T. stellata
— Longer calyx teeth much longer than calyx tube. Pod generally longer than 1 cm.
                                                                                17. T. monspeliaca
16 (13). Racemes umbellate (i.e. all flowers and pods arising from one point). Pod straight
    or slightly curved, with thin longitudinal nerves between the thick transverse ones.
    Peduncles shorter than leaves.   **5. T. maritima**
— Racemes spike-like (i.e. flowers and pods scattered along rhachis). Pod strongly falcate,
    semicircular or fishhook-shaped. Peduncles as long as or longer than leaves   17
17. Pod (mature) fishhook-shaped. Calyx teeth one third or one half as long as tube.
                                                                                    4. T. moabitica
— Pod and / or calyx not as above   18
18. Peduncles 2 to 4 times as long as leaves. Fruiting racemes 5–8 cm. long.
                                                                                 7. T. corniculata
— Peduncles about as long as or shorter than leaves. Fruiting racemes 2–3 cm. long.
                                                                                     3. T. hamosa
19 (11). Flowers 4–6 mm. Mature pod more or less regularly falcate to semicircular, less
    than 2 mm. thick at base. Seeds cylindrical.   **11. T. cylindracea**
— Flowers 0.7–1 cm. or more. Mature pod arcuate, at least 2 mm. thick at base, gradual-
    ly tapering towards apex. Seeds ovoid to oblong.   **10. T. kotschyi**

Sect. EROSAE Sirj., Publ. Fac. Sci. Univ. Masaryk 102 : 28 (1928). Annuals. Stipules
pinnatifid. Racemes umbellate. Calyx subcampanulate. Pod 1–8-seeded, papery, reflexed, straight, transversely nerved. Seeds ovoid, minutely tuberculate.

1. Trigonella schlumbergeri Boiss., Fl. Suppl. 163 (1888); Sirj., Publ. Fac. Sci. Univ.
Masaryk 102 : 28 (1928); Vass., Acta Inst. Bot. Acad. Sci. URSS ser. 1, 10 : 176
(1953). [Plate 181]
    Annual, nearly glabrous, 10–20 cm. Stems erect, ascending or procumbent, branch-
ing mostly from base. Stipules minute, linear-lanceolate, pinnatifid; leaflets 4–8 × 3–7

mm., obovate to obtriangular, truncate, retuse, mucronulate, coarsely dentate above, glabrous on both sides. Peduncles as long as or longer than leaves, aristate. Racemes 2–4-flowered. Pedicels about 3 mm. Flowers about 5 mm. Calyx about 2 mm., almost campanulate, whitish, glabrous; teeth somewhat shorter than tube, triangular or lanceolate. Corolla white with purplish tip on keel; standard somewhat longer than wings, obovate, deeply notched. Pod 1–2 × 0.7–1.2 cm., papery, white, flat, semiovate, glabrous, transversely striate; dorsal suture convex, ventral straight, both with a dentate, eroded, 1–2 mm. broad wing. Seeds 1 mm., ovoid-oblong, minutely tuberculate. Fl. March–April.

Hab.: Deserts. Judean Mts., Judean Desert, Negev, Lower Jordan Valley, Dead Sea area, Moav, Edom.

Area: Saharo-Arabian.

Sect. PECTINATAE Boiss., Fl. 2:67 (1872). Stipules pinnatifid or incised. Racemes umbellate or shortly spicate. Calyx subcampanulate. Pod reflexed, arcuate, denticulate-ciliate along both sutures, transversely nerved. Seeds tuberculate or wrinkled.

2. Trigonella arabica Del. in Laborde, Voy. Arab. Pétr. 86, f. 5 (1830); Boiss., Fl. 2:90 (1872); Sirj., Publ. Fac. Sci. Univ. Masaryk 102:33 (1928); Vass., Acta Inst. Bot. Acad. Sci. URSS ser. 1, 10:179 (1953). *Pocockia arabica* (Del.) Boiss., Diagn. ser. 1, 9:13 (1849). [Plate 182]

Annual, nearly glabrous, 10–50 cm. Stems erect or ascending, diffuse, branching from base. Stipules triangular-ovate, dentate-incised, glabrous; leaflets 0.5–1.5 × 0.3–1 cm., obtriangular to cuneate-obcordate, entire or few-toothed above, glaucous, glabrous. Peduncles longer than leaves, slender. Racemes umbellate, (3–)5–8-flowered. Pedicels 2–3 mm., filiform, slightly hairy, first erect then deflexed. Flowers 0.8–1 cm. Calyx about 3 mm., campanulate, glabrous or glabrescent; teeth about half as long as tube, triangular. Corolla white (rarely slightly yellow) with purple point at tip of keel (rarely the entire corolla violet); standard ovate, deeply notched, somewhat longer than wings, the latter much longer than keel. Pod 1.5–3 × 0.5–0.8 cm., short-stipitate, parchment-like, flat, broadly linear, arcuate, obtuse, marked with fine transverse anastomosing nerves, spiny-ciliate along both sutures. Seeds 2–8, about 1.5 mm., compressed, ovoid, dark brown, minutely tuberculate. 2n = 16. Fl. February–April.

Hab.: Steppes and coastal sand flats. Sharon Plain, Philistean Plain, Lower Galilee, Shefela, Judean Mts., Judean Desert, W. and N. Negev, Upper and Lower Jordan Valley, Dead Sea area, Moav, Edom.

Area: Saharo-Arabian, with slight extensions into adjacent territories of the Mediterranean region.

One of the most common desert species of *Trigonella*. A fairly good pasture plant.

Sect. FALCATULAE Boiss., Fl. 2:66 (1872). Stipules dentate or incised. Racemes umbellate or spicate. Flowers yellow. Pod mostly terete to compressed, linear, hardly beaked, with conspicuous nerves along both sutures. Seeds ovoid or oblong.

3. Trigonella hamosa L., Syst. ed. 10, 1180 (1759); Boiss., Fl. 2 : 84 (1872); Sirj., Publ. Fac. Sci. Univ. Masaryk 102 : 43 (1928); Vass., Acta Inst. Bot. Acad. Sci. URSS ser. 1, 10 : 188 (1953). [Plate 183]

Annual, green, sparingly hairy or glabrescent, 10–30 cm. Stems erect or procumbent, diffuse, branching from base. Stipules dentate; leaflets 0.8–1.5 × 0.5–0.8 cm., obovate-oblong, cuneate, retuse or truncate, dentate above, glabrous or sparingly hairy. Peduncles about as long as subtending leaves, aristate, hairy. Racemes (3–)5–10-flowered. Pedicels about 1.5 mm., hairy. Flowers 4–5 mm. Calyx 1.5–2 mm., campanulate, hairy; teeth half as long as tube, triangular. Corolla yellow; standard longer than wings, obovate. Pod 0.7–1 (–1.2) × 0.15 cm., subcylindrical to linear, falcate to semicircular, obtuse, mucronate, glabrous or appressed-hairy, with thickened transverse to slightly oblique nerves. Seeds many, about 1.5 mm., ovoid, finely mottled, smooth. Fl. March–April.

Hab.: Fields and sandy places. C. Negev, Lower Jordan Valley.

Area: Sudanian, with extensions into adjacent Saharo-Arabian and Mediterranean territories; also adventive in N. Europe.

The above description refers to var. *typica* Sirj., l.c.

4. Trigonella moabitica Zoh.* [Plate 184]

Annual, green-glaucous, 10–25 cm. Stems many, erect or ascending, diffuse, glabrous or sparingly appressed-hairy. Stipules short, semisagittate, the lower stipules dentate; leaflets 0.3–1.2 × 0.3–0.6 cm., obovate to oblong or obcordate-cuneate, dentate. Peduncles slender, as long as or longer than leaves, ending with an awn 3 mm. Racemes capitate-umbellate, 5–10-flowered. Flowers 5–7 mm. Calyx one third to one half as long as tube, triangular-lanceolate. Corolla yellow; standard a little longer than keel and wings, obovate, retuse. Pod 1–1.8 × 0.1–0.15 cm., flat or cylindrical, fishhook-shaped or irregularly semicircular, tapering above, shortly mucronate, obliquely and transversely nerved. Seeds many, about 1.5 mm., smooth. Fl. March.

Hab.: Steppes. Moav, Edom.

Area: Probably Irano-Turanian.

Differs from *T. cylindracea* Desv., Journ. Bot. Appl. 3 : 77 (1814) in its slender and short peduncles, its semisagittate stipules, and especially in its fishhook-shaped pods and the transverse, not longitudinal nerves of the pod. Close to *T. uncata* Boiss. et Noë in Boiss., Diagn. ser. 2, 2 : 12 (1856), but the pod of the latter is falcate, not tapering above, and terminates in a rounded beak.

5. Trigonella maritima Del. ex Poir. in Lam., Encycl. Suppl. 5 : 361 (1817); Boiss., Fl. 2 : 85 (1872); Sirj., Publ. Fac. Sci. Univ. Masaryk 102 : 49 (1928); Vass., Acta Inst. Bot. Acad. Sci. URSS ser. 1, 10 : 190 (1953). *T. maritima* Del., Fl. Aeg. Ill. 71 no. 721 (1813) *nom. nud.* [Plate 185]

Annual, green, puberulent or glabrous, 5–40 cm. Stems procumbent, diffusely branching. Stipules semisagittate, dentate or incised; leaflets 0.4–1 × 0.3–0.6 cm., obtriangular or obcordate, shortly denticulate. Peduncles 1–2 cm., mostly shorter than

---

* See Appendix at end of this volume.

leaves, shortly aristate, later thickening. Racemes capitate-umbellate, (3–)5–10-flowered. Pedicels 1–1.5 mm., deflexed. Flowers 5–7 mm. Calyx 2–2.5 mm., one third to one half as long as corolla; teeth one third or one half as long as tube, triangular. Corolla yellow; standard somewhat longer than wings, obovate, deeply notched. Pod 0.7–1.3 × 0.2 cm., strongly deflexed, somewhat compressed, linear, slightly curved to arcuate, tapering above, acute, appressed-hairy, with longitudinal nerves crossed by prominent, transversely oblique ridges. Seeds many, about 1 mm., ovoid, smooth. Fl. March–May.

Hab.: Deserts. C. Negev. Also recorded from Philistean Plain by Bové (Boiss., l.c.).

Area: Mainly S. Mediterranean, extending into adjacent deserts.

6. Trigonella stellata Forssk., Fl. Aeg.-Arab. 140 (1775); Boiss., Fl. 2:85 (1872); Sirj., Publ. Fac. Sci. Univ. Masaryk 102:51 (1928); Vass., Acta Inst. Bot. Acad. Sci. URSS ser. 1, 10:191 (1953). [Plate 186]

Annual, glabrescent, 5–40 cm. Stems many, prostrate, branching from base and indurated in lower part. Leaves long-petioled; stipules semisagittate, the lower stipules more or less dentate; leaflets 0.5–1 × 0.5–0.7 cm., obovate or obtriangular, cuneate, retuse or truncate, toothed above, glabrous or almost glabrous on both sides. Racemes umbellate, almost sessile, (3–)5–10-flowered. Pedicels thick, deflexed or spreading. Flowers 3–5 mm. Calyx two thirds as long as corolla, tubular; teeth as long as or somewhat shorter than tube, triangular-lanceolate to linear, glabrous or sparingly pilose. Corolla yellow; standard longer than wings and keel, obovate, notched. Pods 0.4–0.8(–1) × 0.1–0.2 cm., stellately spreading, terete to slightly compressed, mostly slightly falcate, tapering above, acute, glabrous or sparingly hairy, with prominent, transversely oblique nerves. Seeds many, 1.5 mm., ovoid, smooth. 2n = 16. Fl. February–March.

Hab.: Roadsides, wadis and hills, mainly in hot deserts. Sharon Plain, Judean Mts., Judean Desert, Negev, Lower Jordan Valley, Dead Sea area, Arava Valley, deserts of Ammon, Moav and Edom.

Area: Saharo-Arabian, also extending into W. Irano-Turanian deserts.

7. Trigonella corniculata (L.) L., Syst. ed. 10, 1180 (1759); Boiss., Fl. 2:83 (1872); Sirj., Publ. Fac. Sci. Univ. Masaryk 110:7 (1929); Vass., Acta Inst. Bot. Acad. Sci. URSS ser. 1, 10:195 (1953). *Trifolium (Melilotus) corniculata* L., Sp. Pl. 766 (1753). [Plate 187]

Annual, glabrous or sparingly hairy, 10–30 cm. Stems erect or procumbent, diffuse. Leaves long-petioled; stipules dentate or incised at base, with subulate-lanceolate upper portion; leaflets (0.5–)1–3(–4) × (0.3–)0.8–1(–2) cm., obovate to oblong-obovate, dentate, glabrous above, sparingly hairy beneath. Peduncles slender, mostly 2–4 times as long as leaves. Racemes spicate, 10–15- or more-flowered. Flowers up to 1 cm. Calyx about 3 mm., hairy or glabrescent; teeth half as long as to as long as tube, broadly lanceolate. Corolla yellow; standard somewhat shorter than keel, obovate, deeply notched. Pod 1–1.5(–2.5) × 0.15–0.25 cm., flattened, more or less curved-falcate, tapering-acuminate, usually glabrous, with prominent, transverse, anastomosing nerves. Seeds oblong, finely tuberculate. 2n = 16. Fl. April.

Hab.: Fields. Judean Mts. (recorded by Post, Fl. Syr. Pal. Sin. 224, 1883–1896 et ed. 2, 1 : 317, 1932).

Area: Mainly N. Mediterranean.

8. Trigonella spinosa L., Sp. Pl. 777 (1753); Boiss., Fl. 2 : 75 (1872); Sirj., Publ. Fac. Sci. Univ. Masaryk 128 : 5 (1930); Vass., Acta Inst. Bot. Acad. Sci. URSS ser. 1, 10 : 197 (1953). [Plate 188]

Annual, sparingly hairy, 10–30 cm. Stems erect or ascending, branching from base. Stipules minute, subsagittate, incised-dentate, entire, the upper stipules narrower; leaflets 0.7–1.6 × 0.2–0.8 cm., obovate-cuneate to oblong-cuneate, mostly notched or almost 2-lobed and sharply dentate at apex, glabrous or glabrescent. Peduncles very short to 0, aristate. Racemes 2–6-flowered. Pedicels about 2 mm., rather thick. Flowers 4–5 mm., erect, deflexed after anthesis. Calyx 2.5–3.5 mm., tubular; teeth unequal, triangular-lanceolate, the longer teeth longer than tube. Corolla yellow; standard longer than wings, obovate, somewhat notched. Pod 2–6 × 0.2 cm., many-seeded, deflexed, terete-compressed, semicircular to circular, acute, glabrous, transversely nerved. Seeds about 2.5 mm., cylindrical, densely tuberculate. Fl. March–April.

Hab.: Batha and fallow fields. Acco Plain, Sharon Plain, Philistean Plain, Upper and Lower Galilee, Mt. Carmel, Esdraelon Plain, Samaria, Shefela, Judean Mts., Judean Desert, Dan Valley, Upper and Lower Jordan Valley, Gilead, Ammon.

Area: Mainly E. Mediterranean.

Pods vary greatly in number, size and degree of curvature.

Sect. VERAE Sirj., Publ. Fac. Sci. Univ. Masaryk 110 : 14 (1929). Annuals. Stipules dentate or incised, rarely uppermost stipules entire. Racemes umbellate or almost so, (1–)2–9-flowered. Pod terete, sometimes uncinate at apex, longitudinally nerved or with somewhat oblique, anastomosing nerves and with distinct sutures. Seeds cylindrical or oblong, finely tuberculate.

9. Trigonella caelesyriaca Boiss., Diagn. ser. 1, 9 : 19 (1849); Sirj., Publ. Fac. Sci. Univ. Masaryk 110 : 19 (1929; "*coelesyriaca*"); Vass., Acta Inst. Bot. Acad. Sci. URSS ser. 1, 10 : 202 (1953). [Plate 189]

Annual, almost glabrous, 10–60 cm. Stems many, ascending or erect, diffuse, branching, sometimes hollow. Stipules semisagittate, deeply incised or dentate, the upper stipules entire; leaflets (0.8–)1–1.5(–2.5) × 0.6–1.7 cm., obovate-cuneate to ovate-elliptical, rounded, truncate or retuse at apex, dentate, glabrous. Peduncles as long as or somewhat longer than subtending leaves, elongating in fruit. Racemes umbellate, 5–12(–18)-flowered. Pedicels 2–3 mm., first erect then deflexed. Flowers 0.8–1.2 cm. Calyx campanulate, whitish, often glabrous; teeth about one third as long as tube, almost equal, triangular to triangular-lanceolate. Corolla yellow; standard much longer than keel, ovate or oblong, notched. Pod (2.5–)3–5 × 0.2–0.3 cm., terete to somewhat flattened, slightly curved to arcuate and semicircular, rarely circular, acute, mucronate, glabrous, marked with longitudinal, somewhat oblique (often obsolete) nerves. Seeds many, 1.5–2.5 mm., cylindrical or subquadrangular, very finely tuberculate. Fl. March–April.

1. Stems up to 60 cm., thick, hollow. Leaflets 2–2.5 cm. Flowers up to 1.2 cm.

var. **gaillardotii**

– Plants of medium size (10–30 cm.). Leaflets 0.8–1 (–1.5) cm. Flowers
about (0.8–)1 cm.   2

2. Pod about 3 mm. broad, slightly curved to arcuate, compressed, not torulose. Seeds
up to 2 mm. broad.   var. **caelesyriaca**

– Pod not as above   3

3. Pod short, up to 3 cm. long, circular or semicircular.   var. **aleppica**

– Pod longer, arcuate or straight, torulose.   var. **torulosa**

Var. **caelesyriaca**. *T. caelesyriaca* Boiss., l.c. *T. caelesyriaca* Boiss., Fl. 2 : 80 (1872)
excl. var. *β*. Stems 10–30 cm. Leaflets 0.8–1 (–1.5) cm. Flowers about (0.8–)1 cm.
Pod up to 4 cm. long, about 3 mm. broad, flattened, straight or slightly curved to
arcuate.

Var. **aleppica** (Boiss. et Hausskn.) Sirj., l.c. 20. *T. aleppica* Boiss. et Hausskn. in Boiss.,
Fl. 2 : 79 (1872). Stems and leaves as in the former variety. Pod 2.5–3 cm. long, up
to 2 mm. broad, circular or semicircular.

Var. **torulosa** Post, Fl. Syr. Pal. Sin. 223 (1883–1896) et ed. 2, 1 : 315 (1932). Stems
and leaves as in the latter variety. Pod straight or somewhat curved, torulose.

Var. **gaillardotii** (Boiss.) Boiss., Fl. 2 : 80 (1872). *T. gaillardoti* Boiss., Diagn. ser. 2,
5 : 78 (1856). Stems up to 60 cm., thick, hollow. Leaflets 2–2.5 cm. Flowers up to
1.2 cm.

Hab. of species : Fields and field edges. Sharon Plain, Philistean Plain, Upper and
Lower Galilee, Mt. Carmel, Esdraelon Plain, Mt. Gilboa, Samaria, Judean Mts.,
Judean Desert, Upper Jordan Valley, Gilead, Ammon.

Area of species : E. Mediterranean (Palestine–Turkey).

Though these varieties are not separated from each other geographically and although
some intermediate forms occur, they seem to be genetically more or less constant taxa.

Sect. CYLINDRICAE Boiss., Fl. 2 : 66 (1872); Sirj., Publ. Fac. Sci. Univ. Masaryk
110 : 22 (1929). Annuals. Stipules entire. Racemes head-like. Fruiting pedicels deflexed.
Corolla white, yellow or violet. Pod cylindrical, curved (rarely straight), sometimes
torulose, narrowing into a beak; valves with longitudinal nerves or furrows.

10. Trigonella kotschyi Fenzl ex Boiss., Diagn. ser. 1, 9 : 15 (1849); Sirj., Publ. Fac.
Sci. Univ. Masaryk 110 : 27 (1929). [Plate 190]

Annual, appressed-hairy, 10–30 cm. Stems ascending or erect, diffuse. Stipules
lanceolate-subulate, entire; leaflets 0.8–1.5 × 0.5–0.8 cm., obovate to oblong-cuneate,
acutely dentate, appressed-pubescent on both sides. Peduncles 2–3 times as long as
leaves, short-aristate. Racemes head-like, (8–)10–14 (or more) -flowered. Pedicels about
2 mm., deflexed in fruit. Flowers 0.7–1 (–1.2) cm. Calyx about 4 mm., campanulate,
hairy, prominently nerved; teeth unequal, lanceolate-subulate, the longest teeth almost
as long as the tube. Corolla yellow or whitish; standard shorter than or as long as the
wings, rounded to somewhat acute or retuse at apex. Pod (1.2–)1.5–2.5 × 0.2–0.25

cm., semicircular or otherwise curved, appressed- or sparsely patulous-hairy, with long-itudinal furrows at both sutures, rarely transversely wrinkled, sometimes smooth al-together, tapering from base into a seedless, acute beak. Seeds few, ovoid or oblong, minutely tuberculate.

Var. **hierosolymitana** (Boiss.) Sirj., l.c. *T. hierosolymitana* Boiss., l.c. et Fl. 2 : 81 (1872); Vass., Acta Inst. Bot. Acad. Sci. URSS ser. 1, 10 : 205 (1953). Corolla yellow; stand-ard somewhat retuse at apex, considerably shorter than keel (especially before anthesis). Fl. March–April.

Hab.: Batha and grassy sites. Sharon Plain, Mt. Gilboa, Shefela, Judean Mts., Judean Desert, Upper Jordan Valley, Gilead, Ammon, Moav, Edom.

Area: E. Mediterranean.

T. sibthorpii Boiss., Diagn. ser. 1, 9 : 14 (1849) et Fl. 2 : 81 (1872), recorded by Dins-more (in Post, Fl. Syr. Pal. Sin. ed. 2, 1 : 316, 1932) from Jaffa, has not been found by others, nor is it recorded from Palestine by Sirjaev (l.c.) or by Vassilchenko (l.c.) who synonymizes this species with *T. torulosa* Griseb., Spicil. Fl. Rumel. 1 : 40 (1843).

11. Trigonella cylindracea Desv., Journ. Bot. Appl. 3 : 77 (1814); Sirj., Publ. Fac. Sci. Univ. Masaryk 110 : 30 (1929). [Plate 191]

Annual, appressed- or patulous-hairy, 10–30 cm. Stems many or few, erect or decumbent, diffuse, branched. Stipules minute, lanceolate-subulate, entire; leaflets (0.2–)0.4–1.2 × 0.3–0.6 cm., oblong to obovate-cuneate, truncate or rounded at apex, acutely dentate. Peduncles slender, about twice as long as subtending leaves, erect, pilose, short-aristate. Racemes capitate, 6–8(–12)-flowered. Pedicels 1 mm., hairy, de-flexed in fruit. Flowers 4–6 mm. Calyx about half as long as corolla, campanulate, prominently nerved, appressed-hairy; teeth one half to one third as long as tube, triangular. Corolla yellow; standard longer than wings and keel, ovate, notched. Pod (1–)1.5–2.5 × 0.15 cm., cylindrical, arcuate to semicircular, appressed-hairy, with obscure longitudinal nerves, tapering into a seedless acute beak, more or less bent outwards. Seeds few, 2–2.5 × 1 mm., cylindrical, smooth. Fl. February–April.

Var. **cylindracea**. *T. cylindracea* Desv., l.c.; Boiss., Fl. 2 : 82 (1872); Vass., Acta Inst. Bot. Acad. Sci. URSS ser. 1, 10 : 206 (1953). Pod 1.5–2.5 cm. Leaflets 0.7–1.2 cm.

Hab.: Batha, steppes and fallow fields; sandy soil. Acco Plain, Sharon Plain, Phi-listean Plain, Shefela, Negev.

Var. **minima** Sirj. et Eig in Sirj., Publ. Fac. Sci. Univ. Masaryk 170 : 21 (1933). Pod 1–1.2 cm. Leaflets 2–3 (–8) mm.

Hab.: Sand flats. W. Negev.

Area of species: E. Mediterranean.

Forma *jaffensis* Sirj., Publ. Fac. Sci. Univ. Masaryk 110 : 31 (1929) is not a fixed form – there are all intermediates between obovate and narrowly oblong leaflets.

12. Trigonella filipes Boiss., Diagn. ser. 1, 9 : 16 (1849); Sirj., Publ. Fac. Sci. Univ. Masaryk 110 : 31 (1929) et 170 : 21 (1933). [Plate 192]

Annual, appressed-pubescent, 10–15 cm. Stems few, erect or ascending, diffuse, branching. Stipules minute, lanceolate-subulate, entire; leaflets 0.6–1 × 0.3–0.6 cm., obovate to oblong, cuneate, rounded at apex, denticulate, appressed-pubescent on both sides. Peduncles filiform, twice as long as leaves, short-aristate. Racemes head-like, many-flowered. Bracts subulate. Pedicels about 1 mm., hairy, erect in flower, deflexed in fruit. Flowers 3–4 mm. Calyx about 2 mm., tubular, hairy; teeth shorter than tube, unequal, triangular. Corolla yellow; standard somewhat longer than wings and keel, oblong, notched. Pod 1–1.5 cm. long and 1.5 mm. broad at base, lanceolate-cylindrical, arcuate, covered with appressed and patulous hairs, tapering to a long, seedless, subulate, somewhat recurved beak. Seeds 1–2, about 2 mm., cylindrical, slightly curved, dark brown, smooth. Fl. March–April.

Var. **filipes**. *T. filipes* Boiss., l.c. et Fl. 2 : 82 (1872); Vass., Acta Inst. Bot. Acad. Sci. URSS ser. 1, 10 : 207 (1953). *T. minima* Paine, Palest. Explor. Soc. Statement 3 : 101 (1875). Racemes about 2.5 cm. in diam. Pod 1.5 mm. thick.

Hab. : Steppes, hillsides. Gilead, Ammon, Edom.

Var. **gracilior** Bornm. ex Opphr., Bull. Soc. Bot. Genève ser. 2, 22 : 320 (1931); Sirj., l.c. 170 : 21 (1933). Racemes about 1.5 cm. in diam. Pod thinner.

Hab. : As above. Ammon.

Area of species : W. Irano-Turanian.

13. Trigonella lilacina Boiss., Diagn. ser. 1, 9 : 17 (1849) et Fl. 2 : 82 (1872); Sirj., Publ. Fac. Sci. Univ. Masaryk 110 : 33 (1929) et 170 : 21 (1933); Vass., Acta Inst. Bot. Acad. Sci. URSS ser. 1, 10 : 208 (1953). [Plate 193]

Annual, appressed-hairy, 15–45 cm. Stems few or many, erect or ascending. Stipules 5 mm., lanceolate-subulate, entire, puberulent; leaflets 0.6–1.6 × 0.4–1 cm., obovate-oblong, cuneate, mostly rounded above, denticulate, appressed-pubescent on both sides. Peduncles slender, 2–3 times as long as leaves, appressed- or patulous-hairy. Racemes head-like, many-flowered. Pedicels 1–1.5 mm., deflexed in fruit. Flowers 6–8 mm. Calyx 3–4 mm., sparingly puberulent and prominently nerved; teeth unequal, the longest teeth as long as tube. Corolla lilac; standard about as long as wings, oblong. Pod 1.5–2 × 0.1–0.2 cm., 2–3-seeded, cylindrical or slightly flattened, arcuate, appressed- and patulous-hairy or glabrescent, obsoletely longitudinally nerved, tapering into a long, acute beak. Seeds 2 mm., cylindrical. Fl. March–May.

Hab. : Batha and grassy places. Upper and Lower Galilee, Esdraelon Plain, Samaria, Upper Jordan Valley (endemic).

Area : E. Mediterranean.

Sect. BUCERATES Boiss. emend. Sirj., Publ. Fac. Sci. Univ. Masaryk 128 : 12 (1930). Annuals. Racemes short, sessile or pedunculate. Corolla yellow; wings adnate to keel by teeth. Pedicels erect or spreading, not deflexed. Pod flat or terete, with thickened nerves along both sutures.

14. Trigonella astroites Fisch. et Mey., Ind. Sem. Hort. Petrop. 1 : 40 (1835). [Plate 194]

Annual, appressed-pubescent, 5–20 cm. Stems few, ascending or procumbent, diffuse. Stipules semisagittate, dentate to incised or entire, pilose; leaflets 3–8 mm. across, obtriangular to obovate, truncate or retuse at apex, acutely denticulate above, appressed-hairy. Peduncles longer to shorter than leaves, sometimes 0, thickening in fruit. Racemes umbellate, 6–12-flowered. Bracts 1 mm., membranous, lanceolate. Flowers about 4 mm., sessile. Calyx about 3 mm., tubular-campanulate, appressed-hairy; teeth about as long as tube, lanceolate-subulate. Corolla yellow; standard somewhat longer than wings, oblong, notched. Pods 1.3–3 × 0.1–0.15 cm., erect or stellately spreading, 4–6-seeded, somewhat compressed, linear-cylindrical, straight or somewhat curved, tapering, acute, densely appressed-pilose to glabrescent, prominently transversely reticulate-wrinkled; dorsal suture more or less sinuate, ventral entire. Seeds 2 × 0.75 mm., cylindrical, brown, tuberculate-wrinkled. Fl. March–April.

Var. **astroites**. *T. astroites* Fisch. et Mey., l.c.; Boiss., Fl. 2 : 72 (1872); Sirj., Publ. Fac. Sci. Univ. Masaryk 128 : 26 (1930); Vass., Acta Inst. Bot. Acad. Sci. URSS ser. 1, 10 : 217 (1953). Peduncles as long as or longer than leaves.
    Hab.: Steppes. N. Negev, Upper Jordan Valley, Gilead, Edom.

Var. **subsessilis** Zoh.* Peduncles very short or 0.
    Hab.: Steppes. N. Negev.
    Area of species : W. Irano-Turanian.

15. Trigonella monantha C. A. Mey., Verz. Pfl. Cauc. 137 (1831); Boiss., Fl. 2 : 77 (1872); Sirj., Publ. Fac. Sci. Univ. Masaryk 136 : 3 (1931); Vass., Acta Inst. Bot. Acad. Sci. URSS ser. 1, 10 : 221 (1953). [Plate 195]
    Annual, appressed-pubescent, 5–15 cm. Stems solitary or few, ascending, branching. Stipules subulate-lanceolate, semisagittate at base, hairy; leaflets 3–8 × 3–6 mm., obovate, rarely oblong, acutely dentate or incised near tip, rounded or truncate at apex. Peduncles very short or 0. Racemes 1 (–2)-flowered. Bracts subulate. Flowers about 6 mm., sessile or very short-pedicelled. Calyx two thirds as long as corolla, hairy; teeth about as long as tube, triangular-lanceolate. Corolla pale yellow; standard much shorter than wings, obovate. Pod 5–7 × 0.15 cm., erect, terete, straight or slightly curved, hairy, ending in a sharp-pointed hook; valves densely appressed-hairy and obliquely to longitudinally nerved. Seeds many, 1–2 mm., cylindrical, not tuberculate. Fl. April–June.
    Hab.: Grassy patches in steppes. Ammon, Edom.
    Area : W. Irano-Turanian.

16. Trigonella noaeana Boiss., Diagn. ser. 2, 2 : 11 (1856) et Fl. 2 : 77 (1872; "*noëana*"); Sirj., Publ. Fac. Sci. Univ. Masaryk 136 : 7 (1931); Vass., Acta Inst. Bot. Acad. Sci. URSS ser. 1, 10 : 223 (1953). [Plate 196]
    Annual, hairy or glabrescent, 10–20 cm. Stems few, erect or procumbent, diffuse. Stipules semisagittate, the lower stipules dentate at base; leaflets 5–8 × 3–6 mm., obovate to oblong, cuneate, truncate at apex, dentate towards tip, sparingly appressed-hairy on both sides. Peduncles 0 or sometimes conspicuous. Racemes 1–2 (–3)-flowered.

* See Appendix at end of this volume.

Pedicels short, thickened in fruit. Flowers 6–8 mm. Calyx much shorter than corolla; teeth almost as long as tube, linear-lanceolate. Corolla pale yellow; standard obovate, notched. Pod (4–)5–7 × 0.15–0.2 cm., terete-compressed, falcate, rarely semicircular, appressed-hairy, net-veined, with prominent, transversely oblique nerves and areoles. Seeds many, 1.5–2 mm., cylindrical, transversely tuberculate. Fl. March–April.

Hab.: Steppes. Ammon, Moav, Edom.
Area: Irano-Turanian.

Sect. REFLEXAE (Sirj.) Vass., Acta Inst. Bot. Acad. Sci. URSS ser. 1, 10 : 228 (1953). Subsect. *Reflexae* Sirj., Publ. Fac. Sci. Univ. Masaryk 136 : 20 (1931). Annuals. Racemes head-like, many-flowered, sessile or subsessile. Corolla yellow, somewhat exserting from calyx. Pods sessile, stellately spreading or deflexed.

17. Trigonella monspeliaca L., Sp. Pl. 777 (1753); Sirj., Publ. Fac. Sci. Univ. Masaryk 136 : 20 (1931); Vass., Acta Inst. Bot. Acad. Sci. URSS ser. 1, 10 : 228 (1953). [Plate 197]

Annual, appressed-hairy or glabrous, 3–30 cm. Stems few, erect or prostrate, simple or branching, sometimes 0. Stipules semisagittate, the lower stipules mostly dentate or incised, the upper stipules entire; petiole often very long; leaflets 0.5–1 × 0.3–0.7 cm., ovate, obovate or obtriangular, somewhat cuneate, acutely denticulate or incised above, mostly appressed-pubescent on both sides. Peduncles inconspicuous or 0, rarely considerable. Racemes capitate, 4–14(–18)-flowered. Bracts linear-subulate. Flowers about 5 mm., subsessile or sessile. Calyx about 3 mm., hairy; teeth about as long as tube or longer, linear-subulate. Corolla yellow; standard longer than wings, obovate, notched. Pods (0.6–)0.8–2.5 × 0.15–0.2 cm., stellately spreading, somewhat deflexed, compressed, slightly curved to arcuate, hairy or glabrous, with elevated, obliquely transverse, somewhat anastomosing nerves. Seeds 1–1.5 mm., transversely wrinkled. 2n = 16. Fl. February–April.

An extremely polymorphic species; most of its forms occur in Palestine.

1. Petiole twice as long as blade or longer. Stems 0 or very short   2
 – Petiole shorter. Stems or branches rather considerable   3
2. Pod hairy.   var. **petiolata**
 – Pod glabrous.   var. **eigii**
3(1). Leaflets denticulate   4
 – Leaflets incised   6
4. Pod glabrous.   var. **leiocarpa**
 – Pod hairy   5
5. Pod 0.8–1.5 cm.   var. **monspeliaca**
 – Pod 1.7–2.5 cm.   var. **macrocarpa**
6(3). Pod hairy.   var. **naftolskyi**
 – Pod glabrous.   var. **nuda**

Subsp. **monspeliaca.** *T. monspeliaca* L. ssp. *caulescens* Feinbr., Beih. Bot. Centralbl. 51, 2 : 396 (1934). Stems more or less elongated. Petiole less than twice as long as blade.

Var. **monspeliaca**. *T. monspeliaca* L., l.c.; Boiss., Fl. 2 : 76 (1872). Leaflets denticulate. Pod hairy, 0.8–1.5 cm.

Hab. : Fields. Acco Plain, Sharon Plain, Philistean Plain, Upper and Lower Galilee, Mt. Carmel, Esdraelon Plain, Samaria, Shefela, Judean Mts., Judean Desert, N. Negev, Hula Plain, Upper and Lower Jordan Valley, Gilead, Ammon, Moav.

Var. **macrocarpa** Bornm., Verh. Zool.-Bot. Ges. Wien 48 : 577 (1898). Leaflets denticulate. Pod hairy, 1.7–2.5 cm.

Hab. : Fields. Upper and Lower Galilee, Mt. Carmel, Esdraelon Plain, Shefela, Judean Mts., Gilead, deserts of Ammon.

Var. **leiocarpa** Koch in Röhling, Deutschl. Fl. ed. 3, 5 : 313 (1839). *T. monspeliaca* L. var. *liocarpa* Aschers. et Graebn., Syn. Mitteleur. Fl. 6, 2 : 386 (1907). *T. monspeliaca* L. var. *glabrata* Eig, Bull. Inst. Agr. Nat. Hist. 6 : 10 (1927). Leaflets denticulate. Pod glabrous.

Hab. : Fields and steppes. Sharon Plain, Upper Galilee, Shefela, Judean Mts., N. and C. Negev, Upper and Lower Jordan Valley.

Var. **naftolskyi** Eig, l.c. Leaflets incised-serrate. Pod hairy.

Hab. : As above. Philistean Plain, W. Negev, Upper Jordan Valley.

Var. **nuda** Sirj., l.c. 24 (*pro form.*). *T. monspeliaca* L. var. *leiocarpa* Eig, l.c. non Koch, l.c. Leaflets incised. Pod glabrous.

Hab. : As above. W. and C. Negev, Upper Jordan Valley.

Subsp. **subacaulis** Feinbr., l.c. Stems 0 or very short. Petiole twice as long as leaf or longer.

Var. **petiolata** Post, Fl. Syr. Pal. Sin. 222 (1883–1896) et ed. 2, 1 : 313 (1932); Sirj., l.c. 24. *T. monspeliaca* L. var. *moabitica* Sirj. et Eig in Sirj., l.c. 24. Petiole 3–4 cm.; leaflets denticulate. Pod hairy.

Hab. : Batha and steppes. Judean Mts., Judean Desert, Lower Jordan Valley, Gilead, Ammon, Moav.

Var. **eigii** Sirj., l.c. 24 (*pro form.*). Leaflets denticulate. Pod glabrous.

Hab. : As above. Judean Mts., Judean Desert, C. Negev, Ammon, Moav.

Area of species : Mediterranean, with extensions into adjacent regions.

The above varieties, kept by Sirjaev (l.c.) as formae, show little geographical and ecological differentiation but are more or less constant genetically.

Sect. UNCINATAE Boiss., Fl. 2 : 67 (1872). Annuals. Stipules entire or almost so. Racemes capitate or spicate. Pod 1–2-seeded, short, reticulately nerved, with a long, uncinate beak. Seeds somewhat compressed, ovoid.

18. Trigonella spicata Sm. in Sibth. et Sm., Fl. Gr. Prodr. 2 : 108 (1813); Boiss., Fl. 2 : 86 (1872); Sirj., Publ. Fac. Sci. Univ. Masaryk 128 : 9 (1930); Vass., Acta Inst. Bot. Acad. Sci. URSS ser. 1, 10 : 233 (1953). [Plate 198]

Annual, glabrous or glabrescent, 15–40 cm. Stems erect or ascending, simple or branching from base to middle. Stipules lanceolate-subulate, semisagittate, the lower stipules sometimes dentate; leaflets 0.8–2.5 × 0.2–0.6 cm., lower leaflets obovate, the upper leaflets oblong-lanceolate or oblong-elliptical to linear, somewhat tapering at base, obtuse or truncate and mucronulate at apex, acutely or obsoletely denticulate almost to base, glabrous or sparingly hairy beneath. Peduncles 2–3 times as long as leaves, 2–6 cm. in flower, up to 8 cm. in fruit, erect. Racemes up to about 2 cm. in flower, elongating in fruit, spike-like, many-flowered. Pedicels about 2 mm. Flowers 6–8 mm., deflexed. Calyx 4–5 mm., tubular, almost 2-lipped; teeth about as long as tube, unequal, triangular-lanceolate, mucronate. Corolla yellow; standard somewhat longer than wings, ovate-oblong, notched. Pods (excl. beak) about 5 × 3 mm., densely crowded, 1-seeded, compressed, ovoid-oblong, long-pilose, later glabrescent, slightly and loosely net-veined, with strongly hooked beak about as long as seed-bearing portion. Seeds about 2.5 × 1.5 mm., ovoid, minutely tuberculate. Fl. April–June.

Hab.: Batha. Coastal Galilee, Judean Mts.

Area: E. Mediterranean, with Irano-Turanian extension areas.

Sect. TRIGONELLA. Annuals. Racemes 1–2- to many-flowered. Calyx tubular. Corolla rather large. Pod long, lanceolate or linear-lanceolate to linear, narrowing to a long beak. Seeds finely tuberculate.

19. Trigonella foenum-graecum L., Sp. Pl. 777 (1753); Boiss., Fl. 2 : 70 (1872); Sirj., Publ. Fac. Sci. Univ. Masaryk 148 : 28 (1932); Vass., Acta Inst. Bot. Acad. Sci. URSS ser. 1, 10 : 241 (1953). [Plate 199]

Annual, hairy to glabrescent, 15–50 cm. Stems single or few, erect or rarely ascending. Stipules triangular-lanceolate, acuminate, entire, pilose; leaflets 1–3 × 0.8–1.5 cm., oblong to obovate-oblong, obtuse, denticulate above, glabrous. Racemes sessile or subsessile, (1–)2-flowered. Flowers 1.3–1.8 cm. Calyx about half as long as corolla, tubular; teeth somewhat shorter than tube, linear-lanceolate, long-pilose. Corolla white to cream-coloured; standard much longer than wings, obovate, retuse; keel half as long as wings. Pod 6–15 × 0.4–0.5 cm., somewhat flattened, linear, straight or curved, glabrous or pilose, marked with remote, longitudinal and anastomosing nerves, gradually attenuating into a straight beak 2–4 cm. Seeds many (10–20), 4–5 × 2–3 mm., ovoid, minutely tuberculate. Fl. March–April.

Hab.: Cultivated and subspontaneous.

Area: Widely cultivated; origin probably S. W. Asia.

20. Trigonella berythea Boiss. et Bl. in Boiss., Diagn. ser. 2, 2 : 10 (1856). [Plate 199a]

Annual, hairy or glabrescent, 10–30 cm. Stems single or few, erect or ascending. Stipules ovate-acuminate; leaflets 1–3 × 0.8–1.8(–2.5) cm., obovate with cuneate base, rarely obovate-oblong, rounded or truncate at apex, usually somewhat retuse, acutely or obsoletely denticulate towards tip, glabrous. Racemes sessile or subsessile, 1(–2)-flowered. Flowers 0.8–1.6 cm. Calyx submembranous, about half as long as corolla, tubular, sparingly hairy or glabrous; teeth two thirds as long as tube, linear-lanceolate. Corolla pale blue or cream-coloured or bluish and cream-coloured; standard much longer than wings, oblong, notched; keel about half as long as wings. Pod 6–11 × 0.5 cm., very slightly flattened, linear, more or less curved, glabrous or sparingly pilose, marked with dense parallel longitudinal nerves, tapering into a 2–4 cm. long beak. Seeds 3–5 × 2–3 mm., ovoid, minutely tuberculate. Fl. March–April.

Var. **berythea**. *T. berythea* Boiss. et Bl. in Boiss., l.c. et Fl. 2 : 70 (1872); Sirj., Publ. Fac. Sci. Univ. Masaryk 148 : 38 (1932); Vass., Acta Inst. Bot. Acad. Sci. URSS ser. 1, 10 : 244 (1953). Flowers 1.2–1.6 cm. Corolla pale blue or cream-coloured and blue.

   Hab.: Batha. Sharon Plain, Philistean Plain, Upper and Lower Galilee, Mt. Carmel, Mt. Gilboa, Samaria, Judean Mts., Hula Plain, Upper Jordan Valley.

Var. **leucantha** Zoh.* Flowers usually smaller (0.8–1 cm.). Corolla cream-coloured.
   Hab.: As above. Judean Mts.
   Very close to *T. foenum-graecum*; represents perhaps an ancestral race of the latter.
   Area of species: E. Mediterranean (Palestine–Turkey).

34. FACTOROVSKYA Eig

Annuals. Leaves stipulate, 3-foliolate. Racemes axillary, 1–2-flowered. Flowers minute, pedicellate. Calyx tubular; teeth 5. Standard with suborbicular limb, notched at apex; keel obtuse. Stamens diadelphous; filaments not dilated at apex; anthers uniform. Ovary stipitate, 2-celled, 2-ovuled, forming after flowering an acute angle with the pedicel and the greatly elongating gynophore; the latter buries the ovary in the ground. Pod subterranean, 2-celled, ovoid to lenticular; cells 1-seeded, the upper lenticular cell often abortive. Radicle of seed parallel to dorsal suture of pod and descending towards its base.
   One species in the E. Mediterranean countries.

1. Factorovskya aschersoniana (Urb.) Eig, Bull. Inst. Agr. Nat. Hist. 6 : 18 (1927). *Trigonella aschersoniana* Urb., Verh. Bot. Ver. Prov. Brandenb. 23 : Sitz.-Ber. 67 (1882). [Plate 200]
   Annual, glabrous or almost so, 3–10 cm. Stems many, prostrate, diffuse. Leaves 2–3 cm.; stipules ovate to ovate-lanceolate, incised-dentate with 2–5 linear-subulate teeth; petiole 0.4–1.2 cm.; leaflets 2–3.5(–6) × 2.5–4.5(–6.5) mm., obtriangular to obovate, cuneate at base, truncate to emarginate at apex, with 2 teeth on each side of mucro, upper surface glabrous, lower surface sparingly hairy; lateral leaflets short-, terminal long-petiolulate. Peduncles shorter than petiole. Flowers 2.5–4 mm. Calyx pilose; teeth half as long as tube, triangular to lanceolate-triangular. Corolla yellow, often remaining closed; standard nearly twice as long as calyx; keel twice as broad as wings, straight. Ovary cylindrical, on a stipe (gynophore) much elongating and pushing the ovary into the ground; style falcate; stigma capitate. Pod subterranean, 0.8–1 cm., usually appressed-tomentose. Seeds 2, rarely 1. Fl. January–March.

---

* See Appendix at end of this volume.

Hab.: Fallow fields and batha. Sharon Plain, Philistean Plain, Upper and Lower Galilee, Mt. Carmel, Esdraelon Plain, Judean Mts., Judean Desert, Negev, Upper and Lower Jordan Valley, Dead Sea area.

Area: E. Mediterranean.

35. MEDICAGO L.

Annual or perennial herbs, rarely half-shrubs or shrubs. Leaves alternate, stipulate, 3-foliolate, with toothed leaflets. Racemes axillary, pedunculate, many- or few-flowered. Flowers small, pedicellate. Calyx short, tubular or campanulate, 5-toothed or -lobed. Corolla mostly yellow, rarely violet; standard obovate to oblong, tapering at base, often reflexed; wings oblong; keel obtuse. Stamens diadelphous; filaments not dilated at apex. Ovary 1-, few- to many-ovuled; style subulate or filiform; stigma terminal. Pod mostly indehiscent, exserted from calyx, straight or reniform to falcate, often spirally coiled, mostly with prickly or tuberculate dorsal suture. Seeds usually reniform; cotyledons not jointed beneath blade.

About 100 species in the Mediterranean region, S. W. and Central Asia, S. Africa.

Literature: J. Urban, Prodromus einer Monographie der Gattung *Medicago* L., *Verh. Bot. Ver. Prov. Brandenb.* 15 : 1–85 (1873). M. Evenari, *Medicago,* in: H. R. Oppenheimer et M. Evenari, Florula Cisiordanica, *Bull. Soc. Bot. Genève,* Ser. 2, 31 : 279–285, pls. 1–12 (1941). C. C. Heyn, The annual species of *Medicago, Scr. Hieros.* 12 : 1–154 (1963).

Most of the species recorded here are highly palatable pasture herbs which have been introduced as such into many countries; they also constitute an important part of the grazing resources in the Middle East.

1. Pod a 1-seeded, slightly curved, net-veined nutlet, 2–3 mm. across. Racemes 15–20(–40)-flowered. **3. M. lupulina**
– Pod usually many-seeded, elongated, spirally coiled or falcate 2
2. Perennial herbs woody at base. Pod of 2–3 coils with pervious centre or pod falcate, not coiled. Racemes 5–15(–20)-flowered 3
– Annual herbs. Centre of pod closed or rarely pervious, but then pod with only 1 coil and the diameter of pod 1.5–2 cm. Racemes mostly few-flowered, rarely many-flowered 4
3. Tomentose-canescent littoral plants. Pod spirally coiled, prickly or unarmed. Flowers yellow. **5. M. marina**
– Green, glabrous or hairy plants. Pod falcate, not coiled and not prickly. Flowers blue, rarely yellow. **4. M. sativa**
4(2). Pod 1.5–2 cm. across, of 1 coil only, with overlapping ends and ciliate-fringed margin. Desert plants. **1. M. radiata**
– Pod not as above 5
5. Pod 1–1.5 cm. across, flat, biconvex to lenticular, of 2 or 3 (rarely up to 5) coils; margin unarmed, wing-like. Seeds more than 2 in each coil. **2. M. orbicularis**
– Pod not as above 6
6. All or some of the coils concave or cup-like; the larger coils partly enclosing the smaller ones 7
– Not as above 8

7. All coils of pod distinctly concave with the cavities directed upwards, each coil partly enclosing the subsequent one; coils not spiny. **6. M. scutellata**
– Pod biconvex, middle coils of pod flat; coils sometimes spiny. **8. M. blancheana**
8 (6). Pod spineless, discoid, with 2½–5 coils; surface of coils with thick radial veins, reaching the very thick dorsal suture and often anastomosing near latter. **7. M. rugosa**
– Pod usually spiny or strongly tuberculate at margin, rarely unarmed 9
9. Pod minute, 1–3 mm. in diam., coils 1–2, loose; spines vertical, 10 or more on each margin of the very broad suture. Flowers usually 6–16 in each raceme. **10. M. coronata**
— Pod and flowers not as above 10
10. Desert plants. Pod globular (rarely cylindrical); surface of coil with 6–16 prominent S-shaped radial veins not reaching the suture but confluent with a peripheral vein behind it; spines usually longer than radius or diameter of pod, the longer usually hooked at tip. **11. M. laciniata**
— Plants not as above 11
11. Pod usually globular (convex and not truncate at ends), with spines 2–4 mm., delicate, slender; coil surface net-veined; coils and spines hairy and/or glandular-hairy 12
— Pod discoid, cylindrical, ovoid or ellipsoidal, not as above 13
12. Pod 2–5 mm. in diam.; spines often longer than diameter of pod. Stipules entire or minutely denticulate. **12. M. minima**
— Pod 1.2–1.5 cm. in diam.; spines much shorter than diameter of pod. Stipules laciniate or deeply dentate. **22. M. intertexta**
13 (11). Coil surface of pod with a dense, irregular net of thin veins, not differentiated into radial and/or peripheral veins. Pod glabrous. **9. M. rotata**
— Coil surface distinctly differentiated into radial or radial and peripheral veins, often anastomosing near suture 14
14. Pod discoid or cylindrical; all coils, except for the lowermost and uppermost ones, equal in width 15
— Pod ellipsoidal or ovoid; coils gradually diminishing in width towards base and apex 19
15. Coils of mature pods usually over 2 mm. thick, compact (strongly appressed to one another); peripheral vein and dorsal suture equally thick. Littoral plants. **15. M. litoralis**
— Coils of mature pod 2 mm. thick or less, not compact (not strongly appressed to one another); dorsal suture much more prominent than peripheral vein 16
16. Coil margin with a distinct furrow between dorsal suture and peripheral vein; spines vertical, i.e. forming a right angle with the coil surface. Racemes 1–3-flowered. **16. M. truncatula**
— Coil margin not furrowed or with only a shallow furrow between dorsal suture and peripheral vein. Racemes (1–)2- to many-flowered 17
17. Stipules short-dentate. Pod of 4–7 coils, villose, rarely glabrous, coils then unarmed or more than 8 mm. in diam.; coil surface with 12–17 radial veins anastomosing near peripheral vein. **17. M. rigidula**
— Stipules deeply dentate or incised. Pod of less coils than above or otherwise different from above 18
18. Pod of 1–2½ coils; spines, if present, usually shorter than radius of coil. Fruiting racemes usually ascending, with 5 or more pods. **14. M. tornata**
— Coils usually more than above; spines, if present, usually as long as or longer than radius of coil. Fruiting racemes deflexed, with 2–4 pods. **13. M. polymorpha**

19(14). Radial veins of coil surface strongly arcuate, almost concentric in their distal part. **18. M. constricta**

— Radial veins not as above 20

20. Coil surface with 12–17 radial veins anastomosing near peripheral vein; pod villose, rarely glabrous, spines then 0 or diameter of pod exceeding 8 mm. Stipules short-dentate. **17. M. rigidula**

— Pod not as above. Stipules incised or very long-dentate 21

21. Coil surface with a broad veinless zone near margin 22

— Coil surface with anastomosing radial veins; no veinless zone near margin 23

22. Leaflets glabrous, rarely with a few hairs beneath, deeply dentate-serrate to doubly serrate. **20. M. turbinata**

— Leaflets hairy on both sides, dentate. **21. M. murex**

23(21). Pod usually hairy and/or glandular-hairy. Seeds yellow to yellowish-brown. Corolla slightly longer than calyx. **19. M. aculeata**

— Pod glabrous or sparingly hairy. Seeds dark reddish-brown to black. Corolla more than twice as long as calyx. **23. M. granadensis**

Sect. MEDICAGO. Pod flattened, with $\frac{1}{2}$–$1\frac{1}{2}$ coils, fringed or not at dorsal and ventral suture. Seeds more than 2 in each coil; seedcoat ridged or wrinkled; radicle as long as cotyledons.

1. Medicago radiata L., Sp. Pl. 778 (1753). *Trigonella radiata* (L.) Boiss., Fl. 2:90 (1872). [Plate 201]

Annual, densely pubescent, 10–25 cm. Stems prostrate or ascending. Stipules lanceolate-subulate, few-toothed at base; leaflets about 0.6–1 × 0.4–0.6 cm., obovate to oblong, dentate-serrate at apex. Peduncles shorter than to nearly as long as leaves. Racemes 1–2-flowered. Flowers 5–6 mm. Calyx teeth about as long as tube, subulate. Corolla deep yellow; standard obovate to elliptical. Pod (1.2–)1.5–2 cm. in diam., membranous, orbicular, with dense radial veins; dorsal suture spiny-ciliate, ventral fimbriate; coils $\frac{1}{2}$–$1\frac{1}{2}$. Seeds 4–7, up to 3 mm., ovoid, yellowish-brown, wrinkled. Fl. March–May.

Hab.: Steppes and deserts. Judean Mts., Judean Desert, Negev, Gilead, Ammon, Moav, Edom.

Area: Irano-Turanian, with slight extensions into Mediterranean borderland.

Sect. ORBICULARES Urb., Verh. Bot. Ver. Prov. Brandenb. 15:48 (1873). Pod lenticular or discoid, with 2–3(–5) coils, usually spineless, glabrous or hairy. Seeds tuberculate; radicle as long as cotyledons.

2. Medicago orbicularis (L.) Bart., Cat. Piant. Siena 60 (1776); Heyn, Scr. Hieros. 12:135 (1963). *M. orbicularis* (L.) All., Fl. Ped. 1:314 (1785); Boiss., Fl. 2:97 (1872). *M. polymorpha* L. var. *orbicularis* L., Sp. Pl. 779 (1753). [Plate 202]

Annual, usually glabrous, 15–40 cm. Stems usually procumbent, profusely branching from base. Stipules ovate, incised; leaflets 0.7–1.2 × 0.6–1 cm., obovate-cuneate, mostly retuse, apiculate, serrate-dentate above. Peduncles shorter than petiole, later elongating. Racemes 1–3 (–5)-flowered. Pedicels longer than calyx. Flowers 3–5 mm. Calyx glabrous or sparsely hairy; teeth about as long as tube. Corolla twice as long as calyx or less, bright yellow; standard twice as long as wings and keel. Pod 1–1.5 cm. in diam., lenticular or discoid, glabrous or hairy, not spiny; margin thin, wing-like; coils 2–5; coil surface with a net of anastomosing radial veins. Seeds 3–6 in each coil, about 3 mm., trigonous, yellow to reddish-brown, tuberculate; radicle about as long as cotyledons. 2n = 16. Fl. March–May.

Hab.: Batha, cultivated and fallow fields, roadsides. Acco Plain, Sharon Plain, Philistean Plain, Upper and Lower Galilee, Mt. Carmel, Esdraelon Plain, Mt. Gilboa, Samaria, Judean Mts., Judean Desert, C. Negev, Hula Plain, Upper and Lower Jordan Valley, Gilead, Ammon, Moav.

Area: Mediterranean and Irano-Turanian, extending into Euro-Siberian and Sudanian territories.

An excellent pasture plant; also cultivated for hay and green manure.

Sect. LUPULARIA Ser. in DC., Prodr. 2:172 (1825) emend. Urb., Verh. Bot. Ver. Prov. Brandenb. 15:47 (1873). Pod of a single 1-seeded coil, reniform or lenticular. Seed smooth; radicle about half as long as cotyledons.

3. Medicago lupulina L., Sp. Pl. 779 (1753); Boiss., Fl. 2 : 105 (1872). [Plate 203]

Perennial, biennial or annual, pubescent, 15–60 cm. Stems procumbent or ascending. Stipules ovate or lanceolate, subcordate at base, acuminate, entire, dentate or incised; leaflets 0.3–2 × 0.3–0.8 cm., obovate, cuneate, retuse to obcordate, apiculate, finely serrate in the upper half, appressed-hairy. Peduncles elongating in fruit, slender, much longer than petiole. Racemes spike-like, (5–)10- to many-flowered. Pedicels as long as or longer than calyx tube. Flowers 2–4 mm. Calyx teeth nearly as long as tube, triangular-lanceolate. Corolla bright yellow. Pod 2 (–3) mm., of a single, 1-seeded coil, reniform or lenticular, appressed-hairy or glabrous, spineless, black when ripe, with prominent arcuate-reticulate veins. Seeds small, yellowish-brown, smooth. Fl. May–July.

Hab.: Batha and maquis. Sharon Plain, Upper Galilee, Judean Mts., Upper Jordan Valley.

Area: Mediterranean, Euro-Siberian and Irano-Turanian; also introduced into other regions.

Sometimes grown as a green fodder, green manure or hay crop.

Sect. FALCAGO Reichb., Fl. Germ. Exc. 504 (1832). Perennials. Pod unarmed, of 2–3 remote coils, linear or falcate. Seed smooth; radicle about half as long as cotyledons.

4. Medicago sativa L., Sp. Pl. 778 (1753); Boiss., Fl. 2 : 94 (1872). [Plate 204]

Perennial, woody at base, glabrous or appressed-hairy, 10–50 cm. Stems many, procumbent, branching, leafy. Stipules ovate-lanceolate, acuminate, entire; leaflets 1–1.5 × 0.3–0.6 cm., those of the lower leaves obovate-oblong, those of the upper leaves lanceolate, cuneate, rounded or truncate and mucronate at apex, dentate above. Peduncles much longer than subtending leaves. Racemes 8–20-flowered. Pedicels as long as or twice as long as calyx tube. Flowers 0.6–1 cm. Calyx about 5 mm., sparingly hairy; tube as long as subulate teeth, campanulate. Corolla blue or yellow; standard ovate, longer than wings, the latter longer than keel. Pod of 2–3 remote coils, or uncoiled and linear or falcate, hairy, unarmed, net-veined. Seeds straight or slightly curved. Fl. April–May.

Hab.: Damp places in steppes. Edom. Rare.

Area: Euro-Siberian, Mediterranean and W. Irano-Turanian.

The above description was made from a few flowering specimens only, so that there is no possibility of referring them to one of the many subspecific taxa of this species. The fruit was drawn from an Anatolian specimen.

Sect. SPIROCARPOS Ser. in DC., Prodr. 2 : 174 (1825). Annuals or perennials. Pod of 2 or more coils, spineless or furnished with tubercles or short spines; coils 1–2-seeded. Seeds smooth; radicle about half as long as cotyledons.

5. Medicago marina L., Sp. Pl. 779 (1753); Boiss., Fl. 2 : 96 (1872). [Plate 205]

Perennial, woolly-canescent, 10–20 cm. Stems ascending to prostrate. Stipules ovate-lanceolate, nearly entire; leaflets 0.8–1.5 × 0.5–0.8 cm., obovate-cuneate, obtuse, mucronulate, dentate above, tomentose. Peduncles nearly as long as subtending leaves. Racemes 5–12(–14)-flowered. Pedicels as long as filiform bracts. Flowers about 0.7–1 cm. Calyx canescent; teeth longer than tube. Corolla twice as long as calyx, yellow. Pod 5–6 mm. across, discoid or cylindrical, truncate on both ends, canescent; coils 3 or less, loose, coil surface with radial, anastomosing veins confluent with the peripheral nerve, dorsal suture obtuse, broad, flattened, unarmed or remotely beset with short-conical spines. Seed 1 in each coil, 3 × 2 mm., reniform, brown. Fl. February–June.

Hab.: Maritime sands. Coastal Galilee, Acco Plain, Sharon Plain, Philistean Plain.

Area: Mediterranean.

6. Medicago scutellata (L.) Mill., Gard. Dict. ed. 8, no. 2 (1768); Heyn, Scr. Hieros. 12 : 38 (1963); *M. scutellata* (L.) All., Fl. Ped. 1 : 315 (1785); Boiss., Fl. 2 : 96 (1872). *M. polymorpha* L. var. *scutellata* L., Sp. Pl. 779 (1753). *M. inermis* (Lam.) Lam. ex Steud., Nom. 513 (1821) *pro syn.* p.p. [Plate 206]

Annual, usually glandular-hairy, 25–50 cm. Stems ascending, branching from base. Stipules ovate-lanceolate, dentate to laciniate, glandular-hairy beneath; leaflets 1–2.5 × 0.5–1.2 cm., oblong-obovate, serrate, glabrous above, hairy or glandular-hairy beneath. Peduncles shorter than or as long as petiole, ending in a weak cusp. Racemes 1–4-flowered. Pedicels shorter than bracts. Flowers 6–9 mm. Calyx glandular-hairy; teeth as long as or longer than tube, lanceolate, acute. Corolla less than twice as long as calyx, yellow to yellowish-orange; standard larger than keel; wings slightly shorter. Pod 0.7–1.5(–1.8) cm. in diam., made of 5–8 cup-shaped, glandular-hairy, spineless, net-veined coils, each partly enclosing the next. Seeds 1–2 in each coil (except for the

1–2 upper coils which are seedless), 4–7 × 2.5–4 mm., reniform, light yellow to brown; radicle less than half as long as cotyledons. 2n = 32. Fl. March–May.

Hab.: Heavy soils, mostly among crops or in fallow fields. Acco Plain, Sharon Plain, Philistean Plain, Upper and Lower Galilee, Mt. Carmel, Esdraelon Plain, Mt. Gilboa, Samaria, Judean Mts., Upper Jordan Valley.

Area: Mediterranean, with extensions into adjacent Euro-Siberian territories. Elsewhere adventive.

Sometimes grown as a hay or pasture plant.

7. Medicago rugosa Desr. in Lam., Encycl. 3 : 632 (1792); Heyn, Scr. Hieros. 12 : 41 (1963). *M. rugosa* Desr. var. *graeca* Heldr. ex Nym., Consp. 167 (1878). *M. rugosa* Desr. var. *incisa* (Moris) Urb., Verh. Bot. Ver. Prov. Brandenb. 15 : 64 (1873). *M. elegans* Jacq. ex Willd., Sp. Pl. 3 : 1408 (1802); Boiss., Fl. 2 : 98 (1872). [Plate 207]

Annual, hairy or glandular-hairy, 15–30 cm. Stems ascending or procumbent, branching from base. Stipules broadly ovate, unequally dentate, hairy beneath; leaflets (0.7–)1–1.5 × 0.7–1 cm., obovate-cuneate or oblong to oblanceolate, those of upper leaves rhombic, obtuse to slightly retuse, mucronate, usually serrate or laciniate at upper part, glabrous above, hairy beneath. Peduncles shorter than petiole, aristate at tip. Racemes 2–7-flowered. Pedicels longer than bracts. Flowers 2.5–4 mm. Calyx hairy and glandular-hairy; teeth shorter than tube. Corolla light to dark yellow; standard longer than keel; wings slightly shorter than standard. Pod 3–5 mm. thick, disk-like, of 2½–5, 1-seeded coils, hairy and glandular-hairy, unarmed; coil surface with 12–30 slightly curved radial veins, much anastomosing and thickened near dorsal suture. Seeds 3–4 mm., yellow; radicle less than half as long as cotyledons. 2n = 32. Fl. March–April.

Hab.: Heavy soils, among crops and in fallow fields. Philistean Plain, Upper and Lower Galilee, Mt. Carmel, Esdraelon Plain, Mt. Gilboa, Samaria, Judean Mts., Judean Desert, Upper Jordan Valley.

Area: Mediterranean.

8. Medicago blancheana Boiss., Diagn. ser. 2, 5 : 75 (1856); Heyn, Scr. Hieros. 12 : 44 (1963). [Plate 208]

Annual, hairy or glandular-hairy, 15–30 cm. Stems usually ascending, branching from near the base. Stipules lanceolate-subulate, dentate; leaflets 1–1.8 × 0.5–0.8 cm., usually obovate or ovate to lanceolate, truncate, apiculate, serrately dentate above, hairy on either side and glandular beneath. Peduncles twice as long as petiole, deflexed, aristate. Racemes 1–3-flowered. Pedicels longer than bracts. Flowers 6–8 mm. Calyx hairy and glandular-hairy; teeth as long as tube. Corolla twice as long as calyx or shorter, pale to dark yellow; standard nearly twice as long as keel and wings. Pod 0.9–1.2 cm. thick, biconvex, glandular-hairy (rarely glabrous), spiny or not; coils 4–6, the middle coil the broadest, 0.8–1.2 cm. in diam., the others decreasing in width towards base and apex; coil surface with a dense net of 20–30 veins, running into the dorsal suture; spines (when present) varying in size and direction. Seeds 1–2 in each coil, 4–5 mm., yellow to light brown, smooth; radicle half as long as cotyledons. 2n = 16. Fl. March–May.

Var. **blancheana**. *M. blancheana* Boiss., l.c. et Fl. 2 : 97 (1872). Coils of pod with 2 rows of spines.

Hab. : Among winter crops and in fallow fields. Philistean Plain, Upper and Lower Galilee, Esdraelon Plain, Shefela, Judean Mts., Lower Jordan Valley, Gilead.

Var. **bonarotiana** (Arcang.) Arcang., Comp. Fl. Ital. 61 (1882). *M. bonarotiana* Arcang., Nuov. Giorn. Bot. Ital. 8 : 6 (1876). *M. blancheana* Boiss. var. *inermis* Post, Fl. Syr. Pal. Sin. 227 (1883–1896). Pod spineless; veins sometimes protruding beyond margin of coils.

Hab. : As above. Acco Plain, Sharon Plain, Upper Galilee, Mt. Carmel, Esdraelon Plain, Shefela, Judean Mts., Hula Plain, Gilead.

Area of species : E. Mediterranean.

9. **Medicago rotata** Boiss., Diagn. ser. 1, 2 : 24 (1843); Heyn, Scr. Hieros. 12 : 48 (1963). [Plate 209]

Annual, hairy, 15–30 cm. Stems usually ascending, branching from near base. Stipules ovate, long-acuminate, dentate; leaflets 0.8–2 × 0.4–0.8 cm., usually obovate to oblong, rarely ovate or oblanceolate, truncate, mucronulate, serrate at upper third, sometimes laciniate. Peduncles about twice as long as petiole, slender, erect-deflexed, aristate. Racemes 1–5(–6)-flowered. Flowers 6–8 mm. Calyx hairy; teeth as long as tube. Corolla up to twice as long as calyx, yellow; standard nearly twice as long as keel and wings. Pod 0.4–1 cm. thick and 0.5–1 (–1.2) cm. across, cylindrical, flat on one or both surfaces, usually glabrous, spiny; coils 3–5(–7), indurated at maturity, all equally broad except for the two extreme ones; coil surface with a dense net of veins; spines 0.5–3 mm., almost vertical and appressed to pod (at right angles to coil surface), often very irregular in shape, some forked. Seeds 1–2 in each coil, 3–5 mm., light to yellowish-brown, smooth; radicle half as long as cotyledons. 2n = 16, 18. Fl. March–May.

Var. **rotata**. *M. rotata* Boiss., l.c. et Fl. 2 : 97 (1872). *M. rotata* Boiss. var. *longispinea* Evenari in Opphr. et Evenari, Bull. Soc. Bot. Genève ser. 2, 31 : 283 (1941). Leaflets serrate, very rarely laciniate. Racemes 1–4-flowered. Pod 0.8–1.2 cm. across; coils 4–6, the last one flat.

Hab. : Among winter crops and in fallow fields. Upper and Lower Galilee, Mt. Carmel, Esdraelon Plain, Samaria, Judean Mts., Hula Plain, Upper and Lower Jordan Valley, Dead Sea area, Gilead, Ammon, Moav.

Var. **eliezeri** Eig, Bull. Inst. Agr. Nat. Hist. 6 : 20 (1927) emend. Heyn, l.c. 49, f. 13 C. Leaflets laciniate. Racemes 4–6-flowered. Pod 5–8 mm. across; coils 3–5, the last one concave.

Hab. : As above. Philistean Plain, Upper and Lower Galilee, Esdraelon Plain, Samaria, Shefela, Judean Mts., Upper Jordan Valley.

Area of species : E. Mediterranean.

10. **Medicago coronata** (L.) Bart., Cat. Piant. Siena 61 (1776); Heyn, Scr. Hieros. 12 : 51 (1963); *M. coronata* (L.) Desr. in Lam., Encycl. 3 : 634 (1792); Boiss., Fl.

2 : 101 (1872). *M. polymorpha* L. var. *coronata* L., Sp. Pl. 780 (1753). *M. coronata* Lam. var. *brevipedunculata* Eig, Bull. Inst. Agr. Nat. Hist. 6 : 22 (1927). *M. coronata* Lam. var. *multiflora* Eig, l.c. [Plate 210]

Annual, hairy or glandular-hairy, 5–15 (–20) cm. Stems ascending, diffusely branching. Stipules ovate to lanceolate, dentate especially at base, the upper stipules mostly entire; leaflets 0.5–1.2 × 0.4–0.6 cm., obovate, rarely oblanceolate, cuneate, often retuse at apex, mucronate, dentate-serrate, especially above. Peduncles longer than petiole, short-aristate. Racemes head-like, (3–)6–16-flowered. Flowers 2–3 mm. Calyx teeth shorter than tube, one tooth usually longer than the rest. Corolla usually less than twice as long as calyx, pale yellow; standard slightly longer than keel and wings. Pod minute, 1–4 mm. thick and 1.5–3 mm. broad, short-cylindrical, often hairy, spiny; coils 1–2½, loose, with 5–8 prominent radial veins on the surface; spines vertical (at right angles to coil surface), about 10 on each coil, forming a crown-like structure on both sides of the pod; suture 0.5–1.5 mm. thick. Seeds 1–3 in each pod, 2–3 mm., irregularly shaped, yellow to yellowish-brown, smooth; radicle over half as long as the cotyledons. 2n = 16. Fl. February–April.

Hab.: Batha and stony hillsides. Sharon Plain, Philistean Plain, Upper and Lower Galilee, Mt. Carmel, Samaria, Judean Mts., Judean Desert, Upper and Lower Jordan Valley, Gilead, Edom.

Area : N. and E. Mediterranean, with slight extensions towards Irano-Turanian territories.

11. Medicago laciniata (L.) Mill., Gard. Dict. ed. 8, no. 5 (1768); Heyn, Scr. Hieros. 12 : 55 (1963). [Plate 211]

Annual, hairy, 5–30 cm. Stems procumbent, rarely ascending, branching. Stipules ovate, dentate to laciniate, hairy beneath; leaflets 0.5–1 × 0.2–0.5 cm., obovate to oblong-cuneate, with a truncate to retuse and mucronulate apex, dentate-serrate to laciniate above or all over, hairy beneath. Peduncles shorter or longer than petiole, aristate. Racemes 1–2(–3)-flowered. Flowers 3–5(–6) mm. Calyx teeth shorter than tube, hairy. Corolla less than twice as long as calyx, pale to dark yellow; standard longer than keel; wings slightly shorter. Pod 3–8 mm. thick, 2.5–6 mm. across (excluding spines), short-cylindrical or globular to ovoid, usually glabrous, rarely hairy, spiny; coils 3–7, soft, with 6–16 prominent, S-shaped radial veins on surface, some of them branching, all confluent with a broad peripheral vein; spines (1–)3–6 mm., slightly spreading to horizontal, grooved, the longer spines hooked. Seeds 1–2 in each coil, 2–3 mm., yellow to yellowish-brown, smooth; radicle over half as long as cotyledons. 2n = 16. Fl. April–May.

Var. **laciniata**. *M. laciniata* (L.) All., Fl. Ped. 1 : 316 (1785); Boiss., Fl. 2 : 104 (1872). *M. polymorpha* L. var. *laciniata* L., Sp. Pl. 781 (1753). Stipules laciniate; leaflets more or less deeply serrate or laciniate. Pod globular or ovoid, with 5–7 coils (rarely less). Peduncles longer than petiole.

Hab.: Deserts; stony ground. Judean Desert, W., C. and S. Negev, Upper and Lower Jordan Valley, Dead Sea area, Arava Valley, Ammon, Moav.

Var. **brachyacantha** Boiss., Diagn. ser. 1, 9 : 10 (1849) et Fl. 2 : 104 (1872). *M. laci-*

niata All. var. *pilosa* Nab., Publ. Fac. Sci. Univ. Masaryk 35 : 68 (1923) p.p. *M. aschersoniana* Urb., Verh. Bot. Ver. Prov. Brandenb. 15 : 77 (1873). Stipules dentate, not laciniate; leaflets serrate, only exceptionally slightly laciniate. Pod cylindrical; coils 2–5. Peduncles shorter than petiole.

Hab. : Mainly deserts. Sharon Plain, Arava Valley, Edom.

Area of species : Saharo-Arabian.

12. Medicago minima (L.) Bart., Cat. Piant. Siena 61 (1776); Heyn, Scr. Hieros. 12 : 60 (1963); *M. minima* (L.) Desr. in Lam., Encycl. 3 : 636 (1792); Boiss., Fl. 2 : 103 (1872). *M. polymorpha* L. var. *minima* L., Sp. Pl. 780 (1753). *M. minima* (L.) Lam. var. *longiseta* DC. ex Ser. in DC., Prodr. 2 : 178 (1825). [Plate 212]

Annual, hairy and / or glandular-hairy, 5–30 cm. Stems ascending or procumbent, branching from base. Stipules ovate, acute, entire or minutely denticulate; leaflets 0.5–0.8 (–1.2) × 0.2–0.7 cm., usually obovate, rounded to emarginate, mucronulate, upper third serrate-dentate. Peduncles shorter to longer than petiole, aristate. Racemes (2–)3–6 (–8)-flowered. Flowers 2–6 mm. Calyx teeth about as long as tube, unequal. Corolla less than twice as long as calyx, yellow; standard distinctly longer than keel; wings slightly shorter. Pod 3–5 mm. thick, 2.5–4.5 (–6) mm. in diam., somewhat depressed, almost globular, hairy and / or glandular-hairy, spiny; coils 3–5, loose, thin; coil surface with 6–8 strongly curved radial veins terminating at a broad veinless strip around the margin; length of spines varying from shorter than to twice the diameter of the pod (mostly as long as the diameter of the pod), spreading horizontally, often hooked at apex. Seeds 1–2 in each coil, minute, 1.5–2 mm., yellowish-brown to light brown, smooth; radicle slightly more than half as long as the cotyledons. $2n = 16$. Fl. March–April.

Hab. : Batha, maquis and fallow fields. Sharon Plain, Upper Galilee, Judean Mts., Judean Desert, Upper and Lower Jordan Valley, Gilead.

Area : Euro-Siberian and Mediterranean, with extensions into adjacent Irano-Turanian and Saharo-Arabian territories.

13. Medicago polymorpha L., Sp. Pl. 779 (1753) emend. Shinners, Rhodora 58 : 5 (1956); Heyn, Scr. Hieros. 12 : 71 (1963). *M. hispida* Gaertn., Fruct. 2 : 349 (1791) emend. Urb., Verh. Bot. Ver. Prov. Brandenb. 15 : 74 (1873). [Plate 213]

Annual, glabrescent, 10–30 cm. Stems many, procumbent or ascending, branching from base. Stipules ovate-oblong, acuminate, laciniate; leaflets 0.8–2 × 0.7–1.5 cm., obovate to obovate-cuneate, obtuse, usually retuse, mucronulate, serrate or dentate at upper third. Peduncles shorter or longer than petiole. Racemes (1–)2–10-flowered. Flowers 3.5–6 mm. Calyx sparingly hairy; teeth about as long as tube, often some-what shorter. Corolla usually twice as long as calyx, bright yellow; standard longer than wings and keel. Pod 0.2–1.2 cm. thick and (0.25–)0.35–1 cm. in diam. at the broadest coil, discoid to cylindrical, glabrous, spiny or unarmed; coils 1½–6, loose, soft or indurated at maturity; coil surface with many radial veins; spines slender or thick. Seeds 1–2 in each coil, 2–4 mm., yellow to yellowish-brown, smooth; radicle about half as long as cotyledons. $2n = 14, 16$. Fl. March–April.

1. Pod not spiny; margin of coils smooth or tuberculate.   var. **brevispina**
 – Pod spiny   2
2. Broadest coil 0.5–1 cm. in diam.; number of coils 4–6, sometimes less than 4 – but then
    coil over 6 mm. broad.   var. **polymorpha**
 – Broadest coil 2.5–4.5 mm. in diam.; number of coils $1\frac{1}{2}$–$3\frac{1}{2}$.   var. **vulgaris**

Var. polymorpha. *M. denticulata* Willd. var. *lappacea* (DC.) Boiss., Fl. 2 : 103 (1872).
M. denticulata Willd. var. *pentacycla* (DC.) Boiss., l.c. Racemes (1–)2–5-flowered. Pod
with thick and hardened spines; coils $(3\frac{1}{2}$–)4–6, indurating at maturity; diameter of
broadest coil 0.5–0.8(–1) cm. 2n = 14.

Hab. : Batha, fields and roadsides. Acco Plain, Sharon Plain, Philistean Plain, Upper
and Lower Galilee, Mt. Carmel, Esdraelon Plain, Samaria, Shefela, Judean Mts.,
Judean Desert, Upper and Lower Jordan Valley, Arava Valley, Gilead, Ammon,
Moav.

Var. vulgaris (Benth.) Shinners, Rhodora 58 : 310 (1956) emend. Heyn, l.c. 75. *M.
denticulata* Willd. var. *vulgaris* Benth., Cat. Pyr. 103 (1826) p.p. Racemes 5–10-
flowered. Pod with slender spines; coils $1\frac{1}{2}$–$3\frac{1}{2}$, usually soft also at maturity; diameter
of broadest coil (2.5–)3–4(–4.5) mm. 2n = 14.

Hab. : As above. Acco Plain, Philistean Plain, Upper and Lower Galilee, Mt. Carmel, Esdraelon Plain, Mt. Gilboa, Judean Mts., N. Negev, Upper Jordan Valley,
Gilead.

Var. brevispina (Benth. emend. Heyn) Heyn, l.c. 77. *M. denticulata* Willd. var. *brevispina* Benth., Cat. Pyr. 103 (1826) p.p. Racemes (1–)2–10-flowered. Pod unarmed;
margin of coils nearly smooth or tuberculate; coils (2–)3–5, often indurating at maturity; diameter of broadest coil (2.5–)3–4(–5.5) mm. 2n = 14.

Hab. : Fallow fields. Upper Jordan Valley. Rare.
Area of species : Mediterranean, W. Irano-Turanian and Euro-Siberian; elsewhere
introduced.

14. Medicago tornata (L.) Mill., Gard. Dict. ed. 8, no. 3 (1768); Heyn, Scr. Hieros.
12 : 85 (1963). *M. polymorpha* L. var. *tornata* L., Sp. Pl. 780 (1753). *M. obscura* Retz.,
Obs. Bot. 1 : 24 (1779) emend. Urb., Verh. Bot. Ver. Prov. Brandenb. 15 : 66 (1873).
M. italica (Mill.) Steud. ex Fiori, Nuov. Fl. Anal. Ital. 1 : 832 (1925). [Plate 214]

Annual, densely hairy, 15–40 cm. Stems usually procumbent, branching from base.
Stipules broadly ovate, entire to laciniate; leaflets 0.8–1.6 × 0.5–0.8 cm., obovate to'
oblanceolate, obtuse, rarely retuse, serrate-dentate above. Peduncles usually much
longer than petiole, aristate at tip. Racemes (3–)8–15(–25)-flowered. Flowers about
4 mm. Calyx hairy; teeth longer than tube. Corolla about twice as long as calyx,
yellow; standard longer than wings and keel. Young pod contracted and concealed
within calyx; mature pod discoid to cylindrical, glabrous, spiny or unarmed; coils
1–$2\frac{1}{2}$(–3–8), flat; coil surface with about 10 radial veins; dorsal suture and peripheral
vein not separated by a furrow. Seeds 1–2 in each coil, 3–4 mm., yellow to yellowish-
brown, smooth; radicle less than half as long as cotyledons. 2n = 16. Fl. February–
April.

1. Pod unarmed.   var. **rugulosa**
– Pod spiny   2
2. Pod of 1–2½ coils.   var. **aculeata**
– Pod of 3–6(–8) coils.   var. **spinulosa**

Var. **aculeata** (Guss.) Heyn, l.c. 89. *M. obscura* Retz. var. *aculeata* Guss., Pl. Rar. 315 (1826). Pods of 1–2½ coils, at least some pods on each plant with less than 2 coils; margin spiny.

Hab.: Sandy soils. Acco Plain, Sharon Plain, Philistean Plain.

Var. **spinulosa** (Moris) Heyn, l.c. 87. *M. helix* Willd. var. *spinulosa* Moris, Fl. Sard. 1:438 (1837). Pod slightly angular; coils 3–6(–8), armed with slender spines.

Hab.: Judean Mts. (single specimen from environs of Jerusalem).

Var. **rugulosa** (Ser.) Heyn, l.c. 88. *M. obscura* Retz. var. *rugulosa* Ser. in DC., Prodr. 2:174 (1825). *M. helix* Willd., Sp. Pl. 3:1409 (1802). Pod of 1–2½ coils, at least some pods on each plant with less than 2 coils; margin unarmed, smooth or wrinkled.

Hab.: Sandy soils. Acco Plain, Sharon Plain, Mt. Carmel.

Area of species: Mediterranean; adventive in many other regions.

Data on *M. helix* Willd. var. *spinosa* Guss., Fl. Sic. Prodr. 2:557 (1828), recorded from Palestine by Dinsmore (in Post, Fl. Syr. Pal. Sin. ed. 2, 1:323, 1932), are to be referred to *M. tornata* var. *aculeata*.

15. Medicago litoralis Rhode ex Loisel., Not. Pl. Fr. 118 (1810; "*littoralis*"); Boiss., Fl. 2:98 (1872); Heyn, Scr. Hieros. 12:91 (1963). [Plate 215]

Annual, hairy, 7–15 cm. Stems procumbent, branching from base. Stipules lanceolate, dentate to laciniate; leaflets 3–8 × 2–7 mm., obovate to obcordate, rounded or truncate at apex, mucronulate, serrate above, pubescent on either side. Peduncles about as long as petiole, aristate at tip. Racemes 1–3-flowered. Flowers 3–6 mm. Calyx short-toothed, hairy. Corolla about twice as long as calyx; standard longer than keel and wings. Pod 0.3–1 cm. thick, cylindrical or discoid, flat at both ends, glabrous, spiny (with spines varying from very short to longer than radius of coil) or tuberculate, rarely smooth, hardening at maturity; coils 2–8, very compact, with thickened suture; coil surface with about 10 radial veins emerging from ventral suture and confluent with the peripheral vein; spines spreading to horizontal. Seeds 1–2 in each coil, 2–3.5 mm., yellow, smooth; radicle less than half as long as cotyledons. 2n = 16. Fl. February–May.

Var. **litoralis**. "*M. littoralis* Rohde in Loisel." var. *breviseta* DC. in Lam. et DC., Fl. Fr. ed. 3, 5:568 (1815). Pod discoid to cylindrical, usually consisting of 2½–6 coils, with spines varying from very short to longer than radius of pod.

Hab.: Mainly littoral sandy soils. Coastal Galilee, Acco Plain, Sharon Plain, Philistean Plain, Mt. Carmel, N. Negev, Gilead.

Var. **inermis** Moris, Fl. Sard. 1:439 (1837). "*M. littoralis* Rohde in Loisel." var. *subinermis* Boiss., Fl. 2:99 (1872). Pod discoid to cylindrical, consisting of 3–8 coils; margin of coils smooth or short-tubercled.

Hab.: As above. Acco Plain, Coast of Carmel, Sharon Plain, Philistean Plain.

Area of species: Mainly Mediterranean, with slight extensions into the Saharo-Arabian borderland; elsewhere adventive.

16. Medicago truncatula Gaertn., Fruct. 2 : 350 (1791) emend. Urb., Verh. Bot. Ver. Prov. Brandenb. 15 : 67 (1873); Heyn, Scr. Hieros. 12 : 95 (1963). [Plate 216]

Annual, hairy, 15–30 cm. Stems ascending or procumbent, branching from near the base. Stipules lanceolate, acuminate, deeply dentate to laciniate; leaflets 0.8–1.5 × 0.7–1.2 cm., obovate-cuneate, truncate, often retuse, dentate-serrate, sometimes laciniate. Peduncles about equal to petiole, aristate at tip. Racemes 1–3-flowered. Flowers 6–8 mm. Calyx hairy, with long slender teeth. Corolla less than twice as long as calyx; standard longer than keel and wings. Pod (0.5–)0.6–1.2 cm. thick, (0.6–)0.7–1.2 cm. in diam., cylindrical or discoid, often hairy, spiny; coils (2–)2½–8, more or less compact and indurated at maturity; coil surface with about 10 radial veins confluent with the peripheral vein; spines 6–10 at each coil margin, varying in length and shape. Seeds 1–2 in each coil, 3–3.5 mm., yellow, smooth; radicle less than half as long as cotyledons. $2n = 16$. Fl. March–May.

1. Pod of 5–8 coils   2
   − Pod of 2–4 coils.   var. **tricycla**
2. Pod longer (thicker) than broad; coils very compact; spines not curved, more or less appressed to pod.   var. **truncatula**
   − Pod as long as broad or even shorter; coils rather loose; spines curved and not appressed to pod.   var. **longiaculeata**

Var. **truncatula**. *M. tribuloides* Lam. var. *truncatula* Koch, Syn. Fl. Germ. Helv. 162 (1835). "*M. tribuloides* Desr." sensu Boiss., Fl. 2 : 99 (1872) p.p., incl. var. *breviaculeata* Boiss., l.c. Pod 0.7–1.2 cm. in diam., longer than broad, cylindrical; coils at least 5, compact; spines thickened at base, mostly rather short, straight or very slightly curved, appressed to pod, especially when mature.

Hab.: Fallow fields; terra rossa, basalt and alluvial soils. Sharon Plain, Upper Galilee, Mt. Gilboa, Samaria, Judean Mts., Upper and Lower Jordan Valley, Gilead.

Var. **longiaculeata** Urb., Verh. Bot. Ver. Prov. Brandenb. 15 : 67 (1873; "*longeaculeata*"). *M. tribuloides* Desr. in Lam., Encycl. 3 : 635 (1792); "*M. tribuloides* Desr." sensu Boiss., l.c. excl. var. *β* p.p. *M. truncatula* Gaertn. var. *tribuloides* (Desr.) Fiori in Fiori et Paol., Fl. Anal. Ital. 2 : 36 (1900). Pod 0.7–1 cm. in diam., shorter than broad, discoid to short-cylindrical; coils at least 5, rather loose; spines usually slender, curved, not appressed to pod.

Hab.: As above. Sharon Plain, Philistean Plain, Mt. Carmel, Samaria, Shefela, Judean Mts., N. Negev, Upper and Lower Jordan Valley, Gilead, Ammon.

Var. **tricycla** (Nègre) Heyn, l.c. 99. *M. truncatula* Gaertn. var. *genuina* (Koch) Briq. subvar. *vulgaris* Briq. f. *tricycla* Nègre, Compt. Rend. Soc. Sci. Nat. Maroc 7 : 90 (1951). Pod discoid to cylindrical, 5–6 mm. thick and 6–8 mm. broad; coils 2–3(–4), not compact, 6–8 mm. in diam.; spines usually slightly divergent.

Hab.: Wadis in deserts. W. and C. Negev.

Area of species: Mainly Mediterranean, with slight extensions into Euro-Siberian and Saharo-Arabian territories.

17. Medicago rigidula (L.) All., Fl. Ped. 1 : 316 (1785) quoad syn.; Heyn, Scr. Hieros. 12 : 103 (1963); *M. rigidula* (L.) Desr. in Lam., Encycl. 3 : 634 (1792). [Plate 217]

Annual, hairy or glandular-hairy, 10–25 cm. Stems procumbent, branching from base. Stipules ovate to oblong, acuminate, with 3–6 short teeth; leaflets 4–8 × 3–6 mm., obovate-cuneate to broadly obovate, obtuse to truncate, serrate-dentate above. Peduncles usually longer than petiole. Racemes 1–2 (–6)-flowered. Flowers (3–)6–8 mm. Calyx hairy; teeth about as long as tube. Corolla less than twice as long as calyx; standard about as long as keel; wings distinctly shorter. Pod 0.5–1.2 cm. thick and 0.5–1 (–1.5) cm. in diam., discoid, cylindrical, rarely ovoid, much indurating at maturity, hairy or glabrescent, with spiny, tuberculate or smooth margins; coils 4–7, compact or not; coil surface with 12–17 strongly bent radial veins, anastomosing near peripheral vein. Seeds 1–2 in each coil, 3–4 mm., yellow to yellowish-brown, smooth; radicle less than half as long as the cotyledons. 2n = 14, 16. Fl. March–May.

1. Pod ovoid-ellipsoidal, densely hairy, tuberculate, not spiny; coils compact, 6–9 mm. in diam. var. **submitis**
- Pod discoid to cylindrical, coils not compact 2
2. Pod densely hairy or villose; coils thin, not exceeding 8 mm. in diam. var. **rigidula**
- Pod glabrescent or glabrous; coils thick, more than 8 mm. in diam. var. **agrestis**

Var. **rigidula**. *M. polymorpha* L. var. *rigidula* L., Sp. Pl. 780 (1753). Pod discoid to cylindrical, spiny, densely hairy or glabrescent; coils up to 8 mm. in diam., thin, not compact in mature pod.

Hab.: Fields; heavy soils. Sharon Plain, Upper and Lower Galilee, Mt. Carmel, Judean Mts., Judean Desert, Upper and Lower Jordan Valley.

Var. **submitis** (Boiss.) Heyn, l.c. 106. "*M. gerardi*" (orth. err.) Waldst. et Kit. ex Willd. var. *submitis* Boiss., Fl. 2 : 101 (1872). Pod ovoid-ellipsoidal, not spiny or short-tuberculate at margin, densely covered with short hairs; coils thickened, compact, 6–9 mm. across; dorsal suture not protruding beyond peripheral vein.

Hab.: As above. Ammon, Edom.

Var. **agrestis** Burnat, Fl. Alp. Marit. 2 : 102 (1896). *M. rigidula* Desr. var. *gileadensis* Eig in herb. Pod short- or long-cylindrical, spiny, hairy, most often glabrescent or glabrous; coils thickened, exceeding 8 mm. in diam., not compact; dorsal suture slightly protruding beyond peripheral vein.

Hab.: As above. Judean Mts., Judean Desert, Lower Jordan Valley, Gilead, Ammon.

Area of species: Mainly Mediterranean, with extensions into adjacent Irano-Turanian territories.

18. Medicago constricta Durieu, Extr. Cat. Grains Bord. 10 : 17 (1873) et Acta Soc. Linn. Bord. 29 : XVI (1873); Heyn, Scr. Hieros. 12 : 108 (1963). *M. globosa* Urb., Verh. Bot. Ver. Prov. Brandenb. 15 : 71 (1873) non J. et C. Presl, Deliciae Prag. 45 (1822). [Plate 218]

Annual, pubescent, 10–30 cm. Stems usually procumbent, branching from base. Stipules oblong-lanceolate, dentate, upper part elongated; leaflets 0.3–0.8 (–1.4) ×

2–7 cm., obovate-oblong, cuneate, obtuse, truncate or retuse, mucronulate, dentate-serrate above. Peduncles longer than petiole, short-aristate at tip, hairy and glandular-hairy. Racemes 1–2-flowered. Flowers 4–5 mm. Calyx hairy; teeth irregular, about equal to tube. Corolla nearly twice as long as calyx, yellow; standard longer than keel; wings shorter. Pod 0.6–1.2 cm. thick, spherical to ovoid, glabrous, spiny, the young pods contracted and concealed within calyx; coils 6–8, hardened at maturity, very compact, coil surface with 6–10 strongly arcuate radial veins. Seeds 1–2 in each coil, about 4 mm., yellow to yellowish-brown, smooth; radicle slightly less than half as long as cotyledons. Fl. March–May.

Hab.: Sandy soils. Acco Plain, Sharon Plain, Philistean Plain, Upper Galilee, Judean Mts., Upper Jordan Valley.

Area: E. Mediterranean.

19. Medicago aculeata Gaertn., Fruct. 2:349 (1791); *M. aculeata* Willd., Sp. Pl. 3:1410 (1802); Heyn, Scr. Hieros. 12:111 (1963). *M. turbinata* (L.) Willd., Sp. Pl. 3:1409 (1802) quoad descr. non quoad typum emend. Moris, Fl. Sard. 1:444 (1837); Boiss., Fl. 2:100 (1872). [Plate 219]

Annual, pubescent, 20–50 cm. Stems ascending or procumbent, branching from base. Stipules ovate-lanceolate, dentate to laciniate; leaflets 1–2 × 0.5–1 cm., obovate to oblanceolate, apiculate, dentate-serrate above. Peduncles longer than petiole, often aristate at tip. Racemes 1–2-flowered. Flowers 4–6 mm. Calyx hairy; teeth about as long as tube. Corolla slightly longer than calyx, bright yellow; standard longer than keel; wings shorter. Pod 0.7–1.5(–2) cm. thick, (0.6–)0.8–1 cm. in diam., almost globular to ovoid, hairy and/or glandular-hairy, rarely glabrescent, spiny, strongly hardened to woody when ripe; young pod contracted and concealed within calyx; coils 5–7, compact; coil surface with about 10 slightly bent anastomosing radial veins, joining the peripheral vein which consists of arches between adjacent spines. Seeds 1–2 in each coil, 4–6 mm., yellow to yellowish-brown, smooth; radicle less than half as long as cotyledons. 2n = 16. Fl. February–May.

Hab.: Damp, heavy soils. Upper Galilee.

Area: Mediterranean.

20. Medicago turbinata (L.) All., Fl. Ped. 1:315 (1785); Heyn, Scr. Hieros. 12:116 (1963). *M. tuberculata* (L.) Willd., Sp. Pl. 3:1410 (1802). [Plate 220]

Annual, densely pubescent, 15–40 cm. Stems procumbent or ascending, branching from base. Stipules ovate-lanceolate, dentate; leaflets 1.2–1.6 × 0.6–0.8 cm., the lower leaflets obovate to ovate, the upper leaflets oblanceolate, obtuse to apiculate, dentate-serrate or doubly serrate. Peduncles aristate at tip, longer than petiole. Racemes (1–)3–8(–10)-flowered. Flowers 5–8 mm. Calyx hairy; teeth about as long as tube. Corolla less than twice as long as calyx, orange-yellow; standard longer than keel; wings shorter. Pod 0.6–1.2(–1.5) cm. thick and 0.5–0.8 cm. in diam., barrel-shaped to sub-globular or ovoid with truncate base, glabrous; pod surface usually tuberculate, rarely smooth or spiny; coils 4–9, thickened, indurated and very compact in mature pods; coil surface with slightly arcuate radial veins terminating at a broad veinless strip around the dorsal suture; spines, when present, up to 5 mm., spreading or erect, straight or bent. Seeds 1–2 in each coil, 4–5 mm., yellow to light brown, smooth; radicle half as long as cotyledons. 2n = 16. Fl. March–May.

1. Mature pod unarmed or with short conical protrusions or with spines strongly appressed to pod.   var. **turbinata**
- Mature pod not as above   2
2. Spines slender, emerging near margin of coils; coil margin nearly entire. Racemes usually 3–8-flowered.   var. **apiculata**
- Spines thick, especially at base, fairly remote from margin; coil margin sinuate. Racemes 1–3-flowered.   var. **aculeata**

Var. **turbinata**. *M. polymorpha* L. var. *turbinata* L., Sp. Pl. 780 (1753). *M. tuberculata* (L.) Willd., Sp. Pl. 3 : 1410 (1802). *M. tuberculata* Willd. var. *vulgaris* Moris in Moris et De Not., Florula Caprar. 36 (1839). *M. tuberculata* Willd. var. *warburgina* Evenari in Opphr. et Evenari, Bull. Soc. Bot. Genève ser. 2, 31 : 284 (1941). *M. tuberculata* Willd. var. *submutica* Boiss. ex Evenari, l.c. Racemes (3–)5–8-flowered. Mature pod usually smooth or tuberculate, not spiny; coil margin slightly sinuate.

Hab.: Fields and batha. Acco Plain, Sharon Plain, Philistean Plain, Upper and Lower Galilee, Mt. Carmel, Esdraelon Plain, Mt. Gilboa, Samaria, Shefela, Judean Mts., Upper and Lower Jordan Valley. Common.

Var. **apiculata** (Urb.) Heyn, l.c. 118. *M. tuberculata* Willd. var. *apiculata* Urb., Verh. Bot. Ver. Prov. Brandenb. 15 : 72 (1873) sensu Urb. non Bast., Fl. Maine-et-Loire 280 (1809). "*M. tuberculata* Willd." sensu Boiss., Fl. 2 : 99 (1872). *M. tuberculata* Willd. var. *spinulosa* (DC.) Tod. ex Dinsmore in Post, Fl. Syr. Pal. Sin. ed. 2, 1 : 324 (1932). Racemes (3–)5–8-flowered. Mature pod spiny; spines slender, with base sunk in tubercle; coil margin nearly entire.

Hab.: As above. Philistean Plain, Upper Galilee, Mt. Carmel, Mt. Gilboa, Shefela, Judean Mts., N. and C. Negev, Hula Plain, Upper Jordan Valley, Gilead, Moav.

Var. **aculeata** (Moris emend. Heyn) Heyn, l.c. 119. *M. tuberculata* Willd. var. *aculeata* Moris, l.c. emend. Heyn, l.c. 119. Racemes 1–2(–3)-flowered. Mature pod spiny; spines emerging from surface of coil far beyond the dorsal suture, more or less thickened, often with thin base sunk in a thick tubercle.

Hab.: As above. Acco Plain, Upper and Lower Galilee, Mt. Carmel, Judean Mts., Upper Jordan Valley.

Area of species: N. and E. Mediterranean; elsewhere adventive.

21. Medicago murex Willd., Sp. Pl. 3 : 1410 (1802); Heyn, Scr. Hieros. 12 : 122 (1963). [Plate 221]

Annual, usually glabrous, 10–30 cm. Stems usually procumbent, branching from base. Stipules ovate-lanceolate, dentate to laciniate; leaflets 0.7–1.5 × 0.5–1.2 cm., obovate to cuneate, serrate-dentate above; apex truncate to retuse, apiculate. Peduncles shorter than petiole, short-aristate at tip. Racemes 1–2(–5)-flowered. Flowers 3–5 mm. Calyx hairy; teeth as long as tube. Corolla less than twice as long as calyx, bright yellow; standard longer than wings, the latter longer than keel. Pod 0.6–1.4 cm. thick and 0.4–1 cm. across, globular to ovoid, glabrous, spiny or rarely spineless, the young pods with contracted coils, concealed within calyx; coils 5–9, hardened at maturity, very compact; coil surface with 4–8 slightly arcuate, unbranched radial veins, terminating at a broad veinless strip near margin; spines (where present) 0.5–3 mm. Seeds 1–2 in each coil, 3–5 mm., smooth, yellow to yellowish-brown; radicle half as long as cotyledons. 2n = 16. Fl. March–May.

Var. **murex.** Pods all spiny; spines 0.5–3 mm. long, slightly varying in length in the same individual and even in the same pod.

Hab.: Sandy soils. Sharon Plain, Philistean Plain, Upper Galilee (latter after Rech. f., Ark. Bot. ser. 2, 2, 5 : 359, 1952).

Var. **inermis** (Guss.) Urb., Verh. Bot. Ver. Prov. Brandenb. 15 : 73 (1873). *M. sphaerocarpa* Bertol. var. *inermis* Guss., Fl. Sic. Syn. 2 : 374 (1844?). Pods all, or at least some in each individual, spineless.

Hab.: As above. Sharon Plain, Judean Mts.

Area of species: Mediterranean; probably adventive in some countries of C. Europe.

22. Medicago intertexta (L.) Mill., Gard. Dict. ed. 8, no. 4 (1768; orth. err. "*intortexta*") emend. Heyn, Scr. Hieros. 12 : 125 (1963). *M. polymorpha* L. var. *intertexta* L., Sp. Pl. 780 (1753). [Plate 222]

Annual, sparingly hairy or glabrous, 30–50 cm. Stems procumbent or ascending. Stipules ovate, dentate to laciniate, with distal tooth 2-fid and longer than others; leaflets 0.6–2 × 0.5–1.5 cm., obovate to oblong and oblanceolate, shortly apiculate, rarely retuse, dentate-serrate above. Peduncles about equal to petiole, aristate at tip. Racemes 1–4(–10)-flowered. Flowers 5–9 mm. Calyx hairy; teeth as long as or shorter than tube. Corolla about twice as long as calyx, yellow; standard longer than keel; wings shorter. Pod 1–2 × 0.9–1.5(–1.7) cm., globular to ovoid, densely covered with many-celled hairs or glabrescent to glabrous, spiny; coils 3–10, loose; coil surface covered with a distinct net of about 7 anastomosing veins; spines 1–5(–8) mm., erect to spreading, glabrous or covered with many-celled hairs. Seeds 1–2 in each coil, about 5 mm., dark reddish-brown to brownish-black; radicle less than half as long as cotyledons. 2n = 16, 18. Fl. March–May.

Var. **ciliaris** (L.) Heyn, l.c. 129. *M. polymorpha* L. var. *ciliaris* L., Sp. Pl. 780 (1753). *M. ciliaris* (L.) Willd., Sp. Pl. 3 : 1411 (1802); Boiss., Fl. 2 : 104 (1872). Leaflets usually 1.5–2 × 0.8–1.5 cm. Pod covered with many-celled hairs, globular, rarely slightly ovoid, coils 6–10; spines 2–4 mm.

Hab.: Damp, heavy soils and swamps. Acco Plain, Sharon Plain, Philistean Plain, Upper and Lower Galilee, Mt. Carmel, Esdraelon Plain, Samaria, Judean Mts., Hula Plain, Upper Jordan Valley.

Area of species: Mainly Mediterranean; adventive in the C. and W. provinces of the Euro-Siberian region.

23. Medicago granadensis Willd., Enum. Pl. Hort. Berol. 803 (1809); Heyn, Scr. Hieros. 12 : 132 (1963). *M. galilaea* Boiss., Diagn. ser. 1, 9 : 10 (1849) et Fl. 2 : 102 (1872). *M. galilaea* Boiss. var. *incisa* Post, Fl. Syr. Pal. Sin. 229 (1883–1896). *M. intertexta* Mill. var. *glandulosa* Eig, Bull. Inst. Agr. Nat. Hist. 6 : 23 (1927). [Plate 223]

Annual, hairy, rarely glabrous, 15–40 cm. Stems procumbent or ascending, branching. Stipules ovate to oblong, dentate-laciniate, with distal tooth much longer than others, glabrous or sparingly hairy; leaflets 1–2 × 0.5–0.8 cm., obovate to elliptical, mucronulate, dentate-serrate, glabrous or sparingly hairy. Peduncles longer than petiole. Racemes (1–)2–4(–6)-flowered. Flowers 4–5 mm. Calyx hairy; teeth as long as tube. Corolla more than twice as long as calyx, yellow to orange-yellow; standard as long as keel or longer. Pod 0.5–0.8 cm. thick and 0.7–1(–1.2) cm. in diam., barrel-shaped, glabrous or rarely hairy, spiny; coils 5–7, rather loose; coil surface with a distinct net of about 12 anastomosing radial veins; spines 1–2 mm., grooved, strongly apiculate, more or less appressed to pod. Seeds 1–2 in each coil, about 5 mm., dark reddish-brown to brownish-black, smooth; radicle less than half as long as the cotyledons. $2n = 16, 17, 18$. Fl. April–May.

Hab.: Cultivated and fallow fields. Acco Plain, Sharon Plain, Philistean Plain, Lower Galilee, Mt. Carmel, Esdraelon Plain, Shefela, Judean Mts., Hula Plain, Upper Jordan Valley, Gilead.

Area: E. Mediterranean; elsewhere adventive.

36. MELILOTUS Mill.

Annuals, biennials or short-lived perennials with erect, often branched stems. Leaves usually alternate, 3-foliolate; stipules adnate to petiole, subulate, entire or dentate; leaflets orbicular, obovate, rhombic or oblong, with dentate, rarely entire margin; middle leaflet long-petiolulate, lateral leaflets almost sessile. Racemes axillary, few- or many-flowered, loose or dense, ebracteate. Flowers small, pedicellate. Calyx glabrous or hairy, with 5 almost equal teeth. Petals not or rarely persistent, free, white or yellow; standard obtuse or slightly retuse at apex, equal to or sometimes longer than wings; keel broad, obtuse at apex. Stamens diadelphous, the connate filaments united to one third of their length. Ovary 2–8-ovuled, glabrous or hairy, with a long, persistent style; stigma capitate. Pod indehiscent, 1- or rarely 2–3-seeded, much exserted from calyx, globular, ovoid or elongated, with reticulate, transverse or concentric wrinkles, folds or pits. Seeds ovoid, smooth or tuberculate.

About 32 species in the Mediterranean and the Euro-Siberian regions.

Some species of this genus are known as fodder, pasture and medicinal plants.

Literature: O. E. Schulz, Monographie der Gattung *Melilotus, Bot. Jahrb.* 29: 660–735, pls. VI–VIII (1901). V. V. Suvorov, Sweetclover—*Melilotus* (Tourn.) Adans. em., in: *Flora of Cultivated Plants of the USSR,* 426–627, Jerusalem, 1950 (English translation). A. E. Clarke, The number and morphology of chromosomes in the genus *Melilotus, Univ. Calif. Publ. Bot.* 17: 435–444 (1934).

1. Flowers white. Stems up to 2 m. Pod brownish-black at maturity, with transverse or reticulate wrinkles. Ovary 3–4-ovuled. Stipules linear-subulate, entire.   **1. M. albus**
– Flowers yellow or pale yellow. Plants not as above   2
2. Pod with concentric wrinkles or folds   3
– Pod with parallel or reticulate but not concentric wrinkles or folds   4
3. Pod 5–8 mm., obliquely ovoid, tapering at both ends and distinctly acute-mucronate at apex.   **2. M. siculus**

– Pod 2–3(–4.5) mm., rounded at apex.   **3. M. sulcatus**
4(2). Flowers 2.5–2.8 mm. Pod 1.8–3(–4) mm., almost globular, with reticulate ridges
   or wrinkles.   **6. M. indicus**
– Flowers and pod larger. Pod otherwise wrinkled or folded   5
5. Ridges of pod very prominent, irregularly winding or curved. Flowers about 6 mm.
                                                               5. M. italicus
– Ridges or wrinkles of pod all transverse and almost parallel. Flowers smaller than above.
                                                               4. M. elegans

Sect. MELILOTUS. Pod compressed, ovoid or ellipsoidal, reticulately wrinkled.

1. Melilotus albus Medik. ex Desr. in Lam., Encycl. 4:63 (1797); Boiss., Fl. 2:109
(1872; "*alba*"); *M. alba* Medik., Vorl. Churpf. Phys.-Oken. Ges. 2:382 (1787) *nom.
nud. M. kotschyi* O. E. Schulz, Bot. Jahrb. 29:699 (1901). [Plate 224]

Biennial or annual, 0.75–2 m. Stems erect, more or less branching. Stipules linear-
subulate, entire; leaflets of lower and middle leaves obovate or rhombic, rarely ovate,
leaflets of upper leaves linear or narrowly elliptical, sparsely dentate. Racemes 3–5 cm.,
more or less compact in flower, later largely elongating. Flowers 3.5–4.5 mm. Calyx
2–2.6 mm.; teeth half as long as tube, lanceolate, acute. Corolla white; standard
usually somewhat longer than wings, the latter longer than or as long as keel. Pod
3–3.5 mm., 1–2-seeded, somewhat compressed, rather ellipsoidal, with a short, sharp,
curved beak at apex, brownish-black when ripe, reticulately wrinkled. Seeds 2–2.2
mm., yellow or brownish, warty. Fl. April–October.

Hab.: Moist places, swamps and by streams. Sharon Plain, Philistean Plain, Upper
Galilee, Mt. Carmel, Judean Mts., Coastal Negev, Hula Plain, Upper and Lower
Jordan Valley, Dead Sea area, Moav.

Area: Euro-Siberian, Mediterranean and Irano-Turanian.

Used as food for livestock; a good honey plant.

Sect. GYRORYTIS Koch, Syn. Fl. Germ. Helv. ed. 2, 184 (1843). Pod somewhat
compressed; ventral suture with thick and smooth margin and hardly visible keel
wrinkles semicircular, concentric.

2. Melilotus siculus (Turra) B. D. Jacks., Ind. Kew. Suppl. 2:199 (1895). *Trifolium
M. sicula* Turra, Farset. Nov. Gen. 12 (1765); Vitm., Summa Pl. 4:326 (1790)
M. messanensis (L.) All., Fl. Ped. 1:309 (1785); Boiss., Fl. 2:107 (1872). *Trifolium
(Melilotus) messanense* L., Mant. Alt. 275 (1771). [Plate 225]

Annual, 10–40 cm. Stems thin, ascending or procumbent, much branched. Stipule
7–8 mm., those of lower leaves triangular-lanceolate, often dentate, those of upper
leaves smaller, broadened at base, entire; leaflets obovate to lanceolate, cuneate a
base, truncate to retuse, mucronulate, dentate above. Racemes 1–2.5 cm., shorter than
subtending leaves, 5–10-flowered, somewhat elongating in fruit. Flowers 5 mm. Caly
short, sharp-toothed. Corolla yellow; standard as long as wings, somewhat longe
than keel. Pod 5–8 × 3.5–4.5 mm., somewhat flattened, obliquely ovoid, tapering a
both ends, with distinctly concentric wrinkles or folds; beak about 2 mm., sharp

Seeds solitary, 3–3.5 mm., flattened, broadly ovoid, brown, tuberculate. Fl. March–May.

Hab.: Damp and saline fields. Acco Plain, Sharon Plain, Philistean Plain, Lower Galilee, Esdraelon Plain, Mt. Gilboa, Samaria, Shefela, Judean Mts., Coastal Negev, Dan Valley, Hula Plain, Upper Jordan Valley.

Area: Mediterranean, with slight extensions into adjacent Irano-Turanian territories.

3. Melilotus sulcatus Desf., Fl. Atl. 2 : 193 (1799; "*sulcata*"). [Plates 226, 227]

Annual, hairy, 10–60 cm. Stems thin, erect or ascending, rarely prostrate, branching from base. Stipules 6–9 mm., broadened at base and incised-dentate, subulate at apex, those of the uppermost leaves subulate, entire; leaflets obovate-cuneate or oblong-cuneate to linear, dentate all over or above. Racemes 1–4 cm., up to 10–50-flowered, dense, elongating in fruit. Flowers 3–5 (–6) mm. Calyx small, with more or less equal teeth somewhat shorter than tube, sparingly hairy to glabrous. Corolla yellow; keel slightly longer than the obtuse standard, the latter longer than the wings. Pod 2–3 (–4.5) mm., somewhat flattened, almost globular to obovoid, with numerous, thin, elevated and concentric wrinkles. Seed 1, flattened, ovoid, distinctly tuberculate. Fl. March–May.

Var. **sulcatus**. *M. sulcata* Desf., l.c.; Boiss., Fl. 2 : 106 (1872). *M. sulcata* Desf. var. *genuina* Godr. in Gren. et Godr., Fl. Fr. 1 : 400 (1849). *M. sulcata* Desf. var. *angustifolia* Willk. et Lange, Prodr. Fl. Hisp. 3 : 377 (1877). *M. sulcata* Desf. var. *libanotica* Ser. in DC., Prodr. 2 : 189 (1825). *M. longifolia* Ten., Prodr. Fl. Nap. Suppl. 1 : 43 (1811–1815). [Plate 226]. Pod 2.5–3 mm., often broader than and about twice as long as calyx, subglobular; young pods not stipitate, with broad base. Leaves mostly oblong-cuneate to linear.

Hab.: Fields and field borders. Coastal Galilee, Acco Plain, Sharon Plain, Philistean Plain, Upper and Lower Galilee, Mt. Carmel, Esdraelon Plain, Samaria, Shefela, Judean Mts., Upper and Lower Jordan Valley, Dead Sea area, Gilead, Edom.

Var. **segetalis** (Brot.) Rouy in Rouy et Fouc., Fl. Fr. 5 : 61 (1899). *M. segetalis* (Brot.) Ser. in DC., Prodr. 2 : 187 (1825). *Trifolium Melil. segetalis* Brot., Fl. Lusit. 2 : 484 (1804). *M. segetalis* (Brot.) Ser. var. *salzmannii* O. E. Schulz, Bot. Jahrb. 29 : 724 (1901). [Plate 227]. Pod 3–4 mm., 3–4 times as long as calyx, obovoid; young pods with abruptly narrowing and stipitate base. Leaves, at least the lower ones, obovate-cuneate.

Hab.: Swamps and damp fields. Coastal Galilee, Acco Plain, Sharon Plain, Philistean Plain, Upper and Lower Galilee, Mt. Carmel, Esdraelon Plain, Shefela, Judean Mts., Dan Valley, Hula Plain, Upper Jordan Valley, Beit Shean Valley, Gilead.

Area of species: Mediterranean.

This species is very variable as to stature, branching, and shape and size of leaf and fruit. The two above varieties are distinguishable mainly by their pods, the size and shape of the leaflets varying greatly. All the local forms display small flowers, 3–4 (–5) mm.

The true *Melilotus infestus* Guss., Fl. Sic. Prodr. 2 : 486 (1828) does not occur in Palestine.

Sect. PLAGIORYTIS Ser. in DC., Prodr. 2 : 188 (1825; *"Plagiorutis"*) p.p. Pod some-what compressed, transversely and sigmoidally wrinkled; ventral suture with a thin and smooth margin and a prominent thick keel.

4. Melilotus elegans Salzm. ex Ser. in DC., Prodr. 2 : 188 (1825); Boiss., Fl. 2 : 107 (1872). [Plate 228]

Annual, 0.5–1 (–1.5) m. Stems erect, branched. Stipules of lower leaves broadened at base, short-mucronate, dentate, those of upper leaves narrower, with a longer mucro; leaflets 1–2 × 0.6–1 cm., obovate to rhombic and oblong-cuneate, upper third sharply dentate. Flowering racemes 1.5–3.5 cm., much longer than leaves, elongating in fruit, loose or compact. Flowers 4.5–5 (–6) mm. Calyx short-toothed. Corolla yellow; keel as long as standard; wings somewhat shorter. Pod 3.5–5 mm., obovoid-ellipsoidal, mucronate, with few, distinct, transverse and nearly parallel ridges or wrinkles. Seeds solitary, rarely 2–3, about 2 mm., greenish or brown, warty. Fl. April–May.

Hab.: Moist places. Mt. Carmel, Judean Mts., Upper Jordan Valley.

Area: Mediterranean; also occurring in E. Sudanian territories.

Sect. LACCOCARPUS O. E. Schulz, Bot. Jahrb. 29 : 709 (1901). Pod globular, irregularly reticulate-wrinkled; ventral suture more or less undulate, furrowed, more or less distinctly keeled.

5. Melilotus italicus (L.) Lam., Fl. Fr. 2 : 594 (1778; *"italica"*); Boiss., Fl. 2 : 107 (1872). *Trifolium (Melilotus) italica* L., Sp. Pl. 765 (1753). [Plate 229]

Annual, sparingly hairy above, 20–100 cm. Stems erect, branching, thick, stout. Stipules acutely lanceolate, the lower stipules broadened at base and sharply dentate; leaflets 2–4.5 × 1–2 cm., entire or dentate, those of lower leaves broadly obovate, cuneate, laciniate-dentate, those of upper leaves oblong-cuneate. Racemes about 5 cm., much longer than leaves, rather loose, much elongating in fruit. Flowers 6 mm. or more. Calyx teeth shorter than tube, unequal. Corolla about 3 times as long as calyx, yellow; standard nearly as long as wings; keel shorter. Pod 3.5–5 mm., deflexed, globular-obovoid to oblong, obtuse, beaked, with prominent ridges irregularly winding or curved. Seeds 1 or 2, 3–3.5 mm., ovoid, greenish or brown, distinctly warted. Fl. March–May.

Hab.: Batha and maquis. Upper Galilee, Mt. Carmel, Samaria, Judean Mts.

Area: Mediterranean.

6. Melilotus indicus (L.) All., Fl. Ped. 1 : 308 (1785; *"indica"*). [Plate 230]

Annual, hairy above, 15–50 cm. Stems branching, thin, flexuous. Stipules lanceolate, broadened at base, acute, 1–2-dentate, slightly hairy; leaflets 0.8–2 × 0.4–1 cm., obovate to oblong-cuneate, upper half sharply dentate or rarely entire. Racemes 1–2 cm., compact, elongating in fruit up to 5 cm. or more. Flowers 2.5–2.8 mm., short-pedicelled. Calyx minute, slightly dentate. Corolla pale yellow; wings somewhat shorter than standard and keel. Pod 1.8–2.5 (–4) mm., almost globular, obtuse, mucronulate, yellow, with reticulate ridges or wrinkles. Seeds 1.5–2 mm., light cinnamon-coloured or greenish-grey, minutely tuberculate. Fl. March–April.

Var. **indicus**. *Trifolium (Melilotus) indica* L., Sp. Pl. 765 (1753) excl. var. *β. M. parviflora* Desf., Fl. Atl. 2 : 192 (1799); Boiss., Fl. 2 : 108 (1872). Stems mostly erect. Pod 1.8–3 mm.

Hab.: Fields, roadsides and devastated batha; on light, heavy and damp soils, also in salines. Coastal Galilee, Acco Plain, Coast of Carmel, Sharon Plain, Philistean Plain, Mt. Carmel, Esdraelon Plain, Samaria, Shefela, Judean Mts., W. Negev, Hula Plain, Upper Jordan Valley, Beit Shean Valley, Lower Jordan Valley, Dead Sea area, Edom. Very common.

Var. **tommasinii** (Jord.) O. E. Schulz, Bot. Jahrb. 29 : 714 (1901). *M. tommasinii* Jord., Pugill. Pl. Nov. 55 (1852). Stems often procumbent. Pod 3–4 mm.

Hab.: Sandy soils. Coastal Galilee, Sharon Plain, Philistean Plain, Esdraelon Plain, Coastal Negev. Rather rare.

Area of species: Probably Mediterranean by origin; introduced into many temperate and tropical regions.

Forms with laciniate leaflets often occur in this as in other species of the Trifolieae tribe. Var. *pinnatifida* Eig, Bull. Inst. Agr. Nat. Hist. 6 : 24 (1927) refers to such a form. The wide ecological range of this species is probably correlated with a wide ecotypic diversity.

Grown in some countries as a fodder plant.

37. TRIFOLIUM L.

Annual or perennial herbs with erect, ascending or procumbent stems, sometimes with creeping rootstocks. Leaves with 3, rarely with 5 (or 7) dentate or entire leaflets; stipules partly connate and adnate to petiole, entire or rarely dentate. Racemes axillary or terminal, often head-like or spike-like or umbellate, pedunculate or sessile, many-, rarely few-flowered, sometimes involucrate by free or connate bracts. Flowers pedicellate or sessile, bracteate or not, all or rarely only the outer (lower) flowers fertile. Calyx mostly tubular or campanulate, 5-, 10- or 20 (rarely 30–36)-nerved, with 5 equal or unequal teeth; sometimes calyx 2-lipped, with upper teeth often shorter or longer and partly connate at base; throat of calyx open or closed by a callosity or by a ring of hairs; tube of calyx sometimes inflated in fruit. Corolla persistent, marcescent or caducous, white, yellow, purple, pink, flesh-coloured, lilac, violet or 2-coloured; standard free or connate at base with wings and keel; the latter two sometimes connate with one another and mostly adnate to the stamens; wings often longer than keel. Stamens diadelphous; all the filaments, or 5 of them, dilated at apex; anthers uniform. Ovary sessile or stipitate, with 2–8 ovules. Pod indehiscent, mostly 1–2 (rarely 4–8)-seeded, enclosed in the persistent calyx and sometimes also in the persistent corolla, rarely exserted, usually membranous, rarely leathery, ovoid to oblong or linear. Seeds globular to ovoid and oblong, sometimes reniform or lenticular. Dispersal units: seed, fruiting calyx or entire head.

About 250 species mostly in temperate Eurasia, Africa and America; the Mediterranean region is the main centre of distribution of the genus.

A large number of the 46 clover species recorded here are highly important as fodder and pasture plants. Some of them, e.g. *T. repens, T. fragiferum, T. alexandrinum, T. resupinatum, T. subterraneum,* have been in cultivation since ancient times, others are basic components of natural pastures and potential fodder plants of the future.

Literature : G. Gibelli & S. Belli, Intorno alla morfologia differenziale esterna ed alla nomenclatura delle specie di *Trifolium* della sezione *Amoria* Presl, crescenti spontanee in Italia, *Atti Accad. Sci. Torino Cl. Fis. Mat.* 22 : 412–456 (1886–1887). G. Gibelli & S. Belli, Rivista critica e descrittiva delle specie di *Trifolium* italiane e affini comprese nella sezione *Lagopus* Koch, *Mem. Accad. Sci. Torino* Ser. 2, 39 : 245–427 (1889). G. Gibelli & S. Belli, Rivista critica delle specie di *Trifolium* italiane comparate con quelle del resto d'Europa e delle regioni circummediterranee, etc., *Mem. Accad. Sci. Torino* Ser. 2, 41 : 149–222, 3 pls.; 42 : 179–222, 3 pls.; 43 : 177–222, 3 pls. (1890–1893). M. Lojacono, Clavis specierum Trifoliorum, *Nuovo Giorn. Bot. Ital.* 15 : 225–278 (1883). H. R. Oppenheimer, Essai d'une révision des trèfles de la Palestine, *Bull. Soc. Bot. Fr.* 108 : 47–71 (1961). M. Hossain, A revision of *Trifolium* in the Nearer East, *Notes Roy. Bot. Gard. Edinb.* 23 : 387–481 (1961). J. Katznelson & F. W. H. Morley, A taxonomic revision of sect. *Calycomorphum* of the genus *Trifolium* I, *Israel Journ. Bot.* 14 : 111–134 (1965). J. Katznelson, A taxonomic revision of sect. *Calycomorphum* of the genus *Trifolium* II, *Israel Journ. Bot.* 14 : 171–183 (1965).

1. Inner (upper) flowers of head without corolla, sterile   2
- All flowers corollate, fertile   6
2. Fruit maturing within the soil, sterile flowers serving as a drilling mechanism by means of which the fertilized flowers penetrate the soil; fruiting heads not cottony nor silky   3
- Fruit not subterranean; fruiting heads globular, densely cottony or silky   4
3. Leaflets mostly obovate, with rounded or truncate apex. Corolla red or violet, 1.4–1.8 cm., 3–4 times as long as calyx teeth.   **46. T. israëliticum**
- Leaflets mostly deeply notched. Corolla white, sometimes striped with pink, 0.8–1.4 cm., about twice as long as calyx teeth.   **45. T. subterraneum**
4(2). Fertile flowers 1–2(–3). Hairy cover of fruiting head translucent at margin.
                                                                            43. T. pilulare
- Fertile flowers 3–7. Hairy cover of fruiting head not translucent at margin   5
5. Fruiting heads 0.8–1 cm., hairs white-cottony.   **44. T. eriosphaerum**
- Fruiting heads 1.2–1.5 cm., hairs not cottony but silky, greyish-white or pinkish.
                                                                           42. T. pauciflorum
6(1). Calyx tube 5-nerved. Flowers short-pedicelled, at length deflexed. Petals persistent, becoming scarious and serving as a wing-like accessory to fruiting calyx. Throat of calyx open; the 2 upper calyx teeth much shorter than the 3 lower teeth. Pod stipitate   7
- Calyx tube 10- or more-nerved (rarely 5-nerved, pedicels then as long as calyx). Petals not as above   12
7. Flowers yellow or cream-coloured   8
- Flowers pink or purple or flesh-coloured   10
8. Heads 2–6-flowered. Flowers 2–3(–4) mm. Leaves small, sessile.   **8. T. micranthum**
- Heads 10- or more-flowered. Flowers longer. Leaves mostly petiolate   9
9. Lower calyx teeth ciliate or terminating in bristles. Corolla about 8–9 mm.; standard

folded below, spoon-shaped above when in fruit. Style almost as long as pod.
6. T. boissieri

– Lower calyx teeth glabrous. Corolla 5–6(–7) mm.; standard flattish or spoon-shaped all along when in fruit. Style much shorter than pod. Fruiting heads cone-like, with imbricated corollas.
5. T. campestre

10(7). Flowers 0.9–1.2 cm. Heads 1–2 cm. broad.
4. T. philistaeum

— Flowers 4–7 mm. Heads 0.6–1 cm. broad
11

11. Heads ovoid, semiglobular or globular, 0.6–1 cm. across. Standard folded in fruit.
7. T. erubescens

— Heads spike-like, oblong-cylindrical, 1.5–3 cm. long. Standard flat in fruit.
3. T. billardieri

12(6). Fruiting calyx 2-lipped, unilaterally gibbous-inflated, vesicular and net-veined, glabrous or hairy or covered with dense wool; upper calyx teeth 2–5 times as long as lower teeth; tube 10-nerved
13

— Fruiting calyx not at all inflated, or symmetrically inflated and then calyx teeth equal in length and tube 20–30-nerved
18

13. Perennials with creeping or erect stems. Calyx 3.5–7 mm. long. Corolla not resupinate, i.e. with standard above and keel below
14

— Annuals. Calyx 2–2.5(–3) mm. long. Corolla resupinate, i.e. with standard below and keel above
15

14. Stems rhizomatous, creeping. Heads 1–1.3 cm. broad, involucrate at base by connate bracts.
12. T. fragiferum

— Stems not rhizomatous. Heads 1.5–2 cm. broad, not involucrate at base by connate bracts.
13. T. physodes

15(13). Fruiting calyces forming a stellately lobed head, each fruiting calyx pear-shaped, with 2 divergent, bristle-like upper calyx teeth. Flowers 0.6–1 cm., fragrant. Peduncles often longer than subtending leaves; leaflets of uppermost leaves obovate-rhombic, cuneate.
14. T. resupinatum

— Fruiting calyces forming a more or less even, continuous or very slightly interrupted, globular head. Plants not as above
16

16. Fruiting heads with remains of marcescent corollas; all heads with long, arcuate peduncles bent above middle.
15. T. clusii

— Fruiting heads without marcescent corollas. Peduncles 0 or erect or symmetrically arcuate
17

17. Fruiting heads densely cottony or fleecy, and then individual calyces not clearly discernible, sometimes heads less cottony and then fruiting calyx teeth conspicuous. Peduncles 0 or erect or rarely some of them arcuate.
16. T. tomentosum

— Fruiting heads 3–8 mm., glabrous or somewhat hairy but never cottony or fleecy; individual fruiting calyces clearly discernible. Calyx teeth minute (1–2 mm.), sometimes reduced to callose protuberances. All peduncles delicate, symmetrically arcuate.
17. T. bullatum

18(12). Stipules dentate throughout, not ending with a subulate or cuspidate apex
19

— Stipules entire, mostly with a subulate, acuminate or cuspidate apex
20

19. Leaflets oblong or linear, dentate; stipules or leaflets or both sometimes with stalked glands. Calyx small, glabrous or almost so.
18. T. glanduliferum

— Leaflets obovate or obcordate, entire; stipules and leaflets not glandular. Calyx large (over 1 cm.), densely villose.
19. T. stellatum

20(18). Flowers each subtended by a clearly discernible bract. Throat of fruiting calyx neither hairy within nor closed by a callosity
21

—   Flowers without bracts. Throat of fruiting calyx closed by a callosity or provided
      with a hairy or callose ring, rarely throat glabrous and open   25
21. Fruiting calyx tube inflated, 20- or more-nerved. Corolla scarious, persistent; standard
      longitudinally striate   22
—   Fruiting calyx tube not inflated, 10-nerved, sometimes nerves concealed by hairs.
      Corolla and standard not as above   23
22. Fruiting calyx tube much inflated, longitudinally and transversely striate-nerved.
      Heads 2–3.5 cm.   **10. T. spumosum**
—   Fruiting calyx tube slightly inflated and only longitudinally striate-nerved. Heads
      about 1–1.5 cm.   **11. T. argutum**
23 (21). Dwarf, stemless annuals. Heads minute, 2–3 mm., sessile, few-flowered, all crowded
      at base of plants, in the axils of very long-petioled leaves.   **9. T. suffocatum**
—   Plants not as above. Heads moderate or large, 0.6–3 cm., long-peduncled. Flowers
      conspicuously pedicellate   24
24. Perennials. Flowers 0.9–1.5 cm. Pedicels 4–7 mm. Pod 3–4-seeded.   **1. T. repens**
—   Annuals. Flowers 6–8 mm. Pedicels usually shorter than above. Pod (in ours) usually
      1-seeded.   **2. T. nigrescens**
25 (20). Calyx tube 20-nerved; throat of fruiting calyx open, glabrous or hairy within   26
—   Calyx tube 10-nerved (nerves sometimes concealed by the hairy cover); throat of
      fruiting calyx closed by a callosity or bearing a thickened callose or hairy ring, rarely
      throat open and glabrous within   27
26. Heads sessile, involucrate. Calyx tube densely hairy. Fruiting heads depressed, flat,
      separating as a whole from stem and functioning as a dispersal unit.   **22. T. cherleri**
—   Heads long-peduncled, not involucrate. Calyx tube glabrescent or glabrous. Fruiting
      heads usually persistent, not separating from stem.   **21. T. lappaceum**
27 (25). Leaflets with thick nerves, curved downwards near margin. Heads small, 1 cm.
      or less, sessile in the leaf axils along stem. Corolla whitish, shorter to slightly longer
      than calyx. Teeth of fruiting calyx rigid, spinescent, spreading or recurved. Fruiting
      heads separating as a whole from plant.   **20. T. scabrum**
—   Plants not as above   28
28. Uppermost leaves opposite   29
—   All leaves, including the uppermost ones, alternate   43
29. Leaflets of cauline leaves ovate or obovate, less than twice as long as broad   30
—   Leaflets of all cauline leaves, or of upper leaves only, oblong, elliptical or linear, at
      least twice as long as their maximum width   32
30. Flowers white or pink, 2 cm. long or more.   **39. T. clypeatum**
—   Flowers cream-coloured, much shorter than above   31
31. Lower calyx tooth broadly lanceolate in fruit, 3–5-nerved; calyx tube almost glabrous.
                                                                      40. T. scutatum
—   Lower calyx tooth lanceolate-subulate in fruit, 1 (–3)-nerved; calyx tube appressed-
      hairy.   **41. T. plebeium**
32 (29). Corolla as long as or a little longer than calyx. Fruiting calyces with urceolate
      tube, sparingly long-villose, readily separating from one another. Fruiting heads
      globular, about 1 cm. across.   **37. T. leucanthum**
—   Not as above   33
33. Flowers white or cream-coloured   34
—   Flowers purple, flesh-coloured, pink or violet, or 2-coloured   39
34. Fruiting heads globular or nearly so, spiny; fruiting calyces not separable from one
      another or from head. Tube of fruiting calyx whitish, nerveless, smooth; throat of calyx

tightly closed by a thick, white callosity; teeth erect or somewhat spreading; tips of calyx teeth purple or blackish.   **38. T. echinatum**

— Plants not as above   35

35. Fruiting calyces persistent (i.e. not separating from rhachis), white and membranous between nerves; throat open, appressed-hairy; lower calyx tooth much broader than the others, clearly 3-nerved at base; lower calyx tooth of lower flowers sometimes oblique or irregularly 2-fid; tips of calyx teeth not purple nor blackish. Seeds up to 2 mm. or more long. Plants cultivated or escaped from cultivation.

                                                                                    35. T. alexandrinum

— Fruiting calyces readily separating from rhachis after maturity; calyx throat closed by a callosity or by a ciliate ring, or open   36

36. Fruiting calyx throat completely closed by a 2-lipped callosity; teeth of fruiting calyx stellately divaricate, purple-tipped; tube urceolate in fruit. Flowers loosely and somewhat bifariously arranged on a more or less long rhachis.   **36. T. constantinopolitanum**

— Calyx throat open or with a narrow callose or ciliate ring; teeth of fruiting calyx usually erect or only partly stellately spreading, or deflexed   37

37. Throat of fruiting calyx open, without a callosity and without a hairy ring; teeth with purplish tips; lower tooth of fruiting calyx spreading, often twice as long as the others or more, that of the lower flowers deflexed.   **34. T. vavilovii**

— Throat of fruiting calyx not closed but carrying a ring of patulous hairs or narrowed by a protruding callose ring; teeth green, not purple-tipped   38

38. Throat of fruiting calyx provided with a ring of spreading hairs; calyx grey- and brownish-hairy.   **32. T. berytheum**

— Throat of fruiting calyx somewhat narrowed (but not closed) by a protruding callosity; calyx sparingly whitish-hairy.   **31. T. salmoneum**

39 (33). Fruiting heads almost globular, 1 cm. or less in diam.; mature calyces connate with one another at base and also not separable from rhachis. Fruiting calyx tube glabrous or glabrescent and nerveless; teeth with purple tips.   **38. T. echinatum**

— Fruiting heads ovoid or oblong or cylindrical, usually much longer than 1 cm. Fruiting calyx tube villose or appressed-silky or hispid; fruiting calyces readily separable from rhachis   40

40. Throat of fruiting calyx not closed but carrying a hairy ring.   **33. T. meironense**

— Throat of fruiting calyx entirely closed by a callosity   41

41. Corolla 2–3 times as long as calyx. Calyx teeth distinctly unequal. Flowering heads of 2 colours. Pod sessile. Stems patulous-hairy.   **28. T. dichroanthum**

— Corolla as long as calyx or distinctly longer. Calyx teeth equal or almost so. Flowering heads not 2-coloured. Pod stipitate. Stems appressed- or subappressed-hairy   42

42. Calyx 1.5–2 cm. Petals as long as calyx. Fruiting heads ovoid.   **29. T. dasyurum**

— Calyx 1 cm. or less. Petals longer than calyx. Fruiting heads cylindrical or oblong.

                                                                                    30. T. prophetarum

43 (28). Stems patulous-hispid. Leaflets dentate above, mostly obtuse, mucronate. Heads ovoid to oblong. Corolla white, about 1.5 cm., as long as or slightly longer than calyx. Fruiting heads about 2 cm. Littoral plants.   **27. T. palaestinum**

— Not as above   44

44. Calyx about twice as long as corolla; calyx teeth equal in length, setaceous, plumose, 2–3 times as long as tube.   **23. T. arvense**

— Calyx shorter than corolla; lower calyx teeth considerably longer than others   45

45. Corolla 0.7–1 cm., lilac or pink. Calyx 5–7 mm. Flowering heads ovoid to globular, about 1 cm. across; fruiting heads up to 2 cm. Leaflets elliptical, up to 1 cm. long.

Littoral decumbent plants.   **26. T. blancheanum**
— Plants not as above   46
46. Corolla 1–1.3 cm., hardly exserted from calyx. Calyx teeth sharp-pointed.
                                                             24. T. angustifolium
— Corolla 1.3–1.8 cm., much exserted from calyx. Calyx teeth truncate   47
47. Flowers pale pink at anthesis, later turning pale purple or dark lilac; heads thus
    often 2-coloured. Stems patulous-hairy.   **28. T. dichroanthum**
— Flowers intensely purple at and after anthesis; heads not 2-coloured. Stems appressed-
    hairy.   **25. T. purpureum**

Sect. AMORIA (C. Presl) Lojac., Nuov. Giorn. Bot. Ital. 15 : 125, 228 (1883). Gen. *Amoria* C. Presl, Symb. Bot. 1 : 47 (1831). Racemes umbellate or capitate. Flowers bracteate and usually pedicellate. Calyx mostly 10-nerved. Petals white, pink or red; standard with a short broad claw, free or only shortly connate with other petals. Pod mostly sessile, (1–)2–8-seeded.

1. Trifolium repens L., Sp. Pl. 767 (1753). [Plate 231]

Perennial, glabrous, 10–30 cm. Stems rhizomatous, prostrate, creeping and rooting from nodes. Leaves long-petioled; stipules broad at base with subulate upper part, scarious, with reddish or green nerves; leaflets 1–2 × 1–1.5 cm., broadly obovate to orbicular, truncate or somewhat notched at apex, sharply serrulate, with parallel lateral veins forked towards margin. Peduncles much longer than subtending leaves, weak. Heads 1.5–3.5 cm. in diam., umbellate, 20–40-flowered, rather loose, nearly globular. Bracts shorter than pedicels, oblong, acuminate. Pedicels as long as or longer than calyx tube, becoming deflexed early. Flowers fragrant. Calyx half as long as corolla; tube campanulate, 10-nerved, glabrous; teeth about as long as tube, somewhat unequal, lanceolate. Corolla white or pinkish; standard oblong; wings somewhat spreading. Pod 4–5 mm., mostly 3–4-seeded, linear-oblong, constricted between seeds. Seeds ovoid to reniform, brownish. Fl. March–September.

Var. **repens.** *T. repens* L., l.c.; Boiss., Fl. 2 : 145 (1872). *T. repens* L. var. *genuinum* Aschers. et Graebn., Syn. Mitteleur. Fl. 6, 2 : 498 (1908). Heads 1.5–2 cm. in diam. Leaflets 1–2 cm. Flowers (5–)6–7 mm.

Hab.: Damp and swampy soils; also in lawns. Acco Plain, Philistean Plain, Judean Mts., Dan Valley, Hula Plain.

Var. **giganteum** Lagrèze-Fossat, Fl. Tarn et Garonne 95 (1847). All the parts of the plant larger. Heads up to 3.5 cm. in diam.

Hab.: As above. Upper Galilee, Dan Valley, Hula Plain.

Area of species: Mediterranean, Euro-Siberian and Irano-Turanian; also introduced into other regions.

Although the two above varieties intergrade, they should be maintained as such until further study is made on this species in the southernmost part of its area. The fact that both varieties grow in the same site suggests the constancy of these taxa.

2. Trifolium nigrescens Viv., Fl. Ital. Fragm. 12, t. 13 (1808). [Plate 232]

Annual, glabrous, (8–)10–60 cm. Stems prostrate, ascending or erect, branching from base. Leaves, except for the uppermost ones, long-petioled; stipules membranous, triangular-lanceolate, abruptly subulate-cuspidate; leaflets 0.5–2.5 cm., obovate to rhombic, truncate to rounded or emarginate at apex, sharply denticulate above or all over. Peduncles longer than subtending leaves. Heads 1–2 cm., many-flowered, globular. Bracts as long as or longer than pedicels, oblong, acuminate. Pedicels often as long as calyx tube or longer. Flowers 5–8 mm. Calyx white, glabrous or sparingly hairy, 5- to 10-nerved; teeth shorter or longer than tube, triangular to lanceolate, with or without cuspidate tip, recurved in fruit. Corolla pink or white, turning yellowish or brownish in fruit. Ovules 2–4(–6). Pod 1–3-seeded, linear, with crenate margin or constricted between seeds. Seeds ovoid, dark brown. Fl. (January–) March–October.

This species should be subdivided into ssp. *nigrescens* (with flowers white also after anthesis and crenate pods containing 2–4 seeds) and ssp. *petrisavii* (with pink flowers turning brownish after anthesis and pods deeply constricted between upper and lower segments, but containing only 1 seed). In Palestine (and adjacent countries) ssp. *petrisavii* was found to be the only representative of *T. nigrescens*.

Subsp. **petrisavii** (Clem.) Holmboe, Bergens Mus. Skr. n.r. 1, 2 : 106 (1914). *T. petrisavii* Clem., Sert. Or. 32, t. 7, f. 2 (1855) et Mem. Accad. Sci. Torino ser. 2, 16 : 268, t. 7, f. 1 (1857); Boiss., Fl. 2 : 144 (1872). *T. meneghinianum* Clem., Sert. Or. 31, t. 7, f. 1 (1855) et Mem. Accad. Sci. Torino ser. 2, 16 : 267, t. 7, f. 1 (1857); Boiss., l.c. Stems solid or fistulous, (8–)10–60 cm. Leaflets 0.5–2.5 cm., obtriangular to rhombic-obovate. Calyx teeth half as long as to as long as tube. Pod deeply constricted in lower part. Seeds usually solitary.

Hab.: Damp and swampy soils. Coastal Galilee, Acco Plain, Sharon Plain, Philistean Plain, Upper and Lower Galilee, Mt. Carmel, Esdraelon Plain, Samaria, Judean Mts., Dan Valley, Hula Plain, Upper Jordan Valley, Ammon.

Area of species : Mediterranean, with extensions into adjacent regions.

T. meneghinianum and *T. petrisavii,* described by Clementi from the environs of Istanbul, are no doubt two minor habitat forms. The publication of these binomials has greatly confused the students of the E. Mediterranean trifolia and caused much controversy in naming the local forms of *T. nigrescens. T. nigrescens* Viv. ssp. *petrisavii* is an extremely polymorphic taxon which can readily be divided into a series of varieties, according to the shape of leaflets and calyx teeth and the stature and branching of the plants. However, such a division cannot be made without appropriate constancy tests.

Sect. CHRONOSEMIUM Ser. in DC., Prodr. 2 : 204 (1825). Racemes capitate or spicate. Calyx 5-nerved, without commissural nerves. Corolla variously coloured, persistent in fruit, serving as an anemochorous means of seed dispersal; standard deflexed, tapering at base, not or only shortly united with other petals. Pod stipitate, 1–2-seeded.

3. Trifolium billardieri Spreng., Syst. Veg. 3 : 211 (1826; "*billarderii*"). *T. comosum* Labill., Ic. Pl. Syr. Dec. 5 : 15, t. 10 (1812) non L., Sp. Pl. 767 (1753); Boiss., Fl. 2 : 150 (1872). [Plate 233]

Annual, glabrous except for the patulous-hairy peduncles, 10–15 cm. Stems erect or ascending, simple or branching from base. Leaves long-petioled, the uppermost leaves opposite; stipules long, oblong-lanceolate, acute; leaflets 0.8–1.8 cm., obovate-oblong to elliptical, cuneate at base, obtuse or truncate to emarginate at tip, denticulate mainly in the upper half; terminal leaflet long-petiolulate. Peduncles stout, rather short. Heads 1.5–3 cm., spike-like, cylindrical. Pedicels very short. Flowers 6–8 mm. Calyx patulous-hirsute; tube membranous, very short; upper teeth minute, triangular, lower teeth linear-lanceolate, obtuse, prominently nerved, ciliate with hairs tuberculate at base. Corolla pink to lilac or flesh-coloured; standard with orbicular limb, denticulate at margin, strongly nerved and scarious in fruit; wings divergent, much shorter than standard and somewhat longer than keel. Pod long-stipitate, 1-seeded, membranous. Seed ovoid-oblong, yellowish. Fl. March–April.

Hab.: Sandy loams. Sharon Plain, Philistean Plain.

Area: E. Mediterranean (Palestine and Lebanon).

4. Trifolium philistaeum Zoh. (nom. nov.). *T. stenophyllum* Boiss., Diagn. ser. 1, 9 : 30 (1849) non Nutt., Journ. Acad. Philad. n.s. 1 : 151 (1847). [Plate 234]

Annual, glabrous or hairy, 10–25 cm. Stems single or few, ascending, dichotomously branched above, terete. Lower leaves long-petioled, upper short-petioled; stipules herbaceous, ovate to oblong, entire, sparingly patulous-hirsute, many-nerved, lower half adnate to petiole, upper half tapering, lanceolate; leaflets 1–2(–2.5) cm., oblong or elliptical to linear and filiform, long-dentate in upper half or entire, glabrous to appressed- or patulous-hairy, terminal leaflet long-petiolulate. Heads (1–)2–6 × 1.5–2 cm., long-peduncled, many-flowered, ovoid, elongating in fruit. Flowers about 1 cm., short-pedicelled, at first erect, later deflexed. Calyx small, membranous, 2-lipped; upper lip with 2 short, glabrous, triangular teeth, lower lip patulous-hairy, with 3 lanceolate-subulate, almost equal teeth, twice as long as the upper. Corolla white to pinkish-white, turning pink or violet or flesh-coloured; standard 2–3 times as long as calyx, with oblong-spatulate, obtuse, many-nerved limb, denticulate at margin, prominently keeled at base, longer than the divergent wings; keel erect, much shorter than wings. Pod stipitate, 1-seeded, membranous, keeled. Seeds 1–2 mm., ovoid, yellowish-brown. Fl. March–May.

Var. **philistaeum**. *T. stenophyllum* Boiss., l.c. et Fl. 2 : 151 (1872). Leaflets all toothed; uppermost leaflets oblong to linear.

Hab.: Sandy soils. Coastal Galilee, Sharon Plain, Philistean Plain, Coastal Negev, Esdraelon Plain (probably adventive here).

Var. **filifolium** Zoh.* All leaflets, or those of the uppermost leaves only, filiform, entire.

Hab.: As above. Philistean Plain, Coastal Negev.

Area of species: E. Mediterranean (Palestine and northern Sinai).

Trifolium speciosum Willd., Sp. Pl. 3 : 1382 (1802) [non "*T. speciosum* Fl. Pelop." sensu Boiss., Diagn. ser. 1, 2 : 33 et 34 (1843)], recorded by Boiss. (Fl. 2 : 151, 1872) from Palestine, has not been observed by others.

* See Appendix at end of this volume.

5. Trifolium campestre Schreb. in Sturm, Deutschl. Fl. 1, 16 : t. 253 (1804). *T. agrarium* L., Sp. Pl. 772 (1753) p.p.; Boiss., Fl. 2 : 153 (1872) p.p. *T. procumbens* L., Fl. Suec. ed. 2, 261 no. 673 (1755) p.p. non L., Sp. Pl. 772 (1753); Boiss., l.c. 154 p.p. [Plate 235]

Annual, hairy or almost glabrous, 10–30 cm. Stems erect, ascending or prostrate, simple or branched. Leaves petiolate; stipules herbaceous, ovate to oblong, long-acuminate; leaflets 0.8–1.6 × 0.4–0.8 cm., ovate to oblong-elliptical, often with cuneate base, truncate or retuse at apex, denticulate in upper half; terminal leaflet long-petiolulate. Peduncles as long as or longer or shorter than leaves. Heads 0.8–1.3 × 0.7–1 cm., many-flowered, often globular. Pedicels shorter than calyx, becoming deflexed early. Flowers rather dense, later becoming densely imbricated. Calyx white, 5-nerved, glabrous or rarely slightly hairy; tube membranous; the 2 upper teeth very short, triangular or lanceolate, the others about twice as long as tube or longer, long-subulate. Corolla (4–)5–6(–7) mm., yellow to pale yellow, turning brown in fruit; standard 4–5 mm., with orbicular limb, flat or spoon-shaped, denticulate at margin, many-nerved. Pod longer than style, stipitate. Seeds solitary, 1 mm., ovoid-lenticular. Fl. February–April (–October).

Hab.: Fields, batha and roadsides. Coastal Galilee, Acco Plain, Sharon Plain, Philistean Plain, Upper and Lower Galilee, Mt. Carmel, Esdraelon Plain, Mt. Gilboa, Samaria, Judean Mts., Negev, Dan Valley, Hula Plain, Upper Jordan Valley, Beit Shean Valley, Gilead, Ammon, Moav. Common.

Area: Mediterranean, with extensions into the Euro-Siberian and the Irano-Turanian regions.

Our specimens of *T. campestre* include, among others, forms with the following combinations of characteristics: (1) Long-peduncled heads and appressed-hirsute stems. (2) Short-peduncled or subsessile heads and more or less patulous-pubescent stems. (3) Short-peduncled heads, appressed-pubescent stems. (4) Medium-sized peduncles and appressed hairs. One can name the first form *T. campestre* Schreb. var. *campestre*, and the second *T. campestre* Schreb. var. *subsessile* (Boiss.) Hay., Prodr. Fl. Pen. Balc. 1 : 848 (1926), but the other two forms are doubtless transitional. As to the glaucescence, it may also appear in all the four forms mentioned. Thus, there is no room for a varietal subdivision of this species within the local populations. The record on var. *thionanthum* (Hausskn.) Dinsmore in Post, Fl. Syr. Pal. Sin. ed. 2, 1 : 351 (1932), is very doubtful.

Most of the local plants could be assigned to var. *subsessile* (Boiss.) Hay., l.c., but there are also forms, mainly confined to mesic habitats, which correspond to var. *campestre*.

6. Trifolium boissieri Guss. ex Boiss., Fl. 2 : 152 (1872). *T. boissieri* Guss., Fl. Sic. Syn. 2 : 858 (1845; "*boisseri*") nom. nud. "*T. speciosum* Willd." sensu Boiss., Diagn. ser. 1, 2 : 33 (1843). [Plate 236]

Annual, patulous-villose above, 15–30 cm. Stems few or many, erect, branched in upper part, terete. Leaves long-petioled; stipules oblong-lanceolate, acuminate; leaflets 1–2 cm., ovate to elliptical or obovate, obtuse, truncate or slightly emarginate at apex, dentate; terminal leaflet long-petiolulate. Peduncles rather thick, often longer than subtending leaves, rarely as long as them or shorter. Heads ovoid. Pedicels as long as or longer than calyx tube, first erect or spreading, then deflexed. Calyx membranous, white, glabrous, 5-nerved; upper 2 calyx teeth triangular, the others lanceolate-subulate, twice or more as long as the upper teeth, ciliate or terminating with long, scattered bristles. Corolla 7–9 mm., yellow or cream-coloured in flower, chestnut-coloured in fruit; standard with obovate, denticulate limb and boat-shaped claw, 2–3 times as long as calyx, much longer than wings, the latter somewhat longer than keel. Pod as long as style, long-stipitate, 1-seeded, oblong. Seeds 1.2 mm., oblong, yellowish-brown. Fl. April–May.

Hab.: Shady places; batha, maquis and forests. Upper and Lower Galilee, Esdraelon Plain, Mt. Gilboa, Hula Plain, Upper Jordan Valley.

Area: E. Mediterranean, with slight extensions into the Irano-Turanian borderland.

Not common in Palestine; rather uniform, except in the size of flowering heads; in some specimens the calyx tube is slightly hairy.

7. Trifolium erubescens Fenzl, Pugill. 5 (1842); Boiss., Fl. 2 : 151 (1872). [Plate 237]

Annual, appressed- or patulous-pubescent, 10–30 cm. Stems few or many, erect or ascending, rarely decumbent, diffuse, branched above, slender, terete. Leaves petiolate; stipules herbaceous at margin, oblong, acute; leaflets 0.6–1 × 0.3–0.6 cm., obovate to oblong, cuneate at base, rounded or almost truncate at apex, denticulate in upper half, all with very short petiolules or without. Peduncles axillary, 2–3 times as long as subtending leaves, almost filiform; terminal peduncles shorter. Heads 0.6–1 cm. across, many-flowered, loose, broadly ovoid to globular. Pedicels shorter than calyx tube. Calyx glabrous; tube membranous, white, obscurely 5-nerved; upper teeth almost as long as tube, triangular, the 3 lower ones mostly 2–3 times as long as tube, linear-lanceolate to subulate, often with a few hairs at apex. Corolla 4–6 mm., pink or lilac, turning flesh-coloured to dark brown in fruit; standard longer than wings and keel, oblong-spatulate in outline, with spoon-shaped limb and boat-shaped claw. Pod somewhat longer than the curved style, long-stipitate, 1-seeded. Seeds 1 mm., ovoid, brown. Fl. March–May.

Hab.: Mainly in shady places; batha, maquis and forests. Sharon Plain, Philistean Plain, Upper and Lower Galilee, Mt. Carmel, Mt. Gilboa, Judean Mts., Gilead.

Area: E. Mediterranean (Palestine and Lebanon).

8. Trifolium micranthum Viv., Fl. Lib. Spec. 45, t. 19, f. 3 (1824). *T. filiforme* L., Sp. Pl. 773 (1753) p.p. non L., Fl. Suec. ed. 2, 261 (1755); Boiss., Fl. 2 : 155 (1872). [Plate 238]

Annual, glabrous except in upper parts, 10–30 cm. Stems few or numerous, erect or procumbent, filiform. Lowest leaves petiolate, the others sessile or subsessile; stipules free almost from base, oblong, acute; leaflets 5–8 mm., obovate to oblong, cuneate at base, truncate or retuse at apex, denticulate above. Peduncles longer than subtending leaves, capillary, later recurved. Heads loosely 2–6-flowered. Pedicels shorter than calyx, becoming deflexed. Calyx about 2 mm., membranous, white, glabrous, 5-nerved; teeth unequal, linear, upper teeth as long as or shorter than tube, 3 lower teeth longer than tube, often ending in 2 bristles. Corolla 2.5–3 mm., persistent, yellow, membranous in fruit; standard oblong, keeled, somewhat longer than keel and wings. Pod stipitate, dehiscent, 1–2-seeded, slightly exserted from corolla, lenticular to orbicular. Seeds somewhat flattened, ovoid-reniform, brown, shiny. Fl. April–May.

Hab.: Seasonally inundated ground. Sharon Plain, Jordan Valley (?).

Area: Mediterranean and Euro-Siberian.

This species has not been observed in Palestine since 1928 and is probably on the verge of extinction here. The nomenclature of this species is discussed at length by Ascherson and Graebner, Syn. Mitteleur. Fl. 6, 2 : 476 (1907).

Sect. MICRANTHEUM (C. Presl) Gib. et Belli, Mem. Accad. Sci. Torino ser. 2, 41 : 197 (1891). Gen. *Micrantheum* C. Presl, Symb. Bot. 1 : 47 (1831). Annuals. Heads axillary, sessile or almost so. Flowers bracteate. Calyx 10-nerved, with open throat; teeth almost equal, at length recurved. Pod sessile, 2-seeded, included in calyx.

9. Trifolium suffocatum L., Mant. Alt. 276 (1771); Boiss., Fl. 2 : 142 (1872). [Plate 239]

Annual, dwarf, stemless or almost stemless, glabrous or very sparingly hairy, 3–8 cm. Leaves almost all at base of plant, very long-petioled, erect or ascending; stipules membranous, ovate, acute; leaflets small, broad, cuneate-triangular, notched at apex, finely serrate above, prominently nerved at lower surface. Heads minute, few-flowered, densely crowded, all at base of plant and in axils of broad, membranous stipules. Flowers 5–6 mm., very short-pedicelled or sessile, subtended by minute, lanceolate bracts. Calyx sparingly pilose or glabrous; tube prominently 10-nerved; teeth as long as the ovoid fruiting calyx tube, lanceolate, 3-nerved, recurved or falcate in fruit. Corolla about half as long as calyx, white. Pod 3–4 mm., 2-seeded, membranous, ovoid-oblong, somewhat constricted between seeds, obliquely mucronate. Seeds lenticular to reniform, yellowish, obscurely tuberculate. Fl. March–April.

Hab.: Grazed places and roadsides. Sharon Plain, Upper and Lower Galilee.

Area: Mediterranean, with slight extensions into adjacent provinces.

A very rare plant, mainly on heavy soils. Presents one of the most interesting examples of basicarpy, the fruits being crowded at the base of the very short stem and not separating from it.

Sect. MISTYLLUS (C. Presl) Godr. in Gren. et Godr., Fl. Fr. 1 : 415 (1849). Gen. *Mistyllus* C. Presl, Symb. Bot. 1 : 49 (1832). Annual, glabrous herbs with spuriously terminal heads. Bracts large, many-nerved. Calyx 20- or more-nerved, becoming more or less inflated after flowering. Petals long- or fairly long-clawed, persisting and becoming scarious after flowering; standard free. Pod sessile, 2–4-seeded, long-beaked.

10. Trifolium spumosum L., Sp. Pl. 771 (1753); Boiss., Fl. 2 : 138 (1872). [Plate 240]

Annual, glabrous plant, 10–40 cm. Stems few or many, prostrate to erect, diffuse, branched, striate. Lower leaves long-petioled, upper leaves short-petioled; stipules membranous, white, ovate, abruptly long-cuspidate, prominently nerved; leaflets 1–2.5 cm., obovate to rhombic, cuneate at base, often truncate to retuse at apex, denticulate. Peduncles as long as or longer than subtending leaves. Flowering heads 1.5–2 cm., many-flowered, broadly ovoid to globular; fruiting heads 2–4 cm., ovoid to cylindrical. Bracts somewhat shorter than calyx, oblong (the outermost bracts ovate), mucronate-subulate at apex. Pedicels short, thick. Flowers 1–1.5 cm. Calyx membranous; tube ellipsoidal, becoming ovoid or globular in fruit, with 20 longitudinal nerves and numerous transverse veins; teeth about half as long as tube, subulate-linear, recurved in fruit. Corolla longer than calyx, purple or reddish; standard with persistent, ovate limb, longer than divergent wings. Pod 1–1.5 cm. including ensiform beak, sessile, 2–4-seeded, somewhat constricted between seeds. Seeds 1.6–1.8 mm., ovoid, light brown, minutely warty. Fl. March–May.

Hab.: Damp places and maquis. Coastal Galilee, Sharon Plain, Philistean Plain, Upper and Lower Galilee, Mt. Carmel, Esdraelon Plain, Samaria, Shefela, Judean Mts., Dan Valley, Hula Plain, Upper Jordan Valley, Beit Shean Valley.

Area: Mediterranean and W. Irano-Turanian.

11. Trifolium argutum Banks et Sol. in Russ., Nat. Hist. Aleppo ed. 2, 2 : 260 (1794); Eig, Journ. Bot. Lond. 75 : 188 (1937). *T. xerocephalum* Fenzl, Pugill. 5 (1842); Boiss., Fl. 2 : 140 (1872). *T. xerocephalum* Fenzl var. *minus* Boiss., l.c. *T. leiocalycinum* Boiss. et Sprun. in Boiss., Diagn. ser. 1, 2 : 31 (1843). *T. moriferum* Boiss., Diagn. ser. 1, 9 : 28 (1849). [Plate 241]

Annual, glabrous or sparingly pubescent, 10–30 cm. Stems few or many, erect or procumbent, branched. Leaves long-petioled; stipules oblong, with a lanceolate-subulate free part; leaflets 0.6–1.2 × 0.3–0.8 cm., obovate-cuneate to oblong, obtuse and mucronulate at apex, sharply dentate. Heads short-peduncled or sessile and involucrate by upper leaves, ovoid and about 1 cm. in flower, elongating in fruit, many-flowered. Bracts as long as or longer than calyx tube, scarious, oblong-cuneate to obovate, mucronate, membranous-margined. Calyx white; tube villose along two rows, about 36-nerved, becoming somewhat inflated and top-shaped in fruit; teeth half to three quarters as long as tube, more or less equal in length, spreading, subulate with broader base. Corolla 6–7 mm., persistent, scarious, white, pink or reddish, many-striate; limb of standard erect, ovate to oblong, longer than erect keel and divergent or deflexed wings, turning pink or dirty white in fruit. Pod sessile, 1-seeded, with a beak 3–4 times as long as pod proper. Seeds about 1 mm., ovoid, brown. Dispersal synaptospermic, i.e. fruiting head separating as a whole from peduncle. Fl. January–May.

Hab.: Roadsides, fields and batha. Coastal Galilee, Acco Plain, Sharon Plain, Philistean Plain, Upper and Lower Galilee, Mt. Carmel, Mt. Gilboa, Samaria, Shefela, Judean Mts., W. and N. Negev, Dan Valley, Upper Jordan Valley. Common.

Area: E. Mediterranean.

Var. *cruentum* (Bornm.) Eig, l.c. 191. *T. xerocephalum* Fenzl var. *cruentum* Bornm., Verh. Zool.-Bot. Ges. Wien 48 : 581 (1898), based on the colour of the corolla, is an unstable form connected to the typical form by intermediates.

T. multistriatum Koch, Syn. Fl. Germ. Helv. ed. 2, 190 (1843), recorded by Dinsmore (in Post, Fl. Syr. Pal. Sin. ed. 2, 1 : 346, 1932) from the Philistean Plain (Sarona), has not been observed by others in Palestine.

Sect. FRAGIFERA Koch, Syn. Fl. Germ. Helv. 171 (1835). Annual or perennial herbs. Heads capitate. Flowers sessile or short-pedicelled, bracteate. Calyx 2-lipped; upper lip inflated after flowering, net-veined, 2-toothed; teeth growing in fruit.

12. Trifolium fragiferum L., Sp. Pl. 772 (1753); Boiss., Fl. 2 : 135 (1872). [Plate 242]

Perennial, hairy or glabrous, 10–40 cm. Stems creeping, rooting from nodes, with erect petioles and peduncles. Leaves congested or loose and long-petioled; stipules up to 2 cm., lanceolate, with subulate free part; leaflets 0.5–2 × 0.5–1.5 cm., ovate to elliptical, obtuse, often retuse, spinulose-toothed. Peduncles axillary. Heads 0.8–1.2 cm.; involucre 3–6 mm., cleft into oblong, entire or toothed lobes, often concealing the calyx tube of the lower flowers. Bracts longer than calyx tube, lanceolate. Flowers short-pedicelled. Calyx tube pilose to woolly; teeth unequal, the 2 upper teeth spreading, shorter than tube, the lower teeth erect, longer than tube. Corolla considerably longer than calyx, not resupinate; standard pink or flesh-coloured, with ovate, retuse limb, much longer than wings and keel. Fruiting calyx tube deflexed, globularly inflated and reticulate-veined, hairy to hispid, sometimes almost concealing the marcescent corolla. Pod dehiscent, 2-seeded, ovoid, with long beak. Seeds 1–1.2 mm., reniform, brown. 2n = 16. Fl. April–October.

Hab.: Swamps and grassy places on heavy soils. Acco Plain, Sharon Plain, Philistean Plain, Upper and Lower Galilee, Mt. Carmel, Esdraelon Plain, Judean Mts., Dan Valley, Hula Plain, Gilead, Ammon, Moav. Fairly common.

Area: Mediterranean, Irano-Turanian and Euro-Siberian; also introduced into other regions and cultivated as an excellent forage crop.

In the Linnaean Herbarium (London) there are two sheets of *T. fragiferum* – one with the inscription of *T. fragiferum* by Linnaeus. This specimen agrees exactly with that form common in southern Europe and in the Mediterranean region and was rightly regarded by most of the authors as *T. fragiferum* L. and not *T. neglectum* C.A.M. as suggested by Bobrov, Acta Inst. Bot. Acad. Sci. URSS ser. 1, 6 : 249 (1947). The other sheet in the Linnaean Herbarium, which contains a large-headed form and which was considered by Bobrov to be the true *T. fragiferum,* was thus named not by Linnaeus himself but by Smith (See Catalogue of the Linnaean Herbarium by Savage, 1945). In consequence, the name *T. fragiferum* is legitimate for the small-headed form.

T. fragiferum is very variable as to size of leaves, fruiting head and length of peduncles. Among other forms, there is a particularly striking one with very small leaflets and short peduncles which could be named var. *pulchellum* Lange, Meddel. Nat. Floren. 2 (Aart. 7) : 169 (1865), but it clearly intergrades with the large-leaved form. There are also other forms, among them a salt-tolerant one. The present author prefers to postpone the subdivision of this species until these forms are tested for constancy.

13. Trifolium physodes Stev. ex M.B., Fl. Taur.-Cauc. 2 : 217 (1808); Boiss., Fl. 2 : 136 (1872). [Plate 243]

Perennial, glabrous, 20–50 cm. Stems many, procumbent or erect, not rooting, leafy, often covered below with stipules of withered leaves. Leaves long-petioled; stipules membranous between nerves, lanceolate, very long-cuspidate, the upper stipules broader; petiole often hairy; leaflets 1–3 cm., ovate to elliptical, obtuse-retuse at apex, with light-coloured middle nerve. Peduncles shorter to somewhat longer than subtending leaves. Heads 1.5–2 cm., axillary and terminal, not involucrate, ovoid to globular. Bracts shorter than pedicels. Calyx white-hairy or glabrous; tube 3–4 mm., as long as or somewhat shorter than teeth, 10-nerved; teeth subulate-lanceolate, becoming recurved early. Fruiting calyx globularly inflated or helmet-shaped at upper side, tomentose or glabrous. Corolla 1–1.3 cm., pink, not resupinate. Pod 1-seeded, oblong. Seeds 1.2 mm., brown. Fl. April–June.

Var. **psilocalyx** Boiss., Fl. 2 : 136 (1872). *T. sclerorrhizum* Boiss., Diagn. ser. 1, 9 : 28 (1849). Calyx glabrous or very slightly pilose on back.

Hab.: Forest, maquis or open grassy places; often on heavy damp soils. Upper Galilee, Judean Mts. (rare), Gilead.

Area: Mediterranean, with slight extensions into adjacent territories.

14. Trifolium resupinatum L., Sp. Pl. 771 (1753). [Plate 244]

Annual, glabrous or glabrescent, 20–60 cm. Stems ascending or erect, rarely procumbent, branching mainly from lower part, mostly furrowed and hollow. Leaves with hairy or glabrous petioles; stipules united below, membranous, ovate-oblong, longitudinally striate-nerved, free portion as long as or longer than adnate one, subulate; stipules of upper leaves much shorter; leaflets 1–2.5 cm., obovate-oblong to elliptical, tapering at base, rounded or tapering (never truncate or emarginate) at apex, spinulosedentate with alternately larger and smaller upwardly oriented teeth. Peduncles much longer than subtending leaves. Heads (0.8–)1–1.5 cm. across, many-flowered. Pedicels rather thick, one quarter or one half as long as the calyx tube, glabrous. Calyx tube white; teeth much shorter than tube, linear-lanceolate, unequal, the upper ones much longer. Corolla deep pink to purple, resupinate, fragrant; standard (5–)6–8 mm., oblong, notched at apex and apiculate in sinus; wings longer than keel, and about half as long as standard. Fruiting heads globular in outline, stellately lobed. Fruiting calyces up to 8 mm. long, diverging from one another, inflated, ovoid or ellipsoidal to pear-shaped, strongly net-veined; upper teeth long, subulate-setiform, divergent. Pod dehiscing at thickened sutures, 1-seeded, membranous, lenticular. Seeds about 1.2 mm., ovoid, brown. 2n = 16. Fl. March–May.

Var. **resupinatum.** *T. resupinatum* L., l.c.; Boiss., Fl. 2 : 137 (1872) excl. var. β et γ. Plant generally up to 60 cm. Fruiting heads up to 1.5 cm. across. Leaflets usually (1–)1.5–2 cm.

Hab.: Mostly heavy soils; river banks, roadsides and under winter crops. Coastal Galilee, Acco Plain, Sharon Plain, Philistean Plain, Upper and Lower Galilee, Mt. Carmel, Dan Valley, Hula Plain, Upper Jordan Valley, Beit Shean Valley, Lower Jordan Valley, Gilead.

Var. **microcephalum** Zoh.* Plant generally lower. Leaves smaller and stems thinner. Fruiting heads 0.8–1 cm. across.

Hab.: Fields; less moist soils than above, sometimes saline soils. Esdraelon Plain and probably elsewhere.

Area of species: Mediterranean and W. Irano-Turanian, extending into the Euro-Siberian region.

* See Appendix at end of this volume.

Highly appreciated as a pasture plant.

Although there are transitions between these two varieties, their distinction is fairly easy. The relation of var. *microcephalum* to *T. resupinatum* L. var. *gracile* Rouy in Rouy et Fouc., Fl. Fr. 5 : 93 (1899) has not been cleared up.

Var. *resupinatum* is identical with Linnaeus's specimen in the Linnaean Herbarium (London), while Boissier's (l.c.) var. *majus* is most probably identical with *T. suaveolens* Schlecht. in Willd., Enum. Pl. Hort. Berol. Suppl. 52 (1814).

15. Trifolium clusii Godr. et Gren. in Gren. et Godr., Fl. Fr. 1 : 414 (1849). [Plate 245]

Annual, sparsely patulous-hairy or glabrous, 10–20(–30) cm. Stems many, erect or ascending, diffuse, branching from base, slightly furrowed or striate. Stipules adnate to petiole up to over half their length, submembranous, obovate-oblong, green-nerved, free portion as long as or longer than the adnate portion, triangular-lanceolate, acuminate; petioles decreasing in length towards apex of stem; leaflets about 0.7–1 × 0.5–0.7 cm., obovate with rounded (not truncate) apex, remotely spinulose-denticulate, mucronate at apex, often with a lighter stripe across; the uppermost leaflets narrower, cuneate. Peduncles slender, longer than subtending leaves, somewhat thickening and arcuate (bent above middle) in fruit. Heads about 0.7–1 cm. across, many-flowered. Pedicels about one quarter as long as the calyx tube. Calyx tube whitish; lower calyx teeth much shorter than tube, lanceolate-linear, white-margined. Corolla 6–7 mm., pink, resupinate; standard oblong, deeply notched, two thirds as long as wings; wings somewhat longer than keel. Fruiting heads 0.8(–1) cm., deflexed, globular, white to pinkish. Fruiting calyces 3–4 mm., compact (without interspaces), accompanied by the marcescent corollas; tubes unilaterally inflated, obliquely ovoid or globular, hairy or glabrescent, rarely glabrous, net-veined, with 2 long, horizontal or recurved, filiform, glabrous teeth at the neck (conical apex) of the tube. Pod 2 mm., 1(–2)-seeded, membranous, ovoid. Seeds oblong, yellowish-brown. 2n = 16. Fl. March–April.

Var. **clusii**. *T. clusii* Godr. et Gren. in Gren. et Godr., l.c.; Opphr., Bull. Soc. Bot. Fr. 108 : 56 (1961). *T. clusii* Godr. et Gren. var. *glabrum* Evenari in Opphr. et Evenari, Bull. Soc. Bot. Genève ser. 2, 31 : 292 (1941). *T. resupinatum* L. var. *minus* Boiss., Fl. 2 : 137 (1872). Stems erect or ascending, up to 20(–30) cm. Peduncles 2 cm. Fruiting heads hairy to glabrous, not white-cottony, becoming slightly lobed by protrusion of calyx tips. Fruiting calyx with upper teeth borne on a conical or cylindrical neck.

Hab.: Batha, garigue, fields and roadsides. Sharon Plain, Philistean Plain, Upper and Lower Galilee, Mt. Carmel, Esdraelon Plain, Mt. Gilboa, Samaria, Judean Mts., Hula Plain, Upper Jordan Valley.

Var. **gossypinum** Zoh.*? *T. tomentosum* L. var. *longipedunculatum* Hossain, Not. Roy. Bot. Gard. Edinb. 23 : 454 (1961). Fruiting heads spherical, not lobulate. Fruiting calyx densely cottony with the upper teeth hidden in fleece.

Hab.: As above. Sharon Plain, Upper and Lower Galilee, Mt. Carmel, Samaria, Judean Mts., Dan Valley, Hula Plain, Upper Jordan Valley, Beit Shean Valley, Lower Jordan Valley, Gilead, Ammon.

* See Appendix at end of this volume.

Area of species : E. Mediterranean, with extensions to W. Mediterranean and W. Irano-Turanian territories.

T. clusii is one of the most abundant species of the *Fragifera* group in this country. This species has been included within *T. resupinatum* L. by many authors, although the differences between the two are fairly clear at first glance. It is also readily distinguished from *T. tomentosum* L. by its long-arcuate peduncles, by the presence of the marcescent corollas among the fruiting calyces, and by the leaflets.

16. Trifolium tomentosum L., Sp. Pl. 771 (1753). [Plate 246]

Annual, glabrous or sparingly hairy, 10–20 cm. Stems many, erect, ascending or procumbent, mostly branching from base, terete or furrowed. Stipules 0.8–1.2 cm., adnate to petioles up to about half their length, ovate, green or green-striped, with the free portion usually shorter than the united one, triangular to triangular-lanceolate; petiole long, glabrous; leaflets 0.4–1.2 (–1.5) cm., those of lower leaves obovate, those of upper leaves obovate-cuneate to obtriangular-cuneate, acutely dentate, truncate, usually notched at apex, glabrous or slightly hairy beneath. Flowering heads (5–)7–8(–9) mm. across, sessile and mostly involucrate by subtending leaves or pedunculate, many-flowered. Bracts cup-shaped. Pedicels minute. Calyx tubular, hairy above; teeth much shorter than tube, linear to lanceolate. Corolla 3–6(–7) mm., pink, resupinate; standard obovate, notched, less than twice as long as the ovate wings, the latter somewhat longer than keel. Fruiting heads (0.5–)0.8–1(–1.2) cm., cottony to glabrescent, snow-white, dirty white, or yellowish-white to pinkish. Fruiting calyx 3–6(–7) mm., inflated, ovoid, glabrescent or pilose to woolly or felty, tapering above or terminating abruptly with a neck-like column crowned with spreading or curved, subulate, hairy upper teeth. Pod 1–2-seeded, ovoid to globular. Seeds scarcely 1 mm., yellowish to brown, plain or mottled. 2n = 16. Fl. February–April.

T. tomentosum is very polymorphic. The following constant varieties have so far been distinguished in the Palestine populations; chromosome counts were made from specimens of var. *orientale* and var. *lanatum*.

1. Fruiting heads slightly lobed by the protruding tips of the calyces, some with peduncles 1–1.5 cm., most heads sessile. Upper calyx teeth setaceous, strongly recurved, borne on a conical or cylindrical neck, projecting from the spherical surface of the head. Upper leaflets long-cuneate. Desert plants. [Plate 246, f. 7] var. **curvisepalum**
   – Heads evenly globular. Calyx teeth not as above   2
2. Fruiting heads all crowded together at base of plant and overtopped by the long-petioled leaves.   var. **chthonocephalum**
   – Fruiting heads all along the stem or on top of stems and branches   3
3. Fruiting heads glabrescent or pilose, with a clearly visible net of nerves on the calyces. Peduncles conspicuous, straight or bent downwards. Upper calyx teeth horizontal, often appressed to tube. [Plate 246, f. 6]   var. **tomentosum**
   – Fruiting heads cottony or tomentose; nerves of fruiting calyces concealed by the fleecy cover; neck of fruiting calyx and teeth visible or partly hidden among wool   4
4. Flowering heads 5–6 mm. across. Lower calyx teeth lanceolate or triangular. Fruiting heads usually woolly, snow-white to yellowish. [Plate 246, f. 4–5]   var. **lanatum**
   – Flowering heads 7–8(–9) mm. across. Lower calyx teeth linear. Fruiting heads grey, pinkish or dirty white   5

5. Heads all sessile, the upper ones often in pairs. [Plate 246, f. 1–3]   var. **orientale**
   – At least part of the heads short- or long-peduncled.   var. **philistaeum**

Var. **tomentosum**. *T. tomentosum* L., Sp. Pl. 771 (1753); Boiss., Fl. 2 : 138 (1872) p.p. *T. tomentosum* L. var. *pedunculatum* Nab., Publ. Fac. Sci. Univ. Masaryk 35 : 71 (1923). [Plate 246, f. 6]. Fruiting peduncles, at least the lower ones, conspicuous, arcuate. Fruiting heads evenly globular, head surface not interrupted by protruding upper parts of individual calyces. Fruiting calyx slightly pilose or glabrous; tube net-veined, clearly visible; teeth of calyx appressed to tube and hardly visible.
   Hab. : Fields and roadsides. Upper Galilee and probably elsewhere. Rather rare.

Var. **lanatum** Zoh.* [Plate 246, f. 4, 5]. Flowering heads about 5–6 mm. across. Lower calyx teeth lanceolate. Corolla 3–5 mm. Fruiting heads usually 1–1.2 cm. in diam., globular, snow-white to yellowish, woolly, sessile, or some of the heads borne on erect (rarely arcuate) peduncles. Fruiting calyx up to 6–7 mm., tapering into a conical apex bearing the 2 upper, spreading or recurved, subulate, hairy teeth, usually hidden among the wool.
   Hab. : Roadsides, fields, batha and steppes. Coastal Galilee, Sharon Plain, Upper and Lower Galilee, Mt. Carmel, Esdraelon Plain, Mt. Gilboa, Samaria, Judean Mts., N. Negev, Dan Valley, Upper Jordan Valley.

Var. **chthonocephalum** Bornm., Beih. Bot. Centralbl. 31, 2 : 204 (1914). Stemless or very short-stemmed plant. Flowering heads resembling those of var. *lanatum* but smaller, in the axils of long-petioled leaves, all crowded at base of plant or on its very short branches.
   Hab. : Fields, batha, steppes and roadsides. Upper Galilee, Judean Mts., Judean Desert, N. and C. Negev, Ammon.

Var. **curvisepalum** (V. Täckh.) Thiéb., Fl. Lib.-Syr. 2 : 28 (1940). *T. curvisepalum* V. Täckh., Svensk Bot. Tidskr. 26 : 373 (1932). [Plate 246, f. 7]. Tiny desert plant with obtriangular, long-cuneate upper leaflets. Peduncles, where present, mostly 1–1.5 cm., erect or curved. Fruiting heads more or less lobed, i.e., heads less compact than in the preceding varieties, with surface interrupted by the projecting upper parts of the calyces. Upper teeth of fruiting calyx very long, setiform and strongly curved, borne on a conical apex of the fruiting calyx.
   Hab. : Steppes and sandy flats. Philistean Plain, W. and N. Negev.

Var. **orientale** Bornm., Verh. Zool.-Bot. Ges. Wien 48 : 581 (1898). *T. hebraeum* Bobr., Acta Inst. Bot. Acad. Sci. URSS ser. 1, 6 : 259 (1947). [Plate 246, f. 1–3]. Flowering heads up to 7–8 (–9) mm. across. Lower calyx teeth linear. Corolla 5–7 mm. Fruiting heads sessile, evenly globular, pinkish to dirty white and grey. Fruiting calyx 4–5 mm., abruptly ending in a neck bearing 2 upper teeth, spreading or somewhat recurved, subulate, hairy.
   Hab. : Roadsides, fields, batha and steppes. Coastal Galilee, Acco Plain, Coast of Carmel, Sharon Plain, Philistean Plain, Upper and Lower Galilee, Mt. Carmel,

---

* See Appendix at end of this volume.

Esdraelon Plain, Samaria, Shefela, Judean Mts., Coastal and N. Negev, Dan Valley, Hula Plain, Upper Jordan Valley, Beit Shean Valley, Gilead, Moav. The most common variety.

T. tomentosum L. var. *orientale* is uniform in certain characteristics but is considerably polymorphic as to a number of other characteristics, such as pubescence of stem, colour and size of seed, shape of fruiting calyx, etc. There is no doubt that this collective variety includes some constant minor taxa which will only be revealed through further extensive experimental studies.

Var. philistaeum Zoh.* As in var. *orientale*, but at least some of the heads with conspicuous, rarely short, straight or curved peduncles.

Hab.: Sandy clay or sandy soil. Acco Plain, Sharon Plain, Philistean Plain, Judean Mts., Dan Valley, Lower Jordan Valley.

Area of species: Mediterranean, W. Irano-Turanian and W. and C. Euro-Siberian.

17. Trifolium bullatum Boiss. et Hausskn. in Boiss., Fl. 2 : 138 (1872). [Plate 247]

A tiny annual, glabrous or very sparingly hairy, 5–15 cm. Stems solitary or few, erect, branching from base. Stipules ovate, green-nerved, united to over half their length, free portion lanceolate; petiole somewhat canaliculate; leaflets not over 8 × 4 mm., obovate-cuneate, retuse, rather remotely denticulate, glabrous. Peduncles about 1 cm., erect in flower, symmetrically arcuate in fruit. Heads minute, 4–5 mm. across, 10–15-flowered. Pedicels minute. Calyx mostly 2–3 mm., tubular; teeth triangular. Corolla 3 mm., pink or whitish; standard somewhat longer than wings, broadly ovate. Fruiting heads 5–8(–9) mm.; relatively few fruiting calyces, well discernible, glabrous or slightly pilose, reticulately nerved; upper calyx teeth minute, triangular, often reduced to callosities. Pod about 1.2 mm., follicularly dehiscent, 1-seeded, lenticular. Seeds 0.8 mm., ovoid, yellowish. 2n = 16. Fl. March–April.

Var. bullatum. *T. bullatum* Boiss. et Hausskn. in Boiss., l.c.; Evenari in Opphr. et Evenari, Bull. Soc. Bot. Genève ser. 2, 31 : 290 (1941). *T. bullatum* Boiss. et Hausskn. var. *glabrescens* Post, Fl. Syr. Pal. Sin. 241 (1883–1896). *T. tomentosum* L. var. *bullatum* (Boiss. et Hausskn.) Gib. et Belli, Mem. Accad. Sci. Torino ser. 2, 41 : 17 (1890). *T. tomentosum* L. ssp. *bullatum* (Boiss. et Hausskn.) Opphr., Bull. Soc. Bot. Fr. 108 : 56 (1961). *T. tomentosum* L. var. *glabrescens* (Post) Hausskn. et Bornm., Mitt. Thür. Bot. Ver. N.F. 24 : 39 (1908). Fruiting heads 5–6 mm. Upper calyx teeth minute, 1 mm. or less.

Hab.: Fields and roadsides. Sharon Plain, Philistean Plain, Upper and Lower Galilee, Esdraelon Plain, Samaria, Judean Mts., Dan Valley, Hula Plain, Upper Jordan Valley.

Var. macrosphaerum Zoh.* Fruiting heads up to about 8–9 mm. in diam. Calyx teeth considerably longer than in the preceding variety.

Hab.: As above. Sharon Plain, N. and C. Negev, Hula Plain.

Area of species: E. Mediterranean.

* See Appendix at end of this volume.

T. bullatum is easily distinguishable from the related species, mainly by the fruiting calyx, the minute flowers, and the trend towards the reduction of the upper calyx teeth, which in var. *bullatum* are rudimentary. The teeth are still well preserved in var. *macrosphaerum,* which is, no doubt, a connecting link between this species and *T. tomentosum* L. var. *tomentosum.* As in *T. clusii,* there also occur forms with glabrous and hairy fruiting heads. The former has been described by Evenari (l.c. 291) and it is probably identical with *T. bullatum* Boiss. et Hausskn. var. *glabrescens* Post, Fl. Syr. Pal. Sin. 241 (1883–1896).

Sect. PARAMESUS (C. Presl) Griseb., Spicil. Fl. Rumel. 1 : 28 (1843); Godr. in Gren. et Godr., Fl. Fr. 1 : 416 (1849). Gen. *Paramesus* C. Presl, Symb. Bot. 1 : 45 (1831). Annuals. Stipules denticulate. Heads terminal and axillary. Bracts minute. Flowers sessile. Calyx tube 10-nerved; throat open, naked; teeth unequal. Petals connate below, marcescent. Pod 2-seeded, somewhat exserted from calyx tube.

18. T. glanduliferum Boiss., Diagn. ser. 1, 2 : 30 (1843). [Plate 248].

Annual, glabrous or slightly hairy, 10–25 cm. Stems erect or ascending, rarely prostrate, simple or branching, terete. Leaves short-petioled; stipules adnate to petiole up to more than half their length, scarious with green margins, semiovate, obtuse, sharply toothed with teeth sometimes ending in glands, many-nerved; leaflets 1–2 (–3) cm., oblong, elliptical to linear, cuneate at base, obtuse, mucronate, sharply dentate, prominently nerved, with or without sessile or stipitate glands on or between teeth; lower leaflets obovate. Peduncles axillary, much longer than leaves. Heads ovoid to globular, with a fairly conspicuous involucre or without involucre. Bracts reduced to very minute 3-toothed scales. Flowers sessile. Calyx tube white, obconical, glabrous or rarely with some scattered hairs, prominently 10-nerved; teeth unequal, mostly longer than tube, green, lanceolate-subulate, keeled-nerved, spreading or recurved in fruit. Corolla 2 or 3 times as long as calyx, pink to purple (rarely white); standard erect, linear, twice as long as keel, the latter somewhat shorter than wings. Pod longer than calyx tube, stipitate, 2-seeded, oblique, with long-exserted style. Seeds 1–1.2 mm., ovoid to oblong, brown. Dispersal through rupture of upper hardened part of pod from the lower membranous part. 2n = 16. Fl. March–April (–May).

Var. **glanduliferum.** *T. glanduliferum* Boiss., l.c.; Boiss., Fl. 2 : 141 (1872), incl. var. *tmoleum* (Boiss.) Boiss., Fl. 2 : 141 (1872). Involucre small, densely beset with stipitate glands. Leaflets, stipules and calyx teeth abundantly glandular. Fruiting calyx tube white, membranous between nerves. Seeds ovoid.

Hab.: Fields. Judean Mts., Hula Plain.

Var. **nervulosum** (Boiss. et Heldr.) Zoh. (comb. et stat. nov.). *T. nervulosum* Boiss. et Heldr. in Boiss., Diagn. ser. 1, 9 : 25 (1849) et Fl. 2 : 141 (1872). *T. nervulosum* Boiss. et Heldr. var. *galileum* (Boiss.) Boiss., Fl. 2 : 142 (1872). *T. galilaeum* Boiss., Diagn. ser. 1, 9 : 26 (1849). Closely resembling the former variety, but calyx teeth often shorter than tube. Involucre 0. Leaves and calyx teeth not or only sparsely glandular.

Hab.: Grassy places. Coastal Galilee, Acco Plain, Sharon Plain, Philistean Plain,

Upper and Lower Galilee, Esdraelon Plain, Judean Mts., Dan Valley, Gilead, Ammon. Area of species : E. Mediterranean.

After an extensive study of this species and comparison with the lectotypes of *T. glanduliferum* Boiss. and *T. nervulosum* Boiss. et Heldr. in Herbarium Boissier, the conclusion was reached that the whole complex is composed of a series of intergrading forms and the two above taxa cannot be kept on a specific level. While the typical specimens of *T. glanduliferum* from Lydia have rather conspicuous involucres, those from Palestine have smaller but well discernible involucres which are densely glandular. A step further leads to a form where the involucre is altogether lacking but the leaflets, stipules and calyx teeth are still sparsely but consistently glandular. In var. *nervulosum* the leaves and stipules are, according to Boissier, not glandular, but one encounters here and there specimens with sparse glands also in what has been regarded by Boissier as *T. nervulosum*. The length of calyx teeth and presence of hairs between the teeth are very weak diagnostic characteristics.

Sect. TRIFOLIUM. Sect. *Lagopus* (Bernh.) Koch, Syn. Fl. Germ. Helv. 184 (1835). Gen. *Lagopus* Bernh., Syst. Verz. Erf. 229 (1800). Subgen. *Trifolium* (C. Presl) Hossain, Not. Roy. Bot. Gard. Edinb. 23 : 397 (1961). Gen. *Trifolium* sensu C. Presl, Symb. Bot. 1 : 48 (1831). Racemes axillary or spuriously terminal, capitate or spike-like, ebracteate. Flowers sessile. Calyx 10- or 20-nerved; throat mostly narrowed or closed by a callosity or by a hairy ring, rarely open. Petals long-clawed; claws usually united to a tube. Pod mostly sessile, mostly included in calyx tube, 1(–2)-seeded.

19. Trifolium stellatum L., Sp. Pl. 769 (1753); Boiss., Fl. 2 : 121 (1872). [Plate 249]

Annual, patulous- and soft-villose, 10–20 cm. Stems few, mostly erect or ascending, sparsely branched or unbranched. Leaves long-petioled; stipules membranous, ovate, obtuse, dentate, green at margin; leaflets mostly 5–8 × 4–8 mm., obcordate with cuneate base, dentate in upper part. Heads 1.5–2 cm., long-peduncled, many-flowered, broadly obovoid to globular. Flowers 1.5–1.8 cm., loose. Calyx campanulate, densely subappressed-hispid, 10-nerved; tube shorter than the lanceolate-subulate teeth, the latter somewhat connate at base; throat densely fleecy but not closed by a callosity. Corolla mostly shorter than or as long as, rarely somewhat longer than calyx teeth, white or pink; standard with ovate to oblong limb, slightly longer than wings. Fruiting calyx with a long and sharp-pointed base; teeth spreading, broadened at base, with bristles directed upwards. Pod short-stipitate, membranous, lanceolate to pear-shaped. Seeds solitary, ellipsoidal to ovoid, shiny, yellowish. Fl. February–April.

Hab.: Roadsides, fields and batha. Acco Plain, Sharon Plain, Philistean Plain, Upper and Lower Galilee, Mt. Carmel, Esdraelon Plain, Mt. Gilboa, Samaria, Shefela, Judean Mts., Judean Desert, Dan Valley, Hula Plain, Upper Jordan Valley, Gilead, Ammon, Moav.

Area: Mediterranean, with slight extensions into adjacent regions.

20. Trifolium scabrum L., Sp. Pl. 770 (1753); Boiss., Fl. 2 : 130 (1872). [Plate 250]

Annual, appressed-hairy, 6–20 cm. Stems 1 to many, ascending or procumbent, sparsely branched or unbranched, flexuous, striate. Leaves small; upper leaves sessile or subsessile; petioles of lower leaves longer than leaflets; stipules membranous, the free portion short-triangular with subulate tip; leaflets 0.5–1 cm., obscurely or very shortly denticulate, with prominent nerves recurved near margin. Heads 0.7–1 cm., mainly axillary, sessile, few- to many-flowered, ovoid to obovoid. Calyx 5–7 mm.; tube leathery to ligneous, cylindrical, appressed-hairy, ribbed; teeth unequal, the lower one somewhat longer, rigid, lanceolate, prominently 1-nerved. Corolla shorter to slightly longer than calyx, mostly white. Fruiting head prickly, with cuneate base, separating as a whole from plant; calyx with recurved or spreading spiny teeth and mostly closed but not callose throat. Pod membranous, ovoid. Seeds solitary, 1.5 mm., ovoid-oblong, reddish-brown. Fl. January–June.

Hab.: Stony ground and rock crevices. Coastal Galilee, Acco Plain, Coast of Carmel, Sharon Plain, Philistean Plain, Upper and Lower Galilee, Mt. Carmel, Esdraelon Plain, foot of Mt. Gilboa, Samaria, Shefela, Judean Mts., Judean Desert, N. Negev, Upper Jordan Valley, Gilead, Ammon, Moav.

Area: Mediterranean, with slight extensions into the Irano-Turanian and Euro-Siberian borderlands.

21. Trifolium lappaceum L., Sp. Pl. 768 (1753). [Plate 251]

Annual, sparingly hirsute or glabrous, 10–30 cm. Stems many, branching, mostly flexuous. Lower leaves long-petioled, upper leaves subsessile; stipules membranous between green prominent nerves, oblong, free portion lanceolate-subulate; leaflets 0.5–1.5 × 0.3–0.8 cm., ovate to obovate or elliptical, the upper leaflets mostly cuneate at base, rounded or truncate, rarely emarginate at apex, very shortly dentate, sparingly hirsute on both sides. Heads 1–1.4 cm., first subsessile then conspicuously pedunculate, globular. Calyx 6–7 mm.; tube obconical or campanulate, green, white-hairy above, glabrous below, 20-nerved; teeth as long as or longer than tube, equal or almost so, setaceous with triangular 5-nerved base, long-ciliate. Corolla as long as or a little longer than calyx, white or pink; standard almost as long as wings and keel, with darker nerves above. Fruiting heads spinescent, with indurated calyx tubes and erect or slightly spreading, bristly-ciliate calyx teeth; calyx throat open, glabrous or ciliate. Pod membranous with a leathery operculum, ovoid, long-beaked. Seeds solitary, about 1.3 mm., ovoid, brownish, shiny. 2n = 16. Fl. March–May.

Var. lappaceum. *T. lappaceum* L., l.c.; Boiss., Fl. 2 : 119 (1872). Throat of calyx hairy-ciliate.

Hab.: Roadsides, fields and batha. Coastal Galilee, Acco Plain, Coast of Carmel, Sharon Plain, Philistean Plain, Upper and Lower Galilee, Judean Mts., N. Negev, Dan Valley, Hula Plain, Upper Jordan Valley, Beit Shean Valley, Gilead. Very common.

Var. zoharyi Eig, Bull. Inst. Agr. Nat. Hist. 6 : 24 (1927); Dinsmore in Post, Fl. Syr. Pal. Sin. ed. 2, 1 : 334 (1932). Throat of calyx glabrous.

Hab.: As above. Acco Plain, Sharon Plain, Philistean Plain, Upper Galilee, Mt. Carmel, Esdraelon Plain, Shefela.

Area of species: Mediterranean, with extensions into adjacent areas of the Irano-Turanian region.

22. Trifolium cherleri L., Demonstr. Pl. Hort. Upsal. 21 (1753) et Amoen. Acad. 3 : 418 (1756); Boiss., Fl. 2 : 119 (1872). [Plate 252]

Annual, patulous-hirsute, 5–20 cm. Stems few to many, ascending or procumbent, rather thick. Leaves long-petioled; stipules membranous, ovate-oblong, short-caudate; leaflets (0.5–)0.6–1 × 0.4–0.5 cm., obovate with cuneate base, notched, denticulate above. Heads sessile, many-flowered, broadly ovoid, somewhat depressed, subtended by broadened ovate-orbicular stipules. Flowers 6–8 mm. Calyx densely hirsute; tube campanulate, 20-nerved, with more or less equal setaceous teeth longer than tube. Corolla as long as or a little longer than calyx, white, rarely reddish. Fruiting calyx with erect teeth and open but villose throat. Pod membranous, ovoid, narrower at base, with an operculum and oblique style. Seed 1, ovoid-reniform, brown, shiny. Fruiting head separating as a whole from stem. Fl. March–April.

Hab.: Fields and damp places. Sharon Plain, Philistean Plain, Upper and Lower Galilee, Mt. Carmel, Esdraelon Plain, Mt. Gilboa, Samaria, Shefela, Judean Mts., Negev, Upper Jordan Valley, Transjordan.

Area: Mediterranean, with slight extensions into the W. Irano-Turanian borderland.

23. Trifolium arvense L., Sp. Pl. 769 (1753); Boiss., Fl. 2 : 120 (1872), incl. var. *longisetum* (Boiss. et Bal.) Boiss., l.c. [Plate 253]

Annual, silky-, appressed- or subpatulous-hairy, 5–15 cm. Stems solitary or few, erect or ascending, mostly branching above, tender, flexuous, terete. Lower leaves petiolate, upper leaves subsessile; stipules membranous between nerves, ovate-oblong, with long-cuspidate tip; leaflets 1–2 × 0.2–0.3(–0.4) cm., linear-oblong to narrowly elliptical with cuneate base, mucronate at apex, obscurely denticulate at upper part. Heads 1–2 cm., axillary and terminal, ovoid to cylindrical, on short peduncles elongating in fruit. Calyx about 6 mm., subpatulous-hairy; tube cylindrical-campanulate, about one third as long as teeth; throat closed by a ring of hairs, not by a callosity; teeth equal, setaceous and plumose, often purplish or pink. Corolla much shorter than calyx, white or pink. Pod membranous, ovoid. Seed 1, globular, yellow. Fl. March–May.

Hab.: Batha and grassy places. Coastal Galilee, Sharon Plain, Upper Galilee, Hula Plain, Gilead. Rare.

Area: Mediterranean, Euro-Siberian and Irano-Turanian.

24. Trifolium angustifolium L., Sp. Pl. 769 (1753); Boiss., Fl. 2 : 122 (1872). [Plate 254]

Annual, appressed- or subappressed-hirsute, 10–30 cm. Stems solitary or few, ascending or erect, scarcely branched. Lower leaves short-petioled, upper leaves long-petioled; stipules adnate to petiole up to half their length, many-nerved, free portion lanceolate-subulate; leaflets (2–)3–5 × 0.2–0.4 cm., narrowly linear-lanceolate, those of upper leaves acute, those of lower leaves obtuse, entire or nearly so, appressed-pubescent on both sides. Heads 2–6 cm., short-peduncled, spike-like, cylindrical or conical. Flowers 1–1.3 cm. Calyx tubular-campanulate, covered with appressed to spreading stiff hairs arising from tubercles; teeth subulate-setaceous, sharp-pointed, the lower one somewhat longer than the others. Corolla not exceeding calyx teeth, or very slightly so, pale pink to almost purple; standard notched. Fruiting calyx with stellately spreading teeth and entirely closed throat. Pod ovoid, membranous. Seed 1, ovoid, light brown. Fl. March–April.

Hab.: Batha. Mt. Carmel. Very rare.

Area: Mediterranean, with extensions into W. Irano-Turanian territories.

25. Trifolium purpureum Loisel., Fl. Gall. 484, t. 14 (1807). [Plate 255]

Annual, mostly appressed- to subappressed-hirsute, 10–30(–50) cm. Stems few or many, erect, ascending or rarely procumbent, branching above, striate. Leaves with petioles shortening towards apex of stem; stipules 1–1.5 cm., membranous between nerves, oblong-lanceolate, with upper portion subulate; leaflets 2–4(–6) × 0.2–1 cm., oblong-lanceolate to linear or elliptical, acute, mucronulate, obscurely toothed above, mostly hairy only at margins. Heads (1–)1.5–6 cm., at the ends of dichotomous or simple branches, conical or ovoid in flower, ovoid-oblong to cylindrical in fruit. Flowers 1.5–2 cm. Calyx up to 1 cm., subappressed-hirsute; tube 3 mm. or more, almost cylindrical; teeth subulate, the lowermost tooth longer than calyx, slightly longer than to twice as long as the rest. Corolla distinctly longer than calyx, purple above, whitish-lilac below, sometimes lilac or whitish all over; standard with oblong limb distinctly longer than wings. Fruiting calyx tube obconical, prominently nerved; teeth blunt, divergent or spreading, plumose, with bristles arising from tubercle; throat completely closed by a callosity. Pod 1-seeded, ovoid, mucronate. Seeds about 1 mm., ovoid, brown. 2n = 16. Fl. February-May.

Var. **purpureum**. *T. purpureum* Loisel., l.c.; Boiss., Fl. 2:123 (1872). *T. purpureum* Loisel. var. *genuinum* Post, Fl. Syr. Pal. Sin. 235 (1883–1896). *T. desvauxii* Boiss. et Bl. var. *laxiusculum* (Boiss. et Bl.) Boiss., Fl. 2:123 (1872). Stems erect or ascending, usually appressed-pubescent. Leaflets oblong to oblong-lanceolate. Flowering heads (2.5–)3–4 cm., oblong to cylindrical; fruiting heads 3–6 cm. Flowers very numerous in each head, 1.5–1.8(–2) cm.

Hab.: Fields, batha and roadsides. Coastal Galilee, Acco Plain, Sharon Plain, Philistean Plain, Upper and Lower Galilee, Mt. Carmel, Esdraelon Plain, Samaria, Shefela, Judean Mts., W. and N. Negev, Dan Valley, Hula Plain, Upper Jordan Valley, Beit Shean Valley, Gilead, Ammon. Common.

Var. **desvauxii** (Boiss. et Bl.) Post, l.c. 236. *T. desvauxii* Boiss. et Bl. in Boiss., Diagn. ser. 2, 2:12 (1856); Boiss., Fl. 2:123 (1872) p.p. Plant usually 10–15 cm. Stems ascending or procumbent, usually slender, appressed-pubescent above, patulous-hirsute below and along stipules. Leaflets mostly linear-lanceolate, obscurely denticulate at apex. Flowering heads 1.5–2 cm., ovoid or broadly conical, generally loose and with a smaller number of flowers than the preceding variety; fruiting heads about 2 cm. (rarely 3 cm.).

Hab.: Dry and stony places; coastal sands or semisteppe batha. Acco Plain, Philistean Plain, Upper and Lower Galilee, Mt. Carmel, Esdraelon Plain, Samaria, Shefela, Judean Mts., Judean Desert, W. and N. Negev, Dan Valley, Hula Plain, Gilead, Ammon. Common.

Area of species: Mainly Mediterranean, with extensions into adjacent W. Irano-Turanian and Euro-Siberian regions.

26. Trifolium blancheanum Boiss., Diagn. ser. 2, 2 : 13 (1856). *T. desvauxii* Boiss. et Bl. var. *blancheanum* (Boiss.) Boiss., Fl. 2 : 124 (1872). [Plate 256]

Annual, appressed- or subappressed-hairy, 10–20 cm. Stems many, procumbent, diffuse, scarcely branched, striate, leafy especially at base. Leaves small, all short-petioled to subsessile; stipules membranous, oblong, ciliate above, prominently nerved, terminating with a lanceolate-cuspidate apex half as long as lower part; leaflets 0.8–1.5 × 0.4–0.8 cm., oblong-elliptical, obtuse, obliquely apiculate, densely appressed-hairy. Peduncles short in flower, elongating in fruit. Heads 1–1.3 cm., many-flowered, ovoid or globular. Flowers 1–1.2 cm. Calyx tubular; tube 3 mm., densely covered with brown bristles, prominently nerved; teeth as long as or longer than tube, unequal, setaceous, blunt, the lower one longer than the others. Corolla almost twice as long as calyx, lilac or pink; standard ovate-oblong, somewhat shorter than wings. Fruiting heads 1.3–2 cm., not increasing much in size. Fruiting calyx somewhat indurated; teeth erect or stellately spreading; throat closed by a callosity. Pod 1-seeded, membranous. Seeds 1.2 mm., greenish-brown. Mature heads not or very tardily disarticulating. Fl. April–May.

Hab.: Seashore exposed to sea spray. Acco Plain, Sharon Plain. Rather uncommon.

Area: E. Mediterranean (Palestine, Lebanon and Cyprus).

27. Trifolium palaestinum Boiss., Diagn. ser. 1, 9 : 21 (1849) et Fl. 2 : 124 (1872). [Plate 257]

Annual, patulous-hairy, 10–20(–30) cm. Stems many or few, erect, ascending or procumbent, usually not branching, thick, striate. Leaves long-petioled below, subsessile above; stipules 1.5–2 cm., membranous between prominent nerves, oblong-linear with long-cuspidate tips; leaflets 1.5–3.5 × 0.3–0.8 cm., oblong-linear to elliptical, obtuse or acute, apiculate, those of the upper leaves toothed and often broader above. Heads 1.5–2 cm., terminal, ovoid, elongating in fruit up to 2.5(–3) cm. Flowers about 1.5 cm. Calyx densely hispid; tube obconical, much shorter than teeth; teeth slightly unequal, subulate, truncate, plumose. Corolla usually not exceeding calyx teeth, white; standard with oblong-linear limb much longer than wings and keel. Fruiting calyx readily separating from rhachis; teeth stellately spreading or slightly diverging; throat closed by a callosity. Pod membranous, oblong, obtuse. Seeds solitary, 2 mm., ovoid, brown, smooth. 2n = 16. Fl. March–May.

Hab.: Sandy soils. Coastal Galilee, Acco Plain, Sharon Plain, Philistean Plain (endemic). Rather common.

Area: E. Mediterranean.

28. Trifolium dichroanthum Boiss., Diagn. ser. 1, 9 : 20 (1849) et Fl. 2 : 124 (1872). [Plate 258]

Annual, patulous-, subpatulous- or antrorsely hirsute, 10–50 cm. Stems few, erect or ascending, rarely procumbent, striate, often reddish. Leaves long-petioled, upper leaves mostly opposite; stipules membranous between nerves, oblong, upper stipules inflated, semiovate, with long-subulate tips; leaflets 1–3(–4) × 0.2–1 cm., oblong to elliptical and linear, obtuse, often mucronulate, obscurely toothed above. Heads 2–6 × 1.5–2 cm., ovoid to cylindrical in flower, 2-coloured (younger flowers pale pink, older flowers deep pink to purple). Flowers up to 2 cm. Calyx 8–9 mm., densely subappressed-hirsute; tube cylindrical-campanulate, much shorter than the unequal, subulate, truncate, plumose teeth. Corolla about 1.6–1.8 cm.; limb of standard linear, distinctly longer than wings. Fruiting calyx with tube somewhat constricted above and erect or partly spreading teeth; throat closed. Pod 1-seeded, membranous, ovoid, with bent mucro. Seeds ovoid, brown, smooth. Fl. March–May.

Hab.: Sandy soils. Acco Plain, Sharon Plain, Philistean Plain, W. Negev. Rather common.

Area: E. Mediterranean (Sinai, Palestine and Lebanon).

29. Trifolium dasyurum C. Presl, Symb. Bot. 1 : 53, t. 33 (1832). *T. formosum* Urv., Mém. Soc. Linn. Paris 1 : 350 (1822) non Savi, Obs. Trif. 102 (1810) nec Curt. ex DC., Prodr. 2 : 200 (1825); Boiss., Fl. 2 : 124 (1872). *T. formosum* Urv. var. *minus* Post, Fl. Syr. Pal. Sin. 236 (1883–1896) et ed. 2, 1 : 338 (1932). *T. velivolum* Paine, Palest. Explor. Soc. Statement 3 : 103 (1875). [Plate 259]

Annual, appressed- or antrorsely pubescent, 10–30(–40) cm. Stems few or many, ascending, diffuse, often dichotomously branching above, striate. Both branches of each fork, or only one of them, developed and ending with a head. Leaves opposite (when only one branch of the fork develops), petiolate, uppermost leaves subsessile; stipules membranous, inflated, with arcuate nerves and a long, subulate to cuspidate tip; leaflets 1–3.5 × 0.2–1 cm., elliptical to oblong, acute, not dentate or obscurely so. Heads 1.5–3(–4) cm., many-flowered, ovoid. Calyx appressed- to patulous-hairy; tube cylindrical to obconical; teeth about twice as long as tube, equal, subulate, truncate, with lanceolate base. Corolla about as long as calyx, purple above, whitish or pink below; standard with oblong limb, somewhat longer than wings. Fruiting calyx with top-shaped tube, divergent or spreading teeth and closed throat. Pod stipitate, membranous, oblong, obliquely apiculate, with solitary, globular to some-what compressed, smooth seed 1.8 mm. 2n = 16. Fl. March–May.

Hab.: Batha, roadsides and fallow fields. Coastal Galilee, Sharon Plain, Philistean Plain, Upper and Lower Galilee, Mt. Carmel, Esdraelon Plain, Samaria, Shefela, Judean Mts., Judean Desert, Negev, Dan Valley, Hula Plain, Upper and Lower Jordan Valley, Gilead, Ammon, Edom. Common.

Area: E. Mediterranean, with extensions into adjacent territories of the Irano-Turanian region.

30. Trifolium prophetarum Hossain, Not. Roy. Bot. Gard. Edinb. 23 : 421 (1961). [Plate 260]

Annual, appressed-silky, 10–15 cm. Stems few or rarely solitary, erect or ascending, simple, rarely branched, slightly furrowed. Leaves with petioles shortening towards apex, the uppermost leaves falsely opposite (one branch of the fork being suppressed); stipules 4–6 mm., prominently nerved and membranous between nerves, oblong, the lower portion adnate to petiole, the upper portion subulate; leaflets 1–2 × 0.2–0.3 cm., oblong-elliptical to almost linear, terminating with an oblique mucro. Heads 1.5–3.5 cm., often at the end of a false dichotomy, many-flowered, obovoid in flower, becoming oblong or cylindrical in fruit. Flowering calyx 6(–7) mm., appressed-silky; tube about 2 mm., narrowly obconical, 10-nerved; teeth 4–5 mm., 2–3 times as long as tube, equal, setaceous, plumose. Corolla exserted from calyx by one third of its length, upper part lilac to purple; standard, with oblong-lanceolate limb, distinctly longer than wings. Fruiting calyx with spreading teeth and closed throat. Ovary and pod stipitate. Seeds solitary, 1.2 mm., ovoid, brown, smooth. Fl. March–April.

Hab.: Batha. Upper and Lower Galilee, Esdraelon Plain, Mt. Gilboa, Judean Mts., Upper Jordan Valley (endemic). Rare.

Area: E. Mediterranean.

31. Trifolium salmoneum Mout., Fl. Djeb. Druze 128 (1953). [Plate 261]

Annual, glabrous below, sparingly appressed-hairy above, 40–60 cm. Stems many, branching all along, fistulous, prominently striate. Leaves petiolate, the upper ones opposite; stipules membranous, oblong-linear, ciliate, with prominent green nerves, free portion usually shorter than the lower connate one, subulate; petiole of upper leaves shorter than blade; leaflets 1.5–5 × 0.3–1.2 cm., elliptical, upper leaflets linear-lanceolate, cuneate, mucronulate, denticulate near apex. Heads 1.5–2 × 1.2–1.6 cm., terminal and axillary, pedunculate, ovoid. Flowers about 1 (–1.3) cm. Calyx tubular to campanulate; tube about 3 mm., prominently nerved, white-membranous between nerves (especially when in fruit), covered with long or short shiny hairs more or less evenly dispersed along tube; nerves visible, not concealed by hairs; throat of calyx (especially when in fruit) strongly narrowed by a callosity but not closed, finely appressed-hairy or glabrous; teeth unequal, 1-nerved, the lower tooth nearly as long as tube, partly or not at all stellately diverging in fruit, not at all or only sparingly tuberculate-hairy. Corolla cream-coloured; standard with linear limb; wings and keel about two thirds as long as standard. Fruiting heads 1.5–2.5 × 1 cm., ovoid to oblong. Fruiting calyx 4.5(–6) mm. (incl. teeth); tube obliquely campanulate, somewhat constricted above middle, evenly white-pilose; throat oblique; teeth with a very thick nerve at triangular base. Pod membranous. Seeds solitary, 1.2–1.5 mm., yellow, globular or obovoid, somewhat compressed. Fl. April–May (–June).

Hab.: Swampy soils. Upper Galilee. Rare.

Area: E. Mediterranean (Palestine and Lebanon).

32. Trifolium berytheum Boiss. et Bl. in Boiss., Diagn. ser. 2, 2 : 15 (1856); Hossain, Not. Roy. Bot. Gard. Edinb. 23 : 425 (1961). *T. supinum* Savi var. *tuberculatum* Boiss., Fl. 2 : 126 (1872). *T. alexandrinum* L. var. *tuberculatum* (Boiss.) Gib. et Belli, Mem. Accad. Sci. Torino ser. 2, 39 : 390 (1889). *T. alexandrinum* L. var. *berytheum* (Boiss. et Bl.) Trab., Bull. Dir. Agr. Serv. Bot. 48 : 2 (1911); Thiéb., Fl. Lib.-Syr. 2 : 34 (1940); Opphr., Bull. Res. Counc. Israel D, 7 : 212 (1959). *T. echinatum* M.B. var. *berythaeum* (Boiss. et Bl.) Dinsmore in Post, Fl. Syr. Pal. Sin. ed. 2, 1 : 338 (1932). *T. constantinopolitanum* Ser. var. *plumosum* Bornm., Beih. Bot. Centralbl. 31, 2 : 203 (1914). [Plate 262]

Annual, sparingly appressed-hairy or glabrescent, 15–50 cm. Stems solitary or few, branching from base or all along, slightly striate, brownish at base. Lower leaves long-petioled, upper leaves subsessile, uppermost leaves opposite; stipules membranous, oblong-linear with dark prominent nerves, free portion shorter or longer than lower portion, subulate-caudate; leaflets (1–)1.3–2.5(–3.5) × 0.2–0.8(–1) cm., linear-elliptical, elliptical or oblong with cuneate base, obtuse, rarely acute or slightly notched and apiculate, denticulate above, appressed-pubescent. Heads 1–1.5(–2) cm., terminal and axillary, pedunculate or sessile and then involucrate, ovoid or obovoid in flower. Flowers about 1 cm. Calyx tubular or obconical; tube 2.5–3 mm., appressed-hairy below and rather hispid above; throat of calyx open, with a ring of stiff, patulous hairs; teeth unequal, lanceolate to subulate, mostly hispid or ciliate, with long hairs usually arising from tubercles, usually 1-nerved, rarely the base of the lower tooth and the 2 posterior teeth 3-nerved. Corolla 7–9 mm., white to cream-coloured; standard with oblong-linear limb; wings and keel two thirds as long as standard. Fruiting heads 0.8–2 × 0.7–1 cm., ovoid to oblong. Fruiting calyx tube obconical, somewhat thickened; lower tooth often longer than tube, the others usually as long as tube or shorter, erect or stellately spreading. Pod membranous, obovoid, apiculate, upper part somewhat leathery. Seeds solitary, 1.5–1.7 mm., obovoid, yellow or brown. 2n = 16. Fl. March–May.

Hab.: Roadsides, fallow fields and grassy places; heavy soils, mostly flooded in winter. Coastal Galilee, Acco Plain, Coast of Carmel, Sharon Plain, Philistean Plain, Lower Galilee, Mt. Carmel, Esdraelon Plain, Shefela, Judean Mts., Hula Plain, Upper Jordan Valley, Beit Shean Valley. Rather uncommon.

Area: E. Mediterranean (Palestine, Lebanon, Syria and Turkey).

33. Trifolium meironense Zoh. et Lern.* [Plate 263]

Annual, appressed-pubescent, 15–30 cm. Stems many, ascending, slightly striate at lower part. Leaves alternate, uppermost leaves opposite; stipules linear-oblong, lower portion membranous, purple-nerved, free part as long as or shorter than the adnate part, herbaceous, subulate; leaflets 0.8–1.5 × 0.2–0.4 cm., linear-elliptical to oblong with cuneate base, mucronate, denticulate in upper part. Heads 1–1.5(–2) × about 1 cm., terminal and axillary, pedunculate, ovoid-oblong. Calyx 3–4 mm.; tube cylindrical in flower, with long patulous hairs especially at base of teeth, 10-nerved; teeth unequal, lower tooth one and a half times as long as tube, the rest usually as long as or shorter than tube, subulate-acicular, long-hairy, 1–3-nerved at base, all or at least the lower tooth ending in a purple tip. Corolla one and a half times to twice as long as calyx, pale pink; standard with linear limb; wings and keel three quarters as long as standard. Fruiting heads 1–1.8 × 0.6–1.2 cm., oblong to conical. Fruiting calyx up to 5 mm.; tube obconical, thickened, with 10 costate nerves; throat open but provided with a callose and ciliate ring; teeth erect or somewhat spreading, triangular at base. Pod membranous, coriaceous in upper part, narrowly obovoid and apiculate. Seeds solitary, about 1.5 × 1.1 cm., laterally strongly compressed, obovoid to pyriform. 2n = 16. Fl. April–May.

* See Appendix at end of this volume.

Hab.: Batha and maquis. Upper Galilee. Very rare.
Area: E. Mediterranean (Palestine, Turkey).

34. Trifolium vavilovii Eig, Bull. Appl. Bot. Pl. Breed. Leningr. ser. 7, 1 : 108 (1934);
Opphr., Bull. Res. Counc. Israel D, 7 : 208 (1959). *T. carmeli* Boiss. var. *carmeli*
sensu Hossain, Not. Roy. Bot. Gard. Edinb. 23 : 427 (1961) excl. syn. [*T. echinatum*
M.B. var. *carmeli* (Boiss.) Gib. et Belli et *T. constantinopolitanum* Ser. var. *carmeli*
(Boiss.) Thell.]. [Plate 264]

Annual, patulous- to appressed- or crisp-hairy, glabrescent below, 15–50 cm. Stems
ascending to erect, moderately branched. Leaves, except the upper ones, alternate,
with petiole longer than stipules; stipules oblong, dark-nerved, with lanceolate-caudate
free portion as long as the adnate part to much longer in the upper leaves; leaflets
(1–)1.5–3.5 × 0.5–1(–1.5) cm., denticulate above, at least the upper ones mucronulate, silky-hirsute with margin somewhat ciliate; leaflets of the lower leaves obovate,
those of the middle leaves broadly elliptical or tapering at both ends, those of the
upper leaves elliptical to oblong and tapering at base to a short petiolule. Flowering
heads 1–1.5 cm., terminal and axillary; adult heads long-peduncled, ovoid to obovoid.
Flowers (0.8–)1–1.2 cm. Calyx tubular; tube appressed-pubescent, 10-nerved; teeth
shorter than or as long as tube, the lower tooth much longer in the lower than in the
upper flowers, one and a half times to twice as long as the 2 upper teeth or more,
all teeth lanceolate-subulate, purple-tipped, 1-nerved, with hairs not arising from
tubercles. Corolla up to twice as long as calyx, cream-coloured; standard oblong to
linear, somewhat notched at apex, much longer than wings, the latter somewhat longer
than keel. Fruiting heads (1–)2(–3) × 1–1.5 cm., cylindrical to conical. Fruiting
calyx indurated, very short-hairy or partly glabrescent; throat wide open, glabrous
or very slightly appressed-hairy (not ciliate); lower tooth much longer than tube,
reflexed, spinescent, the rest erect, never stellately spreading. Pod membranous below,
somewhat leathery above, obovoid, apiculate. Seed 1, about 1.5 mm., greenish-yellow
or brownish. 2n = 16. Fl. March–May.

Hab.: Abandoned fields, roadsides, herbaceous batha and stony hills. Sharon Plain,
Philistean Plain, Upper and Lower Galilee, Mt. Carmel, Esdraelon Plain, Mt. Gilboa,
Samaria, Judean Mts., Dan Valley, Hula Plain, Upper Jordan Valley, Gilead, Am-
mon. Rather common.

Area: E. Mediterranean (Palestine, Syria and Iraq).

T. vavilovii varies slightly in the proportion of the calyx teeth, the pubescence of the
calyx and the size and shape of the leaves.

T. vavilovii has long been overlooked by students of the flora of the Near East. This
was partly due to the inadequate description by Eig and to the inaccessibility of the Russian periodical in which this species was originally published It is a rather common species
in Palestine and it grows in batha and other rather dry places. It is easily distinguished
from *T. alexandrinum* L. and *T. berytheum* Boiss. et Bl. by the smaller flowers, by the
lower calyx tooth which is often twice as long as the others or more, by the slight pubescence of the calyx tube and its leathery consistency, and by the naked throat of the calyx
and the purple tips of the calyx teeth.

35. Trifolium alexandrinum L., Cent. Pl. 1 : 25 (1755) et Amoen. Acad. 4 : 286 (1759); Boiss., Fl. 2 : 127 (1872) excl. syn. et var. *β*; Opphr., Bull. Res. Counc. Israel D, 7 : 204 (1959). [Plate 265]

Annual, sparingly appressed-pubescent, 20–60 cm. Stems few or many, erect or ascending, mostly branching from base, striate, leafy. Leaves petiolate, the uppermost leaves opposite and sessile; stipules submembranous, longitudinally green-nerved, connate for half their length or more, free portion lanceolate-subulate or caudate, plumose-ciliate; leaflets 1.5–5 × 0.6–1.5 cm., those of lower leaves obovate, those of upper leaves broadly elliptical to oblong, those of uppermost leaves tapering at base or also at apex, much narrower than the others, all denticulate above, mucronate, rarely retuse, sparingly or densely appressed-pubescent. Heads 1.2–2.5 × 1–1.5 cm., terminal and axillary, subsessile to pedunculate, ovoid to conical in flower, ovoid-oblong to conical or cylindrical in fruit, often provided with some bracts forming a minute involucre at base. Flowers 0.8–1.3 cm. Calyx 3.5–4 mm.; tube cylindrical or obconical to campanulate, mostly appressed- and silky-hairy, with 10 prominent nerves diverging in fruit; throat open, with or without a ring of short, not patulous, hairs; teeth unequal, often erect or somewhat spreading, triangular-lanceolate to subulate, plumose with antrorse silky hairs or rarely hispid, with glabrous, white and spinulose tips, the lower tooth much broader, mostly as long as tube and a little longer than the others, sometimes obliquely truncate or irregularly split at apex, 3-nerved at base. Corolla cream-coloured; standard usually one and a half times as long as wings and keel, linear-spatulate. Fruiting calyx broadly campanulate, with erect (very rarely partly spreading) teeth. Pod 2.2–2.5 mm., with membranous lower part and coriaceous apiculate operculum. Seeds solitary, mostly 2–2.2 × 1.4–1.9 mm., yellow. Mature calyces not separating from rhachis of head. 2n = 16. Fl. April–May.

Hab.: Cultivated throughout the area, and frequently escaping from cultivation.

Area: Extensively cultivated in temperate and subtropical regions; origin E. Mediterranean, probably Palestine.

Of the many cultivars of the "Egyptian clover", the two known by the names *fahli* and *muscavi* are the most common. The first is a spring form unable to regenerate after harvesting and therefore grown for seeds only. The second is an early summer crop and regenerates readily after each of the 4–6 harvests. As these physiological varieties have so far not been described morphologically, their descriptions are given here.

Var. **alexandrinum.** Plants unbranched or only slightly branched at base. Stems thin, solid. Free parts of stipules of the upper leaves triangular. Involucre of bracts (at base of head) 0 or very rudimentary. Teeth of calyx almost equal, lower tooth (in lower flowers mainly) more or less symmetrical, not oblique, as long as or shorter than fruiting calyx tube; the latter whitish with prominent nerves. Fruiting heads ovoid, less prickly to the touch. Fl. March–April. Local name of variety : *fahli*.

Widely cultivated as a single-harvest clover in the Mediterranean and in other warm-temperate regions. Linnaeus's specimen of *T. alexandrinum* in the Linnaean Herbarium (London) represents the above variety.

Var. **serotinum** Zoh. et Lern.* Plant profusely branched at base. Stems thick, fistulous.

---

* See Appendix at end of this volume.

Free part of stipules of upper leaves lanceolate-subulate. Involucre of bracts at base of head conspicuous, sometimes minute. The lower tooth of calyx considerably longer than the rest, that of lower calyces mostly with asymmetrical apex (e.g. obliquely acuminate or with a unilateral lobe, etc.), mostly one and a half times as long as tube of fruiting calyx; the latter herbaceous, greyish and less prominently nerved. Fruiting heads more prickly to the touch. Fl. Mainly May–June. Local name of variety: *muscavi*.

Extensively cultivated as a forage plant; yields 4–6 harvests during the vegetative period.

T. alexandrinum can readily be distinguished from its related indigenous species, namely *T. berytheum* Boiss. et Bl., *T. constantinopolitanum* Ser., *T. vavilovii* Eig, *T. salmoneum* Mout. and others, though the phylogenetic relations between these wild species and *T. alexandrinum* are still obscure. While Oppenheimer (1959) considers *T. berytheum* Boiss. et Bl. a variety of *T. alexandrinum* and attributes the ancestry of the latter to *T. berytheum,* it is now clear that there is a wide gap between *T. alexandrinum* and its allied wild species. *T. alexandrinum* is well discernible from its allies not only by its floral parts but also by its mature heads, which do not disarticulate, while the mature heads in the other species of the group disarticulate into the fruit-bearing calyces. This presents an enormous discontinuity between the true *T. alexandrinum* and its allies, similar to that existing between cultivated varieties of wheat or barley and the wild ones.

36. Trifolium constantinopolitanum Ser. in DC., Prodr. 2:193 (1825); Boiss., Diagn. ser. 2, 2:14 (1856) non Boiss., Fl. 2:127 (1872) *pro syn. T. alexandrinum* L. var. *phleoides* (Boiss.) Boiss., Fl. 2:127 (1872); Hossain, Not. Roy. Bot. Gard. Edinb. 23:426 (1961). [Plate 266]

Annual, appressed- or patulous-hirtellous, 15–35(–60) cm. Stems erect or ascending, moderately branching. Leaves alternate, uppermost leaves opposite; stipules membranous, linear, green- or blackish-nerved, free portion as long as or longer than lower one, lanceolate or subulate; leaflets (0.8–)1.5–3 × 0.4–0.8 cm., elliptical to obovate-oblong, cuneate at base or tapering at both ends, acute or mucronate, denticulate at apex, appressed-hirsute. Flowering heads 1–2 cm., terminal, pedunculate, ovoid to obconical, somewhat elongating, cylindrical and spike-like in fruit. Flowers rather loose. Calyx at first cylindrical, then urceolate, constricted near throat, more or less densely appressed-hirtellous; teeth as long as tube, narrowly lanceolate to subulate, purple-tipped, plumose-bristly, 1- or rarely 3-nerved, the lower tooth one and a half times as long as the rest. Corolla 1–1.2 mm., up to twice as long as calyx, cream-coloured; standard with broad, linear to oblong limb, much longer than wings and keel, often with purple tip. Fruiting calyces somewhat bifarious, brown-, grey- or white-hirsute; tube urceolate; throat entirely closed by a callosity, ciliate along slit; teeth stellately spreading. Pod membranous with coriaceous apex, oblong. Seed 1, about 1.5 mm., ovoid, yellowish-brown. 2n = 16. Fl. April–June.

Hab.: Damp fields, grassy places, river banks. Upper Galilee, Dan Valley, Hula Plain. Rather uncommon.

Area: E. Mediterranean (Palestine–Turkey).

37. Trifolium leucanthum M.B., Fl. Taur.-Cauc. 2:214 (1808); Boiss., Fl. 2:128 (1872), incl. var. *declinatum* Boiss., l.c. [Plate 267]

Annual, sparingly appressed- or patulous-hairy, 10–30 cm. Stems few or many, erect or ascending, poorly branching, striate. Leaves long-petioled, uppermost leaves opposite; stipules membranous, oblong to lanceolate with cuspidate or subulate upper portion; leaflets 1.5–2.5 cm., those of lower leaves obovate-cuneate and often notched, those of upper leaves oblong-cuneate, obtuse to truncate, denticulate above. Heads 1–1.5 cm. in diam., long-peduncled, semiglobular to almost globular. Calyx 6–7 mm., on a hispid rhachis; tube 3 mm., obconical, densely covered with long, shiny hairs; calyx teeth almost as long as or longer than tube, slightly unequal, lanceolate-subulate, with or without purple tips, 3-nerved at base. Corolla about as long as or slightly longer than calyx, cream-coloured to pink or violet. Fruiting heads 1–2 × 1.2–1.5 cm., almost globular. Fruiting calyx urceolate, with tube constricted above, throat entirely closed by a callosity, and stellately spreading ciliate teeth. Pod membranous in lower part, coriaceous above, ovoid. Seed 1, about 1.5 mm., globular to obovoid, brown, shiny. Fl. March–April.

Hab.: Shady places. Upper Galilee. Very rare.

Area: Mainly Mediterranean, with extensions into W. Irano-Turanian territories.

Easily distinguished from *T. echinatum* M.B. by its small corolla, which is scarcely, if at all, exserted from calyx, and by its hairy, urceolate fruiting calyx tube.

38. Trifolium echinatum M.B., Fl. Taur.-Cauc. 2 : 216 (1808). [Plate 268]

Annual, appressed- or patulous-pubescent above, glabrescent below, (10–)20–50 cm. Stems erect or ascending, rarely prostrate. Leaves alternate, upper leaves opposite; stipules submembranous, linear-oblong, long-villose, dark-nerved, with free portion usually longer than the adnate one, green, lanceolate or subulate; leaflets (0.8–)1.2–2(–3.5) × 0.4–1.5 cm., those of the lower leaves obovate, often retuse, those of the middle leaves linear to broadly elliptical to oblong-cuneate, and those of the upper leaves narrowly elliptical and tapering on both ends or oblong-elliptical, denticulate at apex, appressed-pubescent on either side. Flowering heads 1–2 × 1–1.8(–2) cm., broadly ovoid, on peduncles which elongate in fruit. Flowers 1–1.3(–1.5) cm. Calyx tube cylindrical to obconical, hirsute above, 10-nerved; teeth very unequal, subulate, with purple tips, usually 1-nerved, all or some of them with bristles arising from tubercles; the lower tooth much longer than tube and about twice as long as the 2 upper teeth. Corolla cream-coloured or pink or cream-coloured with pink-tipped keel; standard 1–1.5 cm., one and a half times as long as wings and keel, oblong-spatulate. Fruiting heads (0.8–)1.2–2.4 cm., globular to ovoid, compact, echinate. Fruiting calyces concrescent at base and partly adnate to rhachis, with campanulate, whitish, smooth, obsoletely nerved tube; throat closed by a 2-lipped callosity with ciliolate or glabrous slit widening secondarily due to the growing seed; teeth erect or rarely spreading, subulate-spinulose, plumose, with broad, thickened, nerveless base. Pod membranous, ovoid, apiculate. Seed 1, about 1.3 mm., ovoid, yellowish-brown. 2n = 16. Fl. March–May.

Var. **echinatum**. *T. supinum* Savi, Obs. Trif. 46, f. 2 (1810); Boiss., Fl. 2 : 126 (1872) excl. var. *β*. Stems mostly appressed-, rarely patulous-hairy to glabrescent. Fruiting heads (0.8–)1–1.6 cm. Leaflets (even the middle ones) generally not exceeding 2 cm. in length, elliptical to cuneate-elliptical. Posterior and lateral calyx teeth sparingly plumose-setulose. Corolla mostly pink, rarely cream-coloured; keel not purple-tipped.

Hab.: Heavy soils in batha and on field edges. Upper Galilee, Mt. Carmel, Samaria, Shefela, Judean Mts. Rare.

In the E. Mediterranean countries this variety is not well delimited from the following one, owing to the occurrence of intermediate forms.

Var. **carmeli** (Boiss.) Gib. et Belli, Mem. Accad. Sci. Torino ser. 2, 39 : 377 (1889). *T. carmeli* Boiss., Diagn. ser. 2, 2 : 16 (1856) et Fl. 2 : 127 (1872); Opphr., Bull. Res. Counc. Israel D, 7 : 207 (1959). *T. constantinopolitanum* Ser. var. *carmeli* (Boiss.) Thell., Viert. Nat. Ges. Zürich 52 : 454 (1907). Stems patulous-pubescent. Leaflets of lower leaves obovate, those of middle leaves broadly elliptical, up to 2.5(–3.5) cm. long and up to 1 cm. or more broad, and those of uppermost leaves narrowly elliptical to cuneate-oblong. Calyx teeth all plumose-setulose, the lower tooth up to 6 mm., serrulate. Corolla cream-coloured with pink spot on top of keel; standard 1.3–1.5 cm. Fruiting heads 1.5–2.3 cm.

Hab.: Batha, fields and field edges. Coast of Carmel, Sharon Plain, Upper and Lower Galilee, Mt. Carmel, Esdraelon Plain, Samaria, Judean Mts. Fairly common.

Area of species: Mainly E. Mediterranean and contiguous areas of the Euro-Siberian and Irano-Turanian regions.

This species has not been well understood by some authors. Despite its variability in indumentum, shape of leaflets and size of heads, there is no ground for dividing it into two species as was done by Boissier (in establishing his *T. carmeli*). At the most, *T. carmeli* should be considered a large-leaved and large-headed variety, though intergrading with var. *echinatum*.

T. echinatum is distinguished from the other species of the "*alexandrinum*" group also by its fruiting calyces which are not separable from one another and from the rhachis, and by the smooth and mostly glabrous calyx tube and the erect, rarely spreading teeth.

39. Trifolium clypeatum L., Sp. Pl. 769 (1753); Boiss., Fl. 2 : 129 (1872). [Plate 269]

Annual, patulous- to retrorsely villose, 10–30 cm. Stems erect or ascending, much branching, furrowed, leafy. Leaves long-petioled; stipules almost membranous, half-ovate, with delicate nerves branching above, free portion almost as long as or longer than adnate part, ovate-triangular, acute; leaflets 1–3 × 0.5–2 cm., obovate to obovate-cuneate, sparingly appressed-hairy, dentate above, upper leaflets mucronate. Flowering heads 2–3 × 1–2.5 cm., long-peduncled, many- to few-flowered, obovoid. Flowers up to 2 cm. or more, loose. Calyx tube tubular, green, prominently nerved, long-villose in the upper part; teeth green, sharp-pointed, tuberculate-bristly, many-nerved, the lower one oblong, 2–4 times as long as the triangular to triangular-lanceolate upper ones. Corolla 2–3 times as long as calyx, pink to white; standard oblong-ovate, obtuse, slightly retuse, slightly or distinctly longer than wings and keel. Fruiting heads 2–3 cm., compact. Fruiting calyx with campanulate, somewhat oblique, glabrescent tube; throat closed by a broad, 2-lipped, glabrous callosity; teeth 3 mm. or more broad, stellately spreading, leaf-like, many-nerved, the lower one oblong-ovate, the lateral teeth broadly ovate, one third as long as the lower one, the upper teeth very short, broadly triangular. Pod 4 mm., membranous-scarious, broadly ovoid, prominently nerved, opening by an apiculate operculum. Seeds solitary, 3 mm., lenticular, brown. Upper fruiting calyces separating from rhachis, the rest remaining on the plant. Fl. January–May.

Hab.: Fields, roadsides and batha. Coastal Galilee, Acco Plain, Sharon Plain, Upper and Lower Galilee, Mt. Carmel, Esdraelon Plain, Mt. Gilboa, Samaria, Shefela, Judean Mts., Judean Desert, Dan Valley, Hula Plain, Upper Jordan Valley, Gilead, Ammon, Moav. Common.

Area: E. Mediterranean (Palestine to Greece).

40. Trifolium scutatum Boiss., Diagn. ser. 1, 2:27 (1843) et Fl. 2:129 (1872). [Plate 270]

Annual, patulous-pubescent, 15–20 cm. Stems ascending or procumbent, much branching. All except the uppermost leaves alternate; stipules membranous, prominently nerved, lower united part triangular-ovate, sparingly villose, free portion long, lanceolate-subulate, green, with long bristles arising from tubercle; leaflets 1–1.4 × 0.5–0.8 cm., obovate with cuneate base, rounded or notched at apex, all alike, denticulate above, appressed-hirsute. Heads 1.8–2.3 × 1.3–1.8 cm., terminal, pedunculate, ovoid to obovoid-globular. Flowers 0.8–1 cm. Calyx about 5 mm.; tube whitish, obconical, glabrous or glabrescent, prominently ribbed; teeth unequal, green, not purple-tipped, the lower one broadly lanceolate to oblong, almost glabrous, 3–5-nerved, somewhat longer and broader than tube, and 2–3 times as long as the other teeth, which are lanceolate, 3-nerved, and sparingly ciliate. Corolla cream-coloured; standard with broadly linear to lanceolate limb, somewhat longer than wings, the latter somewhat longer than keel. Fruiting heads 1.5–2 cm., globular-ovoid, soon becoming detached from peduncle and dispersed as a whole. Fruiting calyx with obconical, almost glabrous, strongly ribbed tube; throat closed by a 2-lipped callosity; teeth stellately spreading, sparingly ciliate, the lower one broadly lanceolate, one and a half times as long as the ovate-triangular, leaf-like, 3–5-nerved, wrinkled, lateral teeth. Pod 2–3 mm., membranous with coriaceous tip, obovoid, apiculate. Seed 1, about 1.8 cm., ovoid, yellowish-brown. Dispersal unit: the entire fruiting head. Fl. March–May.

Hab.: Fields and among shrubs. Upper Galilee, Mt. Carmel, Esdraelon Plain, Samaria, Judean Mts., Dan Valley, Upper Jordan Valley. Not rare.

Area: E. Mediterranean (Palestine–Turkey).

41. Trifolium plebeium Boiss., Diagn. ser. 1, 9:23 (1849) et Fl. 2:129 (1872). *T. alsadami* Post, Journ. Linn. Soc. Lond. Bot. 29:425 (1880), Fl. Syr. Pal. Sin. 238 (1883–1896) et ed. 2, 1:340 (1932); Mout., Fl. Djeb. Druze 129 (1953). [Plate 271]

Annual, densely or sparingly patulous-pubescent, 10–40 cm. Stems mostly ascending and diffuse, rarely few and erect, striate. Leaves long-petioled and alternate, except for the uppermost ones; stipules membranous, oblong, prominently dark-nerved, free portion as long as or longer than the lower part, mostly green, lanceolate; leaflets 0.6–1.2 × 0.3–1 cm., varying in shape in a single plant from almost orbicular to obovate with often cuneate base to oblong, rounded to truncate or retuse at apex, obsoletely dentate above. Heads 1–2 × 1.2–1.8 cm., pedunculate, broadly ovoid to obovoid, later somewhat elongating. Flowers 1–1.5 cm. Flowering calyx (4–)5–7 mm.; tube cylindrical or somewhat campanulate, appressed-hairy, prominently nerved; teeth unequal, purple-tipped, the lower one lanceolate-subulate, tuberculate-ciliate, longer than tube and up to or over twice as long as the other, triangular-lanceolate, teeth. Corolla 1–1.2 cm., usually white or cream-coloured; standard with lanceolate-oblong, slightly notched, limb, one and a half times as long as wings and keel. Fruiting heads about 1.2–2 × 1–1.5 cm. Tube of fruiting calyx ovoid, pubescent, with prominent ribs; throat of calyx closed by a broad, 2-lipped, smooth or ciliolate callosity; upper teeth triangular, lateral teeth triangular-lanceolate, and lower tooth lanceolate-subulate, all stellately spreading, 3-nerved, the lower tooth and often also the lateral teeth recurved. Pod about 2 mm., membranous, ovoid. Seed 1, about 1 mm., globular-compressed, brown. Dispersal usually by entire fruiting heads. 2n = 16. Fl. March–May.

Hab.: Rather dry and open places; mainly in batha. Upper Galilee, Judean Mts., Judean Desert, Dan Valley. Not rare.

Area: E. Mediterranean (Palestine–Turkey).

T. scutatum Boiss. and *T. plebeium* Boiss. are very different from one another in their typical forms (as shown by specimens from Mt. Carmel and from Jerusalem) but where they grow together they probably intercross. Accordingly, some specimens show intermediate characters in their calyx structure. However, even in such specimens *T. scutatum* can still be recognized by its glabrous or almost glabrous calyx tube, by its ovate-lanceolate lower calyx tooth, and by other features.

Sect. TRICHOCEPHALUM Koch, Syn. Fl. Germ. Helv. 171 (1835). Sect. *Calycomorphum* (C. Presl) Griseb., Spicil. Fl. Rumel. 1 : 31 (1843). Racemes capitate. Flowers mostly sessile, ebracteolate, the inner ones without corollas and sterile, developing at or after flowering of the outer, fertile flowers. Pod 1-seeded. Calyces of sterile flowers function as an anemochoric means of dispersal (forming a cottony or silky ball), as a geocarpic one (acting as a drilling mechanism), or as a zoochoric one (adhesive calyx teeth).

42. Trifolium pauciflorum Urv., Mém. Soc. Linn. Paris 1 : 350 (1822) et Enum. Pl. 94 (1822; "*pauci-florum*"); Hossain, Not. Roy. Bot. Gard. Edinb. 23 : 441 (1961); Katznelson, Israel Journ. Bot. 14 : 175 (1965). *T. oliverianum* Ser. in DC., Prodr. 2 : 197 (1825). *T. globosum* auct. nonn. non L., Sp. Pl. 767 (1753). [Plate 272]

Annual, patulous-pubescent, 15–50 cm. Stems few, erect or ascending, slightly branching, striate. Lower leaves long-petioled, upper leaves almost sessile; stipules membranous between nerves, semiovate, long-acuminate; leaflets 0.8–1.2 cm., rhombic to obovate, cuneate at base, mostly apiculate, denticulate at apex. Heads 1.2–1.6 cm., short-peduncled to subsessile, many-flowered, globular. Flowers sessile; corollate (fertile) flowers (4–)5–7(–8) in one row, sterile flowers numerous. Calyces of fertile flowers densely hirsute, with equal teeth as long as or slightly longer than tube; calyces of sterile flowers carrying flexuous, elongating, plumose-silky teeth. Corolla 0.8–1 (–1.4) cm., slightly to distinctly longer than calyx, purple. Fruiting heads 1.2–1.8 cm., compact, globular to ovoid, forming dense, silky, greyish-pink, opaque hair balls. Pod included within calyx tube, membranous, obovoid. Seed 1, compressed, ovoid, shiny.

Dispersal unit: the entire head, with its few seed-bearing calyces enclosed by the sterile calyces, which form the silky cover. 2n = 16. Fl. April–May.

Hab.: Fallow fields; heavy soil. Upper Galilee, Hula Plain, Gilead. Rather uncommon.

Area: E. Mediterranean (Palestine to Greece).

43. Trifolium pilulare Boiss., Diagn. ser. 1, 2 : 29 (1843) et Fl. 2 : 135 (1872). *T. pilulare* Boiss. var. *longepedunculatum* Evenari in Opphr. et Evenari, Bull. Soc. Bot. Genève ser. 2, 31 : 295 (1941). *T. globosum* L. ssp. *pilulare* (Boiss.) Gib. et Belli, Mem. Accad. Sci. Torino ser. 2, 43 : 211 (1893); Katznelson, Israel Journ. Bot. 14 : 180 (1965). [Plate 273]

Annual, appressed- to patulous-hairy, 10–50 cm. Stems many, erect, ascending or prostrate, branching throughout, angulate-furrowed. Lower leaves long-, upper short-petioled; stipules membranous between nerves, ovate, acuminate; leaflets 0.4–1.2 cm., obovate with cuneate base, rounded, truncate or retuse at apex, apiculate, obsoletely toothed in upper part. Heads 6–9 mm., 1–2 times as long as leaves, on capillary peduncles spreading or recurved, ovoid or globular, lengthening in fruit. Flowers sessile; corollate (fertile) flowers 1–2, sterile flowers numerous. Calyces of fertile flowers with densely villose tube and equal, setaceous, loosely plumose teeth as long as or longer than tube; calyces of sterile flowers with long, silky and plumose teeth. Corolla 6–7 mm., usually not exceeding calyx, white; standard a little longer than wings and keel. Fruiting heads 0.8–1 cm., globular, forming a silky, greyish hair ball translucent at margin. Pod included within calyx tube, membranous, ovoid, obtuse. Seeds solitary, 2 mm., ovoid-globular, dark brown, smooth, shiny. Dispersal unit: the entire head, containing the 1–2 seed-bearing calyces which are enclosed by the many sterile calyces. 2n = 14. Fl. February–May.

Hab.: Batha, fields and roadsides. Sharon Plain, Philistean Plain, Upper and Lower Galilee, Mt. Carmel, Esdraelon Plain, Mt. Gilboa, Samaria, Shefela, Judean Mts., Judean Desert, Dan Valley, Hula Plain, Upper Jordan Valley, Beit Shean Valley, Gilead, Ammon. Very common.

Area: E. Mediterranean (Palestine to Greece), with extensions into adjacent Irano-Turanian territories.

44. Trifolium eriosphaerum Boiss., Diagn. ser. 1, 9 : 25 (1849) et Fl. 2 : 134 (1872; "*eriosphoerum*"). *T. globosum* L. ssp. *eriosphaerum* (Boiss.) Gib. et Belli, Mem. Accad. Sci. Torino ser. 2, 43 : 208, t. 1, f. 3 (1893). [Plate 274]

Annual, appressed-hairy, especially in upper part, 10–40 cm. Stems few to many, prostrate to ascending, branching, striate. Lower leaves long-petioled, upper leaves subsessile; stipules adnate to petiole, membranous between nerves, ovate to oblong, upper free part short, acute; leaflets 0.6–1 (–2) cm., obovate, cuneate at base, denticulate near the rounded apex. Heads 1.2–1.8 cm., axillary, ovoid to oblong or cylindrical in flower, with peduncles as long as or longer than leaves, elongating and spreading or recurving in fruit. Pedicels very short. Corollate flowers 4–6 in one row, sterile flowers numerous, all sessile. Calyces of fertile flowers white-woolly, with teeth as long as or somewhat longer than the obscurely nerved tube, filiform with triangular base, plumose; calyces of sterile flowers white-cottony, with spreading, setaceous, flexuous, woolly teeth. Corolla 1.2–1.8 cm., much longer than calyx, purple or flesh-coloured above. Fruiting heads about 1 cm. or less, globular, forming an opaque, white-cottony ball. Pod much shorter than calyx, membranous, oblong, mucronate. Seeds solitary, 1.5 mm., ovoid-oblong, brown, smooth, shiny. Dispersal unit: the entire head, including the many sterile calyces, which enclose the few seed-bearing calyces. Fl. February–May.

Hab.: Mainly batha. Philistean Plain, Upper and Lower Galilee, Esdraelon Plain, Samaria, Judean Mts., Judean Desert, Hula Plain, Upper Jordan Valley, Gilead, Ammon. Fairly common.

Area: E. Mediterranean (Palestine, Lebanon and Syria).

Fairly homogeneous and common. Differs from all other species of this section in its white-cottony heads.

45. Trifolium subterraneum L., Sp. Pl. 767 (1753); Katznelson and Morley, Israel Journ. Bot. 14 : 117 (1965). [Plate 275]

Annual, glabrescent to patulous-hairy, 10–30 cm. Stems few, prostrate or decumbent, sparingly branched or often unbranched, weak, slightly furrowed. Leaves long-petioled; stipules ovate, acute; leaflets 0.8–1.2 (–2) cm., mostly obcordate with cuneate base, denticulate and mostly notched at apex. Heads about 1 cm., long-peduncled, obovoid, loose, the fruiting heads globular. Corollate (fertile) flowers few or many; sterile flowers several, developing after anthesis of the fertile ones. Calyces of corollate flowers glabrous or sparingly pubescent, with cylindrical tube growing in fruit and almost equal, linear-subulate, teeth, about as long as tube; calyces of sterile flowers with solid, stalk-like tube and linear teeth. Corolla about 1 cm., almost twice as long as calyx, white, pinkish-striped; standard elliptical. Fruiting heads deflexed, ripening underground. Pod becoming somewhat exserted from split calyx, membranous, obovoid or obtriangular. Seeds solitary, 2.5 mm., lenticular, black. Fruiting head carrying a few seed-bearing calyces and many wire-like sterile ones, bent downwards, surrounding the fertile flowers and pushing them into the ground. 2n = 16. Fl. March–April.

Var. **subterraneum**. *T. subterraneum* L., l.c.; Boiss., Fl. 2 : 133 (1872). *T. subterraneum* L. var. *genuinum* Aschers. et Graebn., Syn. Mitteleur. Fl. 6, 2 : 597 (1908). Calyx tube as long as or longer than pod, sparingly hairy.

Hab.: Fallow fields and grassy sites. Sharon Plain, Upper Galilee, Esdraelon Plain. Fairly common.

Var. **brachycalycinum** Katznelson et Morley, l.c. 128. Calyx tube half as long as pod, often glabrous.

Hab.: Fallow fields and batha; heavy and light soils. Sharon Plain, Upper and Lower Galilee, Samaria, Shefela, Judean Mts., Upper Jordan Valley. Less common than the preceding variety.

Area of species: Mediterranean and adjacent areas of the Euro-Siberian region.

46. Trifolium israëliticum D. Zoh. et Katznelson, Austral. Journ. Bot. 6 : 179 (1958). *T. subterraneum* L. var. *telavivense* (gram. err. *"tel-avivensis"*) Eig, Bull. Inst. Agr. Nat. Hist. 6 : 25 (1927). [Plate 276]

Annual, sparingly patulous-villose, 5–40 cm. Stems few, prostrate to decumbent, sparingly branched or unbranched, weak, striate. Leaves long-petioled; stipules membranous, ovate to oblong, acuminate; leaflets 1–1.4 × 0.6–1.6 cm., obovate with cuneate base and rounded, rarely slightly emarginate apex, long-denticulate above. Heads axillary, pedunculate, few-flowered, the lower peduncles thick and curved. Corollate flowers 2–5, pedicellate; sterile flowers developing after anthesis of the fertile ones. Calyx tube of fertile flowers tubular, white, glabrous, growing in fruit; teeth somewhat longer than tube, almost equal, setaceous, loosely long-villose. Corolla 1.4–1.8 cm., 3–4 times as long as calyx, red or violet. Pod exserted from the split calyx, much broader than long, leathery, transversely ovoid, dark violet to purplish, transversely wrinkled, upper margin strongly keeled. Seeds solitary, ovoid, usually yellowish. Fruiting heads deflexed, ripening underground, the few seed-bearing calyces surrounded by the many, indurated, stalk-like and long-toothed sterile ones, which are bent downwards and push the entire head into the ground. 2n = 12. Fl. February–April.

Hab.: Forests, batha, maquis and open fallow fields. Sharon Plain, Upper and Lower Galilee, Samaria (endemic). Less common than the preceding species.

Area: E. Mediterranean.

Among other characters, it differs from *T. subterraneum* L. in the usually obovate leaflets with rounded or truncate (not deeply emarginate) apex, in its lower peduncles which are thick (usually twice as thick as petioles) and curved, in the red or violet corolla of the fertile flowers, which is 3–4 times as long as calyx, and in the transversely ovoid mature pod, much broader than long.

Trib. VICIEAE. Leaves mostly pinnate, with rhachis terminating in a tendril, rarely in an awn. Flowers in many- or few-flowered racemes. Stamens diadelphous. Pod dehiscing by 2 spirally twisting valves.

38. CICER L.

Annuals or herbaceous perennials or half-shrubs. Leaves impari- or paripinnate, with dentate stipules mostly adnate to stem and with denticulate leaflets. Racemes 1- to few-flowered. Calyx deeply 5-toothed; calyx tube sometimes gibbous; rim of calyx tube often oblique. Corolla as long as or somewhat longer than calyx; standard ovate to orbicular, clawed; wings obliquely obovate. Stamens diadelphous; filaments more or less dilated above; anthers uniform. Ovary sessile, 2- to many-ovuled; style filiform, not bearded; stigma terminal, capitate. Pod dehiscent, 2-valved, 1–3-seeded, turgid. Seeds globular or obovoid; radicle straight.

About 20 species, mainly in S. and E. Mediterranean countries, as well as S. W. and C. Asia.

1. Cicer pinnatifidum Jaub. et Sp., Ann. Sci. Nat. Bot. ser. 2, 18 : 227 (1842); Boiss., Fl. 2 : 560 (1872). [Plate 277]

Annual, glandular-hirsute, 10–40 cm. Stems prostrate to ascending, branched from base. Leaves 2–4 cm., imparipinnate; stipules 3–4 mm., much shorter than petiole, dentate or pinnatipartite, the uppermost stipules lanceolate; leaflets 3–7-paired, 0.3–0.8(–1) cm., obovate to oblong, cuneate at base, deeply dentate-incised to pinnatifid, hairy on both sides. Peduncles aristate. Pedicels longer than calyx, deflexed. Flowers solitary, 5–7 mm., spreading or deflexed in fruit. Calyx as long as or longer than the violet corolla; teeth longer than tube, lanceolate, 3-nerved. Pod 1–1.5 cm., 1–3-seeded, ovoid, glandular-hairy. Seeds 3–4 mm., obovoid, 2-gibbous at base, with erect rostellum, tuberculate. Fl. March–April.

Hab.: On scree and among dwarf shrubs. Sharon Plain, Philistean Plain, Upper and Lower Galilee, Mt. Carmel, Esdraelon Plain, Samaria, Shefela, Judean Mts., Upper Jordan Valley, Gilead. Fairly common.

Area: E. Mediterranean.

Var. *judaicum* (Boiss.) Pop., Bull. Appl. Bot. Pl. Breed. Leningr. 21 : 176 (1928–1929), based mainly on size of pod and recorded from the Judean Mts., cannot be separated from the typical form because of the occurrence of transitional forms between them.

39. VICIA L.

Annual or perennial herbs, rarely shrubs. Leaves paripinnate, with many, rarely 1–2 pairs of leaflets and branched, rarely simple tendrils; stipules mostly semisagittate. Racemes many- to few-flowered, often reduced to single axillary flowers. Bracts small, caducous. Flowers small to large. Calyx often with oblique tube and equal teeth or with upper teeth shorter than lower. Corolla blue, violet to purple or white to yellow; petals short-clawed; standard mostly obovate to oblong, notched; wings often adhering to keel. Stamens diadelphous; staminal tube oblique; filaments thread-like; anthers uniform. Ovary short-stipitate, many- to several-ovuled, rarely 1–2-ovuled; style hairy above or all around, or bearded, rarely glabrous; stigma terminal. Pod dehiscent, mostly compressed, rarely cylindrical; valves leathery, rarely fleshy. Seeds mostly globular, sometimes angular.

About 200 species, mostly in north-temperate regions; a few in S. America and in mountains of Trop. Africa.

Many species of this genus are well known forage plants; some, e.g. *V. ervilia*, *V. narbonensis*, *V. sativa*, *V. villosa* and others, are widely cultivated and most of their wild progenitors are indigenous in Palestine. Some of the species are highly polymorphic and not always clearly delineated. A most intricate complex is that of *V. sativa* and of *V. villosa*. According to the abundance of local forms of these species, they seem to be at present in the full process of speciation.

Literature: P. F. A. Ascherson & K. O. P. P. Graebner, *Vicia*, in: Aschers. & Graebn., *Syn. Mitteleur. Fl.* 6, 2 : 902–995, 1909. A. I. Tupikova, Botanico-agronomical investigations of annual vetches, *Bull. Appl. Bot. Pl. Breed. Leningr.* 16 : 151–246 (1926). I. N. Sveshnikova, Karyological studies on *Vicia*, *Bull. Appl. Bot. Pl. Breed. Leningr.* 17 : 843–854

(1927). B. Schischkin & E. Bobrov, *Vicia* L., in: *Flora URSS* 13: 406–475, 1948. E. Guinea, *Estudio Botanico de las Vezas y Arvejas Españolas,* 1–227, Madrid, 1953. F. J. Hermann, Vetches of the United States, *Agric. Handb.* 168: 1–84 (1960). D. Mettin & P. Hanelt, Cytosystematische Untersuchungen in der Artengruppe um *Vicia sativa* L., *Kulturpflanze* 12: 163–225 (1964). P. Ball, *Vicia,* in: T. G. Tutin & H. V. Heywood (ed.), *Fl. Europaea* (MS). U. Plitmann, *Biosystematical Studies in the Annual Species of Vicia and Lathyrus of the Middle-East,* Ph. D. Thesis, Jerusalem, 1966 (MS.).

1. Tendrils reduced to a very short awn, 2–8 mm. Pod necklace-shaped, 2–4-seeded. Cultivated and escaped.   **8. V. ervilia**
– Tendrils, if present, longer than above, at least in part of the leaves. Pod not necklace-shaped   2
2. Leaflets, at least part of them, about 1(–1.5) cm. or more broad. Pod flat, hairy, about 1 cm. broad, with denticulate margin   3
– Leaflets usually much narrower than above. Pod not as above   4
3. Corolla purple or violet. Leaflets (2–)4–8.   **20. V. narbonensis**
– Corolla cream to pale lilac and bluish. Leaflets 2–4(–6).   **21. V. galilaea**
4(2). Pod (2–)3(–4) mm. broad, linear, not over 2 cm. long. Flowers less than 1 cm.   5
– Pod 0.5–1 cm. broad or more   7
5. Tendrils mostly branched or forked. Calyx teeth longer than tube.   **9. V. pubescens**
– Tendrils mostly simple. Calyx teeth slightly shorter than tube   6
6. Leaflets (4–)6–12. Peduncles about as long as subtending leaves. Stipules 3–4 mm. Lower calyx teeth longer than upper ones. Pod glabrous.   **10. V. tetrasperma**
– Leaflets 4–6(–10). Peduncles longer than subtending leaves. Stipules usually longer than above. Pod hairy.   **11. V. tenuissima**
7(4). Leaflets all or most of them obovate, one and a half times as long as broad. Pod and corolla glabrous   8
– Leaflets, at least most of them, linear, oblong or elliptical, 2–3 or more times as long as broad, sometimes leaflets shorter but then pods or corolla or both hairy   9
8. Calyx glabrous. Corolla yellowish with blue-tipped keel and standard. Racemes mostly 2- or more-flowered. Pod deflexed.   **6. V. cypria**
– Calyx hairy. Corolla purple. Racemes 1-flowered. Pod erect.   **17. V. cuspidata**
9(7). Pod glabrous   10
–   Pod hairy   16
10. Flowers 2 cm. long or more   11
— Flowers up to 1.5(–1.7) cm. long   12
11. Flowers cream-coloured to whitish-pink. Racemes mostly 3–5-flowered.
                                                                    12. V. galeata
— Flowers purplish-violet. Racemes 1–2-flowered.   **5. V. esdraëlonensis**
12(10). Flowers shorter than 1 cm.   13
— Flowers longer than 1 cm.   14
13. Leaflets 6–10-paired. Racemes (2–)3–8(–9)-flowered.   **3. V. palaestina**
— Leaflets 2–4-paired. Racemes 2-flowered.   **4. V. hulensis**
14(12). Peduncles much shorter than subtending leaves. Racemes 1–3(–4)-flowered.
                                                                    7. V. monantha
— Peduncles as long as to much longer than subtending leaves. Racemes mostly 5–30-flowered   15
15. Perennials. Leaves with (5–)6–12 pairs of leaflets; lateral lobes of stipules half as long as terminal one or less.   **1. V. tenuifolia**

— Annuals. Leaves with 4–10 pairs of leaflets; lateral lobes of stipules almost as long as terminal lobe.   **2. V. villosa**

16 (9). Racemes usually 5–30-flowered.   **2. V. villosa**

— Racemes 1–2 (–3)-flowered   17

17. Leaflets 1–2 (–3) pairs, most of them 3–5 cm. Pod erect or ascending.   **19. V. bithynica**

— Leaflets mostly 4 or more pairs, shorter than above, sometimes part of leaves with 2–3-paired leaflets but then leaflets considerably shorter than above and/or very narrow. Pod deflexed   18

18. Flowers yellow or cream-coloured   19

— Flowers blue, purple, violet or white   21

19. Corolla hairy.   **16. V. hybrida**

— Corolla glabrous   20

20. Leaflets obovate to oblong, retuse.   **15. V. sericocarpa**

— Leaflets linear-lanceolate, not retuse.   **14. V. lutea**

21 (18). Pod 2–3 times as long as broad.   **14. V. lutea**

— Pod 4 times as long as broad or more   22

22. Margin of calyx tube horizontal, even.   **18. V. sativa**

— Margin or calyx tube oblique.   **13. V. peregrina**

Sect. GRACCA (Medik.) S. F. Gray, Nat. Arr. Brit. Pl. 2 : 614 (1821). Gen. *Cracca* Medik., Vorl. Churpf. Phys.-Oken. Ges. 2 : 359 (1787). Peduncles many-flowered. Style frequently pubescent around apex. Pod usually beaked. Perennials or biennials, sometimes annuals.

1. Vicia tenuifolia Roth, Tent. Fl. Germ. 1 : 309 (1788); Boiss., Fl. 2 : 586 (1872). *V. cracca* L. ssp. *tenuifolia* (Roth) Gaudin, Fl. Helv. 4 : 507 (1829). [Plate 278]

Perennial, appressed-hairy or glabrescent, 0.5–2 m. Stems erect, climbing, branched, rigid, angular. Leaves 3–10 cm., appressed-pilose; stipules about 1 cm., narrow, semihastate, hairy; tendrils simple or branching; leaflets 6–12-paired, 0.8–3.5 (–4) × 0.1–0.7 cm., subsessile, oblong-linear to lanceolate, acuminate to obtuse and mucronulate. Racemes one-sided, longer than leaves, long-peduncled, erect, dense, with 11–25 flowers. Pedicels shorter than calyx, pilose. Flowers 1.2–1.4 cm. Calyx 3–6 mm., somewhat gibbous, appressed-pilose; rim of tube slightly oblique; teeth shorter than tube, lanceolate-subulate, the lower teeth longer. Corolla blue; standard longer than wings, with limb twice as long as claw, retuse; wings much longer than the dark blue keel. Style slightly hairy at apex. Pod about 2–3 × 0.6–0.8 cm., short-stipitate, 2–6-seeded, deflexed, flattened, oblong-rhombic, glabrous. Seeds 3–4 mm., subglobular, brown-black, smooth, with an oblong-linear, brown hilum. Fl. May–June.

Hab. : Forests, maquis, batha and fields; in mountains. Upper Galilee, Dan Valley, Gilead (specimens seen only from Gilead).

Area : Euro-Siberian, Mediterranean and W. Irano-Turanian.

V. tenuifolia varies in dimensions of leaflets and flowers. One of its forms is var. **laxiflora** Griseb., Spicil. Fl. Rumel. 1 : 82 (1843) (=var. *stenophylla* Boiss., Fl. 2 : 586, 1872 = *V. elegans* Guss., Fl. Sic. Prodr. 2 : 438, 1828) which differs from the typical form in its longer and narrowly linear leaflets, its looser racemes and its larger flowers. This is the only form occurring in Palestine.

2. Vicia villosa Roth, Tent. Fl. Germ. 2 : 182 (1789). [Plate 279]

Annual, villose or appressed-pilose to glabrescent, 20–80 cm. Stems numerous, erect, climbing, branched, angular. Leaves 2–6 cm., rather short-petioled; stipules 5–9 × 1–5 mm., semihastate or semisagittate to lanceolate, hairy; tendrils branched; leaflets (3–)4–10-paired, 0.8–3(–3.5) × (0.1–)0.2–0.8(–1) cm., ovate-oblong to narrowly linear, acute-acuminate to obtuse, mucronulate. Peduncles generally longer than subtending leaves. Racemes long, (3–)5–30(–40)-flowered. Flowers 1.2–1.8(–2) cm., short-ped-icelled, spreading to pendulous. Calyx 5–8 mm., manifestly gibbous, somewhat violet at apex, villose to slightly pilose; rim of tube oblique; teeth shorter to longer than tube, the lower teeth 1–5 mm., longer than the upper teeth, ciliate or glabrescent. Corolla almost 3 times as long as calyx, purple- or blue-violet to bluish, wings some-times whitish or yellowish; standard as long as or longer than wings, retuse, with claw as long as or shorter (or longer) than limb. Style somewhat flattened, hairy at apex. Pod (1.5–)2–3(–3.5) × 0.7–1(–1.2) cm., 2–8-seeded, deflexed, rhombic to oblong-linear, compressed, glabrous to rarely puberulent. Seeds 3–4 mm., slightly compressed, almost globular, black or purple-brown; hilum short, linear, whitish-brown. 2n = 14. Fl. January–May.

Subsp. **villosa.** *V. villosa* Roth, l.c.; Boiss., Fl. 2 : 591 (1872) et auct. plur.; Post, Fl. Syr. Pal. Sin. 289 (1883–1896), incl. var. *latifolia* Post, l.c. Villose annual or bien-nial. Stipules up to 5 mm. broad; leaflets 8–10 pairs, linear-lanceolate to oblong, acute. Racemes 10–30-flowered. Flowers 1.4–1.8 cm. Calyx teeth as long as or longer than tube, ciliate. Corolla blue to violet; limb of standard equalling claw. Pod usually 2–2.5 cm., more or less glabrescent.

Hab. : Fields, hedges, maquis. Sharon Plain, Philistean Plain, Lower Galilee, Mt. Carmel, Shefela, Judean Mts., N. Negev, Hula Plain. Fairly common.

Subsp. **dasycarpa** (Ten.) Cavill., Ann. Cons. Jard. Bot. Genève 11/12 : 21 (1907–1908). *V. dasycarpa* Ten., Rel. Viagg. Abruz. 81 (1830). *V. varia* Host, Fl. Austr. 2 : 332 (1832). Sparingly appressed-hairy to rather subglabrous. Leaves short-petioled to sessile; stipules narrower than 3 mm.; leaflets 3–10 pairs, narrowly linear to oblong-elliptical, acute to obtuse. Racemes 3–15-flowered. Flowers 1.2–2 cm. Calyx teeth generally shorter than tube. Corolla purple-violet with whitish or yellowish wings; limb of standard shorter than claw. Pod 2–3 cm., more or less puberulent.

Hab. : As above; sometimes cultivated. Acco Plain, Sharon Plain, Philistean Plain, Upper and Lower Galilee, Esdraelon Plain, Judean Mts., Dan Valley. Fairly common.

Area of species : Mediterranean, Euro-Siberian and W. Irano-Turanian.

3. Vicia palaestina Boiss., Diagn. ser. 1, 9 : 116 (1849) et Fl. 2 : 592 (1872). [Plate 280]

Annual, sparingly appressed-hairy, 15–80 cm. or more. Stems climbing, simple to branched, slender. Leaves 2–7.5 cm., subglabrous to pubescent; stipules 2–4 mm., semihastate, those of the uppermost leaves lanceolate to oblanceolate; tendrils often branched; leaflets (5–)6–10-paired, 0.5–3 × 0.05–0.3(–0.5) cm., subsessile, narrowly linear to narrowly oblanceolate, acute to obtuse, mucronulate. Peduncles long but shorter than subtending leaves, muticous. Racemes (2–)3–8(–9)-flowered, generally one-sided. Pedicels about as long as calyx, pubescent. Flowers (5–)6–9 mm., deflexed.

Calyx about 2 mm., somewhat hairy; rim of tube slightly oblique; teeth a little shorter than tube, the lower teeth longer, lanceolate-triangular. Corolla about 3 times as long as calyx; standard longer than wings, blue, slightly retuse at apex; wings white-blue or cream-blue; keel dark blue at apex. Style subcompressed, hairy at apex. Pod (1.3–)2–2.5 × (0.4–)0.5–0.8 cm., stipitate, 1–4-seeded, compressed, rhombic-elliptical to oblong, more or less torulose, short-beaked, glabrous, somewhat net-veined. Seeds 3–6 mm., globular to compressed-ovoid, brown to blackish-brown, smooth; hilum short, linear. 2n = 14. Fl. February–May.

Hab.: Maquis and batha. Acco Plain, Sharon Plain, Philistean Plain, Upper and Lower Galilee, Mt. Carmel, Esdraelon Plain, Samaria, Judean Mts., Judean Desert, Dan Valley, Hula Plain, Upper and Lower Jordan Valley, Gilead, Ammon, Moav. Fairly common.

Area: E. Mediterranean, with slight eastward extensions.

4. Vicia hulensis Plitm., Israel Journ. Bot. 14 : 96 (1965). [Plate 281]

Annual, subglabrous, 30–50 cm. Stems few, ascending to erect, branching. Leaves up to 3 cm.; stipules up to 3 mm., narrow, semihastate; tendrils simple to branched; leaflets 2–4-paired, 0.8–2.1 × 0.2–0.6 cm., short-petiolulate, oblong to oblanceolate-linear, obtuse to usually praemorse or 3-denticulate at apex. Peduncles as long as or longer than subtending leaves, muticous. Racemes 2-flowered. Pedicels about as long as calyx. Flowers 7–8 mm. Calyx 2–3 mm., glabrous; teeth as long as or slightly longer than tube, somewhat unequal, ovate. Corolla 2–3 times as long as calyx, whitish or lilac-blue; standard longer than wings, short-clawed, rather retuse; keel shorter than wings. Style rather compressed and pubescent at apex. Pod about 2 × 0.6 cm., deflexed, compressed, linear-subrhombic, glabrous. Immature seeds 2–5, about 3–4 mm. in diam., smooth. Fl. June–July.

Hab.: Basalt hills. Hula Plain (probably endemic to N. E. Palestine and S. W. Syria). Rare.

Area: E. Mediterranean.

5. Vicia esdraëlonensis Warb. et Eig, Repert. Sp. Nov. 25 : 352 (1928). [Plate 282]

Annual, glabrous to sparingly pilose, 25–30 cm. Stems ascending to erect, branching from base, somewhat rigid, angular. Leaves 2–9 cm.; stipules about 2 mm., semihastate, the uppermost lanceolate-elliptical, with black nectary spot; tendrils mostly branched; leaflets 3–6-paired, 0.7–3.5 × 0.2–0.8 cm., subsessile, linear or oblong-linear to lanceolate or oblanceolate, sometimes obovate, truncate to retuse, rarely acutish, mucronate, subglabrous. Peduncles 0.3–1.7 cm., subglabrous to hairy. Racemes 1–2-flowered. Pedicels much shorter than calyx, sparingly pubescent. Flowers 2–2.2 cm. Calyx 8–9 mm., rather gibbous, more or less hairy, sometimes blue-green; tube with an oblique rim; teeth much shorter than tube, the lower teeth twice as long as the upper. Corolla two to two and a half times as long as calyx, purplish-violet; standard somewhat longer than wings, notched; keel shorter than wings, dark violet at apex. Style hairy at apex. Pod about 4 × 1 cm., 4–8-seeded, deflexed, flattened, oblong-rhombic, with a short curved beak, glabrous. Seeds globular-compressed, dark brown, smooth. 2n = 12. Fl. April.

Hab.: Fields; damp soil. E. Upper Galilee, Esdraelon Plain, Hula Plain (endemic). Rare.

Area: E. Mediterranean.

6. Vicia cypria Ky. in Ung. et Ky., Ins. Cyp. 384 (1865); Boiss., Fl. 2:593 (1872). [Plate 283]

Annual, glabrous, 7–40 cm. Stems ascending to erect or climbing, simple or branched, slender, angular, subglabrous. Leaves 1.5–6 cm.; stipules 3–6 mm., somewhat cuneate, narrowly semihastate to ovate-triangular, acute, the lower stipules 3-partite or 3-dentate, the upper stipules deeply incised; tendrils filiform, branched; leaflets 3–6-paired, 0.3–1.4(–1.6) × 0.2–0.8(–1) cm., subsessile, obovate to elliptical, truncate to emarginate, mucronate. Peduncles elongated in fruit, aristate. Racemes 1–2(–3)-flowered, shorter than subtending leaves. Pedicels about as long as calyx tube, subglabrous. Flowers 1.2–1.8 cm., erect to deflexed. Calyx 5–7 mm., slightly gibbous, pale green; rim of tube rather oblique; teeth about as long as tube, slightly unequal, lanceolate. Corolla 2 to 3 times as long as calyx; standard cream-coloured, dark blue at apex, slightly emarginate, usually reflexed; wings a little shorter than standard; keel a little shorter than wings, yellowish to whitish, blue at apex. Style long-filiform, short-pilose at apex. Pod 2–2.6 × (0.4–)0.5–0.6 cm., 3–6-seeded, pendulous, somewhat flattened, oblong to linear-lanceolate, short-beaked, glabrous. Seeds subglobular, brown- and black-stained. Fl. March–May.

Hab.: Fields and batha. Upper Galilee. Very rare.

Area: E. Mediterranean (Palestine, Lebanon and Cyprus).

Unger and Kotschy, l.c., erroneously described this species as a perennial.

7. Vicia monantha Retz., Obs. Bot. 3 : 39 (1783). [Plate 284]

Annual, sparingly pubescent to appressed- and grey-hairy, 5–60 cm. Stems few to many, procumbent or ascending to erect, branching below, angular. Leaves 2–7(–9) cm.; stipules about 5 mm., semihastate, incised to entire, hairy; tendrils simple or branched; leaflets 4–8-paired, 0.5–2.5(–3) × 0.1–0.5(–0.8) cm., subsessile, narrowly linear to oblanceolate or oblong-elliptical, obtuse to truncate or rarely retuse, mucronulate or not. Peduncles shorter than subtending leaves but longer than calyx, elongated in fruit, usually aristate. Racemes 1–3(–4)-flowered. Pedicels shorter than calyx, pubescent. Flowers 1–1.8 cm. Calyx 3–5 mm., somewhat gibbous; tube with an oblique rim, pubescent, sometimes bluish-green; teeth distinctly shorter than tube, triangular-lanceolate. Corolla 3 times as long as calyx, pale violet to blue; standard longer than the wings and the blue- to violet-tipped keel; wings white and dark blue. Style hairy at apex. Pod 2–4(–4.5) × 0.5–1.2 cm., short-stipitate, 4–6(–7)-seeded, flattened, oblong-linear, slightly torulose, short-beaked, glabrous, nerved. Seeds 3–4 mm., somewhat compressed to almost globular, smooth, dark brown; hilum short, oblong-linear, whitish. 2n = 14. Fl. January–June.

Var. **monantha.** *V. calcarata* Desf., Fl. Atl. 2:166 (1798); Boiss., Fl. 2:590 (1872) excl. var. β. Sparingly pubescent, 20–60 cm. Leaflets broader than 1 mm. Flowers up to 1.7 cm. Pod 2–4(–4.5) × 0.6–1.2 cm.

Hab.: Semideserts; among crops and in fallow fields. Philistean Plain, Judean Mts., Judean Desert, W., N. and C. Negev, Lower Jordan Valley, Dead Sea area, Transjordan. Not rare.

Var. **cinerea** (M.B.) Plitm. (comb. nov.). *V. calcarata* Desf. var. *cinerea* (M.B.) Boiss., l.c. *V. cinerea* M.B., Fl. Taur.-Cauc. 3 : 470 (1819). Appressed- and grey-hairy, 5–30 cm. Leaflets 0.5–1.5 × 0.1 cm., narrowly linear. Flowers 1–1.4 cm. Calyx more pubescent than above. Pod 2–2.5 × 0.5–0.6 cm.

Hab.: As above. W., N. and C. Negev, Lower Jordan Valley, Dead Sea area, Edom. Rather rare.

Area of species : S. Mediterranean and W. Irano-Turanian.

Sect. ERVUM (L.) S. F. Gray, Nat. Arr. Brit. Pl. 2 : 614 (1821). Gen. *Ervum* L., Gen. Pl. ed. 5, 328 (1754) p.p. Annuals. Leaflets usually more than 2 pairs. Flowers 1–8, axillary, rather small. Calyx more or less regular. Style shorter than 3 mm., filiform, glabrous or short-puberulent. Pod short, up to 5 mm. broad, few-seeded, oblong-rhomboidal or linear, mostly torulose.

8. Vicia ervilia (L.) Willd., Sp. Pl. 3 : 1103 (1802); Boiss., Fl. 2 : 595 (1872). *Ervum ervilia* L., Sp. Pl. 738 (1753). [Plate 285]

Annual, glabrous to sparingly appressed-pubescent, 10–50(–60) cm. Stems erect, branched at base, more or less rigid, angular. Leaves (3–)4–10(–12) cm.; stipules 2–4(–5) mm., semihastate, dentate; tendrils 2–8 mm., awn-like; leaflets 5–15-paired, 0.5–1.5(–1.8) × 0.1–0.4 cm., subsessile, narrowly linear to oblong-oblanceolate, obtuse to retuse, mucronate. Peduncles shorter than leaves, aristate. Racemes 1–4(–5)-flowered. Pedicels much shorter than calyx, pubescent. Flowers deflexed. Calyx 5–7 mm., appressed-pubescent; teeth somewhat longer than tube, equal, subulate. Corolla about 1 cm., almost twice as long as calyx; standard white-violet; wings shorter than standard, whitish; keel blue-white with a violet spot at apex. Style filiform, puberulent at apex. Pod 1.2–2.5 × 0.3–0.5 cm., 2–4-seeded, deflexed, oblong-linear, torulose to moniliform, short-pubescent. Seeds 4–5 mm., globular or slightly angular, yellowish to dark brown, smooth; hilum small, ovate. 2n = 14. Fl. February–June.

Hab.: Cultivated ground; grown as a fodder plant and often escaped or subspontaneous. Acco Plain, Sharon Plain, Philistean Plain, Upper and Lower Galilee, Mt. Carmel, Esdraelon Plain, Samaria, Shefela, Judean Mts., Judean Desert, Upper and Lower Jordan Valley, Gilead, Ammon. Not rare.

Area : Origin probably Mediterranean.

9. Vicia pubescens (DC.) Link, Handb. 2 : 190 (1831); Boiss., Fl. 2 : 596 (1872). *Ervum pubescens* DC., Cat. Hort. Monsp. 109 (1813); Ser. in DC., Prodr. 2 : 367 (1825). *V. tetrasperma* (L.) Moench var. *pubescens* (DC. err. "Link") Fiori in Fiori et Paol., Fl. Anal. Ital. 2 : 120 (1900). [Plate 286]

Annual, pubescent, 10–60 cm. Stems erect, climbing, angular. Leaves 2.5–5 cm.; stipules 4–5 mm., semihastate, the upper stipules ovate to linear, pubescent; tendrils filiform, simple to forked; leaflets 3–5-paired, 0.6–2.5 × 0.2–0.6 cm., subsessile, ovate or elliptical to oblanceolate, acute to obtuse, mucronulate. Peduncles as long as or longer than subtending leaves, muticous or short-aristate. Racemes 1–6-flowered. Pedicels shorter than calyx, hairy. Flowers 5–9 mm., spreading to erect. Calyx (2–)3–5 mm., hairy; rim of tube oblique; teeth longer than tube, lanceolate-subulate, the upper teeth shorter. Corolla one and a half times as long as calyx; standard pale blue, somewhat longer than the whitish-blue wings; keel blue to violet at apex. Pod 1.2–2 × (0.2–)0.3(–0.4) cm., stipitate, 4–6-seeded, somewhat compressed, linear, subtorulose, short-beaked, pilose-pubescent to subglabrous. Seeds subglobular, brown-black, smooth; hilum very short, brown. Fl. March–May.

Hab.: Batha, maquis, also in other shady places. Upper Galilee, Mt. Carmel, Esdraelon Plain, Hula Plain. Rather uncommon.

Area: N. and E. Mediterranean, extending into adjacent Euro-Siberian provinces.

10. Vicia tetrasperma (L.) Schreb., Spic. Fl. Lips. 26 (1771); Moench, Meth. 148 (1794); Boiss., Fl. 2:596 (1872). *Ervum tetraspermum* L., Sp. Pl. 738 (1753). [Plate 287]

Annual, subglabrous to appressed-pilose, 15–80 cm. Stems procumbent to erect or climbing, simple or branched, slender, angular. Leaves 1.2–4.2 cm., glabrous to appressed-pilose; stipules 3–4 mm., more or less semihastate, the upper stipules sometimes lanceolate, subglabrous; tendrils short, mostly simple, filiform, in the lowermost leaves 0; leaflets (2–)3–6-paired, 0.3–2.2 × 0.1–0.4 cm., subsessile, narrowly linear to oblong, the lowermost leaflets elliptical, acute to obtuse, mucronulate. Peduncles about as long as subtending leaves, elongating, aristate or muticous. Racemes 1–3-flowered. Pedicels a little shorter than calyx, pilose. Flowers 4–8 mm., deflexed to erect. Calyx about 4 mm.; rim of tube oblique; teeth scarcely shorter than tube, narrowly triangular, the lower teeth longer. Corolla twice as long as calyx; standard pale blue; wings somewhat shorter than standard, whitish-blue; keel slightly shorter than wings. Style filiform, slightly hairy at apex. Pod 0.8–1.7 × 0.2–0.4 cm., stipitate, 4–6-seeded, compressed, linear, subtorulose, very short-beaked, almost glabrous. Seeds about 2 mm., subglobular, brown-black, smooth; hilum short, ovate, brown. 2n = 14. Fl. March–May.

Hab.: Damp soils. Sharon Plain, Philistean Plain, Mt. Carmel, Esdraelon Plain, Samaria. Rare.

Area: Mediterranean, Irano-Turanian and Euro-Siberian; adventive in many countries.

11. Vicia tenuissima (M.B.) Schinz et Thell., Viert. Naturf. Ges. Zürich 58 : 70 (1913). *Ervum tenuissimum* M.B., Tabl. Casp. 185, no. 24 (1798). *V. gracilis* Loisel., Fl. Gall. 460, t. 12 (1807) non Banks et Sol. in Russ., Nat. Hist. Aleppo ed. 2, 2 : 259 (1794); Boiss., Fl. 2 : 596 (1872). *V. tetrasperma* (L.) Schreb. ssp. *gracilis* (Loisel.) Aschers. et Graebn., Fl. Nordostd. Flachl. 449 (1898). [Plate 288]

Annual, subglabrous, 15–50 cm. Stems ascending or climbing, slender. Leaves 5–8 × 3–4 cm.; stipules up to 6 mm., semihastate to semisagittate; tendrils simple; leaflets 2–3(–5)-paired, 0.6–3 × 0.2–0.3 cm., those of the lowermost leaves short-elliptical, the rest narrowly lanceolate or oblanceolate, acute. Peduncles longer than subtending leaves, filiform, muticous or short-aristate. Racemes 1–4 (–6)-flowered. Pedicels scarcely shorter than calyx. Flowers (5–)6–9 mm. Calyx teeth shorter than tube, unequal, lanceolate-triangular. Corolla twice as long as calyx or more, purplish-blue, paler at base; standard somewhat longer than wings, the latter somewhat longer than keel. Pod 1.2–1.9 × 0.3 cm., (3–)5–7 (–8)-seeded, compressed, linear, sparingly appressed-pilose. Seeds subglobular; hilum very short, ovate. 2n = 14. Fl. March–June.

Hab.: Fallow fields and among shrubs; heavy soil. Sharon Plain, Esdraelon Plain. Rather rare.

Area: N. Mediterranean, with slight extensions into adjacent Euro-Siberian territories.

Sect. VICIA. Sect. *Euvicia* Vis., Fl. Dalm. 3 : 317 (1852) emend. Taubert in Engl. et Prantl, Nat. Pflznfam. III, 3 : 351 (1894). Annuals, sometimes perennials, mostly climbing. Leaflets usually more than 3 pairs, small or medium-sized. Flowers in short racemes or 1–2 in leaf axils. Calyx regular to irregular. Style more or less compressed, bearded towards apex. Pod narrower than 1.2 cm., torulose, many-seeded.

12. Vicia galeata Boiss., Diagn. ser. 1, 2 : 103 (1843) et Fl. 2 : 572 (1872). [Plate 289]

Annual, subglabrous, 30–70 cm. or more. Stems climbing, branched, angular. Leaves 3.5–9 (–10) cm.; stipules 2–3 mm., narrowly semihastate to ovate-lanceolate; tendrils usually longer than 1.5 cm., branched; leaflets 4–7-paired, (0.3–)0.6–3 × (0.2–)0.3–1.5 cm., subsessile, linear-oblanceolate or elliptical to oblong-obovate, sometimes obcordate, truncate to notched, often mucronulate, sparingly appressed-pilose. Peduncles shorter than subtending leaves, rather pubescent. Racemes mostly 3–5-flowered. Pedicels much shorter than calyx. Flowers (1.8–)2–3 cm., deflexed. Calyx up to 1 cm., slightly gibbous, with an oblique limb, somewhat pubescent; teeth shorter than tube, narrowly triangular to subulate, the upper teeth shorter than the lower. Corolla about 3 times as long as calyx, pale yellow or cream-coloured or whitish to pink; limb of standard often reflexed; keel twice as long as calyx, shorter than wings, boat- or hood-shaped. Style hairy at apex. Pod 2.5–4 × 1 cm., stipitate, 2–5-seeded, deflexed-pendulous, rather flattened, oblong-linear, beaked, glabrous, net-veined. Seeds about 5 mm., globular, brown to black, smooth; hilum narrowly linear. 2n = 12. Fl. February–June.

Hab.: Swampy soils and river banks. Acco Plain, Sharon Plain, Philistean Plain, Upper Galilee, Mt. Carmel, Esdraelon Plain, Samaria, Shefela, Judean Mts., Judean Desert, Dan Valley, Hula Plain, Upper Jordan Valley, Gilead. Fairly common.

Area: E. Mediterranean.

13. Vicia peregrina L., Sp. Pl. 737 (1753); Boiss., Fl. 2 : 576 (1872). [Plate 290]

Annual, appressed-puberulent or pubescent, 15–60 (–75) cm. Stems procumbent to erect, usually branched, angular. Leaves 1.5–6.5 cm.; stipules 3–4 mm., narrow, semihastate or semisagittate, free portion subulate or lanceolate, pilose; tendrils simple to branched; leaflets (2–)3–7-paired, 1–3 (–4) × 0.1–0.6 cm., subsessile, narrowly linear to oblanceolate, tapering at base, retuse, rarely acuminate, mucronulate. Racemes axillary, mostly 1-flowered. Pedicels about as long as to a little longer than calyx, hairy. Flowers 1.2–2.1 cm. Calyx 6–9 mm., slightly gibbous, with an oblique limb; teeth almost as long as tube, the upper teeth shorter, connivent, lanceolate, acuminate. Corolla about twice as long as calyx, purple or blue-violet, paler at base, sometimes white; standard longer than wings, notched. Style hairy at apex. Pod 2–4.5 × (0.6–)0.7–1.2 cm., short-stipitate, (2–)3–7-seeded, deflexed, more or less compressed, oblong-linear, short-beaked, appressed-hairy to subglabrous, sometimes with violet-purple spots. Seeds 4–7 mm., subglobular, sometimes subangular, mostly dark brown or mottled with black; hilum oblong, dark. 2n = 12, 14. Fl. February–May.

Hab.: Batha and fallow fields. Coastal Galilee, Acco Plain, Sharon Plain, Philistean Plain, Upper and Lower Galilee, Mt. Carmel, Esdraelon Plain, Samaria, Judean Mts., Judean Desert, W., N. and C. Negev, Dan Valley, Gilead, Ammon, Moav, Edom. Common.

Area: Mediterranean and Irano-Turanian.

Var. *parviflora* Post, Fl. Syr. Pal. Sin. 287 (1883–1896) and var. *glabrescens* Post, l.c. 288, are two extreme forms within the wider variation range of *V. peregrina*.

14. Vicia lutea L., Sp. Pl. 736 (1753); Boiss., Fl. 2 : 570 (1872). [Plate 291]

Annual, hairy to glabrescent, 15–80(–100) cm. Stems ascending to erect or climbing, usually branching below, angular. Leaves 1.5–6(–8) cm., subsessile; stipules semi-hastate or triangular, glabrous to pilose, with nectary spot beneath; tendrils filiform, mostly branched; leaflets 4–10-paired, 0.5–2.5(–3) × 0.2–0.6 cm., subsessile, linear to narrowly elliptical or oblong, acute to obtuse or retuse, mucronulate. Flowers solitary, rarely in pairs, 1.7–3 cm., axillary, deflexed, on hairy pedicels much shorter than calyx. Calyx up to 1.3 cm., glabrous, with an oblique limb; teeth very unequal, some longer, others shorter than tube, triangular to lanceolate-subulate. Corolla 2 to 3 times as long as calyx, yellow, rarely purple-violet or pinkish; standard longer than wings, retuse, with limb shorter than claw; keel shorter than wings. Style hairy at apex. Pod 2–3.5 × 0.7–1.2 cm., stipitate, 3–6-seeded, deflexed, rather compressed, oblong-linear to oblong-rhomboidal, beaked, hirsute, often with hairs arising from a tubercle. Seeds subglobular to somewhat compressed, dark brown, smooth; hilum oblong-linear, whitish. 2n = 14. Fl. (February–) March–June.

Var. **lutea.** Subglabrous or sparingly pilose. Leaflets 4–8 pairs. Corolla yellow. Pod sparsely hirsute; tubercles of hairs obsolete.

Hab.: Fields. Sharon Plain. Very rare or casual.

Var. **hirta** (Balbis ex DC.) Loisel., Fl. Gall. 462 (1807); Boiss., l.c. *V. hirta* Balbis ex DC., Syn. Pl. Fl. Gall. 360 (1806). *V. vestita* Boiss., Elench. Pl. Nov. 39 (1838) et Voy. Bot. Midi Esp. 2 : 193 (1839). Densely pilose-hirsute. Leaflets congested, mostly 6–10 pairs. Corolla pale yellow or purple-violet. Pod densely hirsute-silky with hairs arising from a tubercle.

Hab.: Fallow fields and by water. Sharon Plain, Philistean Plain, Lower Galilee. Rare.

Area of species: Mediterranean, with extensions into some territories of the Euro-Siberian and Irano-Turanian regions.

The records on this species from Jerusalem, Dead Sea area and Moav (after Dinsmore in Post, Fl. Syr. Pal. Sin. ed. 2, 1 : 418, 1932) are most probably erroneous.

15. Vicia sericocarpa Fenzl, Pugill. 4 (1842); Boiss., Fl. 2 : 570 (1872). [Plate 292]

Annual, appressed-pilose, 10–60 cm. Stems ascending or procumbent, branched, angular. Leaves 1.5–6 cm.; stipules about 3 mm., semihastate to lanceolate-subulate, subglabrous, with nectary spot beneath; tendrils mostly branched, sometimes short; leaflets 3–8-paired, (0.3–)0.5–1.8(–2.2) × 0.1–0.4 cm., subsessile, linear to obovate, tapering at base, truncate or retuse and mucronulate at apex, sometimes obcordate. Flowers (1.5–)1.8–2.9 cm., axillary, mostly solitary, rather erect on hairy pedicels which are shorter than the calyx. Calyx about 1 cm., gibbous with an oblique limb, densely appressed-pilose; teeth slightly to much shorter than tube, the lower teeth longer than the upper. Corolla about 2–3 times as long as calyx, yellow to pale green; standard longer than wings, glabrous; wings longer than keel. Style hairy at apex. Pod 1.5–3 × 0.7–1 cm., 2–4-seeded, deflexed-pendulous, slightly turgid, oblong-rhomboidal, beaked, appressed-silky. Seeds about 5 mm., subglobular, brown to black-violet, smooth; hilum short, linear, pale. 2n = 12. Fl. March–May.

Var. **sericocarpa.** Leaves 1.5–6 cm.; leaflets 0.5–0.8(–2.2) × 0.1–0.4 cm., linear to obovate, tapering at base, truncate or retuse. Calyx teeth narrow, somewhat shorter than tube, the lower teeth longer.

Hab.: Batha; stony ground. Upper Galilee, Samaria, Judean Mts., Upper Jordan Valley, Ammon. Fairly common.

Var. **microphylla** Boiss., l.c. 571. Leaves shorter than in the preceding variety; leaflets 0.3–1 × 0.2–0.4 cm., more or less obcordate, cuneate at base. Calyx teeth much shorter than tube, almost equal.

Hab.: As above. Esdraelon Plain, Mt. Gilboa, Judean Mts., Hula Plain, Gilead. Rather uncommon.

Area of species: E. Mediterranean and Irano-Turanian.

16. Vicia hybrida L., Sp. Pl. 737 (1753); Boiss., Fl. 2 : 570 (1872). [Plate 293]

Annual, appressed-hairy, 15–80 cm. Stems procumbent to ascending or climbing, branching, especially at base, angular, subglabrous to pubescent. Leaves 1.5–5 cm.; stipules 2–3 mm., semihastate, the upper lanceolate; tendrils simple or branched; leaflets 4–7-paired, 0.5–2(–2.5) × 0.3–0.8 cm., subsessile, obovate to oblong-elliptical, sometimes obtriangular, obcordate or linear, cuneate, truncate to notched, mucronu-late. Flowers (1.8–)2–3(–3.5) cm., axillary, solitary, deflexed, on pedicels shorter than calyx. Calyx about 1 cm., with an oblique limb, hirsute; teeth shorter than tube, lanceolate-linear. Corolla 2–3 times as long as calyx, yellow, sometimes purple-veined; standard with limb as long as or shorter than claw, more or less retuse, appressed-hairy outside; keel shorter than standard and wings, yellow to brownish, hooded. Style filiform, hairy at apex. Pod 2–3.5 × 0.8–1 cm., 2–5-seeded, pendulous, oblong-rhomboidal, somewhat compressed at base, appressed-pubescent. Seeds 3–6 mm., globular, brown or purplish-brown or mottled, smooth or slightly tuberculate; hilum linear. 2n = 12. Fl. February–May.

Hab.: Fields and batha. Sharon Plain, Philistean Plain, Upper and Lower Galilee, Mt. Carmel, Esdraelon Plain, Samaria, Shefela, Judean Mts., Judean Desert, N. Negev, Dan Valley, Hula Plain, Upper and Lower Jordan Valley, Dead Sea area, Gilead, Ammon. Common.

Area: Mediterranean, with extensions into the adjacent territories of the Euro-Siberian and the Irano-Turanian regions.

17. Vicia cuspidata Boiss., Diagn. ser. 1, 2 : 104 (1843) et Fl. 2 : 575 (1872). [Plate 294]

Annual, finely pubescent, 10–50 cm. Stems ascending. Leaves (0.5–)1–4 cm.; stipules up to 5 mm., ovate-semisagittate; tendrils mostly simple; leaflets 1–3-paired, those of upper leaves 4–5-paired, up to 1.2 × 0.3–0.6 cm., obovate-cuneate to oblong-lanceolate, acute or retuse, mucronate. Flowers 1.1–1.4 cm., axillary, solitary, nearly sessile. Calyx appressed-pilose, with rim of tube almost even and teeth almost equal, about as long as tube, lanceolate-subulate. Corolla two to two and a half times as long as calyx, purple; standard with limb as long as claw, ovate, retuse, white-mucronate; wings shorter than standard, much longer than keel, linear-oblong; keel half as long as standard, pale purple-violet. Pod 2–2.7 × 0.3–0.4 cm., erect, subcompressed, linear, long-beaked, usually glabrous. Seeds many, about 3 mm., angular; hilum ovate. Fl. April–June.

Hab.: Recorded by Boissier (Fl. 2 : 576, 1872), from Palestine and by Post (Fl. Syr. Pal. Sin. 287, 1883–1896 et ed. 2, 1 : 420, 1932) from Philistean Plain.

Area: E. Mediterranean.

18. Vicia sativa L., Sp. Pl. 736 (1753). [Plate 295]

Annual, hairy to subglabrous, 20–80 cm. Stems erect to procumbent, branching from base. Leaves 2.5–11 cm.; stipules varying in length, semihastate, dentate, usually with a purple nectary spot beneath; tendrils usually branched; leaflets (2–)4–8(–10)-paired, varying in size and shape, 1–3.5(–4) × (0.2–)0.5–1.5 cm., linear or lanceolate to oblong or obovate, sometimes elliptical, obcordate or cuneate, acutish or obtuse to truncate or retuse, mucronate, mostly entire. Racemes axillary, almost sessile, 1–2(–3)-flowered. Flowers (1–)1.5–2.5(–3) cm. (rarely part of them subterranean and minute), short-pedicelled. Calyx 0.7–2 cm., campanulate, hairy, rim of calyx tube even (not oblique); calyx teeth (0.3–)0.5–1(–1.5) × 0.1–0.2 cm., subequal, linear-subulate or lanceolate, acute-mucronate. Corolla one and a half to two and a half times as long as calyx, sometimes 2-coloured; standard 0.7–1.9 cm. broad, obovate-orbicular, notched, whitish-pink to purplish-violet, claw about as long as limb; wings shorter than standard, bluish-pink to purplish-violet; keel shorter than wings, paler, usually darker at apex. Pod (1–)3.5–7 × 0.4–1.2 cm., (5–)6–12-seeded or, when subterranean, 1–2(–3)-seeded, pods compressed to turgid, linear, torulose or not, more or less pubescent, net-veined, yellowish to brown or black, rarely whitish. Seeds 2.5–6 mm., rarely larger, subglobular, sometimes compressed, plain or variegated, greenish-grey or brown-yellow or black; hilum short, linear. Fl. (February–) March–May (–June).

1. Plant producing both subterranean and aerial flowers and fruits.   ssp. **amphicarpa**
   – Plant with aerial flowers and fruits only   2

2. Leaves 2.5–7 cm.; leaflets mostly narrow, (0.2–)0.4–1(–1.3) cm. broad. Calyx 0.7–1.2 cm.; teeth 3–6 mm. Corolla (1–)1.4–2 cm. Seeds 2.5–4 mm.   ssp. **angustifolia**

– Leaves usually longer, 4–11 cm.; leaflets usually broader than above, 0.5–1.5 cm. broad. Calyx 1.2–2 cm.; teeth usually longer than above, 0.5–1.1(–1.2) cm.   3

3. Leaves 4–9 cm. Seeds 3–5 mm. Calyx teeth abruptly tapering at apex. Pod 3.5–6 × (0.4–)0.5–0.6(–0.7) cm.   ssp. **cordata**

– Leaves 7–11 cm. Seeds 4.5–6 mm. Calyx teeth gradually tapering at apex. Pod 5.5–7 × 0.7–1 cm., torulose.   ssp. **sativa**

Subsp. **sativa**. *V. sativa* L., l.c.; Boiss., Fl. 2 : 574 (1872) p.p. *V. sativa* L. ssp. *obovata* (Ser.) Gaudin, Fl. Helv. 4 : 510 (1829). *V. torulosa* Jord. in Bor., Fl. Centr. Fr. ed. 3, 2 : 173 (1857). Leaves 7–11 cm.; leaflets (5–)8(–9)-paired, 2–3.5 × 0.5–1.5 cm., usually oblong-obovate, more or less truncate. Flowers large, often 2-coloured. Calyx 1.2–2 cm., short-pubescent; calyx teeth 0.5–1.1 cm., narrow, gradually tapering at apex. Corolla 2–2.6 cm.; standard 1.4–1.9 cm. broad, whitish-pink to blue-lilac or purplish-violet, claw about as long as or slightly shorter than limb; wings lilac to blue or purplish-violet. Pod 5.5–7 × 0.7–1 cm., usually (6–)8-seeded, flattened, torulose. Seeds 4.5–6 × 3.5–4.5 mm., subglobular, usually greenish-grey, mottled with black or brown. 2n = 10, 12.

Hab.: Cultivated and escaped, but also spontaneous in fallow fields and elsewhere. Coastal Galilee, Acco Plain, Sharon Plain, Philistean Plain, Upper and Lower Galilee, Esdraelon Plain, Mt. Gilboa, Judean Mts., W. and N. Negev, Dan Valley, Hula Plain, Upper Jordan Valley. Fairly common.

Subsp. **cordata** (Wulf. ex Hoppe) Aschers. et Graebn., Syn. Mitteleur. Fl. 6, 2 : 968 (1909) emend. Plitm. (emend. nov.). *V. cordata* Wulf. ex Hoppe in Sturm, Deutschl. Fl. 1, 32 : t. 497 (1812). *V. angustifolia* Roth var. *cordata* (Wulf.) Boiss., l.c. 575. *V. angustifolia* L. var. *segetalis* (Thuill.) Kosteletzky (1824) et *V. angustifolia* Roth var. *segetalis* (Thuill.) Koch, Syn. Fl. Germ. Helv. 197 (1835); Dinsmore in Post, Fl. Syr. Pal. Sin. ed. 2, 1 : 419 (1932). *V. cuneata* Guss., Fl. Sic. Prodr. 2 : 428 (1828); Godr. in Gren. et Godr., Fl. Fr. 1 : 459 (1849). Stems 20–100 cm., procumbent to ascending or climbing. Leaves 4–9 cm.; leaflets 5–7-paired, 1.3–3.5 × (0.6–)1–1.4 cm., oblong or elliptical to obovate or obcordate, obtuse or truncate to retuse, mucronate. Flowers solitary or in pairs, (1.5–)2–2.7 cm. Calyx 1.2–2 cm., pubescent; calyx teeth 0.7–1.2 × 0.1–0.2 cm., abruptly tapering at apex, more or less ciliate. Corolla usually 2-coloured; standard 1.4–1.8 cm. broad, purple or violet to pinkish-blue or lilac, with claw somewhat longer or shorter than blade; wings darker, purple or violet. Pod 3.5–6 × 0.4–0.7 cm., 9–11-seeded, compressed to cylindrical, not torulose, yellow-brown to brown-black. Seeds 3–5 mm., subglobular, mostly yellowish-brown or mottled, sometimes black. 2n = 10, 12.

Hab.: Fields, batha, steppes and roadsides; preferring moist soils; sometimes cultivated or escaped. Coastal Galilee, Acco Plain, Sharon Plain, Philistean Plain, Upper and Lower Galilee, Mt. Carmel, Esdraelon Plain, Mt. Gilboa, Samaria, Shefela, Judean Mts., Dan Valley, Hula Plain. Very common.

Subsp. **angustifolia** (L.) Aschers. et Graebn., l.c. 971 non Gaudin, l.c. 503. *V. angustifolia* L., Fl. Angl. 21 (1754) et Amoen. Acad. 4 : 105 (1759); *V. angustifolia* Roth,

Tent. Fl. Germ. 1 : 310 (1788); Boiss., l.c. 574 p.p. *V. sativa* L. var. *angustifolia* (L.) Wahlenb., Fl. Carp. 218 (1814). Stems 10–50 cm., procumbent or ascending. Leaves 2.5–7 cm.; leaflets (2–)4–8 (–10)-, usually 6-paired, 1–3 (–4) × (0.2–)0.4–1.1 (–1.3) cm., linear or oblanceolate to oblong-obovate, sometimes elliptical, acutish to retuse. Flowers smaller than in ssp. *sativa,* mostly almost 1-coloured. Calyx 0.7–1.2 cm., short-pubescent, with narrow teeth gradually tapering at apex, 3–6 mm. Corolla (1–)1.4–2 cm.; standard 0.7–1.4 cm. broad, whitish-pink or blue-lilac or pale violet, claw as long as or slightly longer than limb; wings pinkish or lilac or bluish-violet. Pod 3.5–6 × 0.4–0.6 cm., (6–)7–12 (–13)-seeded, somewhat compressed, not torulose, brown to black. Seeds 2.5–4 mm., subglobular, yellow or mottled. 2n = 12.

Hab.: Fallow fields and among crops, also in steppes. Coastal Galilee, Acco Plain, Sharon Plain, Philistean Plain, Upper and Lower Galilee, Mt. Carmel, Esdraelon Plain, Mt. Gilboa, Shefela, Judean Mts., Judean Desert, W. and N. Negev, Dan Valley, Hula Plain, Upper Jordan Valley, Beit Shean Valley. Very common.

Subsp. **amphicarpa** (Dorth.) Aschers. et Graebn., l.c. 974. *V. amphicarpa* Dorth., Journ. Phys. 35 : 131 (1789); *V. amphicarpa* L., Sp. Pl. ed. 2, 1030 (1763) *nom. V. angustifolia* Roth var. *amphicarpa* (Dorth.) Alef., Bot. Zeit. 20 : 362 (1862); Boiss., l.c. 575. Leaves and leaflets shorter than in preceding subspecies, rarely narrowly linear, more or less cuneate. Flowers of two kinds: the upper ones well-developed on aerial branches, the subterranean ones borne on stolon-like white shoots arising from the epicotyl; aerial flowers generally smaller than in preceding subspecies, lilac-blue to purple, 1-coloured; subterranean flowers minute, corolla 0 or abortive. Aerial pod as in ssp. *angustifolia* but shorter, subterranean pod about 1–1.5 cm., 1–2 (–3)-seeded, oblong, torulose, with leathery whitish valves and larger seeds. 2n = 14.

Hab.: Screes and fields, also in batha and steppes. Sharon Plain, Philistean Plain, Upper and Lower Galilee, Samaria, Shefela, Judean Mts., Judean Desert, W., N. and C. Negev. Not rare.

Area of species: Mainly Mediterranean, with wide extensions into the Irano-Turanian and Euro-Siberian regions.

According to Mr. Izhaki (personal communication) the three first-mentioned subspecies are to be regarded as independent species for morphological, cytological and genetical reasons.

Each of the four subspecies, especially the first and the last, displays a large array of forms, most of them taxonomically ill-delineated, because of intergrading. There are probably also gene interchanges between the varieties of the various subspecies.

V. sativa varies mainly in shape of leaflets and size of pods as well as in dimensions of flowers and colour of corolla. Thus, *V. angustifolia* Roth var. *albiflora* Boiss., Fl. 2 : 575 (1872) is merely an extreme form included within the variation range of ssp. *angustifolia.*

V. lathyroides L., Sp. Pl. 736 (1753), recorded by Post (Fl. Syr. Pal. Sin. 287, 1883–1896 et ed. 2, 1 : 420, 1932) from Gilead, has not been found by us.

19. Vicia bithynica (L.) L., Syst. ed. 10, 1166 (1759); Boiss., Fl. 2 : 587 (1872). *Lathyrus bithynicus* L., Sp. Pl. 731 (1753). [Plate 296]

Annual, hairy to almost glabrous, 20–60 cm. Stems erect, ascending or climbing, more or less branching, slender, 4-angled. Lower leaves with 1 pair of leaflets, upper leaves with 2–3 pairs; stipules 0.7–1 cm., sagittate, incised; tendrils mostly simple; leaflets of lower leaves ovate-elliptical to obovate, those of upper leaves elliptical to oblong-lanceolate or linear, all mucronate, most of them 3–5 × 0.4–1 cm. Peduncles as long as or shorter than subtending leaves but longer than calyx. Racemes 1–2 (–3)-flowered. Flowers about 2 cm., pedicellate. Calyx teeth longer than the hairy tube, more or less equal, lanceolate. Corolla violet to purple, keel and wings yellowish; standard notched. Pod 2.5–3.5 × 0.7–0.9 cm., compressed, oblong-rhombic in outline, beaked, scabrous-hairy at margin or hairy all over. Seeds globular, brown to brownish-red, spotted with red; hilum small. 2n = 14. Fl. April–May.

Hab.: Damp places. Philistean Plain. Rare; probably casual.

Area: N. Mediterranean, with slight extensions into adjacent territories of the Euro-Siberian region.

20. Vicia narbonensis L., Sp. Pl. 737 (1753). [Plate 297]

Annual, subglabrous to sparingly pubescent or hirsute, 15–50 cm. Stems ascending, procumbent to erect, branched, thick, angular. Leaves 1.5–9 cm.; stipules semihastate to semiorbicular, entire or dentate to incised, with a dark nectary spot beneath; tendrils simple or somewhat branched, lacking in the lower leaves; leaflets (1–)2–3 (–4)-paired, 1–6 (–7) × (0.6–)1–3 cm., subsessile, elliptical or oblong-lanceolate or ovate to obovate, obtuse or rarely acute, rounded or truncate to retuse, mucronulate, entire or dentate-serrate at margin or denticulate near apex, sparingly to densely hairy, especially along nerves, ciliate at margin. Peduncles very short and thick. Racemes (1–)3–6-flowered. Flowers 1.8–3.2 cm., short-pedicelled, deflexed to erect. Calyx 0.7–1.3 cm., sparingly hairy; tube with oblique rim; teeth unequal, the lower teeth longer, as long as tube, mostly ciliate. Corolla 2–2½ times as long as calyx, purple-violet; standard longer and keel shorter than wings. Style hairy at apex. Pod 3.5–6.5 × 0.8–1.5 cm., short-stipitate, flattened, linear to oblong-rhomboidal, curved and beaked, hairy or glabrescent, ciliate and tuberculate-denticulate at margin, often nerved. Seeds 4–6 mm., subglobular, brown-black, more or less smooth; hilum oblong-elliptical to oblong-ovate, whitish. 2n = 14. Fl. February–June.

1. Mature pod with hairs tuberculate at base.   var. **pilosa**
– Mature pod glabrous or glabrescent, but with dentate-tuberculate and ciliate margins   2
2. Leaflets entire.   var. **narbonensis**
– Leaflets, at least some of them, dentate or serrate.   var. **serratifolia**

Var. **narbonensis**. *V. narbonensis* L., l.c.; Boiss., Fl. 2 : 577 (1872). Leaflets 2–4-paired, ovate to elliptical, entire. Pod about 1 cm. broad, glabrescent towards maturity.

Hab.: Spontaneous and sometimes also cultivated; fallow fields. Acco Plain, Sharon Plain, Philistean Plain, Upper and Lower Galilee, Mt. Carmel, Esdraelon Plain, Judean Mts., W. and N. Negev, Upper and Lower Jordan Valley, Gilead, Ammon, Moav. Fairly common.

Var. **pilosa** Post, Fl. Syr. Pal. Sin. 288 (1883–1896). Leaflets 1–3-paired, large, obovate to ovate-orbicular. Pod over 1 cm. broad, hairy all over, also at maturity.

Hab.: Fields and maquis. Philistean Plain, Upper and Lower Galilee, Esdraelon

Plain, Samaria, Judean Mts., Hula Plain, Lower Jordan Valley, Ammon, Moav. Rather uncommon.

Var. **serratifolia** (Jacq.) Ser. in DC., Prodr. 2 : 365 (1825). *V. serratifolia* Jacq., Fl. Austr. 5 (App.) : 30, t. 8 (1778); Boiss., Fl. 2 : 578 (1872). Pubescent. Leaflets obovate to oblong-lanceolate, all, or only the upper or the lower leaflets, dentate or serrate.

Hab. : Under crops and in fallow fields. Philistean Plain, Judean Mts., W., N. and C. Negev, Lower Jordan Valley, Gilead. Fairly common.

Area of species : Mediterranean, with extensions into adjacent Euro-Siberian and Irano-Turanian territories.

21. Vicia galilaea Plitm. et Zoh. in Plitm., Israel Journ. Bot. 14 : 91 (1965). [Plate 298]
Annual, more or less pubescent, 10–50 cm. Stems ascending to erect, simple or branched at base, thick. Stipules large, semihastate-semiorbicular, entire or dentate, usually with a dark nectary spot beneath; tendrils shorter than leaves, simple to branched, almost 0 in lowermost leaves; leaflets 1–2(–3)-paired, up to 6 × 4 cm., ovate-orbicular, rounded, mucronulate, sparingly or densely pubescent, ciliate at margin. Racemes axillary, 1–3-flowered. Flowers 2–3.5 cm., subsessile to short-pedicelled, deflexed to erect. Calyx glabrescent; rim of tube oblique; teeth lanceolate, ciliate. Corolla about twice as long as calyx, lilac to cream-coloured and bluish, resembling that of *V. faba*; wings and keel shorter than standard, each with a dark violet tip. Pod 1 cm. or more broad, 4–6-seeded, somewhat flattened, oblong or oblong-rhomboidal, beaked, long- or short-pilose, tuberculate-denticulate and ciliate at margin. Seeds black, smooth. 2n = 14. Fl. March–April.

Subsp. **galilaea.** Stems up to 25 cm., pilose along ribs. Stipules dentate; leaflets 2–4, up to 6 × 4 cm., green, shiny, glabrescent to puberulent, minutely ciliate at margin. Flowers solitary in axils, 2–2.5 cm., short-pedicelled. Calyx teeth lanceolate. Pod broader than 1 cm., oblong-rhomboidal, short-beaked, long-pilose.

Hab. : Maquis. Upper Galilee. Rather uncommon.

Subsp. **faboidea** Plitm. et Zoh., l.c. 92. Stems up to 50 cm., pilose. Stipules mostly entire; leaflets 2–4(–6), 2–3.5 cm. broad, greyish-green, pubescent, densely ciliate. Flowers 1–3 in an axil, 2.5–3.5 cm., subsessile to short-pedicelled. Calyx teeth lanceolate-triangular. Pod 1 cm. broad, oblong in outline, beaked, short-pilose.

Hab. : As above. Lower Galilee, Mt. Carmel, Esdraelon Plain, Samaria. Rather uncommon.

Area of species : E. Mediterranean.

40. LENS Mill.

Annual or rarely perennial, erect or climbing herbs. Leaves pari-, rarely imparipinnate; stipules semisagittate; petiole mostly terminating with a tendril or an awn. Racemes axillary, few- or 1-flowered. Flowers small, long-pedicelled. Calyx teeth long, nearly equal. Corolla mostly whitish to bluish; standard obovate; wings adherent to acute, slightly beaked keel. Stamens diadelphous; mouth of staminal tube oblique.

Ovary subsessile, 2–3-ovuled; style dorsally flattened with upper face slightly bearded; stigma capitate. Pod short, 2-valved, 1–2-seeded, compressed. Seeds compressed, lenticular.

Literature : H. I. Barulina, Lentils of the Ud.S.S.R. and of other countries, *Bull. Appl. Bot. Pl. Breed. Leningr.* Suppl. 40 (1930; Russian with an English summary). D. V. Zaitschek, Studies in Palestinian lentils II, *Palest. Journ. Bot. Jerusalem* Ser. 1 : 55–64 (1938).

1. Leaves, even the upper ones, with petioles usually ending in an awn; stipules mostly hastate; leaflets 2–4 pairs. All or part of the peduncles longer than subtending leaves. Racemes 1-, rarely 2-flowered. Flowers 4–6 mm. Corolla violet or bluish, one and a half times as long as calyx. **2. L. ervoides**
– Plants differing in some characters from the above 2
2. Corolla violet to pale blue. Flowers 4.5–6 mm. Peduncles as long as or longer than subtending leaves, inconspicuously aristate. Pod obovate-rhombic in outline, considerably longer than broad. **3. L. orientalis**
– Corolla white, violet-veined, rarely pink or violet. Flowers 5–8 mm. Upper leaves ending in a tendril which is sometimes branched. Peduncles shorter than subtending leaves, long-aristate. Pod ovate-rhombic, slightly longer than broad. **1. L. culinaris**

1. Lens culinaris Medik., Phil. Bot. 2 : 361 (1791). *L. esculenta* Moench, Meth. 131 (1794). *Ervum lens* L., Sp. Pl. 738 (1753); Boiss., Fl. 2 : 598 (1872). [Plate 299]

Annual, 15–50 cm., hairy. Stems few to many, erect, sparingly branching, angular. Leaves paripinnate, at least part of them terminating in a branched tendril; stipules small, lanceolate, entire; leaflets 3–7-paired, 1–2 × 0.2–0.8 cm., oblong-linear to linear. Peduncles shorter than leaves, ending in an awn up to 1 cm. Racemes 1–4-flowered. Flowers 5–8 mm. Calyx short-campanulate; teeth much longer than tube, nearly as long as or longer than corolla, almost equal, filiform-subulate. Corolla white, rarely pink or violet. Staminal tube oblique. Ovary 2–3-ovuled. Pod 1 × 0.8 cm., deflexed, ovate-rhombic. Seeds 1–3, lenticular, rarely almost globular. Fl. April.

Hab. : Widely cultivated and often subspontaneous.

Area : Origin probably E. Mediterranean.

2. Lens ervoides (Brignoli) Grande, Bull. Ort. Bot. Napoli 5 : 58 (1918). [Plate 300]

Annual, 10–40 cm., appressed-pubescent. Stems erect or ascending, slender. Leaves 2–3 cm., paripinnate, ending in an awn or in upper leaves rarely in a simple tendril; leaflets 2–4-paired, 0.5–1.5 cm., oblong to linear, mucronulate. Peduncles 1.7–3.5 cm., occasionally longer than subtending leaves, filiform, not aristate. Racemes 1 (–2)-flowered. Flowers 4–6 mm. Calyx teeth much longer than tube, usually somewhat shorter than the bluish corolla, filiform. Pod 0.7–1.2 × 0.3–0.5 cm., 1–2-seeded, obovate-rhombic, pubescent (rarely glabrous). Seeds 3 mm. in diam., lenticular, brown. Fl. March–April.

Var. **ervoides**. *L. ervoides* (Brignoli) Grande, l.c. *Cicer ervoides* Brignoli, Fasc. Pl. Forojul. 27 (1810). *L. lenticula* (Schreb. ex Hoppe) Alef., Bonplandia 9 : 129 (1861). *Ervum lenticula* Schreb. ex Hoppe in Sturm, Deutschl. Fl. 1, 32 : t. 503 (1812); Boiss., Fl. 2 : 599 (1872). Pod pubescent.

Var. **leiocarpa** (Eig) Zoh. (comb. nov.). *Ervum lenticula* Schreb. var. *leiocarpum* Eig,

Bull. Inst. Agr. Nat. Hist. 6 : 29 (1927). Pod glabrous or rarely somewhat ciliate at margin.

Hab. of species : Fields. Upper Galilee, Judean Mts. Rare.

Area of species : N. and E. Mediterranean, with slight extensions into the adjacent regions.

3. Lens orientalis (Boiss.) Schmalh., Fl. Sred. Juz. Ross. 1 : 297 (1895); Hand.-Mazzetti, Ann. Naturh. Mus. Wien 27 : 80 (1913). *Ervum orientale* Boiss., Diagn. ser. 1, 9 : 115 (1849) et Fl. 2 : 598 (1872). [Plate 301]

Annual, 10–30 cm., appressed-hirsute. Stems erect or ascending, branched. Leaves 2–3.5 cm., paripinnate, usually ending in an awn; leaflets 3–7-paired, 0.5–1 cm., ovate to oblong-elliptical, entire, mucronulate, hirsute. Peduncles 1.5–3 cm., as long as or somewhat longer than subtending leaves, ending with a very short awn. Racemes 1–3 (–4)-flowered. Flowers 4.5–6 mm. Calyx as long as or longer than the violet or pale blue corolla; teeth lanceolate-subulate. Pod 0.8–1 × 0.4–0.5 cm., usually 2-seeded, obovate-rhombic, glabrous. Seeds about 3 mm. in diam., lenticular, brown. Fl. March–May.

Hab. : Stony places. Upper and Lower Galilee, Mt. Carmel, Esdraelon Plain, Mt. Gilboa, Upper Jordan Valley, Ammon, Edom. Rather uncommon.

Area : E. Mediterranean and Irano-Turanian.

41. LATHYRUS L.

Annual or perennial herbs. Stems green, mostly with leafy wings. Leaves pari- or imparipinnate, consisting of 1 or rarely of a few pairs of leaflets, or reduced to leaf-like petioles or to stipules, usually with a tendril or with a terminal awn. Racemes 1- to many-flowered, pedunculate. Flowers rather large. Calyx tube usually having a somewhat oblique rim; calyx teeth equal or the upper teeth somewhat shorter. Standard usually obovate to oblong; wings slightly adhering to keel. Stamens diadelphous; staminal tube not oblique above; filaments filiform or dilated at top; anthers uniform. Ovary stipitate or sessile; style flattened, somewhat twisted, bearded near tip, with terminal, capitate stigma. Pod dehiscing by 2 valves, mostly many-seeded, mostly compressed, linear or oblong-rhomboidal, rarely cylindrical. Seeds mostly globular, sometimes compressed or angular.

About 170 species, mainly in the north-temperate zones of both hemispheres; also in the mountains of Trop. E. Africa and in S. America.

Some species are important as forage and pasture plants; some of them are cultivated; one species, *L. odoratus,* is widely cultivated as an ornamental.

Literature : P. Taubert, *Lathyrus* L., in : Engl. & Prantl, *Nat. Pflznfam.* III, 3 : 353–354, 1894. P. F. A. Ascherson & K. O. P. P. Graebner, *Lathyrus,* in : Aschers. & Graebn., *Syn. Mitteleur. Fl.* 6, 2 : 1000–1063, 1909–1910. V. A. Fedchenko, *Lathyrus* L., in : *Flora URSS* 13 : 479–520, 1948.

1. Leaves with simple or compound blades   2
– Leaves reduced to tendrils and leaf-like stipules.   **14. L. aphaca**

2. Petiole leaf-like; blades of leaves predominantly simple, only those of the upper leaves irregularly divided into lobes (leaflets)   3
- Petiole not leaf-like; blade divided into 2 or more distinct leaflets   4
3. Leaves large, oblong, the uppermost leaves with tendrils. Flowers pale yellow. Seeds smooth.   **15. L. ochrus**
- Leaves small, narrowly linear, without tendrils. Flowers purple-red. Seeds tuberculate.   **13. L. nissolia**
4(2). Leaves of 2–4 pairs of leaflets (very rarely of 1 pair only)   5
- Leaves of 1 pair of leaflets   6
5. Leaflets more or less remote. Flowers whitish to cream-coloured. Pod with 4–5 prominent nerves along each valve. Annuals.   **9. L. gloeospermus**
- Leaflets subdigitately crowded. Flowers purple-blue. Pod not as above. Perennials.   **1. L. digitatus**
6(4). Pod up to 9 mm., reniform to subglobular, mostly 1–2-seeded.   **12. L. lentiformis**
- Pod longer and not as above   7
7. Flowers purple, 0.7–0.8 cm. Leaflets 2–7 × 0.1–0.3 cm., narrowly linear, long-acuminate. Pod 1.5–2 cm., erect, glabrous. Seeds tuberculate.   **11. L. setifolius**
- Not as above   8
8. Tendrils simple, aristate, less than 1 cm. Stems erect, rigid, not winged. Flowers lilac-blue, 6–9 mm. Pod not winged, at least 8 times as long as broad.   **10. L. inconspicuus**
- Tendrils branched, rarely simple but then longer than 1 cm.   9
9. Pod about 2 × 1 cm., with broad wings, ciliate at margin.   **8. L. blepharicarpus**
- Pod longer or / and narrower, not ciliate   10
10. Pod with style (beak) 1 cm. long or more. Flowers yellow (rarely pinkish or red); standard up to 2 cm. broad.   **4. L. gorgonei**
— Not as above   11
11. Pod 5–10 times as long as broad   12
— Pod much shorter   13
12. Petiole mostly 2-winged. Peduncles shorter than subtending leaves. Racemes (1–)2–6-flowered.   **2. L. hierosolymitanus**
— Petiole mostly angular. Peduncles as long as or longer than subtending leaves, 1(–2)-flowered.   **3. L. cassius**
13(11). Valves of pod marked by a prominent longitudinal midrib   14
— Valves of pod without longitudinal midrib   15
14. Leaflets 5–7 cm., narrowly lanceolate to linear, much longer than peduncles.   **6. L. cicera**
— Leaflets shorter than above, elliptical, shorter than peduncles.   **7. L. pseudocicera**
15(13). Leaflets narrowly lanceolate-linear. Seeds plain (not mottled).   **6. L. cicera**
— Leaflets lanceolate to oblong or elliptical. Seeds mottled.   **5. L. marmoratus**

Sect. OROBUS (L.) Godr. in Gren. et Godr., Fl. Fr. 1 : 485 (1849) p.p. Gen. *Orobus* L., Gen. Pl. ed. 5, 325 (1754). Perennials. Stems erect. Leaves of 2–3 or more pairs of leaflets; petiole ending with an awn or mucro. Racemes many-flowered. Pod linear.

1. Lathyrus digitatus (M.B.) Fiori in Fiori et Paol., Fl. Anal. Ital. 2 : 105 (1900); Turrill, Kew Bull. 1937 : 236 (1937). *Orobus digitatus* M.B., Fl. Taur.-Cauc. 2 : 153 (1808). "*L. sessilifolius* (Sibth. et Sm.)" Ten., Fl. Neap. Prodr. App. 5 : 20 (1826).

O. sessilifolius Sm. in Sibth. et Sm., Fl. Gr. Prodr. 2 : 64 (1813); Boiss., Fl. 2 : 618 (1872). [Plate 302]

Perennial herb, glabrous, 25–50 cm. Rhizome short, with thick fibrous roots. Stems ascending to erect, mostly simple, prominently ridged. Leaves sessile or short-petioled; stipules longer than petiole, semisagittate, with linear-subulate, veined lobes; leaflets mostly 2 (–3)-paired, 3–9 × 0.2–0.6 cm., almost digitate, linear to narrowly lanceolate, acute to acuminate, with 5–9 parallel nerves. Peduncles much longer than subtending leaves, erect, angular. Racemes axillary, 4–11-flowered. Bracts minute, almost membranous, subulate. Pedicels as long as calyx. Flowers 1–1.8 cm. Calyx about 7 mm.; teeth as long as or usually a little shorter than tube, slightly unequal, triangular-lanceolate. Corolla 2–3 times as long as calyx, purple-blue; standard with obovate, notched limb, longer than wings and keel. Style almost club-shaped, hairy at apex. Pod 5–7 × 0.5 cm., many-seeded, flattened, linear, beaked, often slightly incurved at apex. Seeds subglobular, brown, smooth. Fl. March–May.

Hab.: Maquis and shady places. Upper Galilee, Gilead.

Area: Mainly E. Mediterranean.

Sect. CICERCULA (Medik.) Godr. in Gren. et Godr., Fl. Fr. 1 : 481 (1849). Gen. *Cicercula* Medik., Vorl. Churpf. Phys.-Oken. Ges. 2 : 358 (1787). Annuals. Flowers solitary or in 2–3-flowered racemes. Leaflets oblong, lanceolate or linear; petioles of upper leaves terminating in tendrils. Pod 3–10-seeded, oblong-obovoid to oblong or linear.

2. Lathyrus hierosolymitanus Boiss., Diagn. ser. 1, 9 : 127 (1849). [Plate 303]

Annual, glabrous, 15–50 cm. or more. Stems ascending or climbing, simple or branched, especially at base, angular, 2-winged. Leaves varying in size; stipules shorter than petiole, semisagittate; petioles shorter than leaflets, those of the lowest leaves with awn-like tips, those of the upper leaves with branched tendrils; leaflets 1-paired, (2–)4–12 (–15) × 0.2–1.5 cm., sessile, linear to lanceolate, acuminate or mucronate, parallel-nerved. Peduncles usually shorter than subtending leaves, later elongating, erect. Racemes 2–5 (–6)-, rarely 1-flowered. Bracts small, narrow, sometimes 0. Pedicels about as long as calyx. Flowers (0.9–)1.2–1.8 cm., deflexed. Calyx 6–7 mm.; teeth almost as long as tube, triangular-lanceolate, acuminate. Corolla yellowish-pink or yellow, 2–3 times as long as calyx; standard yellow with pink veins, often notched, longer than wings and keel. Pod 3–6.5 × 0.5–1 cm., 4–10-seeded, somewhat compressed, linear to oblong, straight or slightly curved, with 3 ridges along ventral suture; valves net-veined; beak short. Seeds about 4 mm., angular to subglobular, wrinkled-tuberculate. 2n = 14. Fl. February–April.

Extremely polymorphic. Some of the following varieties grade towards *L. annuus* L., with which the above species has been confused by some authors.

1. Stems with subterranean flowering shoots.   var. **amphicarpus**
 – Stems with aerial flowering shoots only   2
2. Flowers yellowish. Racemes 1-, rarely 2-flowered.   var. **luteus**
 – Flowers pink to yellowish-pink. Racemes usually 2–5-flowered.   var. **hierosolymitanus**

Var. **hierosolymitanus.** *L. hierosolymitanus* Boiss., l.c. et Fl. 2 : 604 (1872). *L. annuus* L. var. *hierosolymitanus* (Boiss.) Post, Fl. Syr. Pal. Sin. 292 (1883–1896). Racemes 2–5-flowered. Flowers pink to yellowish-pink.

Hab.: Fallow fields and batha. Coastal Galilee, Acco Plain, Sharon Plain, Philistean Plain, Upper and Lower Galilee, Mt. Carmel, Esdraelon Plain, Samaria, W. Negev, Dan Valley, Hula Plain, Upper and Lower Jordan Valley, Gilead, Ammon. Very common.

Var. **amphicarpus** Plitm.* Stems with aerial and subterranean flowering shoots.

Hab.: As above. Mt. Carmel, N. Negev. Very rare.

Var. **luteus** Plitm.* Stems slender, 15–30 cm. Leaflets 2–6 × 0.2–0.7 cm., grass-like. Racemes 1–2-flowered. Flowers 0.9–1.1 cm., yellowish.

Hab.: As above. Philistean Plain. Very rare.

Area of species : E. Mediterranean.

3. Lathyrus cassius Boiss., Diagn. ser. 1, 9 : 128 (1849) et Fl. 2 : 604 (1872). *L. annuus* L. var. *cassius* (Boiss.) Post, Fl. Syr. Pal. Sin. 292 (1883–1896).

Annual, glabrous, 20–50 cm. Stems climbing, slender, narrowly 2-winged. Leaves short-petioled; stipules subulate-lanceolate, semisagittate; petiole longer than blade, angular, that of lower leaves ending with an awn-like cusp, that of upper leaves with a tendril; leaflets 1-paired, narrower and shorter than in preceding species, lanceolate, acute. Peduncles longer than subtending leaves, filiform. Racemes 1 (–2)-flowered. Flowers about 1 cm. Calyx 4–5 mm.; teeth as long as tube, triangular-lanceolate, acute. Corolla dark pink with standard darker than wings and keel. Pods 2.5–4 cm., 6–7-seeded, subcompressed, linear, curved at apex, with 3 ridges along ventral suture, net-veined, the young ones glandular. Seeds globular, tuberculate. Fl. March–April.

Hab.: Fields. Esdraelon Plain. Very rare.

Area : E. Mediterranean.

Despite the occurrence of forms intermediate between *L. hierosolymitanus* Boiss., *L. cassius* Boiss. and *L. annuus* L. (the latter does not occur in Palestine), these species can readily be distinguished from one another by the size of flowers and pods, colour of corolla, number of flowers per raceme, etc.; the two first mentioned taxa could, however, be considered as subspecies of *L. annuus.*

4. Lathyrus gorgonei Parl., Giorn. Sci. Sic. 62 : 3 (1838). [Plate 304]

Annual, glabrous, 15–60 cm. Stems many, ascending or climbing, branched, angular to narrowly winged. Leaves up to 10 cm., conspicuously petiolate; stipules shorter to a little longer than petiole, semisagittate, upper portion lanceolate to ovate, acuminate; petioles shorter than leaflets, winged, all, except for those of lower leaves, ending with branched tendrils; leaflets 1-paired, 1.5–8 × (0.1–)0.2–1.8 cm., subsessile, narrowly linear or oblong-lanceolate to elliptical, acuminate or mucronate. Peduncles glabrous or subglabrous, about as long as subtending leaves. Racemes axillary, 1-flowered. Bracts small, subulate, ciliate. Pedicels shorter than to as long as calyx. Flowers (1–)2–2.5 cm., deflexed. Calyx 7–9 mm.; teeth about twice as long as tube or

---

* See Appendix at end of this volume.

shorter, spreading to deflexed in fruit, lanceolate-subulate, acuminate. Corolla over twice as long as calyx, yellow, rarely pinkish to red; standard notched, pink- and purple-veined, longer than the wings and the pale keel. Style about 1 cm., persistent, ciliate towards apex. Pod 2.5–5 × 0.5–0.8 cm., 4–8-seeded, spreading or deflexed on a long peduncle, somewhat flattened, linear, beaked, 3-ridged along ventral suture, net-veined. Seeds 3–5 mm., subglobular, purple-brown, smooth. 2n = 14. Fl. February–April.

1. Seeds mottled with black-brown; number of seeds sometimes less than 5.
                                                                  var. **variegatus**
– Not as above   2
2. Pod provided with a prominent midrib on each valve. Glabrous or subglabrous plants.
   Flowers red, 2–2.5 cm.   var. **lineatus**
– Pod without a midrib   3
3. Leaflets 1–2 mm. broad. Flowers 1–1.5 cm.   var. **stenophyllus**
– Leaflets up to 0.4–1 cm. broad. Flowers generally larger.   var. **gorgonei**

Var. **gorgonei**. *L. gorgoni* Parl., l.c. *L. amoenus* Fenzl, Pugill. 3 (1842); Boiss., Fl. 2 : 605 (1872). Leaflets 0.4–1 cm. broad. Flowers (1.5–)2–2.5 cm. Pod not marked with a prominent midrib.

Hab.: Fields. Coastal Galilee, Acco Plain, Sharon Plain, Philistean Plain, Upper and Lower Galilee, Mt. Carmel, Esdraelon Plain, Judean Mts., Judean Desert, N. Negev, Dan Valley, Hula Plain, Upper and Lower Jordan Valley, Gilead. Common.

Var. **lineatus** Plitm.* Pod with a prominent midrib on each valve. Glabrous or sub-glabrous plants. Flowers red, 2–2.5 cm.

Hab.: As above. Upper and Lower Galilee, Mt. Gilboa, Beit Shean Valley. Rather rare.

Var. **stenophyllus** (Post) Dinsmore in Post, Fl. Syr. Pal. Sin. ed. 2, 1 : 430 (1932). *L. amoenus* Fenzl var. *stenophyllus* Post, Fl. Syr. Pal. Sin. 293 (1883–1896). Leaflets 1–2 mm. broad. Flowers 1–1.5 cm.

Hab.: As above. Philistean Plain, Judean Mts., Judean Desert. Rare.

Var. **variegatus** Evenari in Opphr. et Evenari, Bull. Soc. Bot. Genève ser. 2, 31 : 277 (1941). Seeds less than 5 in each pod, mottled.

Hab.: As above. Sharon Plain, Philistean Plain. Rare.

Area of species: E. Mediterranean, with slight extensions towards the W. Irano-Turanian region.

5. Lathyrus marmoratus Boiss. et Bl. in Boiss., Fl. 2 : 606 (1872). [Plate 305]
Annual, almost glabrous, 15–30(–60) cm. Stems procumbent to ascending, branched at base, slender, angular, narrowly 2-winged. Leaves petiolate; stipules semisagittate, upper portion lanceolate to ovate, tapering at apex; petioles shorter than leaflets, narrowly 2-winged, those of the lowest leaves ending with a cusp, those of the rest with a tendril; leaflets 1-paired, 1–6 × 0.1–0.7 cm., sessile, lanceolate, acute, mucronate or acuminate, parallel-nerved. Peduncles shorter than subtending leaves, rather erect,

* See Appendix at end of this volume.

glabrous to slightly hairy. Racemes 1-flowered. Bracts minute, somewhat ciliate. Pedicels a little shorter than calyx. Flowers 1.2–1.5 cm. Calyx 7–8 mm.; teeth up to twice as long as tube, lanceolate. Corolla twice as long as calyx, pink-violet; standard longer than keel and wings, notched. Style ciliate, puberulent at its dilated apex. Pod 1.5–3 × 0.6–0.8 cm., 2–5-seeded, deflexed, compressed, linear-subrhomboidal, short-beaked, narrowly 2-winged along ventral suture, net-veined. Seeds 3–6 mm., sub-glabrous, grey-rusty, mottled with brown or black-brown. 2n = 14. Fl. February–April.

Hab.: Fields, steppes and batha. Coastal Galilee, Sharon Plain, Philistean Plain, Judean Mts., Judean Desert, W. and N. Negev, Edom. Rather common.

Area: E. Mediterranean.

6. Lathyrus cicera L., Sp. Pl. 730 (1753). [Plate 306]

Annual, subglabrous, 10–40 cm. Stems procumbent to erect, branched, slender, angular, narrowly 2-winged. Leaves petiolate; stipules lanceolate, semisagittate; petioles shorter than leaflets, winged, those of lower leaves ending with a cusp, those of the others with tendrils; leaflets 1-paired, 2–8 × 0.1–0.5 cm., sessile, linear to narrowly lanceolate, parallel-nerved. Peduncles much shorter than subtending leaves, about as long as stipules or shorter, somewhat hairy. Racemes axillary, 1-flowered. Bracts minute, hairy. Pedicels shorter than calyx. Flowers 1–1.5 cm. Calyx 7–8 mm.; teeth twice as long as tube, lanceolate-subulate. Corolla twice as long as calyx, purple-red; standard longer than keel and wings. Style puberulent at its dilated apex. Pod 2–4 × 0.6–0.9 cm., 3–6-seeded, erect to spreading, somewhat compressed, oblong-linear, short-beaked, canaliculate to narrowly 2-winged along ventral suture. Seeds about 4 mm., subglobular, brown to pale grey, plain or sometimes obsoletely mottled or with a black-brown median line, smooth. Fl. February–April.

Var. **cicera**. L. *cicera* L., l.c.; Boiss., Fl. 2 : 605 (1872). Pod 2–3.5 × 0.9 cm.; valves not marked by a prominent midrib. Seeds plain (not mottled).

Hab.: Fields and batha. Upper Galilee. Rare.

Var. **negevensis** Plitm.* Pod 2–4 × 0.6–0.9 cm., net-veined, with a prominent midrib on each valve. Seeds sometimes obsoletely mottled. 2n = 14.

Hab.: Fields. Philistean Plain, Judean Mts., N. Negev, Ammon, Moav, Edom. Sparse.

Area of species: Mediterranean and Irano-Turanian.

7. Lathyrus pseudocicera Pamp., Nuov. Giorn. Bot. Ital. n.s. 31 : 214 (1924); V. Täckh., Stud. Fl. Eg. 317 (1956). L. *cicera* L. var. *lineatus* Post, Fl. Syr. Pal. Sin. 292 (1883–1896). [Plate 306a]

Annual, somewhat hispid-pubescent, 10–25 cm. Stems procumbent to ascending, branched at base, narrowly 2-winged; wings slightly ciliate. Leaves petiolate; stipules semisagittate, ciliate, upper portion mostly longer than petiole, lanceolate-ovate; petioles of lower leaves terminating in a cusp, and those of upper leaves in a tendril, which is often simple; leaflets mostly shorter than 3 cm., 0.1–0.8 cm. broad, almost sessile,

---

* See Appendix at end of this volume.

lanceolate to lanceolate-elliptical, acute to obtuse, mucronulate, ciliate at margins, parallel-nerved. Peduncles much longer than stipules, longer or shorter than subtending leaves, erect, sparingly hairy. Racemes axillary, 1-flowered. Bracts minute, hairy. Pedicels shorter than calyx. Flowers 1.5–2.2 cm. Calyx 7–8 mm.; teeth twice as long as tube, lanceolate to subulate, glabrous or ciliate. Corolla 2–3 times as long as calyx, purple-red to violet; standard slightly notched. Style ciliate and puberulent at the dilated apex. Pod 2–4 × 0.5–0.9 cm., 2–5-seeded, deflexed on an elongated, thickened peduncle, somewhat compressed, oblong-linear, short-beaked, canaliculate to narrowly 2-winged along ventral suture; valves marked with a prominent midrib, net-veined. Seeds 3–5 mm., angular-subglobular, smooth, pale brown to light grey, obsoletely mottled-punctate, sometimes with a brown median line and a spot of the same colour near hilum. Fl. February–April.

Hab.: Fields, steppes and batha. N. Philistean Plain, Judean Mts., Judean Desert, Lower Jordan Valley, Dead Sea area, Moav, Edom. Fairly common.

Area: E. Mediterranean (Cyrenaica to Syria and Iraq).

8. Lathyrus blepharicarpus Boiss., Diagn. ser. 1, 9 : 126 (1849) et Fl. 2 : 607 (1872). [Plate 307]

Annual, patulous-pubescent to sparingly hairy, 10–30 cm. Stems procumbent, rarely ascending, simple or branched at base, angular, somewhat 2-winged. Leaves 2–7 cm., hairy to glabrescent; stipules hardly as long as petiole, lanceolate, semisagittate; petiole slightly winged, shorter than leaflets; tendrils almost 5 cm. in upper leaves, short and awn-like in lower leaves; leaflets 1-paired, subsessile, narrowly linear to elliptical or lanceolate, mucronulate, usually ciliate, parallel-nerved, those of lower leaves almost oblong. Peduncles as long as or longer than subtending leaves, hairy. Racemes axillary, 1-flowered. Bracts minute, caducous. Pedicels shorter or longer than calyx. Flowers 1–1.8(–2) cm. Calyx glabrous, with ovate-lanceolate, acute, sometimes ciliolate teeth up to twice as long as tube. Corolla twice as long as calyx, purplish; standard somewhat longer than wings; keel slightly shorter than wings, white-lilac, with hairy margin. Style spatulate at apex. Pod 1.8–3.5 × 0.8–1.2 cm., 2–5-seeded, flattened, oblong, broadly winged at upper suture, glabrous, ciliate at margin, net-veined. Seeds 4–6 mm., globular, brown to black, often punctate or mottled, smooth. 2n = 14. Fl. February–April.

Hab.: Fields and batha. Philistean Plain, Upper and Lower Galilee, Mt. Carmel, Esdraelon Plain, Samaria, Judean Mts., Judean Desert, Dan Valley, Hula Plain, Upper and Lower Jordan Valley. Fairly common.

Area: E. Mediterranean.

Very polymorphic in indumentum, leaves, flower size, etc. Eig (Bull. Inst. Agr. Nat. Hist. 6 : 30, 1927) has described a glabrous or glabrescent form as var. *glabratus*. An amphicarpous form, in which part of the fruits develop on subterranean shoots, has also been observed in Palestine. Other forms having, e.g., larger flowers, peduncles longer than leaves or pods ciliate only along one suture also occur in this country. The taxonomic value of these forms cannot be asserted until constancy tests have been made.

Further studies may reveal that *L. blepharicarpus* is identical with *L. amphicarpos* L., Sp. Pl. 729 (1753).

Sect. OROBASTRUM Boiss., Fl. 2 : 601 (1872). Sect. *Orobus* (L.) Godr. in Gren. et Godr., Fl. Fr. 1 : 485 (1849) p.p. Annuals or perennials. Stems slightly or not at all climbing. Leaves with branched tendrils. Pod oblong to linear. Style canaliculate along upper side. Flowers solitary. Leaves petiolate; petiole ending in an awn or tendril, sometimes tendrils branched.

9. Lathyrus gloeospermus Warb. et Eig, Repert. Sp. Nov. 25 : 351 (1928). [Plate 308]
Annual, glabrous, dark green, 30–60 cm. Stems branched, rigid, angular, winged. Leaves 5–12 cm., conspicuously petiolate, the lowest leaves with leaf-like petiole and abortive blade; stipules 0.2–2 cm., linear-lanceolate, semisagittate; petiole and rhachis winged, often ending with simple or branched tendrils; leaflets usually 3–4-paired, 3–7 × 0.1–0.6 cm., petiolulate, linear, acute to mucronate, parallel-nerved. Racemes 1-flowered, on very short peduncles. Pedicels erect, shorter than calyx. Calyx 1–1.5 cm.; teeth as long as the nerved tube, linear-lanceolate, acute, the upper teeth somewhat shorter. Corolla white to cream-coloured; wings somewhat shorter than standard and somewhat longer than keel. Pod 3–8 × 0.9–1.3 cm., erect on a thickened pedicel, 2–7-seeded, flattened, oblong-linear, beaked, glabrous or sparingly hairy, with 4–5 prominent parallel nerves on each valve. Seeds 5–7 mm., subglobular, brown, shiny, smooth, strongly viscid. 2n = 14. Fl. March–April.
    Hab.: Fields. Lower Galilee, Esdraelon Plain, Hula Plain, Upper Jordan Valley, Gilead. Rather rare.
    Area : E. Mediterranean.

The recorded var. *pilosus* Warb. et Eig, l.c. and var. *aaronsohnianus* Opphr., Bull. Soc. Bot. Genève ser. 2, 22 : 334 (1931; err. "*L. gloeocarpus* Warb. et Eig var. *aaronsohnianus* Opphr.*"), based mainly on the degree of pubescence and number of nerves of the pod, are doubtfully constant taxa.

10. Lathyrus inconspicuus L., Sp. Pl. 730 (1753). *L. erectus* Lag., Gen. et Sp. Nov. 22 (1816); Boiss., Fl. 2 : 613 (1872). *L. inconspicuus* L. var. *erectus* (Lag.) Fiori et Bég., Sched. Fl. Ital. Exs. (1901–1902). [Plate 309]
Annual, glabrous or subglabrous, 15–60 cm. Stems erect, simple or branching, slender, angular. Leaves short-petioled; stipules about as long as petiole, semisagittate with linear lobes; petioles ending with a narrowly lanceolate to cuspidate awn shorter than 1 cm., those of uppermost leaves rarely with a simple filiform tendril; leaflets 1-paired, 2–7 × 0.2–0.7 cm., sessile, linear to lanceolate, mucronulate to acuminate, parallel-nerved. Peduncles axillary, very short to almost 0, not awned. Racemes 1-flowered. Pedicels about as long as calyx. Flowers 6–9 mm. Calyx about 4–5 mm., slightly puberulent; teeth as long as tube, narrowly lanceolate. Corolla one and a half times to twice as long as calyx, lilac-blue; standard longer than wings and keel, retuse. Style short, dilated at the somewhat puberulent apex. Pod 3–6 × 0.3–0.5 cm., erect, subcylindrical, slightly torulose, slightly incurved at apex, obsoletely 3-ribbed along ventral suture, glabrous, reticulate-veined. Seeds 4–14, 2–4 mm., almost globular, brown, smooth. Fl. April–May.
    Hab.: Fields, mostly among crops. Philistean Plain, Lower Galilee, Esdraelon Plain, Mt. Gilboa, Judean Mts., Upper Jordan Valley, Gilead, Ammon, Moav. Not common.

Area: Mediterranean and Irano-Turanian.

11. Lathyrus setifolius L., Sp. Pl. 731 (1753); Boiss., Fl. 2 : 612 (1872). [Plate 310]

Annual, glabrous, 30–50 cm. Stems ascending, climbing, branched at base, slender, angular, obsoletely 2-winged. Leaves conspicuously petiolate; stipules semisagittate, with narrow, linear-lanceolate upper portion about as long as petiole; petioles much shorter than leaflets, those of lower leaves cuspidate at tip, those of upper leaves ending with a simple or branched tendril; leaflets 1-paired, 2–7 × 0.1–0.3 cm., sessile, narrowly lanceolate to linear, acuminate or mucronulate, parallel-nerved. Peduncles shorter than subtending leaves, subglabrous. Racemes axillary, 1-flowered. Bracts mostly 0. Pedicels about as long as calyx. Flowers 0.7–1 cm., first erect, then deflexed. Calyx about 5 mm.; teeth about as long as tube, lanceolate-subulate. Corolla longer than calyx, purple; standard a little longer than keel and wings, reflexed. Style short-hairy at apex. Pod 1.5–3 × 0.5–0.8 cm., stipitate, 2–3-seeded, oblong-linear, incurved, beaked, hairy or glabrous but sparingly pilose at margins, flattened, obsoletely net-veined. Seeds 3–6 mm., purple-brown, globular, tuberculate. Fl. April.

Var. **sharonensis** Zoh. et Plitm.* Leaves longer than in typical variety; tendrils mostly simple. Flowers 7–8 mm. Pod 1.5–2 cm., glabrous. Seeds much smaller than in typical variety.

Hab.: Swamps. Sharon Plain. Very rare (probably extinct).

Area of species: Mediterranean, with slight extensions into adjacent Euro-Siberian territories.

Sect. LENTIFORMIA Zoh.* Annuals. Leaves very short-petioled; petioles of lower leaves ending with an awn, those of the upper leaves with a simple tendril. Racemes 1-flowered. Flowers minute. Pod 1(–2–3)-seeded, often indehiscent, separating as a whole from plant.

12. Lathyrus lentiformis Plitm., Israel Journ. Bot. 14 : 90 (1965). [Plate 311]

Annual, glabrous or nearly so, 10–35 cm. Stems many, procumbent to ascending, tufted. Leaves 1–4(–4.5) cm.; stipules usually 0.5–1 cm., longer than petiole, semi-sagittate; petiole shorter than blade; tendrils simple, up to 1.5 cm., shorter than leaf-lets; leaflets 0.6–3.5 × 0.2–0.6 cm., elliptical to linear-oblanceolate, acutish to obtuse, mucronulate. Peduncles slender, shorter to longer than subtending leaves. Racemes axillary, 1–2-flowered. Bracts shorter than pedicels, the latter distinctly shorter than calyx. Flowers about 5 mm. Calyx 2–3 mm.; teeth slightly longer than tube, almost equal, lanceolate to ovate. Corolla about twice as long as calyx, lilac-blue; standard longer than wings, reflexed, obovate to orbicular, short-clawed, roundish at apex; keel as long as wings. Style compressed, short-pilose towards apex. Pod 4–9 × 4–6 mm., indehiscent, 1-seeded, or 2(–3)-seeded (pod then torulose), inflated, obovoid to oblong-subreniform, with thin, scarious valves, glabrous, net-veined, separating from plant as a whole. Seeds 2.5–3.5 mm., subglobular, brown, finely tuberculate. $2n = 16$. Fl. April–May.

* See Appendix at end of this volume.

Hab.: Batha; somewhat damp basalt soils. Upper Galilee (endemic). Very rare.
Area: E. Mediterranean.

Sect. NISSOLIA (Adans.) Reichb., Fl. Germ. Exc. 533 (1832). Gen. *Nissolia* Adans., Fam. 2:330 (1763). Annuals. Stipules small; petioles leaf-like, without tendrils. Flowers purple.

13. Lathyrus nissolia L., Sp. Pl. 729 (1753); Boiss., Fl. 2 : 603 (1872). [Plate 312]

Annual, hairy to glabrous, 20–40 cm. Stems erect to ascending, simple or branching from base, rigid, slender, angular. Leaves reduced to petioles 2–10 × about 0.2 cm., leaf-like, linear-lanceolate, parallel-nerved, acute; stipules rudimentary, subulate; tendrils 0; leaflets 0. Peduncles solitary, shorter than petioles (leaves), erect, filiform. Racemes axillary, 1(–2)-flowered. Bracts minute or 0. Pedicels a little shorter than calyx, hairy. Flowers 0.7–1.2 cm., erect to spreading. Calyx 4–6 mm.; teeth shorter than tube, linear-lanceolate, slightly hairy. Corolla about twice as long as calyx, purplered; standard longer than keel and wings. Style short, somewhat puberulent at apex. Pod 2.5–5 (–6) × 0.3 cm., many-seeded, spreading to deflexed, somewhat flattened, very short-beaked, hairy to glabrous, with longitudinal nerves. Seeds about 2 mm., ovoid, subglobular, brown-black, finely tuberculate. Fl. May–June.

Var. **gramineus** (Kern.) Aschers. et Graebn., Fl. Nordostd. Flachl. 454 (1898). *L. gramineus* Kern., Oesterr. Bot. Zeitschr. 13 : 188 (1863). Plant glabrous. Leaves (petioles) much narrower and longer than in typical variety. Pod glabrous.

Hab.: Batha. Upper Galilee. Very rare.
Area of species: Mediterranean, S. and W. Euro-Siberian.

Sect. APHACA (Adans.) Reichb., Fl. Germ. Exc. 533 (1832). Gen. *Aphaca* Adans., Fam. 2:330 (1763). Annuals. Stipules broad, leaf-like; blade reduced to a tendril.

14. Lathyrus aphaca L., Sp. Pl. 729 (1753); Boiss., Fl. 2 : 602 (1872). *L. aphaca* L. var. *biflorus* Post, Fl. Syr. Pal. Sin. 292 (1883–1896). [Plate 313]

Annual, glaucescent, subglabrous, 10–60 cm. Stems usually erect or ascending, branched mainly at base, flexuous, angular. Leaves abortive, reduced to stipules and tendrils (only the juvenile leaves pinnate); stipules 0.5–4 cm., sessile, simple, leaf-like, ovate, sagittate-hastate or truncate at base, apiculate; tendrils 1–6 cm., simple, filiform. Peduncles as long as tendrils, longer than stipules, muticous or short-aristate. Racemes axillary, 1(–2)-flowered. Pedicels about as long as calyx tube, erect or slightly curved, often hairy. Flowers 1–1.5 cm. Calyx about 1 cm.; teeth much longer than tube, almost equal, lanceolate, acute. Corolla longer than calyx, yellow; standard longer than the wings and the incurved, whitish and pink-veined keel. Pod 3(–4–7)-seeded, 2–3 × 0.4–0.6 cm., erect, compressed, oblong-linear, sometimes falcate, slightly torulose, beaked, reticulately veined. Seeds 2–4 mm., subglobular, brown-black, smooth. 2n = 14. February–April.

Hab.: Fields, field edges and roadsides. Acco Plain, Sharon Plain, Philistean Plain,

Upper and Lower Galilee, Mt. Carmel, Esdraelon Plain, Mt. Gilboa, Samaria, Judean Mts., W. and N. Negev, Hula Plain, Upper Jordan Valley, Gilead, Moav, Edom. Very common.

Area: Mediterranean, Irano-Turanian and Euro-Siberian.

Sect. CLYMENUM (Adans.) DC. ex Ser. in DC., Prodr. 2 : 375 (1825). Gen. *Clymenum* Adans., Fam. 2 : 330 (1763). Annuals. Petioles leaf-like, the upper ones with 2 or more leaflets, the lower ones simple, all bearing tendrils. Standard 2-gibbous at base.

15. Lathyrus ochrus (L.) DC. in Lam. et DC., Fl. Fr. ed. 3, 4 : 578 (1805); *L. ochrus* (L.) Boiss., Fl. 2 : 601 (1872). *Pisum ochrus* L., Sp. Pl. 727 (1753). [Plate 314]

Annual, glaucescent, glabrous, 20–80 cm. Stems procumbent to ascending and climbing, simple to slightly branched, winged. Leaves mostly reduced to 2–13 ×0.5–0.7 cm., decurrent, oblong-elliptical, leaf-like petioles, mostly tendrilliferous at apex; the lower ones with no stipules and no leaflets, the upper ones stipulate and divided into 1–5 lanceolate to elliptical leaflets; stipules (in upper leaves) ovate, semihastate, mucronate, adnate to wings of stem. Peduncles shorter than subtending leaves. Racemes axillary, 1 (–2)-flowered. Pedicels as long as calyx. Flowers 1.2–1.8 cm. Calyx 0.6–1 cm.; teeth almost as long as tube, ovate-lanceolate to triangular, acute, scarious at margin, the upper teeth shorter. Corolla twice as long as calyx, light yellow; standard longer than wings, the latter longer than keel. Style dilated at apex. Pod 3–6 × 1–1.5 cm., deflexed on a thickened peduncle, 4–7-seeded, compressed, oblong, beaked, 2-winged along ventral suture, net-veined. Seeds about 5 mm., globular, dark brown, smooth. 2n = 14. Fl. March–May.

Hab.: Fallow fields, among crops and by ditches. Acco Plain, Sharon Plain, Philistean Plain, Upper and Lower Galilee, Esdraelon Plain, Samaria, Shefela, Judean Mts., Dan Valley, Hula Plain, Upper Jordan Valley. Fairly common.

Area: Mediterranean.

Often grown as fodder for livestock.

42. PISUM L.

Annuals or perennials. Leaves of 1 or more pairs of leaflets and a terminal, often branched, tendril; stipules leaf-like, often larger than leaflets. Racemes 1–3-flowered. Flowers conspicuous. Calyx campanulate; tube oblique; teeth unequal, the upper teeth shorter. Standard obovate to orbicular, 2-gibbous at base; wings adherent to keel. Stamens diadelphous; staminal tube not oblique above; filaments slightly dilated at top; anthers uniform. Ovary subsessile, many-ovuled; style flattened, geniculate at base, curved, bearded and dilated above; stigma subterminal. Pod dehiscent, 2-valved, somewhat compressed, oblong-linear, obliquely truncate, beaked. Seeds almost globular.

Some 6 species mainly in the Mediterranean region and in S. W. Asia.

1. Stipules 4–6 (–8) cm., mostly dentate at base only. Flowers up to 2.5 (–3) cm. Leaflets usually 2–3 pairs.   **1. P. elatius**
– Stipules smaller. Flowers smaller. Leaflets usually 1–2 pairs   2

2. Flowers about 1 cm. Corolla rusty-yellow to reddish-brown. Pod 2.5–3 (–4) cm. Seeds velvety, not mottled.   **3. P. fulvum**
— Flowers somewhat larger, 1.3–1.8 cm. Corolla livid with purple wings. Pod 4–5 cm. Seeds mottled.   **2. P. syriacum**

1. Pisum elatius M.B., Fl. Taur.-Cauc. 2 : 151 (1808); Boiss., Fl. 2 : 623 (1872). [Plate 315]

Annual, glaucous, glabrous, 50–100 cm. Stems few, climbing, striate. Leaves 6–15 cm., spreading; stipules 4–6 (–8) cm., oblong to elliptical or ovate, semicordate, unequally dentate at base; tendrils branched into 3 or more pairs; leaflets 2–3-paired, 2–5 × 0.6–2 cm., often entire. Racemes 1–3-flowered, with peduncles as long as or longer than subtending leaves, decreasing in length towards apex. Flowers up to 2.5 (–3) cm. Corolla pink-purplish with dark purple wings; standard retuse. Pod (7–)8–9 × 0.8–1.5 cm., somewhat compressed, oblong-linear, reticulately veined. Seeds about 5 mm., globular, greyish, mottled with brown, often granular. 2n = 14. Fl. April–May.

Hab.: Maquis and fields. Sharon Plain, Philistean Plain, Upper and Lower Galilee, Mt. Carmel, Esdraelon Plain, Samaria, Judean Mts., Upper and Lower Jordan Valley, Gilead. Sparse.

Area: Mediterranean, with slight extensions into adjacent Euro-Siberian and Irano-Turanian territories.

Intermediates between this and the next species are met with.

2. Pisum syriacum (Berg.) Lehm., Der Züchter 24 : 318 (1954). *P. sativum* L. ssp. *syriacum* Berg. in Hedrick, Veg. New York 17 (1928). *P. humile* Boiss. et Noë in Boiss., Diagn. ser. 2, 2 : 45 (1856) et Fl. 2 : 623 (1872) non Mill., Gard. Dict. ed. 8, no. 2 (1768). [Plate 316]

Annual, glaucescent, glabrous, 20–30 (–50) cm. Stems erect, moderately branched, flexuous, striate. Leaves 6–10 cm., erect-spreading; stipules much larger than leaflets, oblong, usually dentate or incised in lower half and slightly above; leaflets 1–2-paired, 2–3 × 0.5–1.2 cm., oblong-elliptical, dentate to entire. Peduncles somewhat longer than stipules. Racemes 1–2-flowered. Flowers 1.3–1.8 cm. Corolla livid with purple wings; standard retuse to 2-lobed. Pod 4–5 × up to 1 cm., flattened, linear, short-beaked, net-veined. Seeds about 5 mm., globular, brown, mottled, granular. 2n = 14. Fl. February–April.

Hab.: Alluvial and loess soil. Sharon Plain, Philistean Plain, Esdraelon Plain, Samaria, Shefela, Judean Mts., Negev, Lower Jordan Valley. Not rare.

Area: W. Irano-Turanian, with slight extensions into E. Mediterranean territories.

3. Pisum fulvum Sm. in Sibth. et Sm., Fl. Gr. Prodr. 2 : 62 (1813). [Plate 317]

Annual, glabrous, 15–30 cm. Stems ascending or procumbent, rarely erect, slender. Leaves 6–12 cm., spreading; stipules 2–3.5 cm., ovate, semicordate, dentate or incised all around or up to middle; leaflets 1 (–2)-paired, 1.5–2.5 × 1–1.5 cm., ovate, mostly dentate. Racemes 1 (–2–3)-flowered, with peduncles longer than stipules. Flowers about 1 cm. or less. Corolla rusty-yellow or reddish-brown, pale in subterranean flowers;

standard broad, ovate to orbicular, retuse to 2-lobed. Pod 2.5–3(–4) × 0.7–1 cm., short-beaked, net-veined. Seeds about 4 mm., black, velvety, punctulate. 2n = 14. Fl. February–April.

Var. **fulvum**. *P. fulvum* Sm. in Sibth. et Sm., l.c.; Boiss., Fl. 2 : 623 (1872). Plant producing aerial flowers and pods only.

Hab.: Mainly in batha. N. Sharon Plain, Upper and Lower Galilee, Mt. Carmel, Esdraelon Plain, Samaria, Judean Mts., Upper Jordan Valley, Edom. Frequent.

Var. **amphicarpum** Warb. et Eig, Agr. Rec. Inst. Agr. Nat. Hist. 1 : 2, pl. 1 (1926). Plant with aerial and subterranean shoots, the latter bearing 1–3 pale flowers, each in the axil of scale-like stipules. Subterranean flowers and pods smaller than those of aerial shoots.

Hab.: Mainly on scree and pebble heaps. Upper and Lower Galilee, Mt. Carmel, Samaria, Judean Mts. Fairly frequent.

Area of species : E. Mediterranean.

Trib. PHASEOLEAE. Twining annual or perennial herbs or shrubs. Leaves 3-foliolate; leaflets often stipellate. Flowers in racemes. Stamens diadelphous or monadelphous. Pod 2-valved. Primordial leaves opposite.

43. Vigna Savi

Twining, procumbent or erect herbs. Leaves 3-foliolate, each leaflet with 2 minute stipelles. Racemes axillary, long-peduncled. Bracts and bracteoles minute, caducous. Calyx campanulate or tubular, 5-lobed; upper lobes connate or free. Standard orbicular with inflexed auricles at base; wings falcate, somewhat shorter than standard; keel incurved, beakless or with strongly incurved beak. Stamens diadelphous; anthers uniform. Ovary sessile, many-ovuled; style filiform or dilated above, bearded lengthwise on upper surface, with oblique, incurved stigma. Pod dehiscent, 2-valved, many-seeded, subterete, straight or curved, partitioned between seeds.

About 100 species, especially in tropical regions of the Old and New World.

1. Vigna luteola (Jacq.) Benth. in Mart., Fl. Brasil. 15, 1 : 194, t. 50, f. 2 (1859). *Dolichos luteolus* Jacq., Hort. Bot. Vindob. 1 : 39, t. 90 (1770). *V. nilotica* (Del.) Hook. f. et Benth. in Hook. f., Niger Fl. 311 (1849); *V. nilotica* (Del.) Boiss., Fl. 2 : 625 (1872). *D. nilotica* Del., Fl. Aeg. Ill. 69 no. 669 (1813) et Fl. Eg. 109, t. 38, f. 1 (1813). [Plate 318]

Perennial, subglabrous to pubescent herb, 2–3 m. Stems twining, branched. Leaves large, up to 30 cm.; stipules 6–8 mm., lanceolate; petiole usually longer than blade; leaflets 4–10 × 1–4 cm., obovate to elliptical, acuminate; lateral leaflets nearly sessile, terminal leaflets long-petiolulate. Racemes 4–8-flowered, on peduncles 6–12 cm. Pedicels very short, glabrous. Flowers 1–1.5 cm. Calyx about 5 mm.; teeth as long as tube. Corolla green-yellow. Pod up to 6 × 0.3–0.5 cm., many-seeded, pendulous, linear-subterete, partitioned between seeds, becoming black or grey, appressed-hirsute. Seeds 5 × 3 mm., cylindrical, brown with black spots, smooth. Fl. April–December.

Hab.: By rivers and ditches. Sharon Plain, Philistean Plain, Hula Plain, Upper Jordan Valley. Not rare.

Area: Sudanian and other tropical regions.

44. RHYNCHOSIA Lour.

Twining, prostrate, rarely erect herbs or shrubs. Leaves stipulate, 3-foliolate. Racemes axillary; sometimes flowers solitary. Upper teeth of calyx more or less connate or free, the lowest tooth longer. Standard reflexed, obovate-orbicular, with inflexed auricles at base; wings narrow; keel incurved. Stamens diadelphous; anthers uniform. Ovary subsessile, (1–)2-ovuled; style incurved; stigma small, terminal. Pod dehiscent, 2-valved, mostly oblong, falcate, not partitioned between seeds. Seeds 1–2.

About 250 species, mainly in tropical regions.

1. Rhynchosia minima (L.) DC., Prodr. 2:385 (1825). *Dolichos minimus* L., Sp. Pl. 726 (1753). [Plate 319]

Green, minutely puberulent, twining herbs or shrubs. Stems slender. Stipules 3–5 mm., oblong; stipelles minute, setaceous; petiole as long as or longer than blade; leaflets 0.7–2 cm., broadly ovate to almost rhombic, acute or mucronate, entire, almost glabrous on both sides. Racemes much longer than leaves, few-flowered. Flowers 8–9 mm. Corolla yellow. Pod 1.5–2.5 × 0.5–0.6 cm., oblong to obovoid-rhomboidal, glabrous. Seeds ellipsoidal, rusty-yellow, mottled with black. Fl. Spring.

Hab.: Savannah; climbing on acacias. Dead Sea area (Ghor es Safieh, after Hart, 1891).

Area: Sudanian.

Geraniales

56. OXALIDACEAE

Herbs, often rhizomatous or bulbiferous, rarely half-shrubs or trees. Leaves radical or cauline, alternate, with or without stipules, pinnate or digitate, usually 3 (rarely 1)-foliolate. Flowers hermaphrodite, actinomorphic, 5-merous, often heterostylous, solitary, or numerous in cymes or umbels. Sepals 5, persistent, usually imbricated. Petals 5, free, rarely spuriously connate, contorted. Stamens 10, connate at base. Ovary superior, (3–)5-carpelled, (3–)5-celled; placentation axile; ovules 1 to many in each cell, anatropous; styles mostly free; stigmas capitate or 2-lobed. Fruit a capsule with loculicidal dehiscence, rarely a berry. Seeds often with elastic seed coat; endosperm copious, fleshy; embryo straight.

Eight genera and about 950 species, mainly in tropical and subtropical regions of the southern hemisphere; some in north-temperate zones.

1. Oxalis L.

Annual or perennial herbs with or without stems. Leaves mostly ternate. Inflorescences cymose, sometimes umbel-like or flowers solitary. Flowers often heterostylous. Sepals free or slightly connate. Petals free, rarely connate at base, yellow, white, blue or pink, sometimes lilac or violet. Stamens 10, with filaments connate at base, the 5 outer filaments shorter. Ovary 5-celled, 5-angled, ovoid or oblong, with 5 distinct styles ending in capitate stigmas. Fruit a loculicidal capsule. Seeds many, minute, with fleshy aril, bursting out of capsule.

About 800 species, mainly in S. America and S. Africa.

1. Stemless herbs, with vertical bulbiferous rhizomes. Corolla 1.5–3 cm., 3 times as long as calyx.   **1. O. pes-caprae**
- Caulescent herbs, with creeping stems rooting at the nodes. Corolla up to 1 cm., twice as long as calyx.   **2. O. corniculata**

1. Oxalis pes-caprae L., Sp. Pl. 434 (1753). *O. cernua* Thunb., Dissert. Oxal. 14 no. 12, t. 2 (1781); Boiss., Fl. 1 : 867 (1867) *in obs.* [Plate 320]

Perennial, glabrous or sparsely pubescent, (10–)20–50 cm. Rhizomes subterranean, vertical, bulbiferous. Stems 0. Leaves 5–15(–30) cm., radical, on long glabrous petioles; stipules ovate-oblong, partly adnate to petiole; leaflets obcordate to 2-lobed, sub-glabrous above, hairy beneath, hairs intermixed with minute scales. Scapes longer than the leaves, swollen, ending with a many-flowered umbel-like cyme. Pedicels 1–2 cm., at first deflexed, later erect. Flowers (1.5–)2–3 cm. in diam., sometimes double. Calyx about 5–7 mm. Corolla funnel-shaped, deep yellow. Fruit 0. Fl. January–March(–June).

Hab.: Shady sites; a frequent weed, especially among citrus groves, in nurseries, near hedges and elsewhere. Coastal Galilee, Sharon Plain, Philistean Plain, Upper and Lower Galilee, Mt. Carmel, Judean Mts., Dan Valley, Upper Jordan Valley, Golan and probably elsewhere. Locally common.

Area: Origin S. Africa; adventive in almost all the warmer parts of the globe.

A form with double flowers, probably var. *pleniflora* Lowe, Man. Fl. Mad. 1 : 100, 1868 (var. *plena* Fl. Serres 19 : 1964, 1873–1874), is not uncommon in the northern part of the coastal plain.

A heterotristylous plant; as the local populations consist of only one race — that with the shortest styles — no fruits are produced.

Probably introduced at the beginning of the present century.

2. Oxalis corniculata L., Sp. Pl. 435 (1753); Boiss., Fl. 1 : 866 (1867). [Plate 321]

Annual and perennial, hairy, 7–30 cm. Stems many, procumbent, sometimes ascending, rooting at the nodes, weak, leafy. Leaves 1–6 cm., alternate, long-petioled; stipules oblong, adnate to petiole; leaflets 0.5–1 cm., broader than long, obcordate-cuneate, more or less hairy mainly at margins and on lower surface. Peduncles axillary, equalling or exceeding the leaves, bearing 1–6-flowered umbel-like cymes. Flowers 0.6–1 cm.

Calyx 3–5 mm. Petals about twice as long as sepals, yellow. Capsule 1–2 × 0.3 cm., on deflexed pedicel, prismatic-cylindrical, puberulent. Seeds 1–1.5 mm., ovoid, transversely wrinkled. Fl. March–October.

Hab.: Damp places; mainly nurseries and lawns. Sharon Plain, Philistean Plain, Upper and Lower Galilee, Mt. Carmel, Esdraelon Plain, Samaria, Judean Mts., Upper Jordan Valley and probably elsewhere. Fairly common.

Area: Adventive in many warmer parts of the world; origin not known.

57. GERANIACEAE

Annual or perennial herbs, rarely half-shrubs or small trees. Leaves usually alternate, rarely opposite, usually stipulate, toothed, lobed or compound, rarely entire. Flowers hermaphrodite, actinomorphic or slightly zygomorphic, mostly 5-merous, in cymes, umbels, spikes or racemes, rarely flowers solitary. Sepals persistent, usually imbricated. Petals caducous, convolute or imbricated, sometimes alternating with nectar glands, rarely 0. Stamens 5–15, mostly 10, obdiplostemonous, with filaments slightly connate at base, all or only 10 or 5 bearing anthers. Ovary superior; carpels 5 (rarely 2–3 or 8), connate and more or less adnate to a mostly prolonged axis (central column) from which they often separate at maturity along their inner face; placentation axile; ovules 1–2 in each carpel, mostly anatropous; styles free or more or less united; stigmas linear or capitate. Fruit a schizocarp, usually dehiscing septicidally from base to apex, rarely a capsule; mericarps usually 1-seeded. Seeds pendulous, with little or no endosperm; embryo arcuate; cotyledons folded.

Some 11 genera and about 780 species, mainly in the temperate regions.

Literature: R. Knuth, Geraniaceae, in: *Pflznr.* 53 (IV, 129): 1–640, 1912. P. H. Davis & J. Roberts, Materials for a flora of Turkey I, Geraniaceae, *Notes Roy. Bot. Gard. Edinb.* 22: 9–27 (1955).

1. Stamens 15, all anther-bearing.   **4. Monsonia**
– Anther-bearing stamens 5–10   2
2. Mericarps not beaked. Flowers yellow or cream-coloured. Perennials with 2–3-pinnatisect leaves.   **1. Biebersteinia**
– Mericarps beaked. Flowers never yellow   3
3. Anther-bearing stamens 10 (in ours). Beaks of mericarps rolling upwards.   **2. Geranium**
– Anther-bearing stamens 5. Beaks of mericarps twisting spirally.   **3. Erodium**

1. BIEBERSTEINIA Steph.

Perennial herbs, hairy or glandular. Leaves alternate, stipulate, pinnatisect. Flowers actinomorphic, racemose or spicate. Sepals 5, imbricated, growing in fruit. Petals 5, alternating with 5 fleshy nectar glands. Stamens 10, all connate at base into a narrow ring, all anther-bearing. Carpels 5, crustaceous, wrinkled, not beaked, adnate to a short axis from base to middle; ovules solitary in each carpel, anatropous, pendulous on a short funicle; styles distinct but united at apex; stigmas capitate. Mericarps indehiscent, nut-like, hard, not separating from axis, included in the persistent calyx. Seeds curved.

Some 5 species from Greece to C. Asia.

1. Biebersteinia multifida DC., Prodr. 1 : 708 (1824); Boiss., Fl. 1 : 899 (1867). [Plate 322]

Perennial, villose and glandular-hairy, 20–50 cm. Roots vertical, thick, tuberous. Stems branched, especially above, thick, grooved, glandular, scaly above base. Leaves lanceolate in outline, 2–3-pinnatisect into linear acute lobules, hairy, sparingly glandular; stipules brown, hairy. Inflorescences loosely racemose at ends of stems and branches. Bracts obovate, incised or pinnatifid. Pedicels somewhat longer than the calyces, bracteolate. Flowers 1–1.5 cm. Sepals ovate-oblong, acute or obtuse, glandular-hairy, growing in fruit. Petals 6–8 mm., yellow or cream-coloured, oblong-cuneate, often somewhat incised at tip. Filaments narrowing abruptly above, ciliate below. Mericarps glabrous, wrinkled. Fl. April–June.

Hab.: *Artemisia herba-alba* steppes, 800–1,000 m.; grey stony soil. Negev, Edom. Rare.

Area : Irano-Turanian.

2. GERANIUM L.

Annual or perennial herbs, rarely shrubby at base. Stems frequently forked, often swollen at nodes. Leaves usually alternate or the uppermost leaves opposite, stipulate, 3–5-angled or orbicular to reniform in outline, dissected or palmatilobed to -partite. Peduncles axillary, usually 1–3-flowered. Flowers actinomorphic. Nectar glands 5, alternating with petals. Stamens 10, usually all anther-bearing; filaments sometimes somewhat connate at base. Ovary of 5 carpels, each 2-ovuled, terminating with a long beak and with a short stigma on top. Fruit a schizocarp; mericarps usually dehiscent, 1-seeded, separating from axis along their inner face, their beaks rolling upwards but remaining attached by their apex to the top of the axis.

About 300 species in temperate regions and in mountainous areas in the tropics.

1. Perennials with tubers or thick rhizomes. Petals usually over 1 cm.   2
– Annuals. Petals up to 1 cm.   3
2. Sepals 3–5 mm. Rhizomes slender, with ovoid-globular underground tubers.
    1. G. tuberosum
– Sepals (0.8–) 1–1.2 cm. Rhizomes oblique, scaly and thick.   **2. G. libani**
3 (1). Mericarps with 3 keels or wings, the lateral keels pectinate-dentate. Rare plants of Moav and Edom.   **7. G. trilophum**
– Mericarps wrinkled or smooth but not keeled or winged   4
4. Petals obcordate or emarginate, frequently ciliate above base   5
– Petals entire, obtuse, not ciliate above base   7
5. Mericarps much wrinkled; beak 0.8–1.2 cm. Seeds smooth.   **6. G. molle**
– Mericarps smooth; beak up to 1.8–2 cm. Seeds pitted or reticulate   6
6. Mericarps glabrous or glabrescent. Petals 0.7–1 cm. Stems glabrescent to appressed-hirsute.   **3. G. columbinum**

- Mericarps villose. Petals 4–6 mm. Stems retrorsely hispid.   **4. G. dissectum**
7 (4). Mericarps smooth, pubescent. Seeds pitted or reticulate.   **5. G. rotundifolium**
- Mericarps wrinkled. Seeds smooth or dotted   **8**
8. Leaves triangular in outline. Stems pubescent.   **8. G. robertianum**
- Leaves orbicular to 5-angled in outline. Stems glabrous, glossy.   **9. G. lucidum**

1. Geranium tuberosum L., Sp. Pl. 680 (1753); Boiss., Fl. 1 : 872 (1867). [Plate 323]

Perennial, appressed- and crisp-pubescent or -hirsute, 15–35 cm. Rhizome with ovoid-globular underground tubers. Stems single or few, erect, dichotomously branched above. Leaves 2–4 cm.; stipules about 2 mm., lanceolate; petioles of lower leaves 3–5 cm.; blade almost orbicular in outline, 5–9-partite into oblong-lanceolate and deeply serrate to incised segments with obtuse or sometimes acute ultimate lobes. Inflorescences many-flowered. Bracts 1 mm., membranous. Pedicels spreading or ascending. Sepals 3–5 mm., elongating in fruit, ovate, mucronate, hairy. Petals usually up to 1.5 cm., purple, obcordate. Mericarps 3 mm., hirsute, smooth; beak 1.2–2 cm., hirsute. Seeds almost glabrous, finely punctate or smooth. Fl. February–May.

Hab.: Fields, among rocks and under shrubs. Acco Plain, Sharon Plain, Philistean Plain, Upper and Lower Galilee, Mt. Carmel, Esdraelon Plain, Samaria, Judean Mts., Judean Desert, C. Negev, Dan Valley, Hula Plain, Golan, Gilead, Ammon, Moav. Common.

Area: Euro-Siberian, Mediterranean and Irano-Turanian.

Most of our plants belong to var. **tuberosum**, although there are also some slight inclinations towards var. **linearifolium** Boiss. (l.c. 873), manifested by narrowly linear leaf segments.

Tubers edible; used in folk medicine as a styptic, diuretic, and antidiabetic.

2. Geranium libani P. H. Davis in P. H. Davis et Roberts, Not. Roy. Bot. Gard. Edinb. 22 : 25 (1955). *G. libanoticum* Boiss. et Bl. ex Boiss., Diagn. ser. 2, 5 : 73 (1856) *pro syn.* non Schenk, Pl. Sp. Aeg. 39 (1840); Boiss., Fl. 1 : 877 (1867). *G. peloponnesiacum* Boiss. var. *libanoticum* Boiss. et Bl. ex Boiss., Diagn., l.c. [Plate 324]

Perennial, patulous- or retrorsely hairy, 20–45 cm. Rhizome about 1 cm. thick, oblique, scaly, with fibrous roots growing from its undersurface. Stems not much exceeding the radical leaves, erect, 2–3-forked above. Leaves 3–5(–8) cm.; stipules 0.8–1.5 cm., lanceolate to linear; petiole of radical leaves 10–20(–30) cm.; blade 5-angled in outline, palmatipartite into 4–5 rhombic, 2–3-partite or -incised segments; ultimate lobes somewhat obtuse, mucronulate. Inflorescences many-flowered. Bracts 3–4 mm., membranous, lanceolate. Pedicels much longer than the flowers. Sepals (0.8–)1–1.2 cm., ovate, aristate, soft-villose, 5-nerved. Petals 1.5–2.5 cm., spreading, lilac to violet, shallowly notched. Mericarps 5–7 mm., more or less hairy; beak about 3–4 cm. Seeds glabrous, smooth. Fl. April–June.

Hab.: Maquis in mountains. Upper Galilee, Judean Mts. Rare.

Area: E. Mediterranean (Palestine to Syria).

3. Geranium columbinum L., Sp. Pl. 682 (1753); Boiss., Fl. 1 : 881 (1867). [Plate 325]

Annual, glabrescent to appressed-hairy, 20–40 cm. Stems erect or ascending, branching from base. Leaves 3–5 cm.; stipules about 5 mm., acuminate-aristate; petioles of lower leaves 5–10(–20) cm.; blade round to polygonal in outline, palmately 5–7-partite or 3-fid; segments cuneate, divided into 2–3 linear or oblong, obtuse or acute, entire to dissected lobes. Peduncles 3.5–7(–15) cm., 2-flowered. Bracts about 5 mm., membranous, acuminate-aristate. Pedicels 2–6(–10) cm., spreading or deflexed, often curving upwards after flowering. Sepals 0.5–1 cm., growing markedly in fruit (up to 1.5–1.8 cm.), ovate, membranous-margined, appressed-hairy, with an awn 2–5 mm. Petals usually 0.7–1 cm., lilac to purple, obcordate-cuneate, rarely crenulate, ciliate above base. Mericarps 4 mm., slightly keeled at back, glabrescent to glabrous, smooth; beak about 2 cm. Seeds pitted. Fl. March–April.

Hab.: Batha; rocky ground. Mt. Carmel. Very rare.

Area: W. Euro-Siberian and Mediterranean.

4. Geranium dissectum L., Cent. Pl. 1 : 21 (1755) et Amoen. Acad. 4 : 282 (1759); Boiss., Fl. 1 : 881 (1867). [Plate 326]

Annual, retrorsely hispid, 15–50 cm. Stems procumbent to erect, diffusely branched. Leaves 1–2.5(–3.5) cm.; stipules 3–8 mm., ovate to oblong, acuminate-aristate; petioles of lower leaves up to 20 cm.; blade often round to reniform in outline, palmately 5–7-partite or -sect; segments cuneate, divided into 3 oblong-linear, obtuse, mucronate, entire to dissected lobes. Peduncles 0.5–3 cm., usually 2-flowered. Bracts 1–3 mm., acuminate-aristate. Pedicels 0.5–2 cm., spreading or deflexed after flowering. Sepals 3–6 mm., slightly elongating in fruit, ovate-lanceolate, glandular-hairy, with an awn up to 2 mm. Petals about 4–6 mm., lilac to purple, obcordate or somewhat retuse, ciliate at base. Mericarps 2–3 mm., villose, smooth; beak up to 1.8 cm., glandular. Seeds pitted-reticulate. Fl. February–April.

Hab.: Fields and damp places. Coastal Galilee, Acco Plain, Sharon Plain, Philistean Plain, Upper and Lower Galilee, Esdraelon Plain, Samaria, Judean Mts., Hula Plain, Upper and Lower Jordan Valley, Golan, Moav. Fairly common locally.

Area: S. W. Euro-Siberian and Mediterranean, with extensions into the Irano-Turanian region; adventive also in other regions.

5. Geranium rotundifolium L., Sp. Pl. 683 (1753); Boiss., Fl. 1 : 880 (1867). [Plate 327]

Annual, patulous- and glandular-hairy, especially above, 15–40 cm. Stems many, branched from base and middle. Branches erect or ascending. Leaves 1.5–3(–4) cm.; stipules about 3 mm., lanceolate; petioles of lower leaves 8–15(–25) cm.; blade orbicular to reniform in outline, 5–7-fid; segments dentate or lobed into 3–5 or more, triangular, cuneate, obtuse to mucronulate lobes. Peduncles 2(–3)-flowered, glandular. Bracts 1–2(–3) mm., lanceolate. Pedicels 1.5–2 cm., spreading or deflexed after flowering. Sepals 3–6 mm., slightly elongating in fruit, ovate, mucronate, glandular-hairy. Petals 5–8 mm., pink, oblong, cuneate, entire, rarely very slightly emarginate, glabrous. Mericarps about 3 mm., pubescent, smooth; beak 1.5–2 cm., glandular-hairy. Seeds reticulately pitted. Fl. February–April.

Hab.: Batha, roadsides and fields. Acco Plain, Sharon Plain, Philistean Plain, Upper and Lower Galilee, Mt. Carmel, Esdraelon Plain, Mt. Gilboa, Samaria, Judean

Mts., Judean Desert, Dan Valley, Upper and Lower Jordan Valley, Golan, Gilead, Ammon, Edom. Fairly common.

Area: W. Euro-Siberian, Mediterranean and W. Irano-Turanian.

6. Geranium molle L., Sp. Pl. 682 (1753); Boiss., Fl. 1 : 882 (1867). [Plate 328]

Annual, patulous-hairy, often glandular above, (5–)10–20 cm. Stems diffusely branched from base, grooved. Branches procumbent or erect. Leaves 1–3 cm.; stipules 2–4 mm., oblong-lanceolate; petioles of lower leaves 5–18 cm.; blade round to reniform in outline, palmately 5–9-fid; segments cuneate, incised or 3–5-lobed; lobes obtuse to subacute and mucronate. Peduncles 2-flowered. Bracts 1–2 mm., membranous, oblong-lanceolate. Pedicels 1–1.5 cm., ascending, often deflexed at base and curved upwards after flowering. Sepals 3–5 mm., slightly elongating in fruit, ovate, short-mucronate, villose, often also with short glandular hairs. Petals (0.4–)0.5–0.8(–1) cm., pink or purple, deeply 2-fid to obcordate, ciliate above base. Mericarps 1.5–2 mm., glabrous, transversely wrinkled; beak 0.8–1.2 cm. Seeds smooth. Fl. February–May.

Hab.: Roadsides, often shady waste places or fields. Coastal Galilee, Acco Plain, Sharon Plain, Philistean Plain, Upper and Lower Galilee, Mt. Carmel, Esdraelon Plain, Samaria, Judean Mts., Judean Desert, C. Negev, Dan Valley, Upper and Lower Jordan Valley, Golan, Gilead, Ammon, Edom. Common.

Area: Euro-Siberian and Mediterranean.

Our collections contain a few specimens which could be referred to var. *macropetalum* Boiss., l.c., on account of their larger petals.

7. Geranium trilophum Boiss., Diagn. ser. 1, 6 : 30 (1846) et Fl. 1 : 882 (1867). [Plate 329]

Annual, patulous-hirsute, 15–25 cm. Stems erect, dichotomously branched. Leaves 2.5–3.5 cm.; stipules 2–3 mm., lanceolate; lower leaves with long petioles; blade orbicular in outline, palmately 5–7-partite into cuneate, 3-lobed segments; ultimate lobes obtuse, mucronulate. Peduncles very short, 2-flowered. Bracts 2 mm., lanceolate. Pedicels 0.5–1.2 cm., erect. Sepals 5–6 mm., growing markedly in fruit, membranous, ovate, aristate, hirsute. Petals up to 1 cm., twice as long as sepals, pink, obovate-cuneate, retuse, ciliate above base. Mericarps with 3 keels or wings and deep furrows between them; lateral keels pectinate-dentate. Seeds smooth. Fl. March–April.

Var. **maculatum** Bornm., Mitt. Thür. Bot. Ver. N.F. 6 : 53 (1894). Petals spotted at base.

Hab.: Steppes. Moav, Edom. Very rare.

Area of species: E. Sudanian.

8. Geranium robertianum L., Sp. Pl. 681 (1753) var. **purpureum** (Vill.) DC. in Lam. et DC., Fl. Fr. ed. 3, 4 : 853 (1805). *G. purpureum* Vill., Fl. Delph. 72 (1786) et Hist. Pl. Dauph. 1 : 272 (1786), 3 : 374, t. 40 (1788); Boiss., Fl. 1 : 883 (1867). [Plate 330]

Annual, often reddish, more or less papillose-pubescent and glandular above, 15–40 cm. Stems erect or ascending, di- or trichotomously branched above. Leaves 2–

4 cm.; stipules ovate to lanceolate, long-hairy; petioles of lower leaves 8–12 cm.; blade triangular in outline, 3–5-foliolate, sometimes reddish; leaflets incised or pinnatifid into obtuse or acute-mucronulate lobes. Peduncles much longer than the subtending leaves, 2–3-flowered. Bracts 2 mm., ovate, hairy. Pedicels as long as or longer than the calyx, erect to ascending, glandular-hairy. Sepals 5–8 mm., oblong-lanceolate, aristate, glandular-hairy. Petals 0.6–1 cm., pink, rarely white, obovate-cuneate, rounded at apex. Mericarps 2–3 mm., transversely wrinkled, separating but remaining attached to beak by 2 white fibres; beak 1.5–3 cm. Seeds smooth or finely dotted. Fl. March–June.

Hab.: Batha and maquis. Sharon Plain, Philistean Plain, Upper and Lower Galilee, Mt. Carmel, Esdraelon Plain, Mt. Gilboa, Samaria, Judean Mts., Upper Jordan Valley, Arava Valley, Gilead. Fairly common.

Area: Mainly Mediterranean, extending slightly into the adjacent provinces of the Euro-Siberian region.

Rouy in Rouy et Fouc., Fl. Fr. 4 : 96 (1897), divides his *G. purpureum* Vill. into a series of varieties according to the nature of the carpel, the shape of the corolla, and other features. Our plants best fit var. *modestum* (Jord.) Rouy, l.c. 97.

9. Geranium lucidum L., Sp. Pl. 682 (1753); Boiss., Fl. 1 : 884 (1867). [Plate 331]

Annual, glabrous, glossy, 15–35 cm. Stems erect or ascending, branched from base, flexuous, often reddish. Leaves 1–3 cm.; stipules 2 mm., acute-lanceolate; petioles of lower leaves from 4 to 10 cm.; blade orbicular to 5-angled in outline, cordate, palmately 5–7-fid or -partite, glabrous, glossy; segments cuneate, with 3 obtuse, mucronulate, crenate or incised lobes. Peduncles longer than the subtending leaves, 1 (–2)-flowered. Bracts 1 mm., linear. Pedicels 0.5–2 cm., spreading after flowering, often curving upwards near apex. Sepals 4–6 mm., connivent in flower and fruit, lanceolate, glabrous, transversely wrinkled, with an awn up to 0.5 mm. Petals 0.8–1 cm., pink, rarely white, obovate, rounded at apex. Mericarps about 2 mm., puberulent at apex, wrinkled-reticulate at back; beak 0.7–1 cm. Seeds smooth. Fl. March–June.

Hab.: Shady places; batha and maquis. Upper Galilee, Mt. Carmel, Mt. Gilboa, Samaria, Judean Mts., Gilead, Ammon, Moav. Uncommon.

Area: Euro-Siberian and Mediterranean; also in Trop. Africa, fide Knuth, in Pflznr. 53 (IV, 129): 60 (1912).

3. ERODIUM L'Hér.

Annuals or perennials with or without woody stock. Leaves alternate or opposite, usually pinnate or pinnately lobed, rarely undivided. Inflorescences usually umbellate, pedunculate, bracteate. Flowers actinomorphic or slightly zygomorphic. Sepals 5, equal. Petals 5, alternating with 5 nectar glands. Anther-bearing stamens 5; staminodes 5. Ovary of 5 carpels adnate to central column of flower. Fruit a schizocarp, splitting into long-beaked mericarps; beak separating from the axis and twisting in its lower part; mericarps usually with a pit on either side of apex (beneath the beak) and with

0–3 furrows beneath each pit; beak plumose-hairy or with long and scattered bristles, lower part of beak twisting spirally at maturity. Seed 1 in each mericarp.

About 75 species, mainly Mediterranean with extensions to some adjacent regions; also in S. Africa, N. America and Australia.

Literature: P. Brumhard, *Monographische Uebersicht der Gattung Erodium*, Breslau, 1905. F. Vierhapper, *Erodium*, in: Beiträge zur Kenntnis der Flora Griechenlands, *Verh. Zool.-Bot. Ges. Wien* 69: 112–155 (1919). A. Eig, Revision of the *Erodium* species of Palestine, *Beih. Bot. Centralbl.* 50, 2: 226–240 (1932).

1. Beak of mericarp bristly (not plumose) along its inner side; mericarps with 2 pits (foveoles), 1 on either side beneath beak — 2
- Beak of mericarp plumose; mericarps without pits beneath beak — 17
2. Mericarps with 1–3 furrows beneath each pit — 3
- Mericarps without furrows beneath pits — 14
3. Beneath each pit 1 furrow — 4
- Beneath each pit 2–3 furrows — 12
4. Very rare white-tomentose perennials. Leaves 1–3 cm., undivided or slightly lobed. Petals 1.5–2 cm., with a large dark spot. Mericarps with beak about 6 cm. **10. E. guttatum**
- Not as above — 5
5. Beak of mericarp (6–)8–10(–12) cm.; mericarps 1–1.4 × 0.2 cm. Corolla about 3 cm. in diam. Pits of mericarp finely pitted inside or with a row of bristles along margin — 6
- Beak of mericarp mostly shorter; mericarps and corolla smaller. Pits of mericarp not as above — 7
6. Stems and branches glandular-hairy above or all over. Calyx glandular-hairy. Pits of mericarp with a row of bristles along margin. **12. E. telavivense**
- Stems and branches usually not glandular-hairy. Calyx rarely glandular-hairy. Pits of mericarp without a row of bristles. **11. E. gruinum**
7 (5). Leaves simple, either undivided or 3-lobed or pinnatifid or pinnatipartite — 8
- Leaves all compound, with distinct leaflets; leaflets dentate or pinnatifid or pinnatisect — 9
8. Leaves undivided or shallowly lobed; lobes broader than long, crenate. Mericarps about 5 mm.; furrows broad and deep, mostly beset with glands. **17. E. malacoides**
- Leaves deeply lobed or pinnatipartite; lobes, at least of the lower leaves, longer than broad, acutely incised-dentate. Mericarps 5–8 mm.; furrows narrow and shallow, without glands. **18. E. subtrilobum**
9 (7). Mucro of sepal terminating in 1 or 2 white bristles usually as long as or somewhat longer than mucro. Pits of mericarp not glandular inside — 10
- Mucro of sepal without bristles. Pits of mericarp glandular inside — 11
10. Corolla 2–3 times as long as calyx. Flowering stems leafless (scapes). Perennials. **5. E. acaule**
— Corolla as long as or somewhat longer than calyx. Flowering stems leafy. Annuals, rarely perennating. **6. E. cicutarium**
11 (9). Leaflets dentate or incised. Plants white-hairy, not tomentose. **7. E. moschatum**
— Leaflets pinnatisect into dentate or incised lobes. Plants densely tomentose-pubescent. **8. E. deserti**
12 (3). Flowers 1.5–2 cm. across. Mericarps slender, about 1 mm. thick; pits neither pitted inside nor surrounded by a row of bristles; mature beak with 10 coils or

more. Fruiting calyx about 1.5 cm.   **13. E. botrys**

— Flowers usually 2.5–3 cm. across. Mericarps about 2 mm. thick; pits either pitted inside or surrounded by a row of bristles; mature beak slightly coiled   13

13. Stems, branches and calyx glandular-hairy. Pits of mericarp not pitted inside but surrounded by a row of bristles.   **12. E. telavivense**

— Stems and branches usually not glandular-hairy, calyx sometimes glandular-hairy. Pits of mericarp pitted inside, without a row of bristles.   **11. E. gruinum**

14 (2). Leaves undivided or shallowly lobed, surface of leaf bestrewn with sessile golden glands. Stems hairy, not glandular. Sepals with 1 or more long bristles on top of mucro   15

— Not as above   16

15. Beak 2–3 cm.   **16. E. alnifolium**

— Beak 5–8 cm.   **15. E. subintegrifolium**

16(14). Fruiting calyx about 1.3 cm. Beak of mericarp 7–8 (–12) × 0.2 cm. Stems glandular. Leaves oblong in outline, all 1–2-pinnatisect or -partite.   **9. E. ciconium**

— Fruiting calyx 7–8 (–9) mm. Beak of mericarp (3–) 5–6 (–8) × 0.1 cm. Stems not glandular. Leaves ovate to triangular in outline, lower leaves often undivided.   **14. E. laciniatum**

17(1). Leaves (1–) 2-pinnatisect or -partite into numerous lobes. Roots with globular or ovoid tubers.   **1. E. hirtum**

— Leaves undivided or 3–5-lobed. Root tubers, when present, not globular or ovoid   18

18. Filaments altogether glabrous. Leaves glabrous or sparingly hairy, often somewhat fleshy.   **2. E. glaucophyllum**

— Filaments ciliate. Leaves pubescent or tomentose   19

19. Perennials with woody base. Petals mostly about 1.5 cm. or more. Stipules brown, leathery with membranous margin; leaf blade green, usually crenate or slightly lobed.   **4. E. arborescens**

— Annuals (rarely perennials), not woody at base. Petals 0.8–1 cm. Stipules membranous; leaf blade canescent, deeply 3–5-lobed.   **3. E. bryoniifolium**

Sect. PLUMOSA Boiss., Fl. 1 : 885 (1867). Perennials. Beak of mericarp caducous, plumose with patulous, silky hairs; mericarps without pits beneath the beak.

1. Erodium hirtum Willd., Sp. Pl. 3 : 632 (1800); "*E. hirtum* (Forssk.) Willd." Boiss., Fl. 1 : 894 (1867). *Geranium hirtum* Forssk., Fl. Aeg.-Arab. 123 (1775) non Burm. f., Spec. Geran. 48 no. 64, t. 1 (1759). [Plate 332]

Perennial, greyish-hirsute to glabrescent, 5–30 cm. Roots fusiform, with spherical to ovoid tubers. Stems mostly short, procumbent or ascending. Leaves 4–8 (–10) cm.; stipules about 5 mm., leathery, ovate; blade triangular or ovate in outline, 1–2-pinnatisect or -partite; segments short, decurrent, with oblong to ovate lobes, glabrescent or puberulent to densely white-pubescent or -hispid. Peduncles longer than the subtending leaves. Umbels 3–6-flowered. Bracts membranous, ovate, hairy. Pedicels 2–4 times as long as the calyx, slender, later thickened and deflexed. Flowers showy. Sepals 5–8 mm., mucronate, glabrescent or grey- and long-hirsute, especially at base. Petals 1–1.5 cm., pale purple with a deep purple spot at base, ovate. Filaments ciliate at base. Mericarps 0.5 cm., with 2 furrows beneath beak; beak 8–10 cm., plumose. Fl. February–May.

Hab.: Steppes and deserts; on various soils. Judean Desert, W., N., C. and S. Negev,

Lower Jordan Valley, Dead Sea area, Arava Valley, Ammon, Moav, Edom. Rather common.

Area : Saharo-Arabian.

The tubers and other parts are used as pot herbs.

2. Erodium glaucophyllum (L.) L'Hér. in Ait., Hort. Kew. 2 : 416 (1789); Boiss., Fl. 1 : 895 (1867). *Geranium glaucophyllum* L., Sp. Pl. 679 (1753). [Plate 333]

Perennial, glaucous, glabrous or glabrescent, 10–40 cm. Roots with interrupted, oblong thickenings. Stems few, prostrate, ascending to erect, divaricately branched above. Leaves 2–5 cm., lower leaves crowded; stipules membranous, ovate-oblong, puberulent; blade leathery or somewhat fleshy, ovate to oblong, crenate or lobed, glaucous, glabrescent or sparingly pubescent. Peduncles longer than the subtending leaves. Umbels (2–)3–5-flowered. Bracts ovate-oblong, hairy. Pedicels about twice as long as the calyx. Sepals about 5 mm., elongating in fruit, membranous-margined, glabrous or glabrescent with appressed hairs at nerves, ending with a long purplish mucro. Petals one and a half times as long as sepals, purple. Filaments not ciliate; upper part of the sterile filaments dilated, ovate, 2-toothed. Mericarps 3–5 mm., with 2 furrows beneath beak; beak up to 8 cm., lower part not feathery. 2n = 20. Fl. March–April.

Hab.: Deserts; especially on soils rich in gypsum. Judean Desert, Negev, Lower Jordan Valley, Dead Sea area, Arava Valley, Moav, Edom. Rather common.

Area : Saharo-Arabian, with extensions into W. Irano-Turanian territories.

Roots edible.

3. Erodium bryoniifolium Boiss., Diagn. ser. 1, 1 : 61 (1843; *"bryoniaefolium"*) et Fl. 1 : 896 (1867). [Plate 334]

Annual or rarely perennial, retrorsely or appressed-tomentose or tomentellous, 5–25 (–40) cm. Stems prostrate, rarely ascending or erect. Leaves 1–7 cm., mostly basal; stipules membranous, ovate, acute; blade ovate-cordate, usually obscurely 3–5-lobed with obtuse and crenate or incised lobes, grey-canescent. Peduncles as long as or longer than the subtending leaves. Umbels 3–6-flowered. Bracts lanceolate-subulate, broadly membranous-margined, woolly. Pedicels scarcely as long as the calyx, later elongating and deflexing. Sepals about 5 mm., oblong, hooded, tomentose outside, hirsute inside, ending in a lanceolate green mucro. Corolla markedly zygomorphic; petals 0.8–1 cm., pink, clawed; the 2 upper petals purple at base of claw; the 3 lower petals somewhat longer. Sterile filaments long-ciliate above. Mericarps 4 mm., with 1 very shallow furrow beneath beak; beak about (7–)8–12 cm., slender, feathery all along. Fl. April–May.

Hab.: Deserts; sandy and gravelly ground. Judean Desert, Negev, Arava Valley, Ammon, Moav, Edom. Uncommon.

Area : Mainly E. Saharo-Arabian and E. Sudanian.

We have not observed var. *laxum* Boiss., Fl. l.c.

The view of P. H. Davis (Fl. Turkey 2 : 477, 1967) that *E. bryoniifolium* is conspecific with *E. oxyrrhynchum* M.B. (Fl. Taur.-Cauc. 2 : 133, 1808; *"oxyrhinchum"*) is still to be confirmed through a more fundamental study of the two taxa.

4. Erodium arborescens (Desf.) Willd., Sp. Pl. 3 : 638 (1800). *Geranium arborescens* Desf., Fl. Atl. 2 : 110 (1798). *Erodium hussoni* Boiss., Diagn. ser. 1, 8 : 119 (1849) et Fl. 1 : 885 (1867). [Plate 335]

Perennial with woody base, appressed-puberulent, 15–40 cm. Roots long, with interrupted cylindrical thickenings. Stems many, erect to ascending, branched. Leaves 2–12 cm., mainly basal; stipules about 5 mm., brown with narrow membranous margins, ovate or oblong, densely hairy; blade leathery, ovate-cordate, irregularly crenate to slightly lobed, green, pubescent, prominently nerved. Peduncles much longer than the subtending leaves. Umbels 4–6-flowered. Bracts connate to half their length, ovate, mucronate, brown, membranous at margin. Pedicels 2–3 times as long as the calyx. Sepals about 0.8–1 cm., mucronate, woolly. Petals 1–1.5 (–2) cm., pink with a deep purple spot at base, orbicular. Sterile filaments densely ciliate at base. Mericarps 8 mm., with 2 furrows beneath beak; beak up to 7–8 cm., plumose. Fl. March–April.

Hab.: Hot deserts; mainly in wadis and among stones. C. and S. Negev, Dead Sea region, Arava Valley, Edom. Rare.

Area: Saharo-Arabian.

Sect. BARBATA Boiss., Fl. 1 : 884 (1867) p. max. p. Beak of mericarp persistent, bristly; bristles long below and along inner side and becoming shorter towards apex; mericarps with a pit on each side beneath beak.

5. Erodium acaule (L.) Becherer et Thell. in Becherer, Repert. Sp. Nov. 25 : 215 (1928). *Geranium acaule* L., Syst. ed. 10, 2 : 1143 (1759). *E. romanum* (Burm. f.) L'Hér. in Ait., Hort. Kew. 2 : 414 (1789); Willd., Sp. Pl. 3 : 630 (1800); "*E. romanum* (L.) Willd." Boiss., Fl. 1 : 890 (1867). *G. romanum* Burm. f., Spec. Geran. 30 no. 30 (1759). [Plate 336]

Perennial, sparingly or densely appressed-hairy, 15–25 cm. Roots fleshy, vertical. Stems 0. Leaves 3–9 cm., rosulate; stipules scarious, ovate, mucronate; blade oblong to oblanceolate in outline, pinnate; leaflets sessile, ovate-oblong, pinnatipartite or incised-dentate, ultimate lobes oblong, acute. Umbels 3–8-flowered, borne on scape-like peduncles as long as or longer than the leaves. Bracts about 2 mm., membranous, ovate, mucronate. Pedicels 2–3 times as long as the calyx. Sepals 5–6 mm., oblong, mucronate, tipped with 2 strong white bristles which are usually somewhat longer than the mucro. Petals 2–3 times as long as sepals, nearly equal, pink, not spotted. Filaments glabrous. Mericarps 0.6–1 cm., with 1 furrow beneath each pit; beak 4–5 cm. Fl. July–March (–April).

Hab.: Batha and roadsides. Upper Galilee, Mt. Carmel, Samaria, Judean Mts., Golan, Gilead, Ammon, Moav. Not rare.

Area: Mainly N. Mediterranean.

6. Erodium cicutarium (L.) L'Hér. in Ait., Hort. Kew. 2 : 414 (1789). [Plate 337]

Annual, more or less pubescent with white and often also with glandular hairs all over or above, 10–40 cm. Stems few or many, procumbent or ascending, sometimes erect. Leaves 2–12 (–15) cm.; stipules 5–7 mm., membranous, ovate, acute; blade oblong in outline, pinnate; leaflets 5–11, 0.5–2 cm., ovate in outline, pinnatipartite or mostly pinnatisect, sparsely or densely appressed-hairy, rarely subglabrous. Peduncles much longer than the subtending leaves. Umbels 3–6-flowered. Bracts minute, membranous. Pedicels short, hairy or glabrescent, spreading or deflexed in fruit. Sepals 4–5 mm., elongating in fruit, oblong, short-mucronate with mucro ending in 1 or 2 bristles. Petals as long as sepals or somewhat longer, pink-purple to purple-violet, obovate, often slightly unequal. Mericarps (4–)5–7 mm., with 1 furrow beneath each smooth and glabrous pit; beak (2–)2.5–5 cm. 2n = 20. Fl. February–May (–August).

Var. **cicutarium**. *E. cicutarium* (L.) L'Hér., l.c.; Boiss., Fl. 1 : 890 (1867). *Geranium cicutarium* L., Sp. Pl. 680 (1753) excl. var. *β*. [Plate 337]. More or less papillose-hairy. Beak of mericarp 3–5 cm.

Hab.: Batha, roadsides and waste places. Acco Plain, Sharon Plain, Philistean Plain, Upper Galilee, Esdraelon Plain, Samaria, Judean Mts., Judean Desert, N. Negev, Hula Plain, Upper Jordan Valley, Golan, Ammon and probably elsewhere in Transjordan. Very common; one of the most widespread ruderals.

Var. **viscidum** Nab., Publ. Fac. Sci. Univ. Masaryk 35 : 58 (1923). Entire plant pubescent-viscid with very dense, white, glandular hairs. Sepals white-woolly, viscid. Beak of mericarp about 3 cm.

Hab.: Steppes and deserts. Judean Mts., Judean Desert, Dead Sea area, Gilead, Ammon, Moav, Edom. Rare.

Area of species: Euro-Siberian, Mediterranean and Irano-Turanian.

E. cicutarium is very polymorphic and its division into infraspecific taxa cannot be done without constancy tests. Var. *viscidum* is, therefore, only tentatively and hesitatingly recorded here.

A valuable pasture plant; leaves used as a pot herb.

7. Erodium moschatum (L.) L'Hér. in Ait., Hort. Kew. 2 : 414 (1789); Willd., Sp. Pl. 3 : 631 (1800); Boiss., Fl. 1 : 891 (1867). *Geranium cicutarium* L. var. *moschatum* L., Sp. Pl. 680 (1753). *G. moschatum* L., Syst. ed. 10, 2 : 1143 (1759) et Sp. Pl. ed. 2, 951 (1763); Burm. f., Spec. Geran. 29 no. 29 (1759). [Plate 338]

Annual, sometimes perennating, with white hairs all over and also with glandular hairs above, 10–50 cm. Stem few or many, mostly procumbent, branched, rather thick. Leaves 5–15 cm., pinnate; stipules 0.8–1 cm., scarious, white, broadly ovate to oblong, obtuse; leaflets 7–13, rather remote, usually 2–4 cm., ovate, dentate to incised. Peduncles longer than the subtending leaves. Umbels 2–8(–12)-flowered. Bracts ovate to ovate-oblong, somewhat united at base. Pedicels longer than the calyx, villose and glandular-hairy to subglabrous, pale brown. Sepals 5–7 mm., elongating in fruit, oblong, ending in a stout mucro. Petals slightly longer than sepals, pink, obovate or oblong. Filaments glabrous, the inner ones broadened at base and with a tooth on each side. Mericarps 4–5 mm., with 1 furrow beneath each glandular pit; beak about 3–4 cm. Fl. February–May.

Hab.: Batha, roadsides and waste places. Coastal Galilee, Acco Plain, Sharon Plain, Philistean Plain, Upper and Lower Galilee, Mt. Carmel, Esdraelon Plain, Mt. Gilboa, Samaria, Judean Mts., Judean Desert, N. Negev, Dan Valley, Hula Plain,

Upper and Lower Jordan Valley, Golan, Gilead, Ammon, Moav. Very common.

Area : Mediterranean and Irano-Turanian, with extensions into the Euro-Siberian and Sudanian regions; elsewhere adventive.

Leaves used as a pot herb.

8. Erodium deserti (Eig) Eig in Eig et Zoh., Palest. Journ. Bot. Jerusalem ser., 1 : 311 (1939); Eig, Beih. Bot. Centralbl. 50, 2 : 237 (1932) *in obs. E. moschatum* (L.) L'Hér. ssp. *deserti* Eig, Beih. Bot. Centralbl. 50, 2 : 236 (1932). [Plate 339]

Annual, densely covered with white hairs and also with glandular hairs all over or only above, (5–)10–20 cm. Stems prostrate or ascending. Leaves 2–6(–8) cm.; stipules about 5–8 mm., membranous, oblong, obtuse to acute; blade oblong in outline, pinnate; leaflets 1–2 cm., ovate, pinnatisect. Peduncles very long. Umbels (2–)3–10-flowered. Bracts 2 mm., membranous, ovate. Pedicels up to twice as long as calyx. Sepals (3–)4–5 mm., white-membranous at margin, glabrescent to densely hirsute or setulose, especially at base, with green and somewhat anastomosing nerves, and with a conspicuous obtuse mucro not terminating in a bristle. Petals about as long as sepals, pink. Mericarps 4–8 mm., with 1 furrow beneath each glandular pit; beak 2.5–4 cm. 2n = 20. Fl. February–April.

Hab. : Roadsides and wadis in steppes and deserts. Judean Desert, N. Negev, Upper and Lower Jordan Valley, Dead Sea area, Arava Valley, Ammon, Moav, Edom. Locally common.

Area : Saharo-Arabian.

E. deserti closely resembles *E. cicutarium* (L.) L'Hér., but is readily distinguished from it by the indumentum, the pits of the mericarps and the apices of the sepals.

9. Erodium ciconium (L.) L'Hér. in Ait., Hort. Kew. 2 : 415 (1789) excl. syn. *β*. [Plates 340, 340a]

Annual, patulous-hirsute and glandular-hairy, rarely sparingly puberulent, 10–35(–45) cm. Stems furrowed, sometimes as long as the lower leaves, rarely shorter, often much longer. Branches ascending or procumbent, rarely erect. Leaves 7–10(–15) cm., appressed-hairy; stipules 6 mm., lanceolate, acute; petiole rather long; blade oblong to ovate in outline, 1–2-pinnatipartite or -sect; segments 1 cm. or more, ovate-oblong to linear, crenate, incised or lobed, ultimate lobes obtuse to acute. Peduncles longer than the subtending leaves. Umbels 2–4(–6)-flowered. Bracts ovate-lanceolate, hairy. Pedicels as long as the calyx or longer, glandular-hairy, spreading or deflexed in fruit. Sepals 0.5–1 cm., growing markedly in fruit, elliptical to oblong, acute, long-mucronate, membranous-margined, green-nerved. Petals 1–2.2 cm., as long as to twice as long as sepals, purplish-blue, obovate. Filaments all ciliate below. Mericarps up to 1.5 cm., white-hispid, with deep glandular but very narrow pits and without furrows; beak 7–8(–12) cm., stout and thick. Fl. March–May.

1. Leaves 1-pinnatisect. Corolla twice as long as calyx.   var. **macropetalum**
 – Leaves 2-pinnatipartite or -sect. Corolla as long as or slightly longer than calyx   2
2. Leaf segments 1–3 cm. The whole plant densely glandular. Lower leaves longer than stems.   var. **idumaeum**
 – Leaf segments much longer than above. Plants less densely glandular. Lower leaves usually shorter than stems.   var. **ciconium**

Var. **ciconium**. *E. ciconium* (L.) L'Hér., l.c. excl. syn. *β*; Willd., Sp. Pl. 3 : 629 (1800); Boiss., Fl. 1 : 891 (1867). *Geranium ciconium* L., Cent. Pl. 1 : 21 (1755) et Amoen. Acad. 4 : 282 (1759). [Plate 340]. Sparingly glandular. Stems longer than the lower leaves. Leaves 2-pinnatipartite or -sect; segments oblong, obtuse. Petals as long as or somewhat longer than sepals.

Hab.: Steppes, fields and batha. Coastal Galilee (fide Barbey, Herbor. Levant 124, 1882), Philistean Plain, Judean Mts., N. and C. Negev, Lower Jordan Valley, Dead Sea area, Gilead, Edom. Not rare.

Var. **macropetalum** Zoh.* [Plate 340a]. Hirsute to glabrescent. Leaves mostly 1-pinnatipartite or -sect; segments ovate, crenate or lobed. Petals twice as long as sepals.

Hab.: Fields. Shefela, N. Negev. Rare.

Var. **idumaeum** Eig, Beih. Bot. Centralbl. 50, 2 : 232 (1932; *"edomea"*). Densely glandular. Stems very short, shorter than the lower leaves. Leaves minutely dissected; ultimate lobes 1–3 mm. Petals as long as or somewhat longer than sepals.

Hab.: As above. Judean Mts., Ammon, Moav, Edom. Rare.

Area of species: Mediterranean and Irano-Turanian.

10. Erodium guttatum (Desf.) Willd., Sp. Pl. 3 : 636 (1800). *Geranium guttatum* Desf., Fl. Atl. 2 : 113, t. 169 (1798). [Plate 341]

Perennial, appressed-tomentose, 10–30 cm. Stems branched from base. Branches ascending. Leaves 1–3 cm., almost all basal; stipules triangular, acuminate; blades triangular to ovate, cordate, those of lower leaves entire or crenate-denticulate, those of upper leaves often with dentate lobes. Peduncles much longer than the subtending leaves. Umbels 3–6-flowered. Bracts free, lanceolate. Pedicels deflexed. Flowers about 2 cm. or more. Calyx 0.7–1 cm.; sepals oblong-elliptical, membranous-margined, hairy, with a long mucro. Petals twice as long as sepals or more, purple or violet with a dark blot at base, obovate, somewhat retuse. Sterile filaments short, broadened at base, ciliate. Mericarps 7–9 mm., with strigose hairs arising from a tubercle; pits broad, hairy within; furrow 1 beneath each pit; beak about 6(–8) cm., not plumose. Fl. March.

Hab.: Deserts. Edom. Very rare.

Area: Saharo-Arabian.

11. Erodium gruinum (L.) L'Hér. in Ait., Hort. Kew. 2 : 415 (1789); Willd., Sp. Pl. 3 : 633 (1800); Boiss., Fl. 1 : 892 (1867). *Geranium gruinum* L., Sp. Pl. 680 (1753). *E. gruinum* (L.) L'Hér. var. *subglandulosum* Eig, Beih. Bot. Centralbl. 50, 2 : 233 (1932). [Plate 342]

Annual, sparingly and retrorsely papillose-hirsute, 10–50 cm. Stems erect or ascending, branched, thick, grooved. Leaves 6–15(–20) cm., appressed-papillose, rarely subglabrous; stipules up to 1 cm., ovate, acuminate; blades cordate, ovate to ovate-lanceolate, undivided, crenate in lower leaves, in the other leaves blades ovate-triangular, pinnatisect or -partite into 3–5 acutely dentate to crenate or lobed segments, with

---

* See Appendix at end of this volume.

the terminal segment elongate and dentate or 3–5-lobed. Peduncles longer than the subtending leaves, sparingly bristly to glabrous, rarely slightly glandular. Umbels (1–)3–6-flowered. Bracts 5 mm., lanceolate, mucronate. Pedicels as long as the calyx, later elongating up to 10 cm. Flowers (2.5–)3 cm. across, showy. Sepals about 1 cm., elongating in fruit up to 2 cm., long-mucronate to aristate, white-membranous between nerves, sparingly hirsute at nerves, rarely glandular. Petals much longer than sepals, violet-blue, obovate, with ciliate base. Filaments all glabrous. Mericarps 1.4 cm., pits deep, pitted within; furrows 1–2 beneath each pit; beak 6–8(–10) cm. Fl. February– May.

Hab. : Batha and fallow fields; mostly a pioneer in early stages of succession. Coastal Galilee, Acco Plain, Coast of Carmel, Sharon Plain, Philistean Plain, Upper and Lower Galilee, Mt. Carmel, Esdraelon Plain, Mt. Gilboa, Samaria, Shefela, Judean Mts., Judean Desert, W. and N. Negev, Hula Plain, Upper and Lower Jordan Valley, Golan, Gilead, Ammon, Moav, Edom. Very common.

Area : Mainly E. Mediterranean.

12. Erodium telavivense Eig ex Eig, Beih. Bot. Centralbl. 50, 2 : 233 (1932); Eig, Repert. Sp. Nov. Beih. 63, 1 : 113 (1931) *nom. nud.* [Plate 343]

Annual, glandular-hirsute, 20–50 cm. Stems ascending to erect, branched. Leaves 8–20 cm., appressed-hairy to glabrescent; stipules 0.6–1 cm., much broadened at base, ovate, mucronate; blades of lowermost leaves cordate-ovate, undivided or 3-lobed, those of middle leaves triangular-ovate in outline, pinnate or pinnatisect into 3–5 ovate and crenate-dentate or crenate-incised segments, with the terminal segment much larger and 3–5-lobed, blades of upper and uppermost leaves with lanceolate, acute, coarsely dentate or lobed segments. Peduncles longer than the subtending leaves. Umbels (1–)2–4-flowered. Bracts 5 mm., lanceolate. Pedicels 2–3 times as long as the calyx. Flowers about 3 cm. across. Sepals 0.8–1 cm., growing markedly in fruit, glandular-hairy, 5-nerved, terminating in a long mucro. Petals much longer than sepals, pale lilac, somewhat ciliate at base. Filaments glabrous. Mericarps 1.2–1.4 cm.; pits deep, not pitted within, ciliate at margin; furrows 1–2 beneath each pit; the upper part of the mericarp and especially the furrows and pits sparingly punctate; beak 8–12 cm. 2n = 36. Fl. March–April.

Hab. : Grassy places and batha; sandy soils. Sharon Plain, Philistean Plain. Locally common.

Area : E. Mediterranean.

Differs from *E. gruinum* (L.) L'Hér. in the glandular indumentum, the long stipe of the mericarp, and the nature of the pits and the furrows.

13. Erodium botrys (Cav.) Bertol., Amoen. Ital. 35 (1819). [Plate 344]

Annual, patulous- or retrorsely hispid, 20–50 cm. Stems erect or ascending, moderately branching, grooved. Leaves mostly radical, long-petioled; stipules about 5 mm., membranous, ovate-oblong, acute; blades (2–)5–15 cm., oblong in outline, hirsute or glabrescent, those of lowermost leaves undivided to pinnatifid or -partite, those of upper leaves pinnatipartite to -sect into narrow, acute, incised to pinnatifid segments. Peduncles much longer than the subtending leaves, glandular-hairy. Umbels (1–)3–

5-flowered. Bracts membranous, ovate-oblong, long-mucronate, ciliate. Pedicels 1–3 times as long as the calyx, thickened in fruit, glandular. Sepals 0.7–0.8 (elongating in fruit to 1.3) cm., membranous-margined, hairy and glandular, prominently nerved; mucro mostly with 2(–3) short bristles at top. Petals about one and a half times as long as sepals, violet, oblong. Filaments glabrous. Mericarps 1–1.2 cm.; pits smooth and glabrous within; furrows 2–3 beneath each pit; beak 6–10(–12) cm., slender, appressed-setulose on inner side, sparsely long-setose outside. Fl. January–May.

Var. botrys. *E. botrys* (Cav.) Bertol., l.c.; Boiss., Fl. 1 : 892 (1867). *Geranium botrys* Cav., Monad. Class. Dissert. 218, t. 90, f. 2 (1787). All the leaves divided.

Var. feinbergii Evenari in Opphr. et Evenari, Bull. Soc. Bot. Genève ser. 2, 31 : 302 (1941). Lower leaves undivided. Recorded from Sharon Plain.

Hab. of species: Batha and grassland on sandy soils up to 200 m. above sea level. Coastal Galilee, Acco Plain, Sharon Plain, Philistean Plain. Locally common.

Area of species: Mediterranean.

14. Erodium laciniatum (Cav.) Willd., Sp. Pl. 3 : 633 (1800); Boiss., Fl. 1 : 893 (1867). [Plates 345, 345a]

Annual, densely to sparingly crisp-puberulent and retrorsely or antrorsely hairy to tomentellous, sometimes sparingly glandular-hairy, rarely glabrescent, 20–50 cm. Stems procumbent or prostrate, rarely erect, grooved. Leaves 1–7(–10) cm.; stipules 5–8 mm., membranous, ovate; blades of lower leaves mostly cordate-ovate, obscurely 3-lobed, blades of the others 3-lobed or 1–2-pinnatipartite or -sect into short, narrow, more or less acutish lobes; rarely some of the leaves almost undivided. Umbels 3–8-flowered, on very long peduncles. Bracts 2 or more, 0.25–0.8(–1.2) cm. broad, membranous, more or less ovate, brown or white. Pedicels twice as long as the calyx, hispidulous to glandular-hairy, rarely glabrous. Sepals about 7–8 mm., mucronate, usually patulous- or appressed-hairy. Petals longer than sepals, purple, oblong. Filaments toothless or 1–2-ciliate-dentate. Mericarps 4–8 mm., without furrows beneath pits; beak (3–)4–8 cm., slender. Fl. March–April.

Var. laciniatum. *E. laciniatum* (Cav.) Willd., Sp. Pl. 3 : 633 (1800). *Geranium laciniatum* Cav., Monad. Class. Dissert. 228, t. 113, f. 3 (1787). *E. laciniatum* (Cav.) Willd. var. *involucratum* (Kunze) Willk. et Lange, Prodr. Fl. Hisp. 3 : 539 (1878). *E. triangulare* sensu Muschl., Man. Fl. Eg. 558 (1912). *G. triangulare* Forssk., Fl. Aeg.-Arab. LXIX, 123 (1775) *nom. ambig.** *G. maritimum* Forssk., l.c. LXIX non L., Syst. ed. 10, 2 : 1143 (1759) nec Burm. f., Spec. Geran. 46 (1759). [Plate 345]. Green plants. Bracts mostly 2, usually about 3.5 mm., sometimes up to 8 mm., often much broader than long, orbicular-ovate to reniform, obtuse. Sepals with a mucro 1.5–2 mm. Filaments mostly with a tooth on each side. Indumentum consisting of rather dense to sparse, long, simple, retrorse, rarely appressed and straight hairs, some-

---

* According to Christensen (Dansk Bot. Ark. 4, 3 : 23, 1922), there is no specimen in Herbarium Forsskål which agrees with the description of *G. triangulare*. Instead, a specimen named by Forsskål (l.c. LXIX) *G. maritimum* agrees with *E. laciniatum*.

times upper parts of plant glabrescent or glandular-hairy; stipules and bracts mostly glabrous. Beak of mericarp 4–8 cm.

Hab.: Among shrubs and in grassy places; sandy soils. Coastal Galilee, Acco Plain, Sharon Plain, Philistean Plain, Shefela, Judean Mts., W. and C. Negev, Dead Sea area, Moav. Not rare.

Area: Mediterranean.

Var. **pulverulentum** (Cav.) Boiss., l.c. *G. pulverulentum* Cav., l.c. 272, t. 125, f. 1 (1788) p.p.; Desf., Fl. Atl. 2 : 111 (1798). *E. pulverulentum* (Cav.) Willd., l.c. 632. *E. subtrilobum* Jord. ssp. *pulverulentum* (Cav.) Vierh., Verh. Zool.-Bot. Ges. Wien 69 : 133 (1919) p.p. *E. bovei* Del., Ind. Hort. Monsp. 6 (1838) *nom. nud.*; Del. ex Del., Linnaea 13 : Litter. 104 (1839). [Plate 345a]. Mostly pilose or tomentellous plants. Bracts mostly more than 2, small, usually 2.5 mm., sometimes up to 5 mm., usually triangular-ovate, acutish to obtuse. Sepals with a mucro 0.5–1 mm. Filaments mostly toothless. Indumentum dense, consisting of short, simple, soft, antrorse to appressed, usually crisp hairs; upper parts of plant never glabrescent; stipules and bracts ciliate. Beak of mericarp 3–5 cm.

Hab.: Steppes and deserts; mainly in gravelly wadis. W., N., C. and S. Negev, Dead Sea area, Arava Valley, Ammon, Moav, Edom. Not rare.

Area: Saharo-Arabian.

Vierhapper (Verh. Zool.-Bot. Ges. Wien 69 : 122–140, 1919) has devoted a thorough investigation to the above taxa, regarded by him as subspecies, each with a series of varieties. We were unable to follow Vierhapper in his subdivision, because of the very weak and mostly overlapping characters on which the varieties are based. In the absence of experimental studies it appears best to refrain from further splitting of these two taxa.

15. Erodium subintegrifolium Eig, Beih. Bot. Centralbl. 50, 2 : 230 (1932). [Plate 346]

Annual, sparingly patulous- or retrorsely hirsute, sometimes glabrescent, 10–40 cm. Stems few, erect or ascending, simple or sparingly branched. Leaves 4–7 cm.; stipules 4–8 mm., ovate, brownish; blades ovate to oblong, cordate at base, appressed-hirtellous, with sessile golden glands, those of lower leaves dentate-crenate or more or less shallow-lobed, those of stem leaves usually 3–5-fid or -lobed; rarely all leaves undivided. Peduncles much longer than the leaves. Umbels 3–7-flowered. Bracts membranous, broadly ovate, acutish. Pedicels much longer than the flowers. Sepals 6–8 mm., papillose to patulous-hirsute, ending in a mucro 1 mm., tipped with a bristle. Petals about twice as long as sepals, lilac-pink. Filaments glabrous. Mericarps 6–7 mm., appressed-hairy, with smooth pits and without furrows beneath; beak 5–8 cm. Fl. March–April.

Hab.: Grassy places and coastal batha; sandy soil. Sharon Plain, Philistean Plain (endemic). Rare.

Area: E. Mediterranean.

The relations between this species and *E. laciniatum* (Cav.) Willd. are still to be elucidated. Future studies will probably include this taxon within *E. laciniatum* with which it has many characters in common (e.g. indumentum, size and shape of mericarp, calyx, etc.). The main difference between the two taxa is the trend in *E. subintegrifolium* towards reduced division of the leaves.

16. Erodium alnifolium Guss., Fl. Sic. Prodr. 2 : 307 (1828); Eig, Beih. Bot. Centralbl. 50, 2 : 227 (1932). [Plate 347]

Annual, with long villose and retrorse hairs or with short appressed hairs, 15–20 cm. Stems few, erect, moderately branched. Lower leaves 3–6 cm.; stipules up to 8 mm., membranous, oblong, somewhat brownish, stipules of upper leaves broader; blade ovate, tapering towards base, obtuse to acutish at apex, undivided, dentate to very slightly lobed, appressed-hairy. Peduncles usually longer than the subtending leaves, retrorsely villose. Inflorescences (2–)4–6-flowered. Bracts 2–3 mm., ovate to lanceolate, white. Pedicels twice as long as the calyx or more, glandular. Flowers 5–6 mm. Sepals oblong, obtuse, long-mucronate, narrowly membranous-margined, with fascicles of long hairs. Petals about as long as sepals, ovate-oblong, obtuse. Filaments glabrous. Mericarps about 4 mm., hairy; pits on top of mericarp broad, without furrows beneath; beak 2–3 cm. Fl. March–April.

Hab.: Sandy soils. Sharon Plain. Very rare.

Area: Mainly W. Mediterranean.

17. Erodium malacoides (L.) L'Hér. in Ait., Hort. Kew. 2 : 415 (1789) excl. var. *β*; "*E. malacoides* (L.) Willd." Boiss., Fl. 1 : 893 (1867). *Geranium malacoides* L., Sp. Pl. 680 (1753) et ed. 2, 952 (1763). [Plate 348]

Annual, with patulous, often also glandular, hairs, 15–35(–50) cm. Stems erect or ascending, grooved, leafy. Leaves (3–)5–10(–13) cm., appressed-pubescent; stipules 5–8 mm., membranous, ovate; blade ovate to oblong, crenate-dentate or rarely incised-lobed with lobes often shorter than broad. Peduncles much longer than the subtending leaves, hairy or glandular-hairy. Umbels (3–)5–10-flowered. Bracts ovate, usually glandular. Pedicels much longer than the flowers, glandular-hairy. Sepals 5 mm., scarious-margined, green-nerved, with glandular and simple hairs, and often with a purplish mucro tipped with 2 bristles. Petals somewhat longer than sepals, lilac, obovate. Filaments glabrous. Mericarps 5 mm., with a deep furrow beneath each pit; both pits and furrows usually somewhat glandular; beak 3–4 cm., slender. 2n=40. Fl. January–May.

Hab.: Batha, fields and roadsides. Acco Plain, Sharon Plain, Philistean Plain, Upper and Lower Galilee, Mt. Carmel, Esdraelon Plain, Mt. Gilboa, Samaria, Judean Mts., Judean Desert, Hula Plain, Upper and Lower Jordan Valley, Dead Sea area, Golan, Gilead, Ammon, Moav, Edom. Very common.

Area: Mediterranean and Irano-Turanian, extending slightly into the Euro-Siberian region.

Varies greatly in the size and lobing of the leaf. Transitional forms between this species and *E. subtrilobum* Jord. are rather rare.

Used as a pot herb.

18. Erodium subtrilobum Jord., Pugill. Pl. Nov. 42 (1852); Vierh., Verh. Zool.-Bot. Ges. Wien 69 : 112, 140 (1919). *E. malacoides* (L.) Willd. var. *subtrilobum* (Jord.) Lange, Pugill. Pl. Hisp. 329 (1865); Rouy in Rouy et Fouc., Fl. Fr. 4 : 118 (1897). [Plate 349]

Annual, ashy-pubescent with patulous conical white, sometimes glandular, hairs,

10–20 cm. Stems prostrate to ascending. Leaves 1.5–10 cm., most of them radical; stipules about 5 mm., membranous, ovate, acutish; blades ovate-oblong in outline, those of lower leaves 3–7-lobed or -pinnatifid or -pinnatipartite into acutely incised-dentate lobes, those of upper leaves less divided, all grey to green, appressed-pubescent to glabrescent. Peduncles usually longer than the subtending leaves. Umbels 3–7-flowered. Bracts 3–4 mm., broadly ovate, white. Pedicels usually longer than the calyx. Sepals 5–7 mm., oblong, mucronate, green with white margins, hirsute, prominently nerved. Petals about as long as sepals, somewhat unequal, pink. Filaments glabrous. Mericarps 5–8 mm., with a flat and narrow, not glandular furrow beneath each pit; beak up to 5 (–6) cm. Fl. February–April.

The following varieties have been distinguished among the local populations.

1. Peduncles, pedicels and calyces more or less densely glandular-hairy.
var. subtrilobum
– All the parts of the plant with non-glandular hairs   2
2. Green plants. Leaves glabrescent.   var. glabrescens
– Grey plants. Leaves appressed-pubescent.   var. neuradifolium

Var. **subtrilobum**. *E. subtrilobum* Jord. var. *glanduliferum* (Hal. ex Vierh.) Vierh., l.c. 112, 143 *subs. illegit.*

Hab.: Steppes. Judean Desert, N. Negev ?, Dead Sea area, Arava Valley. Rare.

Var. **neuradifolium** (Del. ex Godr.) Vierh., l.c. 142 ("*neuradaefolium*"). *E. neuradae-folium* Del. ex Godr., Mém. Acad. Montp. (Sect. Médecin.) 1 : 425 (1853 ?). *E. sub-trilobum* Jord. var. *aegyptiacum* (Boiss.) Vierh., l.c. 143. *E. aegyptiacum* Boiss., Diagn. ser. 2, 1 : 111 (1854); Boiss., Fl. 1 : 894 (1867) excl. var. *β*. 2n = 20. [Plate 349]

Hab.: Steppes. Judean Desert, C. Negev, Lower Jordan Valley, Arava Valley, Edom. Locally common.

Var. **glabrescens** (Boiss.) Vierh., l.c. 144. *E. aegyptiacum* Boiss. var. *glabrescens* Boiss., Fl. l.c.

Hab.: Steppes. Judean Mts., Judean Desert, Dead Sea area, Ammon. Uncommon. Area of species : Saharo-Arabian.

4. MONSONIA L.

Annuals or perennials, sometimes woody at base. Leaves opposite or alternate, stipulate, petiolate, toothed or cut. Peduncles axillary, few- to many-flowered. Flowers actinomorphic. Sepals 5. Petals 5, caducous. Nectar glands 5, alternating with petals. Stamens 15, all anther-bearing, connate into a ring at base and united into 5 bundles opposite the petals. Ovary of 5 carpels, each with 2 ovules; styles and stigmas 5. Fruit a schizocarp with indehiscent mericarps separating from the axis as in the genus *Erodium*; beak of carpel pilose or plumose.

About 30 species in the steppes and deserts of Trop. Africa and S.W. Asia.

1. Pedicels 3–4 times as long as the calyx. Calyx appressed-tomentose. Beak of mericarp 4–5 cm. Leaves ovate-oblong.   **1. M. nivea**

– Pedicels as long as the calyx or shorter. Calyx hispid. Beak of mericarp 7–9 cm.
Leaves ovate-cordate.   **2. M. heliotropioides**

1. Monsonia nivea (Decne.) Decne. ex Webb, Fragm. Florul. Aethiop.-Aeg. 59 (1854).
"*M. nivea* (Decne.) Boiss.", Fl. 1 : 897 (1867). *Erodium niveum* Decne., Ann. Sci. Nat.
Bot. ser. 2, 3 : 285 (1835). [Plate 350]

Perennial, silvery-canescent, 15–25 cm. Stems very short, procumbent, simple, rarely
branched, white, hirsute. Leaves 2–5 cm., mostly rosulate, rather long-petioled; stipules oblong-lanceolate; blade ovate-oblong, strongly plicate, crenate-toothed, silvery-
canescent with appressed short white hairs. Peduncles very long, scape-like, 2–6-
flowered. Bracts ovate-oblong, long-acuminate. Pedicels 1–2.5 cm. Sepals (3–)4–6 mm.,
obovate-oblong, slightly mucronate, membranous-margined, appressed-tomentose.
Petals slightly longer than sepals, pink, obovate. Filaments ciliate at base. Mericarps
5 mm., appressed-hirsute, with 2 transverse furrows at apex; beak 4–5 cm., plumose.
Fl. March–April.

Hab.: Hot deserts; often in shallow sandy wadi beds and among stones. C. Negev,
Dead Sea area, Arava Valley. Uncommon.

Area: Sudanian and Saharo-Arabian.

2. Monsonia heliotropioides (Cav.) Boiss., Fl. 1 : 897 (1867; orth. err. "*heliotropoides*").
Geranium heliotropioides Cav., Monad. Class. Dissert. 220, t. 113, f. 1 (1787). [Plate
351]

Perennial, patulous- and white-hispid, 25–40 cm. Rootstock thick, vertical, twisted.
Stems erect, branched. Leaves 2–10 cm., cauline, opposite, long-petioled; stipules
lanceolate-subulate; petiole long-hispid; blade ovate-cordate, acute, crispate-dentate,
white-canescent. Peduncles long, (6–)8–12-flowered. Bracts oblong-lanceolate, acuminate. Pedicels shorter than to as long as the calyx, not elongating in fruit. Sepals about
5 mm., obovate, membranous-margined, hispid, white with a long purple mucro.
Petals as long as sepals or shorter, pink. Filaments ciliate at base. Mericarps 5–6 mm.,
hairy, with 2–3 transverse furrows at apex; beak 7–9 cm., plumose. Fl. January–May.

Hab.: Hot deserts; granite rocks. Arava Valley. Rare.

Area: E. Sudanian.

58. ZYGOPHYLLACEAE

Shrubs or half-shrubs, rarely trees or herbs. Leaves usually opposite, mostly stipulate,
entire, dissected, 2–3-foliolate or pinnately divided, often fleshy. Inflorescences of simple
or compound cymes, or flowers solitary. Flowers hermaphrodite or rarely unisexual,
actinomorphic, rarely zygomorphic, usually 4–5-merous, rarely apetalous. Sepals (3–)4–
5, free, rarely connate. Petals mostly as many as sepals. Receptacle with disk or gynophore. Stamens (4–)8–10, rarely 15; filaments sometimes with ligular appendages.
Ovary sessile or rarely short-stipitate, (2–)4–5 (–12)-celled, angular or winged; placentation axile; ovules 1 to many in each cell; style 1; stigmas 1 or 2–3 or 5–12. Fruit a
capsule or schizocarp, rarely a berry or a drupe. Seeds mostly with endosperm.

Thirty genera and 250 species, predominantly in arid regions or deserts of all continents.

1. Thorny trees or shrubs. Fruit an ovoid drupe up to 3 cm. Leaves of 2 leaflets. Flowers greenish. **8. Balanites**
 – Shrubs or herbs not as above 2
2. Leaves pinnate with 4–6 pairs of leaflets. Fruit winged or prickly or prominently tuberculate. Annual or biennial prostrate plants. **6. Tribulus**
 – Leaves undivided or dissected or 2–3-foliolate 3
3. Flowers (3–)4-merous. Inflorescences spicate. Fleshy annuals. **2. Tetradiclis**
 – Flowers 5-merous. Inflorescences never spicate 4
4. Petals 0. Unarmed perennial herbs with 3-foliolate leaves. **3. Seetzenia**
 – Petals 5. Plants not as above 5
5. Shrubs with spinescent twigs, simple fleshy leaves, white flowers and juicy berry-like fruit. **7. Nitraria**
 – Herbs or shrubs with a different set of characters 6
6. Stipules spiny. **4. Fagonia**
 – Stipules not spiny 7
7. Leaves 2-foliolate or simple and entire. Stamens 8–10. **5. Zygophyllum**
 – Leaves irregularly dissected into linear-lanceolate lobes. Stamens 12–15. **1. Peganum**

Subfam. PEGANOIDEAE. Fruit a 3–4-carpelled loculicidal capsule or a berry. Leaves alternate, stipulate, dissected.

1. PEGANUM L.

Perennial herbs or shrubs. Leaves alternate, irregularly dissected; stipules minute, bristle-like. Flowers hermaphrodite, opposite leaves, forming terminal raceme-like dichasia. Calyx persistent, 5-parted. Petals 5, imbricated. Stamens (8–)12–15, dilated at base, inserted in 2 rows at base of a ring-like or cup-shaped disk. Ovary 3 (–4)-celled, almost globular; ovules numerous; style triquetrous; keels of style stigmatose. Fruit a capsule, usually 3-valved, dehiscing loculicidally, or indehiscent and berry-like. Seeds angular, with spongy coat; endosperm fleshy; embryo curved.

Six species in the more or less arid parts of Eurasia and America.

1. Peganum harmala L., Sp. Pl. 444 (1753); Boiss., Fl. 1 : 917 (1867). [Plate 352]

Perennial, woody at base, green, glabrous, leafy, 30–50 cm. Stems much branched, angular above. Branches erect and ascending. Leaves 5–10 cm., sessile; stipules 1.5–2.5 mm., subulate to setaceous; blade irregularly pinnatisect; lobes 2–4 cm., spreading, linear-lanceolate, acute, entire. Inflorescences terminal, cymose. Flowers large, on long pedicels thickening above. Sepals 1.5–2 cm., linear, sometimes 3-fid, with minute scales of epicalyx between the sepals. Petals about 1.5 × 0.5–0.7 cm., white or yellowish, oblong-elliptical. Capsule 0.8–1 cm., 3-celled, many-seeded, depressed-globular, 3-lobed, glabrous, with persistent style. Seeds about 2 mm., triangular, blackish-brown, tuberculate. $2n = 24$. Fl. March–April.

Hab.: Roadsides and other ruderal sites in deserts and steppes. Philistean Plain, Lower Galilee, Judean Mts., Judean Desert, Negev, Upper and Lower Jordan Valley,

Dead Sea area, Arava Valley, Golan, Gilead, Moav, Edom. Locally fairly common.

Area: Irano-Turanian and Saharo-Arabian, with extensions into Mediterranean and S. Euro-Siberian territories.

Medicinal plant: Seeds (semen harmalae) are used as an emmenagogue, diuretic and emetic; they contain the alkaloids harmin and harmalin.

Subfam. TETRADICLIDOIDEAE. Fruit a 3–4-carpelled loculicidal capsule. Seeds partly free, partly enclosed in the membranous-spongy part of pericarp. Leaves exstipulate, pinnately dissected or entire.

2. TETRADICLIS Stev. ex M.B.

Annuals, succulent, often diffusely branched at base. Leaves sparse, exstipulate, sessile, entire or dissected, lower leaves opposite, cauline alternate. Flowers many, small, hermaphrodite, in terminal, bracteate, mostly spike-like cymes. Calyx (3–)4-parted, persistent. Petals (3–)4, persistent, short-clawed. Disk inconspicuous. Stamens (3–)4, with persistent, subulate filaments. Ovary 3–4-celled, depressed; style with divergent stigmas. Fruit a tetragonous, loculicidally dehiscing capsule; cells divided by portions of the endocarp into 3 secondary compartments, the middle one with 4 seeds or less, the others 1-seeded. Seeds minute, oblong, with thin coat, scanty endosperm and slightly curved embryo; cotyledons fleshy, plano-convex.

A single species, mainly in S.W. Asia.

1. Tetradiclis tenella (Ehrenb.) Litv., Trav. Mus. Bot. Acad. Pétersb. 3 : 122 (1907). *Anatropa tenella* Ehrenb., Linnaea 4 : 404 (1829). *T. salsa* Stev. ex M.B., Fl. Taur.-Cauc. 3 : 277, 648 (1819) *sine nom. sp., descr. gen. monotyp.*; Boiss., Fl. 1 :918 (1867); *T. salsa* C. A. Mey., Verz. Pfl. Cauc. 226 (1831); *T. salsa* Stev. ex Bge., Linnaea 14 : 178 (1840). [Plate 353]

Annual, glabrous, 10–30 cm. Stems many, erect or ascending, branching throughout, slender. Branches mostly opposite. Leaves (0.5–)1–2 cm., few, succulent, linear, auriculate at base, entire or irregularly dissected into linear lobes, glabrous. Flowers small, short-pedicelled, scattered along the upper parts of the branches in a spike-like inflorescence. Calyx 1–2 mm., parted almost to the middle into 3–4 lobes. Corolla twice as long as calyx or more, white. Capsule about 3 mm. in diam., depressed, 4-lobed. Seeds 0.5 mm., oblong, brown. Fl. December–April.

Hab.: Salines in deserts. Judean Desert, Negev, Lower Jordan Valley, Dead Sea area, Arava Valley, Ammon, Moav, Edom. Rare.

Area: W. Irano-Turanian, with extensions into the Saharo-Arabian region.

Subfam. ZYGOPHYLLOIDEAE. Carpels mostly 5. Fruit a capsule or a schizocarp. Seeds free or enclosed in the pericarp. Leaves opposite or sometimes alternate, stipulate, pinnate or 1–3-foliolate.

3. SEETZENIA R. Br.

Perennial herbs. Leaves opposite, stipulate, 3-foliolate. Inflorescences axillary. Flowers small, hermaphrodite. Sepals 5, persistent, valvate. Petals 0. Disk 5-lobed. Stamens 5, inserted on the disk; filaments without appendage at base. Ovary sessile, 5-celled, pentagonous; cells 1-ovuled; styles 5, free, reflexed; stigmas capitate. Fruit a deeply 5-lobed ovoid capsule; carpels 5, 1-seeded, separating from a central pentagonous axis and dehiscing along ventral suture. Seeds flattened, oblong, enclosed in the brittle, waxy endocarp; coat thick; endosperm scanty; cotyledons thick.

One species in N. and S.W. Africa and S.W. Asia.

1. Seetzenia orientalis Decne., Ann. Sci. Nat. Bot. ser. 2, 3 : 281, t. 7 (1835); Boiss., Fl. 1 : 916 (1867); Burtt and Lewis, Kew Bull. 1954 : 397 (1954). [Plate 354]

Perennial, glabrous to scabrous, 15–35 cm. Stems many, procumbent, sparingly branched, herbaceous, somewhat flexuous, striate, scabrous to muricate along ribs, leafy throughout. Leaves 1.5–2 cm., petiolate, 3-foliolate; stipules membranous, re-flexed, triangular, ciliate; leaflets obovate-cuneate, mucronate, the lateral leaflets oblique, smaller than the middle one. Peduncles solitary, longer than the subtending leaves. Sepals 3 mm., persistent, elongating in fruit, somewhat fleshy, oblong-lanceolate. Stamens scarcely exceeding calyx in length. Capsule 8 × 5 mm., ellipsoidal or ovoid; carpels 1-seeded, with 2 darker longitudinal tuberculate stripes on back. Seeds 4–5 mm., flat, oblong, acute at both ends, with a glossy waxy coat. Fl. February–March.

Hab.: Hot deserts; in pebbly wadi beds. S. Negev, Arava Valley. Rare.

Area: Sudanian and S. African.

4. FAGONIA L.

Dwarf shrubs or perennial herbs, rarely annuals, mostly spiny. Leaves opposite, with spiny stipules, mostly 3-foliolate. Peduncles arising between stipules. Flowers herm-aphrodite, solitary. Sepals 5, caducous or persistent, mucronate. Petals 5, imbricated in bud, clawed. Disk inconspicuous. Stamens 10, with scaleless filaments. Ovary sessile, 5-celled, pentagonous; ovules 2, side by side at base of each cell; style persistent, subulate, 5-angled; stigma simple. Fruit a pyramidally pentagonous, septicidal capsule, very deeply 5-lobed, splitting along the axis into 5 carpels; carpels dehiscent, 1-seeded. Seeds compressed, ovate to oblong, with mucilaginous coat, horny endosperm and broad flat cotyledons.

About 40 species, mainly in the deserts of Africa, S.W. Asia and America; 1 species in the Mediterranean region.

Literature: P. Ozenda & P. Quézel, Les Zygophyllacées de l'Afrique du Nord et du Sahara, *Trav. Inst. Rech. Sah.* 14 : 23–83 (1956). M.N. El Hadidi, The genus *Fagonia* in Egypt, *Candollea* 21 : 13–54 (1966).

1. Calyx persistent or semipersistent in fruit   2
– Calyx caducous   4
2. Stipular spines much shorter than leaves.   **2. F. glutinosa**

- Stipular spines longer than or about as long as leaves　　　　　　　　　　　3
3. Plants glabrous or sparingly hairy. Capsule up to 4 mm.　　　**5. F. bruguieri**
- Plants hispid. Capsule up to 7 mm.　　　　　　　　　　　　　　**6. F. mollis**
4(1). Plants glabrous (rarely with few glands)　　　　　　　　　　　　　　5
- Plants covered with ordinary or glandular hairs or with both or with sessile glands　6
5. Leaflets linear, middle leaflet considerably longer than the lateral ones (1.3–1.8 × 0.1–0.2 cm.). Pedicels 2–3 times as long as the capsule.　　　　**4. F. bischarorum**
- Leaflets ovate to broadly elliptical, usually almost equal in length. Pedicels as long as the capsule or shorter.　　　　　　　　　　　　　　　**6. F. mollis**
6(4). Petioles of lower leaves longer than leaflets; stipular spines usually 3–5 mm. (not exceeding 1 cm.); leaflets 0.3–0.7 (–1.2) × 0.1–0.2 cm., linear or linear-oblong to lanceolate or elliptical　　　　　　　　　　　　　　　　　　7
- Not as above　　　　　　　　　　　　　　　　　　　　　　　8
7. Stems brownish-green, with stipitate glands. Capsule usually about 5 mm.　　　**3. F. sinaica**
- Stems greyish-green, with sessile glands or papillae. Capsule usually about 7 mm.　　　**7. F. arabica**
8(6). Delicate annual plants covered with long patulous hairs ending with glands. Lower leaves rosulate; leaflets ovate-orbicular, the middle leaflets of upper leaves broadly ovate, much broader than the lateral leaflets; stipular spines much shorter than the leaflets. Petals 6–7 mm.　　　　　　　　　　　　　　**1. F. latifolia**
- Perennials, mostly shrubby. Leaflets not as above　　　　　　　　　　9
9. Plants covered with sessile glands only. Leaflets linear to linear-elliptical, usually revolute-margined. Flowers about 1 cm., pale pink. Upper leaves usually sessile. Pedicels usually longer than the capsule.　　　　　　　　　**7. F. arabica**
- Plants covered with sessile and usually also with long-stipitate glands. Leaflets ovate to broadly elliptical. Flowers up to 2 cm., intensely pink. All leaves petiolate. Pedicels shorter than or as long as the capsule.　　　　　　　　**6. F. mollis**

1. **Fagonia latifolia** Del., Fl. Aeg. Ill. 62 (1813) et Fl. Eg. 86, t. 28, f. 3 (1813); Boiss., Fl. 1 : 904 (1867). [Plate 355]

Annual slender herb, with long white or brownish patulous rigid hairs ending in glands, 10–20 cm. Stems single or few, 4-angled, dichotomously branched above. Leaves short-petioled, 3-foliolate; stipular spines very short (3–5 mm.), shorter than the leaves; lower leaves rosulate, much larger than the others, with middle leaflet broadly ovate to almost orbicular; upper leaves: middle leaflets 1–1.5 cm., ovate-rhombic, long-mucronate; lateral leaflets short (5–7 mm.), elliptical. Flowers short-pedicelled, small, up to 8 mm. across. Sepals 2–3 mm., caducous, ovate-oblong, mucronate, sparingly hairy. Petals 6–7 mm., pale pink, long-clawed. Fruiting pedicels about as long as the capsule, obpyramidal, hispidulous. Capsule about 4 mm. in diam., obconical, subpatulous-hairy; style shorter than the capsule. Fl. February.

Hab.: Wadis. Dead Sea area. Very rare.

Area: Saharo-Arabian.

2. **Fagonia glutinosa** Del., Fl. Aeg. Ill. 62 (1813) et Fl. Eg. 86, t. 28, f. 2 (1813); Boiss., Fl. 1 : 904 (1867). [Plate 356]

Perennial, grey to green with woody base, densely covered with sessile glands and often with adherent sand grains, 20–40 cm. Stems prostrate, much branched, furrowed or angular. Branches brittle, with rather long internodes. Leaves with conspicuous petioles, usually all 3-foliolate; stipular spines much shorter than the leaves; leaflets 0.3–1 (–1.2) cm.; lateral leaflets oblong-elliptical, mucronulate, the middle leaflet oblong or rhombic to rhombic-cuneate or obovate, usually almost twice as long as the lateral ones. Pedicels shorter to longer than the calyx, later often deflexed. Sepals 3–6 mm., persistent, ovate-oblong. Petals 0.6–1.5 cm., pink or purple, with long claw and ovate limb. Capsule 5–7 mm., obconical, with long hairs interspersed with sessile glands; style short to about as long as the capsule. Seeds 1–1.5 mm., oblong, brown, finely pitted-granular. Fl. March–May.

Var. **glutinosa.** Greenish. Middle leaflet ovate-rhombic to obovate. Petals up to 8 mm. Capsule about 5 mm., with patulous white hairs; style much shorter than the capsule.

    Hab.: Desert; sandy depressions and wadis. Arava Valley. Not rare.

Var. **grandiflora** Boiss., l.c. 905. [Plate 356]. Mostly greyish. Middle leaflet oblong or rhombic, cuneate at base. Petals (0.9–)1–1.5 cm. Capsule about 7 mm., mostly with appressed hairs; style almost as long as or a little shorter than the capsule.

    Hab.: As above. Negev, Dead Sea area, Arava Valley, Moav, Edom. Not rare.

    Area of species: Saharo-Arabian.

Transitions between the above varieties with regard to size of petals are met with; in the Negev a specimen with caducous calyx has been observed. — Var. *pseudo-cahirana* Opphr., Bull. Soc. Bot. Genève ser. 2, 22 : 339 (1931) is one of these transitional forms.

3. Fagonia sinaica Boiss., Diagn. ser. 1, 1 : 61 (1843). *F. kahirina* Boiss. var. *sinaica* (Boiss.) Boiss., Fl. 1 : 905 (1867). *F. kahirina* Boiss., Diagn. ser. 1, 8 : 122 (1849). *F. sinaica* Boiss. var. *kahirina* (Boiss.) Hadidi, Candollea 21 : 37 (1966) et var. *sinaica* sensu Hadidi, l.c. 39. [Plate 357]

    Dwarf shrub, green, sparingly hairy to glandular-hairy, 15–30 cm. Stems many, erect or straggling, much branched, angular. Branches spreading, forked. Leaves 3-foliolate or upper leaves simple; stipular spines less than 1 cm., often 3–5 mm., shorter than the leaves and much shorter than internodes; petioles conspicuous, those of the lower leaves often longer than middle leaflet; leaflets 0.3–1.2 cm., lanceolate to elliptical, obtuse, mucronate. Pedicels shorter than the flowers, elongating in fruit, slightly obconical, ridged, later deflexed. Sepals 3–4 mm., caducous, ovate, glandular-hirsute to glabrescent. Petals 2–3 times as long as sepals, violet, long-clawed. Fruiting pedicels as long as to twice as long as the capsule. Capsule 4–5 (–6) × 5–6 mm., obconical, hairy throughout; style half as long to almost as long as the capsule. Seeds brown, ovate, pitted. Fl. March–April.

    Hab.: Deserts; mainly in plains and wadis, among rocks. Judean Desert, C. Negev, Dead Sea area, Arava Valley. Uncommon.

    Area: Saharo-Arabian.

A thorough examination of our material from Sinai and Palestine has led us to the conclusion that *F. kahirina* Boiss. is absolutely identical with *F. sinaica* Boiss. and that there is no room for dividing the plants of our area into var. *sinaica* and var. *kahirina,* as has been done by some authors. In all specimens observed, the petioles of the lower leaves are longer than the middle leaflet; in the length of the pedicel and the density of the indumentum our specimens show a continuous variation.

4. Fagonia bischarorum Schweinf., Bull. Herb. Boiss. 7 (App. 2): 276 (1899). [Plate 358]

Dwarf shrub, olive-green, glabrous, rarely with sparse stipitate glands at upper part, 10–30 cm. Stems many, erect or ascending, much branched, angular. Branches slender, spreading, forked. Leaves long-petioled, 3-foliolate; stipular spines up to 0.7 (–1) cm., shorter than the internodes and leaflets; leaflets 0.8–1.8 × 0.1 (–0.2) cm., linear, the lateral leaflets shorter than the middle one, somewhat falcate. Pedicels up to 1 cm., often shorter than the flowers, elongating in fruit. Flowers up to 1.5 cm. across. Sepals 3–4 mm., caducous, ovate. Petals 5–8 mm., pink to violet. Fruiting pedicels 2–3 times as long as the capsule, deflexed. Capsule 5–6 mm. across, conical, appressed-hairy, with style as long as the capsule. Seeds ovate, brown, pitted. Fl. March–April (–June).

Hab.: Rocky wadis. Dead Sea area. Rare.

Area: Saharo-Arabian.

5. Fagonia bruguieri DC., Prodr. 1: 704 (1824); Boiss., Fl. 1: 905 (1867). [Plate 359]

Perennial with woody base, green, glandular-hairy or glabrous, 10–30 cm. Stems many, much branched, procumbent, brittle, angular, with short internodes. Lower leaves 3-foliolate, upper leaves simple; stipular spines 1–2 cm., mostly longer than the leaves, almost spreading, weak; petiole shorter than the leaflets; leaflets 0.5–1 cm., rather fleshy, ovate-oblong, often with revolute margins, mucronulate-spinulose. Pedicels shorter than the flowers, erect at first, later horizontal or slightly deflexed. Sepals 2–3 mm., persistent, ovate to acuminate, puberulent. Petals 2–3 times as long as sepals, pink. Capsule up to 4 mm., obconical, hairy, especially along keels; style shorter than the capsule, conical. Seeds about 2 mm., ovate with narrow margins, conspicuously tuberculate, brown, glossy. Fl. March–April.

Hab.: Hot deserts; in wadis and depressions. Dead Sea area, Arava Valley, Edom. Common.

Area: Saharo-Arabian, widely extending into adjacent Irano-Turanian deserts.

The records of *F. myriacantha* Boiss., Diagn. ser. 1, 8: 123 (1849) from Palestine should be referred to the above species.

6. Fagonia mollis Del., Fl. Aeg. Ill. 62 (1813) et Fl. Eg. 76, t. 27, f. 2 (1813). [Plates 360, 361a, b]

Dwarf shrub, green, hairy to hispid, with sessile or stipitate glands or altogether glabrous, up to 40 cm. Stems many, branched. Branches horizontal or ascending, angular, grooved. Leaves short-petioled, all 3-foliolate; stipular spines 1–1.3 (–2) cm., often as long as or longer than the leaves, horizontal; leaflets 0.8–1.2 cm., ovate to obovate or elliptical, obtuse, mucronate-spinulose, the middle leaflet as long as to much longer than the lateral ones. Pedicels shorter than the calyx, later elongating, first erect, later deflexed. Sepals caducous or semipersistent. Petals up to 2 cm., 2–3 times as long as sepals, pink. Capsule 6–7 mm., obovoid-obconical, hirsute-glandular, with a short style. Seeds ovate, brown, punctulate. Fl. March–April.

1. Plants glabrous, rarely with a few sessile glands. Sepals glabrous to glabrescent. Loosely branched dwarf shrubs with short-lived leaves.   var. **mollis**
– Plants hairy to hispid, mostly with sessile to stipitate glands. Sepals hairy to hispid. Intricately and very densely branched dwarf shrubs with persistent leaves   2
2. Green plants with sessile and stipitate glandular hairs. Sepals caducous.
                                                                            var. **glabrata**
– Yellowish plants, densely hispid, often also with long and short glandular hairs. Sepals becoming white-membranous, remaining attached to the mature capsules.
                                                                            var. **glabrata**

Var. **mollis.** *F. mollis* Del., l.c. non auct. *F. grandiflora* Boiss., Diagn. ser. 1, 8 : 121 (1849) et Fl. 1 : 907 (1867). *F. mollis* Del. var. *grandiflora* (Boiss.) Post, Fl. Syr. Pal. Sin. 189 (1883–1896). [Plate 360]. Plants glabrous, rarely with a few sessile glands. Leaflets deciduous. Sepals glabrous to glabrescent.

Hab. : Deserts; especially on chalks and soils rich in gypsum. Judean Desert, Lower Jordan Valley, Dead Sea area, Arava Valley, Moav, Edom. Fairly common.

Var. **glabrata** Schweinf. ex ? V. Täckh., Stud. Fl. Eg. 257 (1956). *F. grandiflora* Boiss. var. *sparse-glandulosa* Bornm., Verh. Zool.-Bot. Ges. Wien 48 : 569 (1898). [Plate 361 a]. Plants fairly hairy with sessile and / or stipitate glandular hairs. Leaflets persistent. Sepals hairy.

Hab. : As above. Judean Desert, Negev, Lower Jordan Valley, Dead Sea area, Arava Valley, Moav, Edom. Fairly common.

Var. **hispida** Zoh.* [Plate 361 b]. Plants hispid with long yellowish glandular hairs mixed with short glandular hairs. Calyx semipersistent, becoming membranous in fruit and adhering to the mature capsule. Leaflets persistent.

Hab. : On rocks, especially on granite, also in sandy or gravelly wadi beds. Negev, Dead Sea area, Arava Valley, Edom. Locally very common.

Area of species : E. Saharo-Arabian.

Var. *hispida* is very near to *F. tristis* as described by Sickenberger, Mém. Inst. Eg. 4 : 201 (1901) and not *F. tristis* var. *tristis* as understood by Hadidi, Candollea 21 : 35 (1966), according to whom leaflets are cylindrical. Our variety differs from *E. tristis* Sickenb. and from *F. tristis* var. *boveana* Hadidi, l.c. 33, in the size of the petals, which are up to 1.8 cm. long, 2–3 times as long as the semipersistent sepals. The whole plant is an intricately branched hemispherical shrublet with erect branches, covered with yellowish ordinary hairs mixed with long and short glandular hairs.

7. Fagonia arabica L., Sp. Pl. 386 (1753). [Plate 362]
Dwarf shrub, woody at base, green, densely covered with short papillae or with sessile glands, sometimes with adhering sand grains, 10–30 cm. Stems many, erect to

---

* See Appendix at end of this volume.

ascending, much branched from base and middle, furrowed. Leaves usually 3-foliolate or some of them simple; stipular spines 0.4–2.5 cm., shorter to much longer than the leaves and often equal to the internodes; petioles as long as the leaflets to much shorter, sometimes (in summer forms) longer; leaflets (0.3–)1–1.5 cm., linear, linear-elliptical or rarely linear-oblong, acute, often with revolute margins, densely covered with sessile glands. Pedicels shorter than the flowers, often elongating in fruit. Flowers about 1 cm. Sepals 3–4 mm., caducous, oblong-lanceolate, glandular. Petals twice as long as sepals, pale pink, short-clawed. Capsule (6–)7–8 mm., deflexed, conical, covered with short patulous hairs and sessile glands; style shorter than capsule, conical. Seeds about 2.5–3 mm., ovate, winged, very finely pitted-punctate. Fl. May–June.

Var. **arabica.** *F. arabica* L., l.c.; Boiss., Fl. 1 : 907 (1867). Stipular spines much longer than the leaves, directed upwards; leaves up to 1.5 cm., petiole shorter than the blade.

Hab.: Desert; mostly on stony ground. C. Negev, Dead Sea area, Arava Valley, Edom. Fairly common.

Var. **negevensis** Zoh.* Stipular spines horizontal, about half as long as the leaves; leaves almost horizontal, mostly simple, very short-petioled, blade up to 2 cm., linear-oblong.

Hab.: Gravelly slopes and wadi beds. Arava Valley. Rare.

Area of species: E. Saharo-Arabian.

F. arabica shows a very pronounced seasonal and habitat polymorphism, and var. *negevensis* may perhaps represent one of these forms. Some of the forms tend towards 1-foliolate or long-petioled leaves and shorter or more horizontal stipular spines.

5. ZYGOPHYLLUM L.

Shrubs, half-shrubs or herbs. Leaves opposite, simple or 2- to many-foliolate; stipules mostly fleshy; leaflets mostly succulent, flat or cylindrical. Flowers hermaphrodite, (4–)5-merous, pedicellate, solitary or in pairs. Sepals (4–)5, persistent or caducous. Petals (4–)5, imbricated, clawed, entire. Disk fleshy, angulate or cup-shaped. Stamens 5–10; filaments with a scale or a wing-like appendage at base. Ovary 4–5-celled, 4–5-angled, narrowed into an angular style, each cell with 2 or more superposed ovules. Fruit a 4–5-winged, 4–5-lobed or 4–5-angled capsule, indehiscent, or dehiscing septicidally or loculicidally. Seeds pendulous, with brittle coat, scanty endosperm and oblong cotyledons.

About 100 species, predominantly in the deserts of Africa, Asia and Australia.

1. Leaves simple. Prostrate annuals.   **5. Z. simplex**
   – Leaves 2-foliolate. Perennials   2
2. Leaflets flat, obovate, usually 1–2 cm. broad. Fruit cylindrical, mostly 2–3 cm.
                                                                          2. Z. fabago
   – Leaflets succulent, cylindrical, oblong or obovoid, 2–4 mm. broad. Fruit much
     smaller   3

* See Appendix at end of this volume.

3. Woody dwarf shrubs. Fruit with broad wings. Petals up to 1.5 cm. **1. Z. dumosum**
− Perennial herbs. Fruit wingless. Petals much shorter   4
4. Plants densely hairy. Pedicels shorter than the flowers and the prominently 5-lobed capsules.   **4. Z. album**
− Plants glabrous when adult. Pedicels longer than the flowers and the 5-angled capsules.
                  3. Z. coccineum

1. Zygophyllum dumosum Boiss., Diagn. ser. 1, 8 : 125 (1849) et Fl. 1 : 911 (1867). [Plate 363]

Dwarf shrub, appressed-canescent, 40–100 cm. Stems intricately branched and woody, except for the current-year branches. Branches erect or ascending, angular. Leaves 2-foliolate; stipules connate at base, triangular; petiole as long as or longer than the leaflets, persistent, fleshy, cylindrical; leaflets 0.6–1 cm., deciduous, fleshy, oblong-cylindrical, entire, hairy. Pedicels slender, as long as the calyx, elongating in fruit. Flowers axillary, solitary. Sepals about 8 mm., oblong, sparingly hirsute. Petals almost twice as long as sepals or more, white, oblong-spatulate. Scales at base of filaments ovate-orbicular, obtuse, toothed at apex. Ovary longer than the scales, glabrous; style persistent. Capsule 1 cm. broad or more, first erect, later deflexed, depressed-globular in outline, with 5 somewhat undulate wings broader than the capsule proper. Seeds 3–4 × 2 mm., oblong-rhomboidal, brown. Fl. March–April.

Hab.: Deserts; stony or rocky ground on hillsides and plateaus. Judean Desert, Negev, Lower Jordan Valley, Dead Sea area, Arava Valley, Moav, Edom. Locally very common.

Area: E. Saharo-Arabian (Palestine-Sinai).

One of the most common shrubs in the deserts of Palestine and Sinai; a leading plant of several plant communities; highly resistant to extreme perennial drought and also to a certain degree of salinity. Attains an age of 200–250 years.

2. Zygophyllum fabago L., Sp. Pl. 385 (1753); Boiss., Fl. 1 : 913 (1867). [Plate 364]

Perennial, green, glabrous herb, 30–80 cm. Stems erect or ascending, sometimes hanging from walls, woody at base. Leaves 2-foliolate; stipules 4–8 mm., connate at base or free, herbaceous, ovate or elliptical; petiole about as long as the leaflets, slightly winged; leaflets 1.5–3 × 1–2 cm., thick, somewhat fleshy, obovate to elliptical, entire, rounded or acute at apex. Pedicels shorter than the calyx. Flowers axillary, solitary. Sepals 5–7 mm., ovate, membranous-margined. Petals almost as long as sepals, whitish-cream, yellow below, obovate, rounded or emarginate. Scales at base of filaments as long as the ovary, linear-oblong, papillose, ciliate. Capsule (1.5–)2–3 × 0.4–0.5 cm., many-seeded, erect to deflexed, oblong-cylindrical, 5-angled; style filiform. Seeds compressed, oblong, tuberculate. Fl. April–June.

Hab.: Walls and ruins. Judean Mts., Ammon. Very rare.

Area: W. Irano-Turanian, with slight extensions into territories of adjacent regions.

3. Zygophyllum coccineum L., Sp. Pl. 386 (1753); Boiss., Fl. 1 : 915 (1867). [Plate 365]

Perennial, canescent when young, later green and glabrous, 20–40 cm. Stems numerous, much branched, woody at base. Branches erect to ascending, whitish, partly with opposite but unequally long twigs. Leaves 2-foliolate; stipules broad, connate at base, membranous, triangular, apiculate; petiole fleshy, longer than the leaflets; leaflets 1–3 cm., fleshy, oblong or cylindrical, entire. Flowers solitary at the ends of younger branches. Sepals 5–6 mm., shorter than the pedicels, ovate, hooded, membranous-margined. Petals 0.8–1 cm., white or pink, spatulate, acuminate, long-clawed. Scales at base of filaments as long as the globular ovary, ovate, obtuse, retuse. Capsule 0.8–1 cm., erect, cylindrical to 5-angled, truncate, with a very short style. Seeds compressed, ovate, acute, tuberculate-wrinkled. Fl. February–April.

Hab.: Hot deserts; gravelly or sandy, often saline, soils. C. and S. Negev, Lower Jordan Valley, Dead Sea area, Arava Valley, Edom. Uncommon.

Area: Saharo-Arabian.

4. Zygophyllum album L.f., Dec. 1, 11, t. 6 (1762) et L., Sp. Pl. ed. 2, 551 (1762); Boiss., Fl. 1 : 915 (1867). [Plate 366]

Perennial, cobwebby-canescent, 15–50 cm. Stems branched from base. Branches ascending or spreading, thick, fleshy, somewhat flexuous, furrowed and angular. Leaves 2-foliolate; stipules connate at base, membranous, triangular; leaflets 0.4–1 cm., fleshy, elliptical or obovate, entire, as long as or somewhat shorter than the fleshy, oblong petiole. Pedicels much shorter than the calyx. Flowers axillary, solitary. Sepals 4–6 mm., ovate-oblong. Petals one and a half times as long as sepals, white, long-clawed; limb obovate to elliptical, deflexed at tip. Scales at base of filaments about as long as the velvety ovary, ovate-oblong, acute, almost entire. Capsule 6–8 (–9) × 4–7 mm., erect or spreading to deflexed, turbinate, prominently 5-lobed above; style very short, rather thick. Seeds oblong, acute, finely tuberculate-wrinkled. Fl. April–July.

Hab.: Sea shores and deserts; sandy and gravelly, usually saline ground. Sharon Plain, Philistean Plain, Dead Sea area, Arava Valley. Rare.

Area: Saharo-Arabian, with extensions into Mediterranean coastlands.

5. Zygophyllum simplex L., Mant. 68 (1767); Boiss., Fl. 1 : 912 (1867). [Plate 367]

Annual, green, glabrous, 10–50 cm. Stems many, all prostrate, more or less divaricately branched, whitish, flexuous. Leaves simple, (0.8–)1–2(–3) cm., fleshy, cylindrical, obtuse; stipules membranous, lanceolate, acute. Pedicels shorter than the calyx, elongating in fruit and becoming deflexed. Flowers axillary, solitary or in pairs, scattered along the branches. Sepals about 2 mm., caducous, obovate, very broadly scarious-margined. Petals longer than sepals, yellow, spatulate, long-clawed. Scales at base of filaments much shorter than ovary, 2-lobed. Capsule 2–2.5 mm., obovoid-globular to turbinate, with 5 prominent, narrowly winged wrinkled carpels; style about as long as the capsule. Seeds compressed, oblong, smooth. Fl. March–May (–June).

Hab.: Hot deserts; stony, sandy, or loamy ground, mostly in saline locations. Judean Desert, Negev, Lower Jordan Valley, Dead Sea area, Arava Valley, Edom. Fairly common.

Area: E. Sudanian.

6. Tribulus L.

Annual or biennial herbs, mostly prostrate. Leaves paripinnate, opposite or, by abortion of 1 leaf of the pair, alternate. Flowers hermaphrodite, axillary or between forks, pedicellate, solitary or forming scorpioid cymes. Sepals 5, persistent or caducous. Petals 5, caducous, spreading. Disk ring-shaped. Stamens 10, rarely 5, inserted on base of disk, shorter than petals, the episepalous stamens shorter; filaments with a gland at base. Ovary sessile, 5-celled (in ours); cells often transversely divided into locelli; ovules 1–5 in each cell, superposed; style 1 or 0; stigma 5-rayed. Fruit a schizocarp; mericarps 5, indehiscent, often separating from axis at maturity, indurated, prickly, tuberculate or winged. Seeds solitary, obliquely pendulous; coat membranous; endosperm 0; cotyledons elliptical.

Twenty species, mainly in N. Africa, S.W. Asia and S. Africa; one species in Trop. S. America.

1. Mericarps with a dentate wing all along or at base only.   **1. T. longipetalus**
– Mericarps wingless, with 2 or 4 prickles (sometimes reduced to tubercles only)   2
2. Petals narrowly linear-oblong. Style 0; stigma pyramidal. Mericarps keeled and crested, usually with 2–4 strong spines.   **3. T. terrestris**
– Petals broadly obovate. Style distinct; stigma capitate or oblong. Mericarps pitted and wrinkled, with 2 short prickles often reduced to tubercles.   **2. T. bimucronatus**

1. Tribulus longipetalus Viv., Pl. Aeg. 10 no. 7 (1831) excl. t. 2, f. 5. *T. alatus* Del., Fl. Aeg. Ill. 62 no. 438 (1813) *nom. confus.* [= *T. pentandrus* Forssk., Fl. Aeg.-Arab. 88 (1775) *nom. confus.*]. [Plate 368]

Annual, appressed-canescent, with sparse patulous bristles, 25–30 cm. Stems prostrate, branched from base, flexuous, striate. Leaves 5–7 cm., usually in pairs; stipules 5–6 mm., ovate-oblong; leaflets 4–6-paired, oblong-elliptical, acute. Flowers 1.5 cm. in diam. Sepals 7–9 mm., lanceolate. Petals about as long as sepals, yellow, obovate-oblong. Stamens 10. Stigma as long as the style or shorter, ovoid. Mericarps about 0.8(–1) cm., hairy, with warty, more or less keeled back and a dentate wing. Fl. March–April.

1. Wings all along the mericarp   2
– Wings only at base of mericarp.   var. **mollis**
2. Wings trapeziform-square, crested; the entire part of the wing much broader than both teeth and seed-bearing part.   var. **macropterus**
– Wings triangular, deeply toothed; the entire part of the wing much narrower than both teeth and seed-bearing part.   var. **longipetalus**

Var. **longipetalus**. *T. longipetalus* Viv., l.c.; Boiss., Fl. 1 : 902 (1867) *pro syn.* "*T. alatus* Del." sensu Boiss., l.c. excl. Ic. Viv., l.c. t. 2, f. 5. [Plate 368]

Var. **macropterus** (Boiss.) Zoh. (comb. et stat. nov.). *T. macropterus* Boiss., Diagn. ser. 1, 1 : 61 (1843) et Fl. 1 : 903 (1867). [Plate 368]

T. macropterus Boiss. is only very slightly different from *T. longipetalus*. The width of the wings varies greatly in the same population and sometimes in the same specimen; the only difference between these two taxa lies in the proportion between the entire and the dentate parts of the wings.

Var. **mollis** (Ehrenb. ex Schweinf.) Zoh. (comb. et stat. nov.). *T. mollis* Ehrenb. ex Schweinf., Beitr. Fl. Aethiop. 29 (1867). "*T. alatus* Del." sensu Viv., l.c. no. 8, t. 2, f. 6a, b.

Hab. of species: Hot deserts; sandy and gravelly ground. Judean Desert, S. Negev, Lower Jordan Valley, Dead Sea area, Arava Valley. Uncommon.

Area of species: Mainly Sudanian.

2. Tribulus bimucronatus Viv., Pl. Aeg. 9 no. 6, t. 2, f. 4 (1831); Boiss., Fl. 1 : 901 (1867). ?*T. pentandrus* Forssk., Fl. Aeg.-Arab. 88 (1775) *nom. confus.* [Plate 369]

Annual, appressed-canescent and patulous-hispidulous, (30–)50–60 cm. Stems many, prostrate, branched from base, flexuous, leafy. Leaves 5–8 cm., in pairs, one shorter and one longer; stipules 4 mm., lanceolate; leaflets 4–8-paired, oblong, oblique, apiculate. Flowers 1–1.2 cm. in diam. Sepals 4–6 mm., lanceolate. Petals somewhat longer than sepals, whitish-yellow, obovate. Stamens 5, rarely 10. Stigma as long as or longer than the style, capitate or oblong. Mericarps about 4 mm., rounded at back, appressed-hairy or canescent, rough-warty, with 4 prickles, the lower prickles or all often reduced to tubercles. Fl. January–April.

Hab.: Deserts; in wadis. S. Negev, Arava Valley. Rare.

Area: E. Sudanian.

3. Tribulus terrestris L., Sp. Pl. 387 (1753); Boiss., Fl. 1 : 902 (1867). [Plate 370]

Annual, green, rarely canescent, appressed-hairy and hispidulous, 30–60 cm. Stems many, prostrate, sparingly branched, striate, leafy. Leaves 4–8 cm., mostly in pairs, the smaller leaf with 5 pairs of leaflets, the larger with 6–8 pairs; stipules 4 mm., lanceolate; leaflets 0.6–1.2 cm., ovate-oblong, apiculate. Flowers up to 1.5 cm. in diam. Sepals 5(–7) mm., lanceolate. Petals up to twice as long as sepals, yellow, oblong-linear. Stamens 10. Stigma subsessile, mostly pyramidal. Mericarps about 1 cm. across, appressed-hairy or canescent, more or less keeled and somewhat crested, with 4 very strong prickles, the lower ones sometimes abortive, very rarely all reduced to conical tubercles. Fl. April–August.

Hab.: Weed in summer crops or in fallow fields. Acco Plain, Sharon Plain, Philistean Plain, Upper and Lower Galilee, Mt. Carmel, Esdraelon Plain, Samaria, Judean Desert, Negev, Dan Valley, Hula Plain, Upper and Lower Jordan Valley, Dead Sea area, Moav, Edom. Common.

Area: Euro-Siberian, Mediterranean, Irano-Turanian and Sudanian; also introduced into many other regions.

Fruit used as a detersive, astringent, purgative and diuretic.

Subfam. NITRARIOIDEAE. Carpels 3. Stamens 10–15; filaments without scales. Fruit a drupe with an ovoid-conical stone. Leaves alternate or clustered, stipulate, simple.

7. NITRARIA L.

Shrubs. Twigs often spinescent, all or only the young ones canescent. Leaves alternate or clustered, simple, fleshy; stipules caducous or indurated. Flowers hermaphrodite, in cymes. Calyx 5-fid, persistent; segments valvate in bud. Petals 5, valvate, hooded, short-beaked at apex. Disk inconspicuous. Stamens 15, inserted at the margin of the disk, naked at base. Ovary 3-celled, oblong-pyramidal, gradually tapering into a short style, silky; ovule 1 in each cell; stigmas 3, connivent. Fruit a conical drupe, with a 1-celled, 1-seeded, indurated and wrinkled endocarp; apex splitting into 6 small subulate teeth. Seeds pendulous, ovoid, acuminate; coat membranous; endosperm 0; cotyledons obovate-elliptical, plano-convex.

Four species in saline deserts: S.W. Europe, N. Africa, S.W. and C. Asia, E. and S. Australia.

1. Nitraria retusa (Forssk.) Aschers., Verh. Bot. Ver. Prov. Brandenb. 18 : 94 (1876). *Peganum retusum* Forssk., Fl. Aeg.-Arab. LXVI, 211 (1775). *N. tridentata* Desf., Fl. Atl. 1 : 372 (1798); Boiss., Fl. 1 : 919 (1867). [Plate 371]

Shrub, 1–2 m.; twigs appressed-canescent. Stems many, erect, profusely branched. Branches erect-spreading. Leaves 1–2(–3) cm., alternate or fasciculate, conspicuously petiolate, fleshy, obovate-cuneate, retuse or 3–5-crenate-dentate at apex, appressed-pubescent or glabrescent; stipules minute, persistent. Flowers 6–8 mm., long-pedicelled, in loose dichotomous cymes at the ends of young twigs. Calyx 2 mm., with persistent, ovate-triangular lobes. Petals twice as long as calyx or longer, white or greenish-white, hispid. Fruit a fleshy, berry-like drupe, 0.6–1 cm., trigonous, foveolate at base, sulcate above. Fl. April–May.

Hab.: Saline deserts. E. Judean Desert, Negev, Lower Jordan Valley, Dead Sea area, Arava Valley, deserts of Ammon, Moav and Edom. Locally common.

Area: Saharo-Arabian, with extensions into adjacent Sudanian territories.

One of the most common shrubs in the halophytic vegetation of the local deserts. Widely used by the Bedouins as a source of fuel; the drupes are sweet and edible.

Subfam. BALANITOIDEAE.* Carpels 5. Stamens 10; filaments without scales. Ovary 1–5-celled. Fruit a large fleshy drupe. Seeds pendulous. Spiny shrubs or trees. Leaves alternate, exstipulate, with 1 pair of leaflets.

8. BALANITES Del.

Small trees with strong axillary spines. Leaves alternate, of 1 pair of leaflets. Flowers hermaphrodite, greenish, axillary, in cymes. Sepals 5, caducous, imbricated, concave. Petals 5, linear-oblong. Disk fleshy, depressed-conical with 10 furrows, hollow at apex. Stamens 10, inserted at base of disk; filament without a scale at base. Ovary half-

* This taxon has recently been given the rank of a family.

immersed in the cavity of the hollow disk, 5-celled; ovule 1 in each cell, linear; style subulate, often 5-sulcate; stigmas 1 or 5, minute. Fruit a fleshy, ovoid or ellipsoidal, oleaginous, 1-celled, 1-seeded drupe. Seeds pendulous; coat fibrous; embryo ovoid; cotyledons thick, oblong, plano-convex.

About 20 species in Trop. Africa and Asia.

1. Balanites aegyptiaca (L.) Del., Fl. Aeg. Ill. 61 no. 427 (1813) et Fl. Eg. 77, t. 28, f. 1 (1813); Boiss., Fl. 1 : 944 (1867). *Ximenia aegyptiaca* L., Sp. Pl. 1194 (1753). [Plate 372]

A thorny shrub or tree up to 6 m. Stems divaricately and very intricately branched. Branches long, spiny, sparingly leafy to almost naked. Twigs terete, mostly hairy; spines 1–3 cm. or more. Leaflets 1–3 × 0.6–1 cm., deciduous, petiolate, leathery, ovate to elliptical or almost orbicular, obtuse, tomentellous. Flowers 0.8–1.2 cm., subsessile, in cymes of 3–5. Sepals about 4 mm., oblong, pubescent. Petals much longer than sepals, greenish, linear-oblong, glabrous. Drupe 2–3 × 1–1.5 cm., fleshy, ellipsoidal, covered with a bluish bloom. Fl. mainly February–July.

Hab.: Hot deserts; oases and wadis. E. Judean Desert, Beit Shean Valley, Lower Jordan Valley, Dead Sea area, N. Arava Valley. Not rare.

Area: Sudanian.

The oil which constitutes up to 40% of the fruit is comestible and also widely used in folk medicine and in soap manufacture.

Believed by some to be the Biblical צֳרִי (e.g. Gen. XLIII : 11 and elsewhere).

59. LINACEAE

Annual or perennial herbs, shrubs, vines or trees. Leaves usually alternate, rarely opposite, mostly stipulate, simple, entire or slightly toothed. Flowers hermaphrodite, often heterostylous, actinomorphic, 4–5-merous, in spicate, paniculate or dichasial cymes. Sepals imbricated. Petals contorted, mostly clawed. Stamens 4–5, equal in number to and alternating with the petals; staminodes often present, small, opposite petals; filaments united at base into a narrow ring; anthers introrse, 2-celled, longitudinally dehiscent. Ovary (2–)3–5-celled; cells often partly partitioned by a false septum; ovules (1–)2 in each cell, anatropous; styles (2–)3–5, free, rarely more or less united. Fruit a loculicidal capsule (sometimes also dehiscing along the false septa) or a drupe or a 1-seeded nutlet. Seeds often with a mucilaginous coat and an aril or with winged appendages; endosperm scanty.

About 25 genera and 500 species, mainly tropical, but also in temperate regions.

1. Linum L.

Annual or perennial herbs or half-shrubs. Leaves alternate or opposite, sessile, narrow, usually entire, with or without stipular glands. Flowers hermaphrodite, actinomorphic, in terminal or axillary cymes, or flowers solitary. Sepals 5, persistent. Petals 5, caducous, more or less free or united by their claws, red, yellow, blue, pink or white. Stamens 5, with filaments dilated and slightly connate at base, alternating with 5 small staminodes. Ovary 5-celled; cells divided entirely or partly by a false septum; ovules 2 in each cell; styles 5, free or slightly connate at base; stigmas filiform, club-shaped or capitate. Fruit a capsule, usually dehiscent, mostly 10-seeded, ovoid or oblong. Seeds flat, smooth, glossy; embryo straight; cotyledons oleiferous.

About 200 species in temperate or subtropical regions; large centres of distribution in the Mediterranean and in S.W. and N. America. Many species display heterostylous flowers.

Literature: H. Winkler, *Linum* L., in: Engl. & Prantl, *Nat. Pflznfam.* ed. 2, 19a: 112–119, 1931. P. H. Davis, Materials for a flora of Turkey II: *Linum* Linn., *Notes Roy. Bot. Gard. Edinb.* 22: 135–161 (1957).

1. Flowers yellow   2
 – Flowers pink, blue or purple   7
2. Petals 1.5–3 cm. Leaves with stipular glands   3
 – Petals 0.7–1 (–1.2) cm. Leaves without stipular glands   5
3. Sepals linear, (2–) 3 times as long as the indehiscent capsule. Annuals.
                                                                           9. L. nodiflorum
 – Sepals ovate to oblong or lanceolate, shorter than to twice as long as the dehiscent capsule. Perennials with woody base   4
4. Leaves tapering towards base and apex, not mucronate. Sepals ovate or oblong, abruptly mucronate, shorter than the capsule. Petals 2 cm. or less. Inflorescences mostly 1-flowered.   7. L. toxicum
 – Leaves clasping at base, mucronate. Sepals lanceolate, long-acuminate, up to twice as long as the capsule. Petals mostly over 2 cm. Inflorescences (2–) 3- to many-flowered.
                                                                         8. L. mucronatum
5 (2). Sepals not longer than the capsule. Perennials.   4. L. maritimum
 – Sepals much longer than the capsule. Annuals   6
6. Inflorescences diffusely corymbose-paniculate. Pedicels slender, about as long as or longer than the calyx. Flowers not overtopped by adjacent leaves.
                                                                         5. L. corymbulosum
 – Inflorescences dense, trapeziform or spike-like. Pedicels thick, shorter than the calyx. Flowers mostly overtopped by adjacent leaves.   6. L. strictum
7 (1). Patulous-hairy plants. Flowers 2–3 cm. Sepals 2–3 times as long as the capsule.
                                                                           1. L. pubescens
 – Glabrous or glabrescent plants. Flowers about 1 cm. Sepals shorter to slightly longer than the capsule   8
8. Sepals oblong-ovate, acuminate, about as long as the capsule. Capsule 5–6 mm.
                                                                             2. L. bienne
 – Sepals ovate to almost orbicular, mucronate, half or two thirds as long as the capsule. Capsule 1 cm.   3. L. peyronii

Sect. DASYLINUM (Planch.) Juz. in Fl. URSS 14: 140 (1949). Subgen. *Syllinum* (Griseb.) Planch. ser. *Dasylinum* Planch., Hook. Lond. Journ. Bot. 6: 598 (1847). Petals lilac, pink or blue, rarely white with violet veins; claws coherent. Leaves alternate, without stipular glands.

1. Linum pubescens Banks et Sol. in Russ., Nat. Hist. Aleppo ed. 2, 2 : 268 (1794); Boiss., Fl. 1 : 860 (1867). [Plate 373]

Annual, sparingly patulous-hairy, 10–50 cm. Stems erect, dichotomously branched from base or above, white. Leaves 1.5–3 (–3.5) × (0.2–)0.3–1 cm., alternate, oblong-ovate to oblong-lanceolate, lower leaves obtuse, upper leaves acute, all more or less hairy to long-villose with glandular hairs or teeth at margin, 3–5-nerved. Inflorescences corymbose, dichotomously branched; branches elongating, becoming long monochasia. Flowers many, showy, heterostylous. Sepals 1–1.2 cm., 2–3 times as long as capsule, abruptly linear-lanceolate from an ovate scarious-margined and 3-nerved base, somewhat glandular at margin. Petals 2–3 cm., pink; claws of petals somewhat connate above; limb broadly ovate to orbicular. Fruiting pedicels short. Capsule about 4–5 mm., ovoid, with beak 1–2 mm. Fl. March–May.

Hab.: Batha and fields. Acco Plain, Sharon Plain, Philistean Plain, Upper and Lower Galilee, Mt. Carmel, Esdraelon Plain, Samaria, Shefela, Judean Mts., N. Negev, Hula Plain, Upper Jordan Valley, Beit Shean Valley, Lower Jordan Valley, Golan, Gilead, Ammon, Edom. Common.

Area: Mainly E. Mediterranean.

Sect. LINUM. Sect. *Eulinum* Griseb., Spicil. Fl. Rumel. 1 : 116 (1843). Petals free, blue, pink or white. Sepals much shorter than petals, eglandular. Leaves alternate, without stipular glands.

2. Linum bienne Mill., Gard. Dict. ed. 8, no. 8 (1768). *L. angustifolium* Huds., Fl. Angl. ed. 2, 134 (1778); Boiss., Fl. 1 : 861 (1867). [Plate 374]

Annual, glabrous or subglabrous, 30–60 cm. Stems single or many, erect or ascending, dichotomously branched mainly above, slender, striate. Leaves 0.6–3 cm., alternate, sessile, linear with broader base, tapering-acuminate at apex, (1–)3–5-nerved below. Inflorescences corymbose, contracted or rarely somewhat diffuse. Pedicels slender, often up to 2 cm. or more. Flowers homostylous. Calyx about as long as the capsule; sepals oblong to narrowly ovate, acuminate, 3–5-nerved, with middle nerve stout and longer than the lateral nerves. Petals 0.9–1.3 cm., free, bluish, obovate, entire, short-clawed. Capsule about 5–6 mm., globular. Seeds 2–3 mm. Fl. March–April.

Hab.: Mainly damp fields and swamps. Acco Plain, Sharon Plain, Philistean Plain, Upper and Lower Galilee, Mt. Carmel, Esdraelon Plain, Samaria, Shefela, Judean Mts., Judean Desert, Dan Valley, Hula Plain, Upper Jordan Valley, Beit Shean Valley, Golan, Gilead. Locally common.

Area: Mediterranean, extending into S. and W. Euro-Siberian and some of W. Irano-Turanian territories.

Believed by some to be the progenitor of the cultivated flax, *Linum usitatissimum* L.

3. Linum peyronii Post, Pl. Post. 3 : 6 (1892), Fl. Syr. Pal. Sin. Add. 8 (1883–1896) et ed. 2, 1 : 253 (1932). [Plate 375]

Annual, glabrous, 20–40 cm. Stems single or few, erect, dichotomously branched above, striate. Leaves 1.5–2.5 × 0.2–0.4 cm., alternate, sessile, linear, tapering towards both ends, acuminate, 3-nerved below. Inflorescences corymbose-paniculate, contracted to somewhat diffuse. Pedicels slender, often 2–3 cm., elongating in fruit. Flowers homostylous. Calyx 5–7 mm., about one half to two thirds as long as the capsule; sepals ovate to very broadly ovate (rarely becoming orbicular in fruit), obtuse or acute, mucronate, scarious-margined and finely denticulate above, 3-nerved, with the middle nerve much longer and thicker. Petals 1–1.2 cm., free, pale blue. Capsule about 1 cm., globular. Seeds 5 mm. Fl. April.

Hab.: Steppes and fields. Gilead, Ammon, Edom. Rare.

Area: Irano-Turanian.

Sect. LINASTRUM (Planch.) Winkl. in Engl. et Prantl, Nat. Pflznfam. ed. 2, 19a: 114 (1931). Subgen. *Linastrum* Planch., Hook. Lond. Journ. Bot. 6: 597 (1847). Leaves mostly alternate, the lower leaves sometimes opposite; stipular glands absent. Petals free, yellow or rarely pinkish to white.

4. Linum maritimum L., Sp. Pl. 280 (1753); Boiss., Fl. 1: 851 (1867). [Plate 376]

Perennial, glabrous, 20–50(–60) cm. Stems many, ascending, with long, sparingly leafy branches. Lower leaves 0.6–1.5 × 0.2–0.4 cm., opposite, elliptical to lanceolate; upper leaves smaller, alternate, lanceolate to linear, acute, mucronulate, more or less scabrous, 3-nerved. Inflorescences diffusely corymbose-paniculate. Pedicels as long as to much longer than the calyx. Flowers homostylous. Sepals 3–5 mm., almost as long as the capsule, ovate, shortly acuminate, not glandular at margin. Petals 0.8–1(–1.2) cm., free at base, yellow, oblong-ovate. Capsule about 5 mm., globular. Fl. April–August (–October).

Hab.: Swamps and marshes. Acco Plain, Sharon Plain, Philistean Plain, Coastal Negev. Uncommon.

Area: Mediterranean, extending to the Atlantic coast of Europe.

5. Linum corymbulosum Reichb., Fl. Germ. Exc. 834 (1832); Boiss., Fl. 1: 852 (1867). *L. strictum* L. var. *corymbulosum* (Reichb.) Planch., Hook. Lond. Journ. Bot. 7: 476 (1848). [Plate 377]

Annual, glabrous to minutely pilose, 10–40(–50) cm. Stems single or few, erect, branched above, slender. Leaves 1.5–2.5 × 0.1–0.2 cm., scattered, alternate, erect, lanceolate to linear, acute to more or less acuminate, scabrous. Peduncles slender. Inflorescences diffusely corymbose-paniculate. Pedicels longer than or about as long as the calyx. Flowers homostylous. Sepals 3–6 mm., one and a half times to twice as long as the capsule, lanceolate, tapering, very long-acuminate, keeled, glabrous, with scarious and glandular margin. Petals 7–8 mm., free at base, yellow, oblong-obovate, retuse. Capsule about 3 mm., globular, apiculate. Fl. (March–) April–May.

Hab.: Batha; stony ground. Coastal Galilee, Sharon Plain, Upper and Lower Galilee, Mt. Carmel, Esdraelon Plain, Judean Mts., Golan. Not rare.

Area: N. Mediterranean and Irano-Turanian.

6. Linum strictum L., Sp. Pl. 279 (1753); Boiss., Fl. 1 : 852 (1867). [Plate 378]

Annual, scabridulous to scabrous, 10–50 cm. Stems erect, simple or branched at base or above, more or less stiff and indurated. Branches few, lateral, often short and appressed. Leaves 0.5–2.5 × 0.1–0.3 (–0.4) cm., crowded, alternate, linear-lanceolate, acute, cuspidate, scabrous, 1–3-nerved. Pedicels shorter than the calyx, thick. Flowers homostylous, crowded in axillary branches on the main axis or on laterals, forming trapeziform or spike-like inflorescences. Sepals 0.5–1 cm., twice as long as the capsule, lanceolate with broad base and acuminate-cuspidate apex, scarious-margined below, with prominent main nerve and 2 obscure lateral ones. Petals 7–9 mm., free at base, yellow, oblong-obovate. Capsule about 3 mm., globular, apiculate. Fl. (February–) March–April.

Var. **strictum**. *L. sessiliflorum* Lam. [var.] α Lam., Encycl. 3 : 523 (1792). *Cathartolinum strictum* (L.) Reichb. var. *sessiliflorum* (Lam.) Reichb., Ic. Fl. Germ. 6 : 62, t. 327, f. 5170a (1841–1844). Cymes in more or less trapeziform inflorescences. Stems and especially inflorescences rather branched.

Var. **spicatum** (Lam. ex Pers.) Pers., Syn. Pl. 1 : 336 (1805). *L. sessiliflorum* Lam. var. *spicatum* Lam. ex Pers., l.c. *L. sessiliflorum* Lam. [var.] γ Lam., l.c. *Cathartolinum strictum* (L.) Reichb. var. *spicatum* (Pers.) Reichb., l.c., f. 5170c. "*L. strictum* L. var. *spicatum* Reichb." Boiss., l.c. [Plate 378]. Cymes in dense, thick, spike-like inflorescences.

Hab. of species : Batha and fallow fields. Coastal Galilee, Acco Plain, Sharon Plain, Philistean Plain, Upper and Lower Galilee, Mt. Carmel, Samaria, Shefela, Judean Mts., Judean Desert, Dan Valley, Hula Plain, Upper Jordan Valley, Golan, Gilead, Ammon, Moav. Common.

Area of species : Mediterranean, slightly extending into W. Irano-Turanian territories.

The two varieties often grow together, and intermediate forms between them have been observed.

Sect. SYLLINUM Griseb., Spicil. Fl. Rumel. 1 : 115 (1843). Petals yellow or white, with coherent claws which separate later. Leaves mostly alternate, often with 2 stipular glands.

7. Linum toxicum Boiss., Fl. 1 : 854 (1867); Evenari in Opphr. et Evenari, Bull. Soc. Bot. Genève ser. 2, 31 : 308 (1941). [Plate 379]

Perennial, glaucescent, glabrous, 15–20 cm. Stems simple or branched, rigid, woody at base. Leaves 0.5–1.4 cm., alternate, somewhat thick, oblong-lanceolate, narrowly membranous-margined, with 2 glands at base; lower leaves obtuse, upper leaves acute. Pedicels very short. Flowers terminal, mostly solitary, heterostylous. Sepals 6–7 mm., scarious, oblong to ovate-oblong, abruptly mucronate, denticulate and glandular at margin. Petals 1.7–2 cm., yellow, obovate, obtuse. Capsule much longer than the sepals, globular-ovoid. Fl. May–June.

Hab.: Ruins and abandoned places. Sharon Plain, Judean Desert, Dan Valley, Lower Jordan Valley. Very rare.

Area: W. Irano-Turanian.

8. Linum mucronatum Bertol., Misc. Bot. 1 : 18 (1842) non Gilib., Fl. Lithuan. 2 : 143 (1781) *nom. inval. L. orientale* (Boiss. et Heldr.) Boiss., Fl. 1 : 855 (1867) p.p. *L. flavum* L. var. *orientale* Boiss. et Heldr. in Boiss., Diagn. ser. 2, 1 : 99 (1854). [Plate 380]

Perennial, glaucous, glabrescent, 10–40 cm. Stems ascending or procumbent, branched from the woody base. Leaves 1–3(–3.5) × 0.2–0.7 cm., alternate, except for the floral leaves; lower leaves oblong-obovate or lanceolate, upper leaves linear-lanceolate, all sessile, mucronate, glaucous, mostly 1-nerved, rarely 3–5-nerved, with 2 glands at base. Inflorescences (2–)3- or more-flowered dichasia. Pedicels 0 or very short in the alar flowers and up to 2 cm. or more in the terminal flowers. Flowers heterostylous. Sepals (0.5–)0.8–1.3 cm., longer than the capsule, lanceolate-acuminate, keeled, membranous-margined, glandular-ciliate. Petals 2–3 cm., yellow, broadly obovate, obtuse, tapering into a short, sometimes purple, claw. Capsule about 6 mm., globular. Fl. March–May.

Hab.: Batha, fields and steppes. Acco Plain, Mt. Carmel, Esdraelon Plain, Samaria, Judean Mts., Judean Desert, N. Negev, Gilead, Ammon, Moav, Edom. Locally common.

Area: W. Irano-Turanian.

Ssp. *assyriacum* P. H. Davis, Not. Roy. Bot. Gard. Edinb. 22 : 155 (1957) and var. *syriacum* (Boiss. et Gaill.) Bornm., Beih. Bot. Centralbl. 31, 2 : 196 (1914) are recorded from Palestine by P. H. Davis (l.c.) and Dinsmore (in Post, Fl. Syr. Pal. Sin. ed. 2, 1 : 251, 1932) respectively. We could not find in our specimens adequate differential characteristics to separate these taxa from typical *L. mucronatum*.

L. balansae Boiss., Fl. 1 : 855 (1867) is mentioned by Bornmueller (Verh. Zool.-Bot. Ges. Wien 48 : 567, 1898) in connection with specimens collected by him in the environs of Jerusalem. In spite of the broader leaves (up to 1 cm.) on the main stem and the larger number of their nerves (up to 7), these specimens should be referred to *L. mucronatum* Bertol., since in Bornmueller's view they represent habitat forms of one and the same species.

9. Linum nodiflorum L., Sp. Pl. 280 (1753); Boiss., Fl. 1 : 853 (1867). [Plate 381]

Annual, glabrous, 10–50 cm. Stems erect or ascending, more or less angular. Leaves 2.5–3 (–4) × 0.2–0.5(–1) cm., alternate, with the exception of the uppermost ones, spatulate to oblong, oblanceolate or linear-lanceolate, scabrous, 1-nerved, with 2 dark glands at base, often scabrous-ciliate at margin. Inflorescences dichasially or mono-chasially branched, with remote, nearly sessile flowers. Flowers homostylous. Sepals 1–1.3 cm., 2–3 times as long as the capsule, linear, prominently 1-nerved, scabrid at margin, glandular at base. Petals about 1.5 cm. (or more), yellow, oblong, cuneate. Capsule about 5 mm., indehiscent, ovoid, acute. Fl. March–May.

Hab.: Batha and fields. Sharon Plain, Philistean Plain, Upper and Lower Galilee, Mt. Carmel, Esdraelon Plain, Samaria, Shefela, Judean Mts. (Judean Desert ?), Dan Valley, Upper Jordan Valley, Golan, Gilead, Ammon. Fairly common.

Area: N. Mediterranean, with extensions into W. Irano-Turanian territories.

The record by Dinsmore (in Post, Fl. Syr. Pal. Sin. ed. 2, 1 : 250, 1932) of *Linum gallicum* L., Sp. Pl. ed. 2, 401 (1762) from Palestine is probably erroneous.

60. EUPHORBIACEAE

Monoecious or dioecious herbs, shrubs or trees, often with milky juice. Leaves usually alternate, rarely opposite or whorled, mostly stipulate, simple or compound. Flowers small, mostly unisexual, actinomorphic, arranged in axillary or terminal racemose or cymose inflorescences. Sepals mostly free or 0. Petals alternating with sepals or 0. Staminate flowers with intrastaminal disk or disk lobes or glands alternating with outer stamens; stamens few or many, sometimes 1, filaments free or more or less connate, anthers 2-celled. Pistillate flowers with or without disk; ovary free, superior, usually 3-celled, with 1–2 anatropous pendulous ovules in each cell. Fruit usually a capsule separating from a persistent central column into 3 cocci, rarely fruit a drupe. Seeds with more or less leathery or fleshy coat, usually carunculate; endosperm fleshy, oleiferous; embryo mostly straight; radicle turned toward hilum.

About 290 genera and 7,500 species, mainly in Trop. America and Africa, in both humid and arid regions; a few genera also in temperate regions.

1. Flowers arranged in cyathia, each cyathium consisting of a cup-shaped involucre containing numerous staminate flowers (each of 1 stamen) around a solitary pistillate flower. Plants with acrid, milky juice. **5. Euphorbia**
 – Flowers not as above. Plants without milky juice 2
2. Dioecious plants. Leaves opposite. Staminate flowers clustered in catkins borne on axillary or terminal peduncles; pistillate flowers 1–2 together, axillary, subsessile. **3. Mercurialis**
 – Monoecious plants. Leaves alternate 3
3. Shrubs or small trees, with peltate, palmate, 7–11-lobed leaves. Capsule prickly, 1–3 cm. **4. Ricinus**
 – Herbs or low shrubs. Leaves entire or slightly lobed, not peltate. Capsule small, not prickly 4
4. Leaves up to 1 cm. **1. Andrachne**
 – Leaves 2–9 cm. or more. **2. Chrozophora**

Subfam. PHYLLANTHOIDEAE. Plants without milky juice. Carpels 2-ovuled.

1. ANDRACHNE L.

Monoecious, prostrate perennial herbs or dwarf shrubs. Leaves alternate, stipulate, mostly petiolate, simple. Flowers small, axillary, frequently in clusters, solitary. Calyx more or less deeply 5-parted. Petals membranous, shorter than calyx or abortive. Disk glands free, opposite petals. Staminate flowers: corolla minute, stamens 5–6, filaments free or somewhat connate at base; pistil abortive. Pistillate flowers: corolla mostly 0; ovary 3-celled, with 2 ovules in each cell, styles 3, 2-fid or 2-partite, stigmas somewhat club-shaped. Fruit a 3-celled capsule with 2 seeds in each cell. Seeds triquetrous, without caruncle; endosperm fleshy; embryo curved; cotyledons broad, flat, radicle rather long.

About 20 species in the Tropics and the Mediterranean region.

1. Glabrous, herbaceous perennials. Leaves usually ovate to obovate. Capsule glabrous.
   1. A. telephioides

– Papillose-scabrous or hirtellous dwarf shrubs. Leaves reniform to orbicular. Capsule hirsute.
   2. A. aspera

1. Andrachne telephioides L., Sp. Pl. 1014 (1753); Boiss., Fl. 4: 1138 (1879). [Plate 382]

Perennial, glaucous, glabrous, 10–40 cm. Stems many, prostrate, simple or branched from base, slender, leafy. Leaves 0.4–1 cm., petiolate, often somewhat fleshy, oblong or ovate to obovate, acute. Flowers 1–3 in an axil, pedicellate. Sepals 2–3 mm., rhombic, white-margined. Petals somewhat shorter than sepals, yellowish, lanceolate. Disk glands 2-lobed. Capsule 3–4 mm., depressed, glabrous. Seeds about 1.5 mm., angular, punctate. Fl. February–August.

Hab.: Waste places and dry hillsides; mostly on stony ground. Philistean Plain, Upper and Lower Galilee, Mt. Carmel, Esdraelon Plain, Samaria, Judean Mts., Judean Desert, N. and C. Negev, Upper and Lower Jordan Valley, Dead Sea area, Arava Valley, Golan, Gilead, Ammon, Moav, Edom. Common.

Area: Mainly Mediterranean and W. Irano-Turanian.

2. Andrachne aspera Spreng., Nov. Prov. 5 (1819) et Syst. Veg. 3: 884 (1826); Boiss., Fl. 4: 1138 (1879). [Plate 383]

Dwarf shrub, glaucous, papillose-scabrous or hirtellous, 10–30 cm. Stems many, arising from a woody base, prostrate to ascending, simple or branched, rigid. Leaves 0.5–1 cm., reniform to orbicular with cordate base, often notched at tip; upper leaves smaller, sessile. Flowers 1–3 in an axil, about 1–2 mm., on pedicels usually shorter than the subtending leaves, upper flowers solitary on long pedicels. Sepals lanceolate, hirsute. Petals shorter than sepals, lanceolate. Disk glands peltate, reniform in staminate flowers, obovate, truncate in pistillate flowers. Capsule about 2–4 mm., depressed, hirsute. Seeds about 1.5 mm., angular. Fl. March–April.

Hab.: Hot deserts; on stony ground. Judean Desert, E. and S. Negev, Lower Jordan Valley, Dead Sea area, Arava Valley, Edom. Rare.

Area: E. Sudanian, slightly extending into adjacent Saharo-Arabian and Irano-Turanian regions.

Roots used by the Bedouins in preparing an eye wash.

Subfam. CROTONOIDEAE. Plants with or without milky juice. Carpels 1-ovuled.

2. CHROZOPHORA Ad. Juss. ("*Crozophora*") corr. Benth.

Monoecious herbs or shrubs with stellate or scurf-like hairs. Leaves alternate, stipulate, petiolate, simple. Flowers unisexual. Sepals 5 or 10, valvate in bud. Disk inconspicuous, 5-lobed, glandular. Staminate flowers in axillary spike-like racemes, sessile or almost so; petals 5, alternating with sepals; stamens 5–15 in 1–3 whorls, filaments connate into a central column, anthers 2-celled with an excurrent, mucronate connective. Pistillate flowers 1–4 in a cyme below the staminate flowers, pedicellate; petals 5, narrow, sometimes 0; staminodes 5 or 0; ovary globular, 3-celled, cells 1-ovuled, styles 3, 2-fid or -parted, stigmatose on one side. Fruit a 3-celled ovoid-globular capsule; cocci 1-seeded, 2-valved. Seeds triquetrous, tapering at tip, without caruncle; embryo central in the oleiferous endosperm; cotyledons broad; radicle short.

Eleven species, mainly in the Mediterranean and tropical countries of Africa and S.W. Asia.

Literature : F. Pax & K. Hoffmann, *Chrozophora* Neck., in : *Pflznr.* 57 (IV. 147. VI) : 17–27, 1912. D. Prain, The genus *Chrozophora, Kew Bull.* (*Bull. Misc. Inform.*) 1918 : 49–120 (1918).

1. Capsule densely stellate-hairy. Stamens about 15, in 3 whorls. Seeds smooth. Surface of blade uneven to strongly plicate.   **1. C. plicata**
– Capsule scurfy-scaled. Stamens 10 or less. Seeds tuberculate. Surface of blade plane   2
2. Leaves green or grey, ovate-rhombic and obscurely lobed, mostly with dispersed stellate hairs. Stamens 10.   **2. C. tinctoria**
– Leaves tomentose, grey to yellowish-white, not lobed but sometimes undulate or dentate, densely stellate-hairy. Stamens 4–6(–7–8)   3
3. Perennial, erect, greyish-tomentose desert shrubs, up to 60 cm. or more. Leaves always oblong-lanceolate, dentate or undulate; lateral nerves of blade 5–9; stellate hairs distinct. Capsule with dentate or ciliate or fringed scales and many prominent tubercles. Seeds up to 5 mm.   **4. C. oblongifolia**
– Annual, often ascending or prostrate plants of segetal habitats, (10–) 20–30 (–40) cm. Leaves ovate or oblong-lanceolate (often both forms in the same specimen), not dentate, rarely undulate; lateral nerves 3–5; stellate hairs very dense and overlapping. Capsule with obtusely lobed scales and without tubercles. Seeds up to 3 mm.
                                                                      3. C. obliqua

1. Chrozophora plicata (Vahl) Ad. Juss. ex Spreng., Syst. Veg. 3 : 850 (1826; "*Crozophora*") excl. syn. [*tinctorium* γ Lam.]; Ad. Juss., Euph. Gen. Tent. 28 (1824; "*Crozophora*") *comb. inval.*; Boiss., Fl. 4 : 1140 (1879). *Croton plicatum* Vahl, Symb. Bot. 1 : 78 (1790). ? *Croton hastatum* Burm. f., Fl. Ind. 205 (typ. err. 305), t. 63, f. 1 (1768). [Plate 384]

Annual, canescent to woolly with stellate hairs, 30–50 cm. Stems branched from base. Branches mostly procumbent, dichotomous above, elongated. Leaves 2–5 cm., long-petioled; stipules linear; blade ovate, plicate, oblique at the subcordate or rarely cuneate base, obtuse, sometimes slightly 3-lobed. Flowers terminal or axillary, in spike-like racemes. Staminate flowers about 3–4 mm., sessile; sepals ovate; petals lanceolate-ovate; stamens about 15, in 3 whorls. Pistillate flowers usually in groups of 3, about 4 mm., pedicellate, deflexed; petals linear. Capsule about 5–6 × 8 mm., on a long pedicel, depressed-globular, covered with stellate hairs. Seeds 3–4 mm., smooth. Fl. April–November.

Hab.: Seasonally inundated depressions in sandy soils. Sharon Plain, Philistean Plain, Negev. Rare.

Area: Sudanian, widely extending into other tropical regions of Africa and Asia.

2. Chrozophora tinctoria (L.) Ad. Juss., Euph. Gen. Tent. 28, 84, 110, t. 7, f. 25 (1824; "*Crozophora*"); Raf., Chlor. Aetn. 4 (1813) *nom. inval.*; Boiss., Fl. 4: 1140 (1879). *Croton tinctorium* L., Sp. Pl. 1004 (1753). [Plate 385; under *C. tinctoria* (L.) Raf.]

Annual, grey, stellate-hirsute to woolly, with minute hairs, not felty, 10–50 cm. Stems erect or procumbent. Leaves 2–9 cm.; stipules narrow, linear; petiole up to 10 cm.; blade ovate-rhombic, subcordate to short-cuneate at base, rounded, obscurely lobed. Flowers 3–4 mm., in terminal or axillary spike-like racemes. Staminate flowers: sepals linear-lanceolate; petals linear; stamens about 10, in 2 whorls. Pistillate flowers: petals minute. Capsule 5–8 mm., on a deflexed pedicel, ovoid-globular, scurfy and tuberculate. Seeds about 4 mm., triquetrous, scabrous-tuberculate. Fl. May–October.

Hab.: Among summer crops or in fallow fields. Acco Plain, Sharon Plain, Philistean Plain, Upper and Lower Galilee, Mt. Carmel, Esdraelon Plain, Samaria, Judean Mts., Negev, Dan Valley, Hula Plain, Upper and Lower Jordan Valley, Beit Shean Valley, Golan, Ammon, Moav, Edom. Very common.

Area: Mediterranean and Irano-Turanian.

Formerly a source of a dye used for colouring linen as well as pastry and cheese.

3. Chrozophora obliqua (Vahl) Ad. Juss. ex Spreng., Syst. Veg. 3: 850 (1826; "*Crozophora*"); Prain, Kew Bull. 1918: 111 (1918); Ad. Juss., Euph. Gen. Tent. 28 (1824; "*Crozophora*") comb. inval. *Croton obliquum* Vahl, Symb. Bot. 1: 78 (1790). *Crozophora verbascifolia* (Willd.) Ad. Juss., l.c.; Spreng., l.c. 851; Boiss., Fl. 4: 1141 (1879). *Crozophora hierosolymitana* Spreng., l.c. 850; Boiss., l.c. *pro syn.* [Plate 386; under *C. verbascifolia* (Willd.) Ad. Juss.]

Annual, rather yellowish-white, tomentose-felty, with dense stellate hairs, 20–40 cm. Stems ascending or procumbent, divaricately branched. Leaves 2–7 cm.; stipules minute, linear; petiole 5–10 cm.; blade very thick, ovate to oblong or lanceolate, rounded or subcordate at base, acute or obtuse at apex, rarely undulate. Flowers 3–5 mm., in terminal and axillary racemes. Staminate flowers subsessile; sepals and petals linear-lanceolate, the petals longer; stamens 3–5 (–7). Pistillate flowers on long reflexed pedicels. Capsule 5–6 mm., scurfy. Seeds about 4 mm., scabrous-tuberculate. Fl. April–November.

Hab.: Fields and waste places. Coastal Galilee, Philistean Plain, Samaria, Judean Mts., W. and N. Negev, Lower Jordan Valley, Dead Sea area, Golan, Moav, Edom. Less common than the preceding species.

Area: S.E. Mediterranean and Irano-Turanian.

There is no justification for separating *C. obliqua* from *C. hierosolymitana,* as transitional forms and also specimens with ovate lower leaves and oblong-lanceolate upper ones have been observed.

The differentiation between *C. oblongifolia* and the narrow-leaved specimens of *C. obliqua* is quite obvious from comparison of the other characters used in the key.

4. Chrozophora oblongifolia (Del.) Ad. Juss. ex Spreng., Syst. Veg. 3 : 850 (1826; "*Crozophora*"); Prain, Kew Bull. 1918 : 100 (1918); Ad. Juss., Euph. Gen. Tent. 28 (1824; "*Crozophora*") *comb. inval. Croton oblongifolium* Del., Fl. Aeg. Ill. 76 no. 903 (1813) et Fl. Eg. 139, t. 51, f. 1 (1813); Boiss., Fl. 4 : 1141 (1879) *pro syn.* [Plate 387; under *C. obliqua* (Vahl) Ad. Juss.]

Perennial herb, woody at base, greyish and stellate-hairy or -woolly, 40–60(–100) cm. Stems many, erect, leafy. Leaves (2–)4–7 × 1–2.5 cm., alternate, short-petioled; stipules minute, caducous, oblong-linear; blade oblong-lanceolate, mostly short-cuneate at base, acute to acuminate, repand or coarsely dentate, prominently nerved beneath. Racemes axillary and terminal. Staminate flowers 4–6 mm., subsessile in spike-like racemes, with obovate-lanceolate sepals and petals, and with 4–6 (rarely 7–8) stamens. Pistillate flowers 1–4 in a cyme; pedicels 0.3–1 cm., elongating in fruit, deflexed; sepals 10, linear; petals as long as sepals; styles 2-parted to middle. Capsule 4–5 × 8 mm., conical-tuberculate and scurfy. Seeds about 4–5 mm., scabrous-tuberculate. Fl. May–September.

Hab.: Wadi beds; sandy soil. S. Negev, Arava Valley. Rare.

Area: Sudanian.

3. MERCURIALIS L.

Dioecious, rarely monoecious herbs. Leaves opposite, stipulate, simple. Staminate flowers in long, narrow, loose spikes or catkins; perianth segments 3–4, valvate; stamens 8–15, anther cells joined by a globular connective. Pistillate flowers axillary, solitary or in clusters, subsessile or pedunculate; perianth segments imbricated; stamens 2–3, reduced to filaments; ovary 2-celled, each cell with 1 ovule, styles short, stigmas rough on their inner side. Fruit a 2-, rarely 3-celled capsule, dehiscing by valves. Seeds pendulous, carunculate; embryo surrounded by a fleshy endosperm.

Eight species in the Mediterranean and Euro-Siberian regions.

1. Mercurialis annua L., Sp. Pl. 1035 (1753); Boiss., Fl. 4 : 1142 (1879). [Plate 388]

Dioecious, glabrescent annual, 20–50 cm. Stems erect, branched, striate, thickened at nodes. Leaves 1.5–6 cm., petiolate, ovate to elliptical-lanceolate, crenate-serrate. Flowers 3–5 mm. across. Staminate flowers clustered in catkins borne on axillary and terminal peduncles much longer than the leaves; perianth of 3 sepaloid, ovate, acute, glabrous segments 1.5–2 mm.; stamens 8–12. Pistillate flowers axillary, solitary or in pairs, subsessile; perianth segments somewhat connate at base, ovate, acute. Capsule 3–4 mm. broad, compressed-obovoid, covered with tubercles which terminate in bristles. Seeds 2 mm., ellipsoidal, pitted and tuberculate. Fl. December–May.

Hab.: Waste places, roadsides and by hedges. Acco Plain, Sharon Plain, Philistean Plain, Upper Galilee, Mt. Carmel, Esdraelon Plain, Samaria, Shefela, Judean Mts., Judean Desert, Hula Plain, Upper and Lower Jordan Valley, Dead Sea area, Golan, Gilead, Ammon, Moav. Very common.

Area: Mediterranean and Euro-Siberian.

Formerly official; purgative.

4. RICINUS L.

Monoecious shrubs with alternate, stipulate, peltate, palmately lobed leaves. Flowers large, in subpaniculate racemes, staminate flowers above, pistillate below. Perianth segments 3–5, valvate in bud. Petals absent. Staminate flowers with numerous stamens connate and branched repeatedly; anther cells 2, globular. Pistillate flowers with a large 3-celled ovary and style 3–6-parted, hirsute, stigmatose all along. Fruit a 3-celled capsule covered with thick prickles; cells 2-valved, 1-seeded. Seeds with a 2-lobed caruncle; endosperm copious, oleiferous; cotyledons large.

One species, presumably of Trop. African origin.

1. Ricinus communis L., Sp. Pl. 1007 (1753); Boiss., Fl. 4 : 1143 (1879). [Plate 389]

Glaucous, glabrous shrub, 1–4 m. Stems erect, much branched above, thick, hollow. Leaves 6–25 cm. or more, petiolate; stipules united, clasping; blade 7–11-lobed; lobes ovate-lanceolate, dentate. Flowers in axillary and terminal racemes. Staminate flowers about 1 cm.; perianth 3–5-lobed; stamens numerous. Pistillate flowers about 1 cm.; perianth 5-lobed, caducous; ovary 3-celled, globular or ovoid; style short, with 3 red, 2-lobed stigmas. Capsule 1–3 cm., oblong-ellipsoidal, covered with soft prickles, rarely smooth. Seeds about 1 cm. or more; coat crustaceous, glabrous, often mottled. Fl. mainly March–November.

Hab.: Subspontaneous in the hotter parts of Palestine; in the Dead Sea area (Arnon River delta) it occurs in dense groves; also common in wadis, at roadsides and in waste places: Sharon Plain, Philistean Plain, Esdraelon Plain, Samaria, Judean Mts., W. and N. Negev, Hula Plain, Beit Shean Valley, Golan, Moav. Fairly common.

Area: Presumably originating in the Sudanian and E. African regions.

This is the Biblical קִיקָיוֹן (e.g. Jonah IV : 6). An important industrial oil plant cultivated since ancient times in tropical and subtropical countries (castor beans); the oil, which constitutes up to 70% of the seed, is used in the chemical industry and as an aviation lubricant; in medicine it is known as a purgative (oleum ricini); ricinine, a toxic alkaloid, is one of the constituents of the seed.

5. EUPHORBIA L.

Monoecious shrubs or herbs with acrid milky juice. Leaves usually alternate, rarely opposite, exstipulate or rarely stipulate, simple; cauline leaves usually differing from the umbellar and floral leaves. Inflorescences simple (of solitary cyathia) or often compound and umbel-like, subtended by "umbellar" leaves below which solitary alternate axillary branches may occur; cyathia subtended by "floral" leaves. Flowers unisexual, very small, greenish, included in a cup-shaped cyathium; each cyathium comprises: 4–5 involucre lobes alternating with 4–5 conspicuous glands; few to many 1-staminate flowers with the stamen borne on a jointed stalk bearing a fringed bracteole at base; a solitary pistillate flower in the middle of the cyathium, often borne on a long pedicel, with a minute (often obsolete) 3–6-lobed calyx; and a 3-celled ovary with 3 styles and 6 stigmas protruding from the cyathium; ovules solitary in each cell. Fruit a capsule of 3 cocci, each 2-valved and 1-seeded, separating from the persistent central column. Seeds smooth or wrinkled, often with a caruncle; endosperm copious; cotyledons large, flat.

About 1,600 species in tropical and temperate regions.

Literature: P. E. Boissier, *Centuria Euphorbiarum*, Leipzig, Paris, 1860. P. E. Boissier, *Euphorbia*, in: DC., Prodr. 15, 2: 7–188, 1262–1266, Paris, 1862–1866. P. E. Boissier, *Icones Euphorbiarum*, etc., 120 pls., Paris, Geneva, Basel, 1866. J. Vindt, *Euphorbia*, in: Monographie des Euphorbiacées du Maroc, *Trav. Inst. Sci. Chérif.* 6: 23–193, 3 pls. (1953). M. S. Khan, Taxonomic revision of *Euphorbia* in Turkey, *Notes Roy. Bot. Gard. Edinb.* 25: 71–161 (1964). K. H. Rechinger & H. Schiman-Czeika, *Euphorbia*, in: K. H. Rechinger, *Flora Iranica*, Contrib. 6: 8–48, pls. 2–20, Graz, 1964.

1. Stipules small, subulate or lanceolate, sometimes fringed; leaves all opposite, mostly with oblique (unequal) base. Glands of cyathium with a pale-coloured, entire or lobulate (rarely obsolete) appendage, never horned. Capsule 1–2 mm., or longer but then altogether glabrous   2
 – Stipules lacking, rarely minute glands at base of leaves; leaves alternate (except for the floral ones), rarely some or all stem leaves opposite but then glands of cyathium horned or capsule white-woolly and 5–6 mm. in diam.   9
2. Plants altogether glabrous   3
 – Plants hirsute   4
3. Seeds smooth. Leaves sessile, 1–1.2 (–1.5) cm. Plants of sandy coasts.   **1. E. peplis**
 – Seeds wrinkled or pitted. Leaves petiolate, 3–6 mm. Plants of hot deserts.
                                                                                         2. E. granulata
4 (2). Cyathia arranged in dense globular pedunculate heads or umbels about 1 cm. or more in diam. Stems procumbent or ascending. Leaves up to 4 cm.   **6. E. hirta**
 – Inflorescences not as above   5
5. Leaves entire all around; base of leaf strongly asymmetrical. Carpels rounded.
                                                                                         2. E. granulata
 – Leaves dentate or crenulate, at least near apex   6
6. Leaves 1.5–2 cm. or more, remote. Plants erect, with stems repeatedly forked above. Inflorescences umbellate.   **7. E. nutans**
 – Leaves 3–9 mm., mostly crowded. Plants prostrate; stems not forked   7
7. Leaves ovate to suborbicular, dentate-crenulate all around. Appendage of gland mostly whitish, often broader than the gland, often 3-dentate.   **3. E. chamaesyce**
 – Leaves oblong to elliptical, dentate near apex only. Appendage of gland not as above   8
8. Carpels appressed- or crisp-hairy all over. Leaves sessile, oblique at base.
                                                                                         4. E. forskalii
 – Carpels patulous-hairy along keel only. Leaves short-petioled, not or only slightly oblique at base.   **5. E. prostrata**
9(1). Villose-canescent annuals. Glands pectinately cleft into setaceous lobes. Capsule woolly. Styles undivided. Seeds tetragonous, tuberculate.   **9. E. petiolata**
 – Not as above   10
10. Glands horned or semilunate, rarely pectinate or 0   11
 – Glands ovate or elliptical, more or less rounded or truncate, not horned   24
11. Seeds tuberculate, reticulate, sulcate or pitted   12
 – Seeds smooth   20
12. Seeds with longitudinal or transverse furrows or with both, or with longitudinal

furrows and pits. Annuals   13
— Seeds reticulate, tuberculate, wrinkled or irregularly pitted. Annuals or perennials   16
13. Seeds with 6 longitudinal furrows.   **26. E. aulacosperma**
— Seeds with 2 longitudinal furrows and 4 longitudinal rows of pits, or with transverse
   furrows only (rarely with transverse pits only)   14
14. Seeds compressed, with 2 rows of 4–6 transverse furrows on either side (rarely furrows of seed reduced to pits).   **25. E. falcata**
— Seeds angular, with 2 longitudinal furrows and with 4 longitudinal rows of pits
   (rarely the latter dash-like)   15
15. Carpels each with 2 wing-like keels at back.   **27. E. peplus**
— Carpels with a single keel, not 2-winged.   **28. E. chamaepeplus**
16(12). Cauline (winter) leaves linear to needle-shaped, caducous, leaving dense scars
   on lower part of stem. Umbellar and floral (spring) leaves broadly ovate to triangular
   or orbicular.   **23. E. aleppica**
— Plants not as above   17
17. Leaves opposite. Seeds tetragonous. Low, rare annuals.   **8. E. densa**
— Leaves (except for the floral ones) not opposite   18
18. Floral leaves lanceolate-triangular, many times longer than broad. Capsule 1–2 mm.
   across. Seeds tetragonous, covered with white transverse tubercles. Tender annuals.
                                                                     24. E. exigua
— Leaves, capsule and seeds not as above   19
19. Perennials, woody at base. Horns of gland short-ovate, one fourth to one half as
   long as the width of the gland.   **30. E. cheiradenia**
— Annuals. Horns of gland narrowly linear, 2–4 times as long as the width of the gland.
                                                                 29. E. reuteriana
20(11). Floral leaves very dilated at base, abruptly caudate-acuminate, deeply serrate-
   pectinate. Glands with 2–4 entire or 2-fid horns, or glands palmately 6–10-cleft.
   Annuals.   **11. E. retusa**
— Floral leaves and glands not as above. Perennials   21
21. Shrubs, 0.5–2 m., with thick woody stems. Leaves 6–10 cm. Plants with depressed-
   globular capsule and laterally compressed carpels, and with horns of gland much
   shorter than the width of the gland.   **10. E. dendroides**
— Not as above   22
22. Cauline leaves usually not exceeding 2 cm. in length, sessile with broad or almost
   cordate base, very densely imbricated, leathery or fleshy, somewhat concave. Seashore shrubs.   **33. E. paralias**
— Cauline leaves not as above   23
23. Leaves acute, entire. Horns of gland shorter than the width of the gland. Capsule
   5–7 mm.   **32. E. macroclada**
— Leaves, at least the lower ones, obtuse, often truncate, mucronulate, all or the upper
   leaves only often finely serrulate near apex. Horns of gland much longer than the
   width of the gland. Capsule about 4 mm.   **31. E. terracina**
24(10). Capsule covered with conical spines or with cylindrical or conical warts, sometimes the latter ending in bristles. Glabrous plants   25
— Capsule glabrous or hairy but without warts, rarely capsule warty but then plants
   villose   26
25. Warts of capsule ending in a long bristle. Annuals growing among crops.
                                                                 22. E. cybirensis

— Warts of capsule without bristle. Woody dwarf shrubs, growing in batha and desert communities.   **13. E. hierosolymitana**

26(24). Seeds transversely furrowed or pitted   27
— Seeds smooth or reticulate or tuberculate   28

27. Seeds 2.5–3 mm., oblong-tetragonous, with 3 transverse furrows on each face and scurfy dots between the furrows.   **18. E. phymatosperma**
— Seeds 1–1.5 mm., compressed, with 2 rows of 4–6 transverse furrows on either side.
                                                                                                   25. E. falcata

28(26). Seeds reticulate or tuberculate   29
— Seeds smooth   33

29. Seeds trigonous, covered with flat, irregular tubercles. Glands somewhat concave.
                                                                                                   34. E. geniculata
— Seeds ovoid or globular, not as above   30

30. Seeds finely tuberculate but not reticulate. Perennials with serrulate and villose leaves. Capsule with short cylindrical warts interspersed with long, soft hairs.
                                                                                                   14. E. verrucosa
— Seeds reticulate. Annuals   31

31. Capsule villose.   **16. E. berythea**
— Capsule glabrous   32

32. Leaves serrulate, obtuse, almost all spatulate; floral leaves obovate to orbicular.
                                                                                                   15. E. helioscopia
— Leaves pectinate-dentate, usually acute, the upper cauline leaves elliptical; floral leaves ovate-triangular.   **17. E. oxyodonta**

33(28). Leaves truncate and with a few scattered teeth at base and apex; floral leaves similar to cauline leaves.   **12. E. isthmia**
— Leaves not as above   34

34. Shrubs. Leaves entire. Very rare plants.   **10. E. dendroides**
— Annuals. Leaves more or less serrate   35

35. Plants densely or sparingly villose. Capsule 3–4 mm. Leaves coarsely serrate.
                                                                                                   19. E. arguta
— Plants glabrous. Capsule (1–)2–3 mm. Leaves finely serrulate throughout or only towards apex   36

36. Capsule globular, not sulcate. Floral leaves usually longer than broad. Seeds with a persistent caruncle.   **21. E. microsphaera**
— Capsule deeply 3-sulcate. Floral leaves as long as broad or shorter. Seeds with a caducous caruncle.   **20. E. gaillardotii**

Sect. ANISOPHYLLUM (Haw.) Roep. in Duby, Bot. Gall. 1 : 412 (1828). Gen. *Anisophyllum* Haw., Syn. Pl. Succul. 159 (1812) non Jacq., Sel. Am. 283 (1763). Leaves stipulate, with auriculate base. Glands of cyathium appendiculate.

1. Euphorbia peplis L., Sp. Pl. 455 (1753); Boiss., Fl. 4 : 1086 (1879). [Plate 390]
   Annual, glabrous, 6–20 cm. Stems branched from base. Branches procumbent, forked. Leaves 1–1.2(–1.5) × 0.5–0.8 cm., almost all alike, opposite, sessile, more or less fleshy, ovate-oblong to rhombic, oblique, with an obtuse auricle at base, obtuse or retuse at apex, repand-dentate or entire; stipules membranous, 2–3-cleft into subulate lobes. Cyathia about 1.5 mm., solitary in axils and at forks, on thick pedicels; involucre campanulate, hirsute at throat, lobes triangular, ciliate; glands concave,

transversely oblong, reddish, with a narrower, entire or lobulate appendage. Styles short, 2-lobed. Capsule 3–4 mm., obovoid, deeply 3-sulcate, glabrous, smooth; carpels rounded. Seeds about 2 mm., ovoid, grey, smooth, without caruncle. Fl. May–October.

Hab.: Maritime sands. Coastal Galilee, Acco Plain, Sharon Plain, Philistean Plain. Not rare.

Area: Mediterranean and Euro-Siberian, with extensions towards W. Irano-Turanian territories.

E. parvula Del., Fl. Eg. 91 (1813), recorded by Barbey (Herbor. Levant 154, 1882) from "Ouadi el-Chalah, ad fines meridionales Palaestinae", has not been observed by us. Barbey's specimen is *E. terracina* L. var. *modesta* (Boiss.) Boiss. in DC., Prodr. 15, 2: 158 (1862).

2. Euphorbia granulata Forssk., Fl. Aeg.-Arab. CXII, 94 (1775); Boiss., Fl. 4: 1087 (1879). [Plate 391]

Annual, densely patulous-hairy or glabrescent to glabrous, 10–40 cm. Stems many, arising from base, unequal, prostrate, sparsely branched above, brittle. Leaves 3–6 × 2–4 mm., almost all alike, opposite, petiolate, obovate to elliptical, oblique at base, entire, hairy on both sides or glabrous; stipules minute, lanceolate, ciliate. Inflorescences forming short leafy racemes along the upper parts of the stems. Cyathia minute, axillary, subsessile; involucre turbinate, hirtellous, lobes ovate, fringed; glands transversely oblong, as broad as the white appendage or narrower. Capsule 1.5 mm. in diam., obovoid, deeply 3-sulcate, hirsute throughout or glabrous, with rounded carpels. Seeds oblong-tetragonous, transversely wrinkled-pitted. Fl. February–March.

Var. **granulata**. Stems, leaves and capsule hirsute.

Var. **glabrata** (J. Gay) Boiss. in DC., Prodr. 15, 2: 34 (1862) et Fl., l.c. *E. forskalii* J. Gay [var.] δ *glabrata* J. Gay in Webb et Berth., Phyt. Canar. 3: 243 (1846–1847). Plants glabrous or glabrescent.

Hab. of species: Wadis in hot deserts. Dead Sea area, Arava Valley, Edom. Uncommon.

Area of species: Sudanian, with extensions into E. African and Saharo-Arabian territories.

3. Euphorbia chamaesyce L., Sp. Pl. 455 (1753); Boiss., Fl. 4: 1088 (1879). *E. canescens* L., Sp. Pl. ed. 2, 652 (1762). [Plate 392]

Annual, reddish, hirsute to canescent, 20–50 cm. Stems prostrate, branched from base into many unequal branches. Leaves 3–7 mm., almost all alike, opposite, petiolate, ovate to suborbicular, oblique at base, obtusely dentate to crenulate, rarely entire, usually hairy, rarely glabrescent; stipules setaceous, often with a small tooth at base. Cyathia about 1 mm., solitary or few in axils, pedicellate; involucre turbinate, glabrous or hirsute, ciliate at throat, lobes ovate-triangular, fringed; glands subconcave, wax-coloured, with a 3-dentate to 3-lobed, mostly white appendage (rarely absent). Capsule about 1.5 mm., globular, 3-lobed, hairy all over or with spreading hairs along keels of carpels. Seeds about 1 mm., ovoid-tetragonous, transversely wrinkled. Fl. April–September.

Hab.: Fields, nurseries and waste places. Coastal Galilee, Acco Plain, Sharon Plain,

Philistean Plain, Upper and Lower Galilee, Mt. Carmel, Esdraelon Plain, Mt. Gilboa, Samaria, Judean Mts., Hula Plain, Upper Jordan Valley, Golan. Fairly common.

Area: Mediterranean and W. Irano-Turanian, extending towards S. and C. Euro-Siberian territories.

A very polymorphic species: varies in shape and dentation of leaves, hairiness of leaves and capsule, width of glands, and appendages.

4. Euphorbia forskalii J. Gay in Webb et Berth., Phyt. Canar. 3: 240 (1846–1847) p.p. excl. syn. [*E. thymifolia* Forssk., Fl. Aeg.-Arab. CXII, 94 (1775)] et var. *β, γ, δ*. *E. aegyptiaca* Boiss., Cent. Euph. 13 (1860), in DC., Prodr. 15, 2: 35 (1862) et Fl. 4: 1088 (1879) *subs. illegit.* [Plate 393]

Annual, greyish, appressed- and/or crisp-hairy, 10–20 cm. Stems many, prostrate, branched from base. Branches leafy. Leaves 6–9 mm., almost all alike, opposite, sessile, oblique at base, oblong to elliptical, remotely serrulate-crenate near apex, the teeth muticous or mucronate; stipules small, lanceolate, ciliate; floral leaves similar to cauline leaves. Inflorescences leafy, compound of short glomerules and racemes. Cyathia about 1–1.5 mm., solitary in axils, subsessile; involucre turbinate, velvety-hirsute, glabrous at throat, lobes ovate, fringed; glands reddish, appendage of gland as broad as gland or narrower. Capsule about 1.5–2 mm., globular, 3-lobed, crisp-hairy; carpels keeled. Seeds 1 mm., oblong-tetragonous, whitish, transversely wrinkled. Fl. February–April.

Hab.: Hot deserts. Coastal Negev (fide J. Gay, l.c.), Dead Sea area, Arava Valley. Rare.

Area: Sudanian.

5. Euphorbia prostrata Ait., Hort. Kew. 2: 139 (1789). [Plate 394]

Annual, 5–15 cm., crisp-hairy, rarely almost glabrescent. Stems many, diffusely prostrate, slender. Leaves 0.3–0.8(–1) cm., almost all alike, opposite, short-petioled, broadly elliptical to oblong-elliptical, obtuse, obscurely serrulate near apex, reddish, obsoletely 3-nerved; stipules minute, triangular-subulate, often incised. Inflorescences leafy, compound of axillary short-peduncled clusters. Cyathia about 1 mm. across; involucre obconical, lobes ovate, fringed; glands transversely ovate to oblong, with pink appendage narrower than gland to as broad. Capsule 1–1.5 mm., ovoid, 3-sulcate, patulous-bristly along keels only. Seeds about 1 mm., quadrangular, whitish, transversely wrinkled. Fl. summer.

Hab.: Roadsides, lawns. Philistean Plain, Judean Mts., Dead Sea area. Locally fairly common; adventive.

Area: Origin N. America; widely distributed over many temperate regions.

6. Euphorbia hirta L., Sp. Pl. 454 (1753). *E. pilulifera* L., l.c. p.p.; Hook., Fl. Brit. Ind. 5: 250 (1887). [Plate 395]

Annual, hispid with crisp hairs, 20–40 cm. Stems many, procumbent or ascending. Leaves 1.5–4 × 1–2 cm., almost all alike, opposite, short-petioled, oblong-elliptical to obovate or oblong-lanceolate, oblique at base, acute, toothed or serrulate; stipules 1–2 mm., membranous, lanceolate-subulate, ciliate. Inflorescences capitate, about 1 cm. in diam., axillary, pedunculate, dense, composed of staminate and hermaphrodite cyathia. Cyathia 1–2 mm.; involucre campanulate, lobes subulate-triangular, fringed, pubescent; glands orbicular, with a very narrow or obsolete appendage. Capsule about 2 mm., globular, 3-sulcate, appressed-hirsute; carpels laterally compressed, keeled. Seeds 1 mm., tetragonous, irregularly transversely wrinkled. Fl. July–November.

Hab.: Irrigated fields and nurseries; recently introduced. Sharon Plain, Philistean Plain, Lower Galilee, Mt. Carmel, Esdraelon Plain, Samaria, Dead Sea area, and probably elsewhere. Uncommon.

Area: Sudanian.

7. Euphorbia nutans Lag., Gen. et Sp. Nov. 17 (1816). *E. hypericifolia* sensu Engelm. in Chapm., Fl. S.U.S. 403 (1860) et auct. non L., Sp. Pl. 454 (1753). [Plate 396]

Annual, sparingly hirsute to almost glabrescent, 15–30 cm. Stems erect, forked repeatedly above, slender. Leaves 1.5–3 × 0.6–1.5 cm., almost all alike, opposite, subsessile, ovate-oblong to lanceolate-linear, somewhat oblique at base, obtuse and dentate-serrate above or throughout, often with a reddish spot; stipules triangular, reddish, fringed. Cyathia 1 mm., solitary or in monochasial rays; involucre campanulate, glabrous outside, hairy within, lobes lanceolate; glands white, ovate to orbicular, with an entire or obscurely sinuate appendage. Capsule 2 mm. or less, globular, 3-sulcate; carpels slightly keeled, glabrous. Seeds 1–1.2 mm., tetragonous-ovoid, blackish, transversely wrinkled. Fl. August–September.

Hab.: Nurseries and waste places. Judean Mts. and probably elsewhere. Uncommon.

Area: Pluriregional.

Sect. TITHYMALUS (Scop.) Boiss. in DC., Prodr. 15, 2: 99 (1862); Scop., Fl. Carn. ed. 2, 1: 332 (1771–1772) *pro gen.* Leaves opposite or alternate; stipules absent. Glands of cyathium entire or 2-horned, not appendiculate.

8. Euphorbia densa Schrenk, Bull. Phys.-Math. Acad. Pétersb. 3: 308 (1845); Boiss., Fl. 4: 1091 (1879). [Plate 397]

Annual, glaucescent, glabrous plant, 5–15 cm. Stems dichotomously branched from base; internodes short. Leaves 1–1.4 × 0.5–1 cm., almost all alike, opposite, sessile, obovate to suborbicular, somewhat tapering at base, mucronulate, scabrous at margin. Inflorescences umbellate, very dense. Cyathia about 3 mm., subsessile; involucre somewhat turbinate, lobes oblong, denticulate; glands transversely oblong, horns long, linear, somewhat acute. Capsule about 3 mm., ovoid, 3-sulcate, borne on a thick pedicel; carpels subcarinate. Seeds 1.5–2.2 mm., tetragonous, white, reticulate or pitted; caruncle small, almost globular. Fl. April.

Hab.: Steppes. Edom. Rare.

Area: Irano-Turanian.

9. Euphorbia petiolata Banks et Sol. in Russ., Nat. Hist. Aleppo ed. 2, 2: 253 (1794). *E. petiolata* Banks et Sol. var. *microphylla* (Post) Eig, Journ. Bot. Lond. 75: 192 (1937). *E. lanata* Sieb. ex Spreng., Syst. Veg. 3: 792 (1826); Boiss., Fl. 4: 1092 (1879). [Plate 398]

Annual, patulous-villose to woolly-canescent, 15–40 cm. Stems erect or ascending, branched all along, striate. Leaves 1–3.5 × 0.8–1.5 cm., gradually decreasing in size, all opposite except for the lower ones, petiolate, ovate-oblong to ovate, spinulose-dentate. Inflorescences umbellate-paniculate. Cyathia about 2 mm., short-pedicelled; involucre campanulate, lobes triangular-ovate, fimbriate; glands transversely oblong, cleft into 2–8 setaceous lobes. Capsule about 5–6 mm., ovoid-subglobular, 3-sulcate, white-villose; carpels keeled. Seeds about 4 mm., tetragonous, truncate at both ends, tuberculate, with a stipitate, transversely oblong caruncle. Fl. May–October.

Hab.: Fallow fields on heavy soil; among summer crops and especially in vineyards. Sharon Plain, Philistean Plain, Upper and Lower Galilee, Esdraelon Plain, Samaria, Judean Mts., N. Negev, Hula Plain, Upper and Lower Jordan Valley, Dead Sea area, Gilead, Ammon, Moav. Fairly common.

Area: Mainly E. Mediterranean and W. Irano-Turanian (also in Algeria).

10. Euphorbia dendroides L., Sp. Pl. 462 (1753); Boiss., Fl. 4: 1093 (1879). [Plate 399]

Shrub, glabrous, 0.5–2 m. Stems erect, di- or trichotomously branched. Old branches marked with leaf scars, new branches leafy. Leaves 6–8(–10) × 0.5–1 cm.; cauline and umbellar leaves sessile, linear to lanceolate, tapering at base, obtuse or acute, entire, paler beneath; floral leaves subcordate or semiorbicular, acute, yellowish, exceeding the campanulate involucre, which is up to 5 mm. long. Umbels 2–10-rayed, dichotomously branched. Cyathia pedicellate; involucre lobes oblong, 2–3-fid, fimbriate; glands transversely ovate, first truncate, then slightly semilunate, often hirsute below. Capsule about 5 mm., depressed-globular, deeply 3-lobed with lobes laterally compressed, glabrous, smooth. Seeds 3 mm., ovoid to subglobular, smooth; caruncle sessile, crested. Fl. March–April.

Hab.: Maritime cliffs. Mt. Carmel. Very rare (probably a relic from an earlier, more humid, climate).

Area: N. and W. Mediterranean.

11. Euphorbia retusa Forssk., Fl. Aeg.-Arab. 93 (1775), t. 13 (1776); Botsch., Novit. Syst. Pl. Vasc. 1964: 360 (1964). *E. kahirensis* Raeusch., Nom. ed. 3, 140 (1797) *subs. illegit. E. cornuta* Pers., Syn. Pl. 2: 17 (1806) *subs. illegit.;* Boiss., Fl. 4: 1093 (1879). [Plate 400]

Annual, glaucous, glabrous, 10–35 cm. Stems erect to ascending, branched from base, rather thick, striate. Leaves 1–3(–5) cm., sessile; cauline leaves linear to oblong, rounded or somewhat clasping at base, retuse or acute at apex, more or less acutely serrate; umbellar and floral leaves opposite, cordate and dilated at base (up to 0.8–2 cm. broad), caudate-acuminate and usually recurved at tip, much more serrate than the cauline leaves. Inflorescence a repeatedly forked umbel. Cyathia about 3 mm., pedicellate; involucre campanulate, lobes triangular, fringed; glands somewhat concave, with 2–4 entire or 2-fid horns, rarely glands palmately 6–10-cleft. Capsule 5–6 mm., ovoid, 3-sulcate, smooth; carpels rounded. Seeds about 2.5 mm., smooth, with yellowish caruncle about 1 mm. Fl. February–April.

Hab.: Deserts; mainly on sandy ground. W. and N. Negev, Arava Valley, deserts of Ammon and Edom. Locally fairly common.

Area: Saharo-Arabian.

Contrary to Botschantzev's statement, the name *"retusa"* is mentioned in L., Amoen. Acad. 3, p. 119 (1756) but as var. β of *E. exigua* and not as a specific epithet. In any case, Forsskål only compared his plant with, and did not base it on Linnaeus's variety.

12. Euphorbia isthmia V. Täckh., Svensk Bot. Tidskr. 26: 374 (1932); Dinsmore in Post, Fl. Syr. Pal. Sin. ed. 2, 2: 829 (1933). [Plate 401]

Annual, glabrous, 10–30 cm. Stems erect or ascending, usually dichotomously branched from base or middle, thick, flexuous, striate; internodes long. Leaves almost all alike, 3–5(–7) × 0.4–0.8 cm., sessile, linear to oblong-lanceolate with broader and sometimes cordate base and truncate apex, dentate with scattered sharp teeth especially at base and apex. Inflorescences dichotomously branched. Cyathia about 2 mm., pedicellate; involucre campanulate, lobes rectangular, fimbriate; glands minute, transversely ovate, truncate. Capsule (6–)7–8 mm., ovoid, smooth; carpels rounded. Seeds about 3 mm., ovoid, smooth, with a conical yellowish caruncle 2.5 mm. Fl. March–April.

Hab.: Deserts, especially in sandy wadi beds. W., N. and S. Negev, Edom. Uncommon.

Area: E. Saharo-Arabian.

13. Euphorbia hierosolymitana Boiss. ex Boiss., Diagn. ser. 1, 12: 110 (1853); Boiss., Pl. Syr. Exs. (1846). [Plate 402]

Dwarf shrub, glabrous, 20–50(–100) cm. Roots thick, fusiform. Stems erect, woody at base. Branches simple or intricately ramose, rigid. Leaves (0.5–)1.5 cm., short-petioled, oblong or obovate, tapering at base, obtuse or acute, entire or somewhat repand; umbellar and floral leaves 0.5–1.5 cm., obovate, obtuse. Rays of umbel (1–)3–5, often dichotomously branched. Cyathia 2–3 mm., pedicellate; involucre broadly campanulate, hirsute within, lobes broadly ovate, denticulate; glands transversely elliptical. Capsule about 4 mm., more or less globular, 3-sulcate, covered with conical and cylindrical warts; carpels rounded. Seeds 3 mm., ellipsoidal, yellowish, glossy, smooth, with a globular-depressed caruncle. Fl. January–April.

Var. hierosolymitana. *E. thamnoides* Boiss., Cent. Euph. 33 (1860), in DC., Prodr. 15, 2: 131 (1862) et Fl. 4: 1104 (1879) *subs. illegit. E. thamnoides* Boiss. var. *hierosolymitana* (Boiss. ex Boiss.) Boiss. in DC., Prodr. l.c. et Fl. l.c.; Post, Fl. Syr. Pal. Sin. 720 (1883–1896). *E. thamnoides* Boiss. var. *dumulosa* Post, l.c. Plants 30–50(–100) cm. Leaves 1.5–5 cm., oblong, mucronulate. Umbels 3–5-rayed; rays mostly 2–3-flowered. Pedicels longer than the involucre.

Hab.: Batha and garigue. Philistean Plain, Upper Galilee, Mt. Carmel, Esdraelon Plain, Mt. Gilboa, Samaria, Judean Mts., C. Negev, Golan, Gilead, Ammon, Moav, Edom. Common.

Var. ramanensis (Baum) Zoh. (comb. et stat. nov.). *E. ramanensis* Baum, Bull. Soc. Bot. Fr. 110: 49, f. 2 (1963). Plants lower. Leaves shorter, 0.5–1.2(–2) cm., obtuse.

Umbels 1–3 (–4)-rayed; rays usually 1 (–2–3)-flowered. Pedicels shorter than the involucre.

Hab.: Rocky ground. Judean Desert, N. and C. Negev. Locally common.

Area of species: E. Mediterranean, with slight extensions into adjacent Irano-Turanian territories.

Sometimes a leading species of batha.

While there are obvious differences between var. *hierosolymitana* and var. *ramanensis*, there are no diagnostic differences between *E. hierosolymitana* and what has been referred to by Boissier in DC., Prodr. l.c. as the typical variety of *E. thamnoides*. The difference in the leaf shape recorded by Boissier is not constant and the two forms of leaves mentioned by Boissier (Fl., l.c.) occur even in the same specimen.

14. Euphorbia verrucosa L., Sp. Pl. 459 (1753); M. S. Khan, Not. Roy. Bot. Gard. Edinb. 25:103 (1964). *E. pubescens* Vahl, Symb. Bot. 2:55 (1791); Boiss., Fl. 4:1106 (1879). [Plate 403]

Perennial, villose, 30–70 cm. Stems erect or ascending, terete, woody below, slightly grooved. Cauline and umbellar leaves 2–4 cm., sessile, oblong or oblong-lanceolate to linear, subcordate at base, acute or acuminate, serrulate, villose; floral leaves about 1 cm., ovate-rhombic, subcordate at base, mucronulate. Rays of umbel about 5, the primary rays trichotomously, the secondary rays dichotomously branched. Cyathia about 3 mm.; involucre campanulate, hirsute, lobes ovate, truncate, ciliate; glands broadly elliptical, ciliate at margin. Capsule 3.5–4 mm., globular, 3-sulcate, covered with short, cylindrical warts interspersed with long, soft hairs. Seeds about 2 mm., ovoid, somewhat tuberculate, with a small, transversely ovoid caruncle. Fl. June–October.

Hab.: Swamps and river banks. Sharon Plain, Dan Valley, Hula Plain. Rare.

Area: Mediterranean, with extensions into the adjacent Euro-Siberian territories.

15. Euphorbia helioscopia L., Sp. Pl. 459 (1753); Boiss., Fl. 4:1107 (1879). [Plate 404]

Annual, glaucous, glabrous or sparsely hairy, 10–40 cm. Stems erect or ascending, simple or branched from base, thick. Cauline leaves 2–4 cm., caducous, spatulate, tapering at base, obtuse at apex, serrulate, glabrous; umbellar and floral leaves often larger, obovate to orbicular. Umbels usually 5-rayed; rays di- or trichotomously branched. Cyathia about 2 mm., pedicellate; involucre lobes fringed; glands transversely ovate, entire. Capsule 3 mm., globular, 3-sulcate, glabrous; carpels rounded. Seeds 1.5–2 mm., ovoid, brown, foveolate-reticulate, with sessile ovoid caruncle. Fl. January–May.

Hab.: Roadsides and fields. Acco Plain, Sharon Plain, Philistean Plain, Upper and Lower Galilee, Mt. Carmel, Esdraelon Plain, Samaria, Shefela, Judean Mts., Judean Desert, Dan Valley, Hula Plain, Upper and Lower Jordan Valley, Golan, Gilead, Ammon, Moav, Edom. Very common.

Area: Euro-Siberian and Mediterranean, extending into the Irano-Turanian and Sudanian regions; elsewhere widely introduced.

Formerly medicinal: purgative and antihelminthic (radix et folia euphorbiae helioscopiae).

16. Euphorbia berythea Boiss. et Bl. in Boiss., Diagn. ser. 2, 4: 82 (1859) et Fl. 4: 1107 (1879). [Plate 405]

Annual, patulous-hairy, 10–30 cm. Stems single or few, erect, branched from base. Leaves 1–3 cm., denticulate; cauline and umbellar leaves spatulate or obovate, tapering at base into petiole, acute, mucronate; floral leaves sessile, triangular-ovate, apiculate. Rays of umbel 3–5, di- or trichotomously branched, villose. Cyathia about 2 mm., pedicellate; involucre turbinate, hirsute within, lobes broad, truncate, ciliate; glands transversely ovate, truncate. Capsule 3–4 mm., depressed-globular, deeply 3-sulcate, villose; carpels keeled. Seeds about 2 mm., globular, brown, finely reticulate-tuberculate with confluent tubercles; caruncle small, globular-conical. Fl. April–May.

Hab.: Batha and fields. Sharon Plain, Upper Galilee, Mt. Carmel, Esdraelon Plain, Mt. Gilboa, Shefela. Uncommon.

Area: E. Mediterranean.

17. Euphorbia oxyodonta Boiss. et Hausskn. ex Boiss. in DC., Prodr. 15, 2: 1267 (1866); Boiss., Fl. 4: 1108 (1879). [Plate 406]

Annual, sparingly villose, 20–50 cm. Stems erect, simple or branched from base. Branches erect or procumbent. Cauline and umbellar leaves 1.5–5 × 1–1.5 cm., deeply pectinate-dentate; lower leaves spatulate to ovate-spatulate, tapering into petiole, usually acute, upper leaves sessile, elliptical; floral leaves 0.5–1.5 cm., ovate-triangular, acute. Inflorescences umbellate with 3–6 dichotomously branched rays. Cyathia about 2 mm., pedicellate; involucre turbinate, glabrous, lobes broad, ciliate; glands transversely ovate. Capsule 3–4 mm., broadly ovoid, deeply 3-sulcate, somewhat truncate at apex, glabrous. Seeds about 2 mm., ovoid, irregularly and prominently reticulate-wrinkled, with a small white caruncle. Fl. February–May.

Hab.: Batha, fields and roadsides. Sharon Plain, Philistean Plain, Upper and Lower Galilee, Mt. Carmel, Esdraelon Plain, Samaria, Judean Mts., Judean Desert, W. Negev, Hula Plain, Upper Jordan Valley, Beit Shean Valley, Lower Jordan Valley, Dead Sea area, Golan, Gilead, Ammon, Moav, Edom. Fairly common.

Area: E. Mediterranean, with extensions towards W. Irano-Turanian territories.

18. Euphorbia phymatosperma Boiss. et Gaill. in Boiss., Diagn. ser. 2, 4: 83 (1859) et Fl. 4: 1109 (1879). [Plate 407]

Annual, glaucous, glabrous, 5–15 cm. Stems erect, usually simple. Cauline leaves 0.5–2 cm., subsessile, obovate to elliptical, obtuse, apiculate, entire; umbellar leaves somewhat longer than the others, ovate to elliptical; floral leaves ovate-rhombic, mucronate. Rays of umbel 3, short, forked. Cyathia about 1 mm., pedicellate; involucre campanulate, lobes broadly ovate, obtuse; glands transversely oblong. Capsule 3–4 mm., ovoid, 3-sulcate; carpels rounded, glabrous. Seeds 2.5–3 × 2 mm., oblong-tetragonous, with 3 transverse furrows and scurfy dots between the furrows; caruncle shortly stipitate, depressed, white. Fl. March–April.

Hab.: Fields. Judean Mts., Gilead. Rare.

Area: W. Irano-Turanian.

19. Euphorbia arguta Banks et Sol. in Russ., Nat. Hist. Aleppo ed. 2, 2 : 253 (1794). [Plate 408]

Annual, glaucous, densely or sparingly villose, 20–60 cm. Stems erect, simple or branched from base, striate. Cauline and umbellar leaves 2–6 (–8) cm., sessile, lanceolate to oblong, sometimes spatulate, coarsely serrate all around; lower leaves petiolate, obtuse; upper leaves sessile, acute; floral leaves smaller, rhombic-ovate, mostly apiculate. Umbels 3–5-rayed; rays di- to trichotomously branched. Cyathia about 1 mm.; involucre turbinate, glabrous, lobes shortly ovate, fringed-dentate; glands transversely oblong. Capsule 3–4 mm., depressed-globular, 3-sulcate, glabrous or hirsute; carpels rounded, slightly grooved at back. Seeds 1.5 mm., globular-ellipsoidal, usually smooth; caruncle depressed-globular. Fl. March–June.

Var. **arguta**. *E. arguta* Banks et Sol., l.c.; Boiss., Fl. 4 : 1097 (1879); Eig, Journ. Bot. Lond. 75 : 188 (1937). Capsule glabrous.

Hab.: Fields; heavy or swampy soil. Acco Plain, Sharon Plain, Philistean Plain, Upper and Lower Galilee, Mt. Carmel, Esdraelon Plain, Samaria, Shefela, Judean Mts., Hula Plain, Upper Jordan Valley, Beit Shean Valley, Lower Jordan Valley, Golan, Gilead, Moav. Fairly common.

Var. **dasycarpa** Plitm.* Capsule hirsute.

Hab.: As above. Sharon Plain, Philistean Plain, Lower Galilee, Mt. Carmel, Lower Jordan Valley. Rare.

Area of species : E. Mediterranean.

20. Euphorbia gaillardotii Boiss. et Bl. in Boiss., Diagn. ser. 2, 4 : 84 (1859) et Fl. 4 : 1097 (1879); Blakelock, Kew Bull. 1950 : 453 (1951). [Plate 409]

Annual, glabrous, 30–50 cm. Stems single, erect, profusely branched below the main 5- or more-rayed umbel, glaucescent-whitish, grooved. Branches and rays of umbel forked repeatedly, each fork subtended by a pair of leaves. Cauline leaves elliptical-lanceolate, tapering at base to petiole, acute, mostly serrulate, deflexing and caducous; upper and floral leaves 0.8–2 cm., as long as or shorter than broad, ovate-triangular to orbicular, subcordate, mucronate. Cyathia 1–1.5 mm., pedicellate; involucre turbinate, hairy at throat, lobes ovate, fringed; glands transversely ovate-triangular. Capsule 1.5–2 mm., ovoid, deeply 3-sulcate, smooth, glabrous; carpels rounded. Seeds 1 mm., almost ovoid, brown, smooth, opaque; caruncle small. Fl. summer.

Hab.: Fields; among summer crops. "Transjordan, Birkat Dân, Sept. 1875, Post 37" fide Blakelock, l.c. Very rare.

Area : E. Mediterranean (Turkey, Syria, Palestine).

According to Blakelock, l.c., the specimen Ky. 398 cited by Boissier does not belong to *E. gaillardotii*.

21. Euphorbia microsphaera Boiss. ex Boiss., Diagn. ser. 1, 7 : 87 (1846) et Fl. 4 : 1098 (1879); Boiss. in Ky., Pl. Pers. Austr. Exs. no. 448 (1845); M. S. Khan, Not. Roy.

---

* See Appendix at end of this volume.

Bot. Gard. Edinb. 25 : 108 (1964). *E. unilateralis* Blakelock, Kew Bull. 1950 : 453 (1951). [Plate 410]

Annual, glabrous, 30–60 cm. Stems erect, branched from base or above, brownish. Leaves more or less serrulate; cauline and umbellar leaves about 3–7 cm., caducous, nearly sessile, oblong-lanceolate, tapering at base, acute at apex; floral leaves 1–2 cm., longer than broad, ovate to suborbicular or deltoid, obtuse or mucronate. Umbels 5-rayed; rays repeatedly forked, one ray of the ultimate fork usually lacking. Cyathia about 3 mm., pedicellate; involucre turbinate, hairy at throat, whitish, lobes ovate, fringed; glands transversely elliptical. Stigmas almost sessile. Capsule 1–2(–3) mm., globular, not sulcate, glabrous, hairy when young; carpels ovoid, rounded. Seeds about 2 mm., ovoid, brown, smooth; caruncle minute. Fl. June–July.

Hab. : Fields. Acco Plain, Sharon Plain, Dan Valley, Hula Plain. Rare.

Area : W. Irano-Turanian.

The specimen, recorded by Oppenheimer (Bull. Soc. Bot. Genève ser. 2, 22 : 341, 1931) from the Hula Plain (Herb. Aaronsohn no. 5751) as *E. gaillardotii* Boiss. et Bl., should be referred to this species.

22. Euphorbia cybirensis Boiss., Diagn ser. 1, 7 : 89 (1846); Boiss., Fl. 4 : 1098 (1879) excl. var. δ. [Plate 411]

Annual, glabrous, 25–50(–80) cm. Stems erect, simple or branched. Leaves 1–4 cm., sessile to somewhat clasping; cauline and umbellar leaves obovate-spatulate to elliptical, acute, sometimes obtuse, serrulate towards apex or rarely entire; floral leaves almost orbicular or triangular-deltoid, obtuse, apiculate or mucronate. Rays of umbel 5, elongated, usually forked once or twice. Cyathia about 3 mm., pedicellate; involucre campanulate, glabrous or hairy, lobes ovate, dentate; glands transversely ovate. Stigmas borne on a very long style. Capsule 2–3 mm., scarcely dehiscent, globular, not 3-sulcate, beset with conical tubercles ending in bristles. Seeds 1–2 mm., compressed, ovoid, brown, smooth; caruncle sessile, disk-shaped. Fl. March–July.

Hab. : A common weed among winter crops and in fallow fields; mainly on heavy soil. Acco Plain, Sharon Plain, Philistean Plain, Upper and Lower Galilee, Mt. Carmel, Esdraelon Plain, Samaria, Shefela, Judean Mts., Dan Valley, Hula Plain, Upper Jordan Valley, Golan, Ammon.

Area : E. Mediterranean, with extensions into W. Irano-Turanian territories.

Rather polymorphic; varies in shape of leaf apex (e.g. var. *acuta* Post, Fl. Syr. Pal. Sin. 720, 1883–1896, err. "var. *acuta* Boiss."), in size of capsule and seeds (e.g. var. *microcarpa* Boiss. in DC., Prodr. 15, 2 : 119, 1862) and also in the density of tubercles on the capsule.

23. Euphorbia aleppica L., Sp. Pl. 458 (1753); Boiss., Fl. 4 : 1109 (1879). [Plate 412]

Annual, glabrous or somewhat pruinose-scabrous, 10–40 cm. Stems usually single and erect or few and ascending, branched above. Leaves sessile, entire; lower cauline leaves 1–2 × 0.1–0.2 cm., caducous, linear to needle-shaped; umbellar leaves 0.5–2 × 0.8–1.5 cm., oblanceolate to oblong and ovate; floral leaves ovate-rhombic to triangular or orbicular, apiculate-mucronate. Rays of umbel 3–7, forked repeatedly. Cyathia about 1 mm.; involucre turbinate-campanulate, lobes small, oblong, fringed;

glands semilunate or 2-horned. Capsule 2–3 mm., depressed-globular, 3-sulcate; carpels keeled. Seeds 1–1.5 mm., white, tuberculate. Fl. May–October.

Hab.: Fields; a conspicuous weed among summer crops. Coastal Galilee, Sharon Plain, Philistean Plain, Upper and Lower Galilee, Mt. Carmel, Esdraelon Plain, Samaria, Judean Mts., Judean Desert, Dan Valley, Hula Plain, Upper Jordan Valley, Golan, Gilead, Moav. Fairly common.

Area: E. Mediterranean and W. Irano-Turanian.

A biseasonal annual, in winter resembling a pine seedling.

24. Euphorbia exigua L., Sp. Pl. 456 (1753); Boiss., Fl. 4:1110 (1879). [Plate 413]

Annual, glaucous, glabrous, 3–15(–20) cm. Stems erect or ascending, branched from base, rarely simple, sulcate, leafy. Leaves (0.4–)0.8–1.5(–2) cm.; cauline leaves linear to oblong-linear, acute, obtuse, truncate or retuse at apex; umbellar leaves triangular-lanceolate; floral leaves dilated and somewhat subcordate at base. Rays of umbel 3–5, forked repeatedly. Cyathia about 1 mm., pedicellate; involucre turbinate, hirtellous at throat, lobes ovate, dentate; glands transversely ovate, with dark brown horns usually longer than the width of the gland. Capsule 1–2 mm., ovoid, 3-sulcate, smooth. Seeds about 1 mm., ovoid-tetragonous, grey, irregularly covered with transverse white tubercles; caruncle depressed. Fl. January–April.

Var. **exigua**. *E. exigua* L. var. *acuta* L., l.c. Cauline leaves acute.

Hab.: Fallow fields and batha. Coastal Galilee, Sharon Plain, Philistean Plain, Upper and Lower Galilee, Mt. Carmel, Esdraelon Plain, Samaria, Shefela, Judean Mts., N. Negev, Upper Jordan Valley. Uncommon.

Var. **retusa** L., l.c.; "var. *retusa* Roth" Boiss., l.c. Cauline leaves obtuse, truncate to retuse. Scarcely a variety.

Hab.: As above. Sharon Plain, Philistean Plain, Upper and Lower Galilee, Mt. Carmel, Mt. Gilboa, Shefela, Upper Jordan Valley. Fairly common.

Area of species: Mediterranean and Euro-Siberian.

25. Euphorbia falcata L., Sp. Pl. 456 (1753); Boiss., Fl. 4:1111 (1879). [Plate 414]

Annual, glabrous or glabrescent, 8–25(–30) cm. Stems many, erect to ascending, simple or branched. Branches forked several times. Leaves alternate, sessile, entire or scabridulous at margin; lower leaves 1–1.5(–2) cm., frequently caducous, spatulate to oblong or lanceolate, tapering at base, usually obtuse or retuse; umbellar and floral leaves 0.3–1(–1.5) cm., ovate to elliptical-ovate, acuminate-mucronulate. Inflorescences umbellate-corymbose; rays 3–5, forked repeatedly. Cyathia about 1 mm., pedicellate; involucre turbinate, lobes ovate, fringed; glands longer than broad, horns long or sometimes short or 0. Capsule (1–)1.5–2.5 mm., ovoid, 3-sulcate; carpels keeled. Seeds about 1 mm., compressed, with 1 row of 4–6 transverse furrows or pits on each of the 4 faces. Fl. March–August.

1. Glands almost without horns. var. **ecornuta**
– Glands with horns much longer than the width of the gland proper 2
2. Floral leaves 0.5–1.5 cm. Furrows of seed elongated, as long as the width of the face of seed. var. **falcata**

– Floral leaves up to 0.5 cm. Furrows of seed reduced to pits.   var. **galilaea**

Var. falcata. Floral leaves 0.5–1.5 cm. Glands with distinct horns. Furrows of seed distinct.

Hab.: Fields; on heavy soil in winter and summer crops. Philistean Plain, Upper and Lower Galilee, Mt. Carmel, Esdraelon Plain, Shefela, Judean Mts., N. Negev, Hula Plain, Gilead, Moav.

Var. galilaea (Boiss.) Boiss. in DC., Prodr. 15, 2 : 140 (1862); Boiss., Fl. l.c. *E. galilaea* Boiss., Diagn. ser. 1, 12 : 116 (1853). Floral leaves smaller, up to 5 mm. Capsule up to 1.5 mm. Furrows of seed reduced to pits.

Hab.: As above. Philistean Plain, Upper Galilee, Mt. Carmel, W. Negev.

Var. ecornuta Boiss., Fl. l.c. [Plate 414]. Horns of gland short or absent.

Hab.: As above. Acco Plain, Sharon Plain, Philistean Plain, Upper Galilee, Mt. Carmel, Esdraelon Plain, Samaria, Shefela, Judean Mts., N. Negev, Upper Jordan Valley, Golan, Ammon, Moav, Edom. Fairly common, more so than the other varieties.

Area of species: Mediterranean and W. Irano-Turanian, with extensions into W. Euro-Siberian territories.

26. Euphorbia aulacosperma Boiss., Diagn. ser. 1, 12 : 117 (1853) et Fl. 4 : 1111 (1879). *E. aulacosperma* Boiss. var. *fossulata* (Boiss. et Gaill.) Boiss. in DC., Prodr. 15, 2 : 141 (1862); Boiss., Fl. l.c. [Plate 415]

Annual, glabrous, 5–15 cm. Stems erect to ascending, simple or branched from base, striate. Leaves 0.8–1.5 cm., alternate below, opposite above, obtuse, somewhat apiculate, entire or obsoletely denticulate; lower leaves obovate-cuneate to spatulate; floral leaves triangular-rhombic, mostly broader than long, oblique. Rays of umbel 2–3, simple or forked. Cyathia about 1 mm., pedicellate; involucre turbinate, lobes ovate, truncate, hirsute within; glands subovate, 2-horned, horns 2–3 times as long as the width of the gland. Capsule about 1.5 mm., depressed-ovoid, deeply 3-sulcate; carpels rounded at back. Seeds 1 mm., short-cylindrical, truncate, very finely tuberculate, with 6 dark longitudinal furrows and a depressed caruncle. Fl. January–May.

Hab.: Fields; among crops. Sharon Plain, Upper and Lower Galilee, Mt. Carmel, Esdraelon Plain, Mt. Gilboa, Samaria, Shefela, Judean Mts., Judean Desert, Upper Jordan Valley, Dead Sea area, Gilead, Ammon, Moav, Edom. Uncommon.

Area: E. Mediterranean (Palestine–Turkey).

27. Euphorbia peplus L., Sp. Pl. 456 (1753); Boiss., Fl. 4 : 1112 (1879). [Plate 416]

Annual, glabrous, 10–30(–50) cm. Stems erect, rarely prostrate, simple or mostly branched. Leaves (0.3–)0.6–2(–3) × (0.3–)0.4–1 cm.; lower leaves petiolate, obovate, tapering at base, obtuse or retuse, entire; umbellar leaves larger, subsessile; floral leaves broadly ovate. Rays of umbel 3, forked repeatedly. Cyathia 1–1.5 mm., pedicellate; involucre turbinate, lobes ovate, fimbriate; glands lunate, with slender horns much longer than the width of the gland. Capsule about 2 mm., short-ovoid, 3-sulcate, smooth or slightly rough at back; carpels with 2 wing-like keels at back. Seeds about 1.5 mm., ovoid-hexagonous, white-grey, with 2 longitudinal furrows and 4 rows of round or elongated pits; caruncle depressed-conical. $2n = 16$. Fl. December–May.

Hab.: Waste places, roadsides, nurseries and fields. Coastal Galilee, Acco Plain, Sharon Plain, Philistean Plain, Upper and Lower Galilee, Mt. Carmel, Esdraelon Plain, Samaria, Shefela, Judean Mts., Judean Desert, C. Negev, Dan Valley, Hula Plain, Upper and Lower Jordan Valley, Dead Sea area, Golan, Gilead, Ammon, Moav, Edom. Very common.

Area: Euro-Siberian, Mediterranean and Irano-Turanian; elsewhere introduced.

This species has been subdivided by some authors into two varieties: the typical variety and var. *minima* DC. in Lam. et DC., Fl. Fr. ed. 3, 3 : 331 (1805) [= *E. peplus* L. var. *β* Willd., Sp. Pl. 2 : 903 (1800; "*β Peplis minor*") = *E. peplus* L. var. *peploides* (Gouan emend. DC.) Vis., Fl. Dalm. 3 : 229 (1850–1852) = *E. peploides* Gouan, Fl. Monsp. 174 (1764); Boiss., l.c.]. The latter is distinguished from the typical form by its dichotomously branched umbel, smaller seeds with fewer pits and suborbicular leaves. As there are intergrading forms between the two taxa, it is practically impossible to delimitate them.

28. Euphorbia chamaepeplus Boiss. et Gaill. in Boiss., Diagn. ser. 2, 4 : 88 (1859) et Fl. 4 : 1113 (1879). [Plate 417]

Annual, glabrous, 5–15 cm. Stems erect, branched from base, rarely simple, grooved. Leaves 3–7(–9) mm., almost all alike, sessile or short-petioled, ovate or elliptical, sometimes oblong, acute, apiculate. Umbels 2–3-rayed; rays simple, rarely forked. Cyathia 0.5–1 mm., pedicellate; involucre almost turbinate, lobes fringed; glands 2-horned, horns slender, much longer than the width of the gland. Capsule about 2 mm., ovoid, deeply 3-sulcate; carpels keeled, not 2-winged. Seeds 1.5 mm., cylindrical-hexagonous, with 2 longitudinal furrows and 4 rows of transverse, regularly or irregularly scattered pits or furrows; caruncle depressed-conical. Fl. February–March.

Var. **chamaepeplus.** Seeds cylindrical or hexagonous, white; pits more or less regularly arranged.

Hab.: Batha, steppes and deserts. Coastal Galilee, Sharon Plain, Philistean Plain, Esdraelon Plain, Samaria, Judean Mts., Judean Desert, N., C. and S. Negev, Upper and Lower Jordan Valley, Dead Sea area, Arava Valley, Gilead, Ammon, Moav, Edom. Not rare.

Var. **sinaica** Hochst. ex Boiss. in DC., Prodr. 15, 2 : 142 (1862); Boiss., Fl. l.c. *E. sinaica* Hochst., in Sched. Pl. Schimp. ed. 2. Seeds obscurely hexagonous; pits irregularly scattered.

Hab.: Steppes. Judean Desert, Coastal Negev, Lower Jordan Valley. Not rare.

Area of species: Irano-Turanian and Saharo-Arabian.

29. Euphorbia reuteriana Boiss., Diagn. ser. 1, 12 : 115 (1853) et Fl. 4 : 1115 (1879). [Plate 418]

Annual, glaucous, glabrous, 10–30(–40) cm. Stems erect, simple or poorly branched. Leaves 1–2.5(–4) cm., sessile, entire, rarely repand; lower cauline leaves minute, obcordate, the rest linear, retuse or retuse-mucronulate; uppermost and umbellar leaves linear to oblong, acute; floral leaves 0.5–1.5 cm., often broader than long, short-cuneate to reniform at base, broadly triangular or rhombic, obtuse, mucronulate. Rays of umbel (2–)3–5, forked repeatedly. Cyathia about 2 mm., pedicellate; involucre campanulate, lobes ovate, fimbriate; glands horned, 2–4 times as long as the width of the gland. Capsule 3–4 mm., ovoid, deeply 3-sulcate; carpels rounded, smooth. Seeds about 2 mm., ovoid, deeply pitted, with short-conical caruncle. Fl. February–June.

Hab.: Fields and batha. Philistean Plain, Upper and Lower Galilee, Mt. Carmel, Esdraelon Plain, Mt. Gilboa, Samaria, Judean Mts., Upper Jordan Valley, Gilead. Uncommon.

Area: E. Mediterranean.

30. Euphorbia cheiradenia Boiss. et Hohen. in Boiss., Diagn. ser. 1, 12 : 112 (1853) et Fl. 4 : 1119 (1879). [Plate 419]

Perennial, glaucescent, glabrous, woody at base, 20–40 cm. Stems erect or ascending, simple, some of them fertile, the rest sterile. Leaves 1–2.5 × 0.3–1 cm., sessile; cauline leaves oblong-oblanceolate to elliptical-lanceolate, obtuse or acute, apiculate, entire, glabrous; umbellar and floral leaves somewhat leathery, ovate to almost orbicular, apiculate or mucronate, denticulate towards apex. Umbels 4–5-rayed; rays short, sometimes forked. Cyathia 2 mm.; involucre campanulate, lobes triangular-ovate, ciliate; glands transversely ovate, short-horned, horns sometimes with accessory dentate appendages and becoming 2-fid at tip. Capsule 4–6 mm., ovoid, 3-lobed; carpels rounded. Seeds obsoletely tetragonous, ovoid, white, pitted; caruncle 1 mm., conical. Fl. April.

Hab.: Steppes. Ammon, Edom. Very rare.

Area: W. Irano-Turanian.

Despite the record by Rechinger f. (Ark. Bot. ser. 2, 2, 5 : 382, 1952) on the occurrence of *E. chesneyi* (Klotsch et Garcke) Boiss. in DC., Prodr. 15, 2 : 152 (1862) in Azraq, all the specimens collected by us in the Transjordan are typical *E. cheiradenia*.

31. Euphorbia terracina L., Sp. Pl. ed. 2, 654 (1762; typ. err. *"serracina"*); Boiss., Fl. 4 : 1123 (1879). [Plate 420]

Perennial (flowering also in the first year), glabrous, 20–80 cm. Stems erect or ascending, sometimes prostrate, branched from base and middle, woody at base. Leaves (1–)2–6 cm.; lower cauline leaves oblong to linear-lanceolate or oblong-linear, mostly obtuse, often truncate-retuse, mucronulate, upper cauline leaves acute, all entire or finely serrulate near apex; umbellar leaves 1.5–3 cm., deflexed, oblong-elliptical; floral leaves shorter, ovate-triangular to semiorbicular. Rays of umbel 3–5, forked repeatedly. Cyathia about 2 mm., pedicellate; involucre campanulate, lobes ovate, fimbriate; glands 2-horned, horns longer than the width of the gland. Capsule 3–4 mm., depressed-globular, 3-sulcate, smooth; carpels keeled. Seeds about 2 mm., smooth; caruncle ovoid, carinate, somewhat beaked, white. Fl. March–August.

Var. **terracina.** Plants erect or ascending.

Hab.: Rocks and batha; near coast. Coastal Galilee, Acco Plain, Sharon Plain, Philistean Plain, Judean Mts., N. Negev. Not rare.

Var. **modesta** (Boiss.) Boiss. in DC., Prodr. 15, 2 : 158 (1862). *E. modesta* Boiss., Cent. Euph. 34 (1860). *E. terracina* L. var. *prostrata* Boiss., Fl. l.c. *subs. illegit.* Plants prostrate.

Hab.: Sandy soil. Judean Mts., N. Negev. Rare.
Area of species: Mediterranean.

32. Euphorbia macroclada Boiss., Diagn. ser. 1, 5 : 54 (1844). *E. macroclada* Boiss. var. *schizoceras* (Boiss. et Hohen.) Dinsmore in Post, Fl. Syr. Pal. Sin. ed. 2, 2 : 504 (1933). *E. tinctoria* Boiss. et Huet ex Boiss. in DC., Prodr. 15, 2 : 166 (1862); Boiss., Fl. 4 : 1129 (1879). *E. tinctoria* Boiss. et Huet ex Boiss. var. *schizoceras* (Boiss. et Hohen.) Boiss. in DC., l.c. et Fl., l.c. 1130. [Plate 421]

Perennial, glabrous to yellowish-pruinose, 20–40(–50) cm., with creeping rhizomes. Stems many, branched from base, short, thick, whitish, sulcate, some of them sterile. Leaves 2.5–8(–10) cm., sessile, leathery; cauline leaves lanceolate, tapering at base, acute-mucronate, entire, with prominent nerves on lower surface; umbellar leaves about 1–2 cm., ovate to oblong, acute; floral leaves 0.7–1.2 cm., rhombic-deltoid, mucronate. Rays of umbel 5–9, forked. Cyathia about 3–4 mm.; involucre campanulate, lobes ovate, truncate, fringed; glands transversely oblong, entire or lobed, usually with 2 simple or 2-fid horns shorter than the width of the gland. Capsule about 5–7 mm., ovoid, obsoletely grooved, glabrous; carpels keeled. Seeds about 3 mm., oblong, smooth. Fl. April–August.

Hab.: Steppes; on rocky ground. Gilead (fide Dinsmore in Post, l.c.), Ammon, Edom. Rare.
Area: Irano-Turanian.

33. Euphorbia paralias L., Sp. Pl. 458 (1753); Boiss., Fl. 4 : 1130 (1879). [Plate 422]

Half-shrub, glaucous, glabrous, 30–50 cm. Roots vertical. Stems many, erect, stiff and leafy, fertile and sterile. Leaves 1–2(–3) × 0.2–0.4 cm., dense, often imbricated, sessile, very thick and fleshy, elliptical to oblong, somewhat concave, with broad or almost cordate base, obtuse or acute at apex, entire; lower leaves sometimes opposite or whorled; umbellar and floral leaves 0.6–1.2 cm., ovate, cordate at base, mucronulate. Rays of umbel 3–5, short, thick, simple or forked. Cyathia about 3 mm., pedicellate; involucre campanulate, hairy at throat, lobes oblong, ciliate; glands transversely oblong, lunate, entire or dentate, with 2 short divaricate horns. Capsule about 4 × 6 mm., depressed-globular, 3-lobed, finely granular-wrinkled; carpels rounded. Seeds 3 mm., ovoid-globular, greyish with darker spots, smooth, with a very small reniform caruncle. Fl. April–August.

Hab.: Maritime sands. Coastal Galilee, Acco Plain, Sharon Plain, Philistean Plain, Coastal Negev. Locally common.
Area: Mediterranean, with extensions into adjacent area of the Euro-Siberian region.

Sect. POINSETTIA (R. Grah.) Boiss. in DC., Prodr. 15, 2 : 10, 71 (1862). Gen. *Poinsettia* R. Grah., Edinb. New Phil. Journ. 20 : 412 (1836). Leaves (in ours) with small stipular glands. Involucres often surrounded by coloured floral leaves; glands without appendage, cup- or funnel-shaped (in ours).

34. Euphorbia geniculata Ortega, Hort. Matrit. Dec. 18 (1797). *E. prunifolia* Jacq., Hort. Schoenbr. 3 : 15, t. 277 (1798) emend. Müll. in Mart., Fl. Brasil. 11, 2 : 694 (1873–1874) excl. var. *α*. [Plate 423]

Annual, sparingly hairy to glabrous, 40–60 cm. Stems erect, dichotomously branched, grooved. Leaves 3–8 × 1.5–3 cm., almost all alike, upper leaves opposite; stipules glanduliform; blade oblong to elliptical, tapering at base, denticulate. Inflorescences umbellate, of 2–3 dichotomously branched rays. Cyathia about 3 mm., pedicellate; involucre cylindrical-obovoid, glabrous, lobes ovate, incised or fringed; glands stipitate, cup- or funnel-shaped. Capsule 3 mm., globular, 3-sulcate, glabrous; carpels slightly keeled at back. Seeds 1.5–2 mm., trigonous, tuberculate. Fl. July-December.

Hab.: Irrigated fields. Sharon Plain, Philistean Plain, Judean Mts., Lower Jordan Valley; adventive. Uncommon.

Area: Origin Trop. America.

Callitrichales *

61. CALLITRICHACEAE

Annual or perennial, slender, aquatic or swamp plants. Stems often much branched and rooting from nodes. Leaves small and narrow, opposite, partly rosulate, exstipulate, simple, entire, glabrous or stellately hairy, 1–3- or more-nerved. Flowers mostly unisexual (plants monoecious), minute, solitary or serially superposed in leaf axils, mostly with 2 falcate bracteoles. Perianth 0. Staminate flowers of 1 stamen with a long filament and a 4-celled anther. Pistillate flowers of a 2-carpelled ovary, falsely partitioned into 4 cells, each with 1 anatropous ovule; styles or stigmas 2. Fruit somewhat compressed laterally; carpels at first united, later separating into 4 drupaceous mericarps, broad-margined or winged. Seeds solitary, with a thin coat, an oleiferous endosperm and a somewhat curved embryo.

One genus with 44 (or 25) species represented in most regions of the globe.

1. CALLITRICHE L.

See description of family.

Literature: G. Samuelsson, Die *Callitriche*-Arten der Schweiz, *Veröfftl. Geobot. Inst. Rübel Zürich* 3 (Festschrift Carl Schröter) : 603–628 (1925). H. D. Schotsman, Les Callitriches, etc., in : P. Jovet, *Flore de France* 1 : 1–152, pls. I–XX & A–F, Paris, 1967.

1. Leaves lanceolate-subulate, broadest at base. Carpels broadly winged.
   3. C. hermaphroditica
 – Leaves oblong-linear to spatulate, long-tapering at base. Carpels narrowly winged   2
2. Fruit sessile.   **2. C. verna**
 – Fruit on 0.5–1 cm. long pedicel.   **1. C. pedunculata**

* The systematic position of this order is strongly disputed in the literature. Recently, some authors have, for embryological reasons, placed the Callitrichaceae within the Sympetalae, close to the Verbenaceae.

1. Callitriche pedunculata DC. in Lam. et DC., Fl. Fr. ed. 3, 4 : 415 (1805); Boiss., Fl. 2 : 756 (1872). *C. naftolskyi* Warb. et Eig, Repert. Sp. Nov. 26 : 84 (1929). [Plate 424]

Tiny perennial, glabrous, light green, up to 20 cm. Lower leaves linear, varying in length, usually 0.8–1.5 cm., upper leaves oblong (rarely obovate), tapering at base, rounded at apex, 1–3-nerved. Pedicels 0.5–1 cm. Fruit about 2 mm., subglobular, with narrowly winged carpels, often maturing underground; styles shorter than the fruit, caducous. Fl. summer.

Hab.: Puddles, small depressions inundated in winter. Sharon Plain, Upper Galilee. Rare.

Area: Euro-Siberian and Mediterranean.

According to Schotsman in P. Jovet, Fl. Fr. 1 : 84 (1967), *C. pedunculata* is only a terrestrial form of *C. brutia* Pet., Inst. Bot. 2 : 9 (1787).

2. Callitriche verna L., Fl. Suec. ed. 2, 2 (1755) emend. Lönnr., Obs. Crit. Fl. Suec. 19 (1854). [Plate 425]

Tiny aquatic up to 10 cm. Leaves light green, varying extremely in size and shape, those of the common form 0.8–2 cm., oblong-linear to spatulate, tapering at base, rounded at apex; upper leaves rosulate. Staminate flowers crowded in the upper part of the plant or scattered, sometimes staminate and hermaphrodite flowers in alternate whorls. Fruit 1 mm. or less, sessile, obovoid; carpels very narrowly winged; styles up to 1–2 mm., caducous, filiform. Fl. summer.

Hab.: Puddles, ditches and ponds. Sharon Plain, Philistean Plain, Hula Plain. Rare.

Area: In many temperate and subtropical regions of E. Holarctis.

Schotsman in P. Jovet, Fl. Fr. 1 : 78 (1967) synonymizes this species with *C. palustris* L., Sp. Pl. 969 (1753); we have been, so far, unable to examine the relevant material.

3. Callitriche hermaphroditica L., Cent. Pl. 1 : 33 (1755) et Amoen. Acad. 4 : 293 (1759). [Plate 426]

Perennial, slender, submerged. Stems branched, yellowish, glabrous, 15–50 cm. long. Leaves 0.8–1.8 ×0.1–0.2 cm., sessile, linear-lanceolate to lanceolate-subulate, mostly broadest at base, attenuate and mostly 2-toothed at apex, green, glabrous, 1-nerved. Fruit 1.5–2 mm. in diam., almost globular in outline, 4-lobed; carpels winged; styles caducous, long; stigmas appressed. Fl. June–November.

Hab.: Ditches and water holes; slow-flowing or stagnant water. Upper Galilee. Very rare.

Area: Euro-Siberian.

Rutales

62. RUTACEAE

Herbs, shrubs or trees, sometimes vines, often with a heavy odour due to an aromatic volatile oil. Leaves alternate, rarely opposite, exstipulate, simple or compound, glandular-dotted. Inflorescences various, mostly cymose. Flowers mostly hermaphrodite, actinomorphic, rarely zygomorphic, 2–5-merous. Sepals imbricated or open in bud, free or connate. Petals inserted on a disk often elongated into a gynophore. Stamens as many as or twice as many as sepals (rarely more); epipetalous stamens sometimes reduced to staminodes; anthers versatile or dorsifixed, 2-celled, introrsely dehiscent. Ovary superior, with as many carpels as sepals; carpels mostly connate at least in stylar part, very rarely free, when connate then ovary 2–4(–5)- or 1-celled; ovules mostly 2 in each cell, rarely numerous, anatropous; style mostly 1; stigma simple. Fruit a drupe, a berry, a loculicidal (rarely septicidal) capsule or a schizocarp separating into as many cocci as carpels. Seeds with or without endosperm; embryo curved or straight.

About 150 genera and 1,600 species, widespread, especially in tropical and subtropical regions.

1. Petals fimbriate or dentate. Flowers, except the terminal ones, 4-merous (in ours).
                                                                            1. Ruta
– Petals entire. Flowers all 5-merous.   **2. Haplophyllum**

1. RUTA L.

Perennial herbs or shrubs, glandular-punctate, with a strong odour. Stems very richly branched. Leaves alternate, frequently pinnately divided. Inflorescences cymose, corymbose or paniculate, bracteate. Flowers 4-merous (the terminal one 5-merous). Calyx 4(–5)-parted. Petals 4(–5), yellow, hooded, fimbriate or dentate, rarely entire. Disk thick, cushion-like. Stamens 8(–10); filaments dilated at base, epipetalous filaments shorter. Ovary 4(–5)-celled, deeply 4(–5)-lobed; cells 6–12-ovuled; placentation axile; style 1, central, with a small stigma. Capsule 4(–5)-lobed; lobes usually dehiscing inwardly. Seeds angular, punctate; endosperm fleshy.

A few species, mainly in the Mediterranean region and S.W. Asia.

1. Ruta chalepensis L., Mant. 69 (1767) emend. Mill., Gard. Dict. ed. 8, no. 4 (1768). *R. chalepensis* L. var. *bracteosa* (DC.) Boiss., Fl. 1 : 922 (1867). *R. bracteosa* DC., Prodr. 1 : 710 (1824). [Plate 427]

Shrub with pungent odour, glabrous, glandular-dotted, 50–70 cm. Stems woody at base, ascending. Leaves 1.5–10 cm., oblong in outline, pinnately divided; segments unequal, 0.3–0.8(–2) cm. oblanceolate or elliptical, obtuse or sometimes acutish, margins sometimes slightly wavy-dentate and revolute. Inflorescences corymbose. Bracts 5–8 mm., sessile, cordate-ovate to ovate-lanceolate. Flowers 0.8–1.5 cm. in diam., pedicellate. Calyx lobes 4, cordate-ovate, acute. Petals 4(–5), about 1 cm., oblong, fringed. Capsule 6–8(–10) mm., 4(–5)-lobed; lobes dorsally grooved, acute, mucronate. Seeds about 2 mm. Fl. February–June.

Hab.: Batha and garigue; sandy and calcareous soils. Acco Plain, Sharon Plain, Philistean Plain, Upper and Lower Galilee, Mt. Carmel, Esdraelon Plain, Samaria, Judean Mts., Upper Jordan Valley, Golan, Gilead. Locally fairly common.

Area: Mediterranean.

Frequently grown as an ornamental in home gardens; it contains a volatile oil (oleum rutae), said to have been used formerly as a condiment; also known to have been used in treating hysteria, worms, amenorrhoea and menorrhagia, and for relieving rheumatic pains.

2. HAPLOPHYLLUM Ad. Juss. (*"Aplophyllum"*) corr. Reichb.

Perennial herbs or half-shrubs. Leaves undivided or 3-parted. Inflorescences corymbose, bracteate. Flowers hermaphrodite, actinomorphic, yellow or reddish. Calyx 5-parted. Petals 5, hooded, entire. Stamens 10; filaments free or connate below, dilated at base, hairy or glabrous. Ovary 5-celled, 5-lobed, depressed, with or without horns at top of carpels; ovules (1–)2 or 4(–8) in each cell; styles united into a cylindrical or club-shaped column. Capsule 5-celled, glandular, separating into carpels, rarely indehiscent. Seeds reniform, transversely wrinkled-tuberculate.

About 65 species, mostly growing in the deserts of N. Africa, and C. and W. Asia.

Literature: C. C. Townsend, *Haplophyllum,* in: K. H. Rechinger, *Flora Iranica,* Contrib. 36: 2–21, pls. 1–8, Graz, 1966. C. C. Townsend, Towards a revision of *Haplophyllum* A. Juss. (Rutaceae), I, *Kew Bull.* 20: 89–102 (1966).

1. Carpels bearing a straight or incurved projecting horn at top. Dwarf shrubs, with oblong-lanceolate to linear leaves usually 1–1.2 cm.   **1. H. fruticulosum**
   – Carpels not horned. Leaves either less than 1 cm. or much longer   2
2. Leaves ovate to lanceolate, about 0.3–0.6 cm. (rarely up to 1 cm.). Dwarf shrubs. Glands, if present, not projecting from surface of leaves or stems.   **2. H. poorei**
   – Not as above   3
3. Flowers red or reddish. Filaments connate at base. Desert plants dotted with glands not projecting above surface.   **4. H. blanchei**
   – Flowers yellow   4
4. Yellowish-green plants. Leaves usually obovate to oblanceolate, often parted into 2–3 linear-lanceolate segments; margins not revolute. Glands, if present, not projecting above surface. Non-desert plants.   **3. H. buxbaumii**
   – Green to grey plants. Some leaves obovate and some linear in the same or in different plants, all undivided; margins often strongly revolute. Glands always tubercle-like, projecting above surface. Desert plants.   **5. H. tuberculatum**

1. Haplophyllum fruticulosum (Labill.) G. Don f., Gen. Syst. 1: 780 (1831; *"Aplophyllum"*); *"H. fruticulosum* (Labill.) Boiss.", Fl. 1: 932 (1867). *Ruta fruticulosa* Labill., Ic. Pl. Syr. Dec. 1: 13, t. 4 (1791). [Plate 428]

Dwarf shrub, short- and patulous-pubescent, 20–40 cm. Stems many, erect to ascending, simple or branched, woody at base. Leaves usually 1–1.2 cm., sessile, leathery, acute, entire; the lowest leaves minute, ovate, the others oblong-lanceolate to linear, tapering to a short petiole. Inflorescences corymbose-umbellate, short, dense, not elongating in fruit. Pedicels shorter to somewhat longer than the flowers. Calyx one third to one half as long as corolla, tomentose; lobes oblong. Petals 5–7 mm., yellow, elliptical, obtuse, glabrous. Filaments shorter than corolla. Ovary white-villose; stylar column club-shaped above. Fruit about 3 mm.; carpels with a straight or incurved horn at top. Fl. April.

Hab.: Steppes; stony soil. Edom. Very rare.

Area: Irano-Turanian (Palestine–Syria).

The illustration of *H. fruticulosum* was made from a plant collected on Mt. Hermon.

2. Haplophyllum poorei C. C. Townsend, Kew Bull. 20: 97, f. 3 (1966). [Plate 429]

Dwarf shrub, glaucescent, short- and patulous-pubescent, up to 25 cm. Stems usually simple, forked, woody at base, the older ones remaining together with those of the current year. Leaves dense, all alike, 0.3–0.6 cm. (rarely up to 1 cm.), somewhat thick, ovate to lanceolate, obtuse, entire, subappressed-hairy, with sparse glandular dots; younger leaves densely imbricated, sessile or semiamplexicaul. Inflorescences first short and capitate, then corymbose-umbellate, 4–6-flowered. Pedicels very short, thickening in fruit and elongating up to 6 mm. Calyx one fifth to one third as long as corolla; lobes broadly ovate to orbicular, densely hirsute. Petals 6–9 × 4–5 mm., reddish-brown along middle and yellowish at the membranous broad margins, ovate, obtuse, hairy or glabrous. Filaments free, with broader and somewhat barbulate base. Ovary frequently glandular-hairy; stylar column cylindrical. Capsule 2–3 mm.; carpels not horned, becoming densely glandular-tuberculate with maturity. Seeds unknown. Fl. March–May.

Subsp. **poorei.** Stems glandular. Leaves not semiamplexicaul, somewhat tapering at base. Lobes of calyx deltoid-ovate, becoming blackish-green. Corolla 5 times as long as calyx, glabrous. Filaments gradually attenuating above, glandular; anthers not hairy. Ovary mainly glandular-hairy.

Hab.: Bare sandstone. Edom (endemic). Very rare.

Subsp. **negevense** Zoh. et Danin *. [Plate 429]. Stems not glandular. Leaves semiamplexicaul. Lobes of calyx almost orbicular, remaining grey-green. Corolla 3–4 times as long as calyx, hairy. Filaments abruptly attenuating above, not glandular; anthers hairy. Ovary hairy and glandular-hairy.

Hab.: In fissures of hard limestone. C. Negev (Ras Ramon; endemic). Rare.

Area of species: W. Irano-Turanian.

This species is very close to *H. fruticulosum* (Labill.) G. Don f., but is distinguished by the usually ovate leaves which are all alike, the shape of calyx lobes and petals, the hornless carpels and the cylindrical stylar column. More thorough studies may determine the taxonomical relations between these two species.

3. Haplophyllum buxbaumii (Poir.) G. Don f., Gen. Syst. 1: 780 (1831; "*Aplophyllum*"); "*H. buxbaumii* (Poir.) Boiss." Boiss., Fl. 1: 937 (1867). *Ruta buxbaumii* Poir. in Lam., Encycl. 6: 336 (1804). [Plate 430]

* See Appendix at end of this volume.

Perennial, yellowish-green, appressed-puberulent, 35–50 cm. Stems erect, branched. Leaves 1–6 cm., entire or 3-sect, dotted with small blackish glands not projecting above surface; the lower leaves obovate to spatulate and oblanceolate, tapering at base, obtuse, usually undivided; the upper leaves often unequally parted into 2–3 linear-lanceolate to oblanceolate segments. Inflorescences usually divaricate leafy corymbs. Flowers 0.7–1.2 cm. Calyx lobes about 1 mm., ovate, yellow, glabrous or hairy. Petals yellow, oblong, tapering at base, obtuse, glabrous. Filaments free to base, barbate. Ovary tuberculate; stylar column club-shaped. Capsule 2–3 mm., glandular-tuberculate. Fl. March–June.

Subsp. **buxbaumii**. Plants yellowish-green throughout. Leaves undivided or upper leaves unequally parted into 2–3 oblanceolate-linear segments, appressed-puberulent. Flowers 0.8–1.2 cm. Capsule about 3 mm. Fl. April–June.

Hab.: Fields; often among winter crops. Acco Plain, Sharon Plain, Philistean Plain, Upper and Lower Galilee, Mt. Carmel, Esdraelon Plain, Samaria, Shefela, Judean Mts., N. Negev, Hula Plain, Upper Jordan Valley, Beit Shean Valley, Lower Jordan Valley, Arava Valley, Golan, Gilead, Ammon, Moav. Rather common.

Area of species: Mediterranean and Irano-Turanian.

The two local varieties, distinguished by Boissier (l.c. 938), are: var. *stenophyllum* Boiss. with most of the leaves divided into spatulate-linear segments, and var. *corymbulosum* (Boiss.) Boiss. with most of the leaves undivided, smaller flowers and glabrous calyx lobes. The varieties intergrade and seem to be inconstant. The other subspecies, *H. buxbaumii* ssp. *mesopotamicum* (Boiss.) C. C. Townsend, Kew Bull. 20 : 92 (1966), has not been found in Palestine.

4. Haplophyllum blanchei Boiss., Fl. 1 : 937 (1867). [Plate 431]

Perennial, green, minutely puberulent to glabrescent and sparsely dotted with black glands, 25–30 cm. Stems many, erect or ascending, branched above, slender. Leaves 0.8–2.5 cm., oblong-linear, tapering at base, with revolute margins; the lowest leaves sometimes spatulate. Inflorescences corymbose or capitate (when young). Flowers short-pedicelled. Calyx one fourth as long as corolla; lobes ovate-orbicular, obtuse, glabrous or ciliate, often with a few glands. Petals 4–6 mm., red or reddish, oblong, obtuse, hooded, glabrous. Filaments connate and ciliate at base. Ovary glabrous; stylar column club-shaped above. Capsule about 3 mm., densely glandular-tuberculate. Fl. March–April.

Hab.: Deserts; gravelly ground. Gilead, Ammon, Edom. Locally frequent.

Area: Irano-Turanian.

Our specimens may belong to a special form with calyx lobes not ciliate and with flowers somewhat larger than in the typical variety.

Haplophyllum rubellulum Thiéb. et Gomb. in Thiéb., Mém. Inst. Eg. 31 (Fl. Lib.-Syr. 1): 165 (1936), recorded by Rechinger f. (Ark. Bot. ser. 2, 2, 5 : 381, 1952) from E. Ammon, should be referred to this species.

5. Haplophyllum tuberculatum (Forssk.) Ad. Juss., Mém. Mus. Hist. Nat. Paris

12 : 528, t. 17 no. 10 (1825; "*Aplophyllum*"); Boiss., Fl. 1 : 939 (1867); C. C. Townsend, Kew Bull. 20 : 99 (1966). *Ruta tuberculata* Forssk., Fl. Aeg.-Arab. 86 (1775).

H. longifolium Boiss., Diagn. ser. 1, 8 : 127 (1849) et Fl. 1 : 941 (1867). [Plates 432, 432a]

Perennial, woody at base, glabrous or crisp-pubescent, mostly with projecting glands or tubercles, 30–40 cm. Stems many, erect to ascending, simple or branched. Leaves (1–)1.5–5 cm., crenate, wavy-margined, often strongly revolute, frequently prominently tuberculate; lower leaves and those of sterile branches obovate or oblong-spatulate, tapering into petiole; upper leaves linear, obtuse; sometimes all leaves linear or all obovate to oblong. Inflorescences corymbose, many-flowered, bracteate, loose, divaricate. Flowers up to 1 cm. or more, subsessile. Calyx up to one fourth as long as corolla; lobes ovate, yellow, hairy or glabrous. Petals 5–8 mm., yellow, oblong, obtuse. Filaments connate at base or free, abruptly dilated towards apex, usually hairy, glandular or not. Ovary glabrescent; stylar column club-shaped, glabrous or hairy. Capsule about 3–5 mm., glabrous or woolly, glandular-tuberculate. Fl. March–April.

Hab.: Steppes and deserts; mostly in wadis, runnels and on sandy plains. Philistean Plain, Judean Desert, N., C. and S. Negev, Lower Jordan Valley, Dead Sea area, Arava Valley, Moav, Edom. Locally fairly common.

Area : Saharo-Arabian.

This is the most variable species of *Haplophyllum*. It occurs in many forms which were considered by some botanists, especially Boissier, as independent species. Recently these binomials were synonymized with *H. tuberculatum* by Townsend, l.c. and in Rechinger f. (Fl. Iranica Contrib. 36 : 16, 1966). *H. longifolium* Boiss. (divided by Bornmueller, Verh. Zool.-Bot. Ges. Wien 48 : 570, 1898, into var. *ciliosum* and var. *eriocalycinum*) has also proven to belong to *H. tuberculatum*. Plate 432a is given here for the sake of comparison to show that particular form which for a whole century has represented *H. longifolium* Boiss. and which, despite the difference from *H. tuberculatum* in the leaves and flowers, has not been considered by Townsend (l.c.) even as a variety.

63. POLYGALACEAE

Herbs, shrubs, climbers or trees. Leaves alternate or rarely opposite, exstipulate, simple, entire. Flowers hermaphrodite, zygomorphic, solitary or in racemes, pedicellate, subtended by 1 bract and 2 bracteoles. Sepals 5, free, imbricated, often petaloid, the 2 inner ones larger than the outer. Petals 3–5, unequal, more or less united and adnate to staminal tube. Receptacle small, rarely forming an annular disk. Stamens usually 8; filaments usually partly connate into a tube. Ovary superior, 1–2- or rarely 3–5-celled, with many anatropous ovules in 2 rows or with 1 ovule in each cell; style simple; stigma 2-lobed, rarely capitate. Fruit a capsule, nut, samara or drupe. Seeds 1 or 2 in each cell, often hairy or winged, usually with endosperm; embryo straight.

Some 13 genera and 800 species throughout the tropical and temperate regions.

1. POLYGALA L.

Herbs or small shrubs. Leaves mostly alternate, rarely opposite or whorled. Flowers mostly in racemes. Sepals persistent, the 2 inner sepals petaloid, wing-like, much larger than the sepaloid outer ones. Petals mostly 3, connate below and adnate to staminal tube, the lower (middle) one mostly the larger, boat-shaped, enclosing the stamens and mostly bearing a fringed crest. Stamens 8; filaments united to about the middle or further into a sheath open on the upper side; anthers 1–2-celled, opening by pores. Ovary 2-celled, with a single anatropous ovule in each cell; style simple. Capsule loculicidally dehiscent, 2-celled, thin, flattened laterally. Seeds mostly hairy, surrounded at base with a lobed caruncle; endosperm hard or oleiferous or 0.

About 700 species in temperate and warm regions.

Literature : R. Chodat, Monographia Polygalacearum I, II, *Mém. Soc. Phys. Hist. Nat. Genève* 31, 1 (Vol. Suppl.), No. 7 : 1–143, pls. 1–12 (1891); ibid. 31, 2, No. 2 : 1–500, pls. 1–23 (1893).

1. Leaves ovate to broadly elliptical, slightly longer than broad, thick. Filaments connate to apex. Low perennials, densely canescent with crisp hairs.   **3. P. hohenackeriana**
– Leaves linear-lanceolate or oblong. Filaments connate to middle. Annuals or spinescent perennials, glabrous to tomentose (and not crisp-hairy)   2
2. Unarmed annuals. Inner sepals 3-nerved. Lateral lobes of corolla longer than the middle one.   **1. P. monspeliaca**
– Woody perennials with rigid, spinescent branches. Inner sepals with dense anastomosing veins. Lateral lobes of corolla shorter than the middle one.   **2. P. sinaica**

1. Polygala monspeliaca L., Sp. Pl. 702 (1753); Boiss., Fl. 1 : 469 (1867). [Plate 433]

Annual, slender, glabrous to tomentose, 10–40 cm. Stems single or few, erect. Leaves 1–3 cm., alternate, sessile, lanceolate to linear-lanceolate, tapering at base, acuminate, somewhat folded at margin. Racemes terminal, spike-like, long, many-flowered. Bracts as long as the pedicels, membranous, subulate. Pedicels short, usually deflexed. Flowers 0.6–1 cm. The 3 outer sepals about 2–3 mm., lanceolate, green; the 2 inner sepals (wings) 0.8–1 cm., elliptical, white, 3-nerved, with veins not anastomosing. Corolla much shorter than inner sepals; lateral petals slightly longer than the middle boat-shaped one. Filaments connate to middle. Capsule about 8 mm., somewhat shorter than the fruiting wings, obovate, notched, glabrous, broadly winged. Seeds 2.5 mm., linear, appressed-silky. Fl. April–June.

Hab. : Batha; mostly on stony ground or in grassy patches. Acco Plain, Sharon Plain, Philistean Plain, Upper Galilee, Mt. Carmel, Esdraelon Plain, Judean Mts., Gilead, Ammon, Edom. Locally fairly common.

Area : Mediterranean, with slight extensions into the adjacent Euro-Siberian territories.

2. Polygala sinaica Botsch., Novit. Syst. Pl. Vasc. 1964 : 368 (1964). *P. spinescens* Decne., Ann. Sci. Nat. Bot. ser. 2, 3 : 275 (1835) non Gill. in Hook. et Walk.-Arn., Hook. Bot. Misc. 3 : 146 (1833); Boiss., Fl. 1 : 470 (1867). *P. spinescens* Decne. var.

glabrescens Zoh. in Eig et Zoh., Palest. Journ. Bot. Jerusalem ser., 1 : 310 (1939). *P. scoparia* auct. non H.B. et K., Nov. Gen. et Sp. 5 : 399 (1823). [Plate 434]

Perennial, shrubby, somewhat velvety-pubescent, 15–30 cm. Stems much branched. Branches virgate, rigid, spinescent, yellowish-green. Leaves 0.6–2 cm., caducous, alternate, sessile, oblong-linear, tapering at base, acutish, pubescent. Racemes terminal, with few to 10 scattered flowers. Bracts usually longer than the pedicels, membranous, oblong-subulate. Pedicels short, first erect, then deflexed. Flowers up to 8 mm. The 3 outer sepals 2.5 mm., almost equal, elliptical, membranous with a broad hairy green midrib; the 2 inner sepals (wings) about 7 mm. or more, white, broadly elliptical, distinctly clawed, densely nerved, with anastomosing veins. Corolla much shorter than the inner sepals; lateral petals much shorter than the middle, purple, helmet-shaped one. Filaments connate to middle. Capsule about 5–6 mm., obovate, truncate, glabrous; fruiting wings 1 cm. Seeds 3–4 mm., appressed-silky. Fl. April–June.

Hab.: Hot deserts; rocky ground. Arava Valley, Edom. Rather rare.

Area : Sudanian.

3. Polygala hohenackeriana Fisch. et Mey., Ind. Sem. Hort. Petrop. 4 : 42 (1838 ?); Boiss., Fl. 1 : 472 (1867). *P. edumea* Zoh., Palest. Journ. Bot. Jerusalem ser., 2 : 89 (1940) *nom. nud.;* Zoh. ex Zoh., Palest. Journ. Bot. Jerusalem ser., 2 : 166, ff. 19–22 (1941). [Plate 435]

Perennial, densely canescent with crisp hairs, about 8–15 cm. Stems procumbent to ascending, sparsely branched, rigid and flexuous. Leaves 0.4–0.7 (–1) cm., alternate, sessile, thick, ovate to elliptical, obtuse or acute, mucronulate, entire, appressed-canescent. Racemes terminal, spike-like, few- to many-flowered, dense. Bracts minute, membranous. Pedicels about 2 mm., first erect, later deflexed. Flowers about 5–6 mm. The 3 outer sepals unequal, elliptical to oblong, broadly membranous-margined, with green midrib; the 2 inner sepals (wings) 2–3 times as long as the outer, mostly white, obovate to elliptical, distinctly clawed, 3-nerved, nerves green, lateral veins not anastomosing. Corolla smaller than the inner sepals, white or pale pink; lateral petals about as long as or somewhat longer than the boat-shaped middle one. Filaments connate to apex. Capsule about 6 × 4 mm., as long as and slightly broader than the fruiting wings, obovate or obcordate, glabrous, with unequally winged margin. Seeds about two thirds as long as capsule, cylindrical-conical, long- and appressed-hairy. Fl. April.

Hab.: Steppes; Nubian sandstone, about 800 m. Edom. Rare.

Area : Irano-Turanian.

Fairly variable in the shape of leaves, the wings and the length of the middle lobe of the corolla.

Sapindales

64. ANACARDIACEAE

Trees or shrubs, evergreen or deciduous. Leaves alternate, rarely opposite, exstipulate or with caducous stipules, simple or compound. Inflorescences racemose or cymose, bracteate. Flowers hermaphrodite or unisexual (plants then monoecious, dioecious or polygamous), actinomorphic, small. Calyx mostly 3–5-parted. Petals as many as the calyx lobes, inserted on the calyx, imbricated or valvate in bud; sometimes petals 0. Disk flat, cup-shaped or annular, entire or lobed, rarely obsolete. Stamens as many or twice as many as the calyx lobes, inserted under or rarely on the disk; filaments usually subulate; anthers basi- or dorsifixed, 2-celled, introrsely dehiscent. Ovary superior, 1–3 (–5)-celled, with 1 anatropous, pendulous or ascending ovule in each cell; styles 1 or more. Fruit usually indehiscent, drupe- or nut-like, 1- or many-seeded, sometimes winged. Seeds with a very thin or no endosperm, a straight or curved embryo, plano-convex cotyledons and a short radicle.

About 80 genera and 600 species mainly in tropical and subtropical regions of the New and Old World; a few genera also in temperate regions.

1. Leaves pinnate; leaflets entire, glabrous.   **1. Pistacia**
 - Leaves 3–5-fid or -parted, or leaves pinnate but then leaflets toothed and hairy.
                                                                       2. Rhus

1. PISTACIA L.

Trees or shrubs with a turpentine resin. Leaves alternate, exstipulate, usually pinnate. Flowers unisexual (plants dioecious), apetalous, small, in axillary racemes or panicles. Staminate flowers: bract 1, bracteoles 2, perianth segments 1–2 (all these together forming a mostly 5-fid spurious perianth); disk small; stamens 3–5(–7) around the disk, with short filaments adnate at base to disk and with long anthers; pistil rudimentary or 0. Pistillate flowers: bract 1, bracteoles 2, perianth segments mostly 2–5, small, scarious, imbricated; disk 0 or almost so; ovary sessile, 1-celled with 1 ovule pendulous from a basal funicle, style short and 3-fid, stigmas capitate and recurved, mostly unequal. Fruit drupe-like. Seeds compressed, with membranous testa; cotyledons thick, oleiferous, curved.

Some 9 species in the Mediterranean region, W., C. and E. Asia, and in southern N. America.

Literature: A. Engler, *Pistacia*, in: A. et C. de Candolle, *Monographiae Phanerogamarum* 4 : 284–293, t. 9, ff. 22–29, Paris, 1883. M. Zohary, A monographical study of the genus *Pistacia*, *Palest. Journ. Bot. Jerusalem Ser.*, 5 : 187–228 (1952).

1. Deciduous trees. Leaves not leathery; leaf rhachis winged or not. Pistillate flowers
   in loose paniculate inflorescences   3
 - Evergreen shrubs or trees with leathery leaves; leaf rhachis winged. Pistillate flowers

in rather congested or almost spike-like inflorescences   2
2. Shrubs. Leaflets usually 2–3-paired, mucronulate; terminal leaflet 0 or similar to the
   others (ovate or oblong-lanceolate to elliptical). Fruit abundant, fertile.
                                                                         5. P. lentiscus
– Trees. Leaflets usually 4–6-paired, usually acuminate-aristate; terminal leaflet much
   narrower and mostly shorter than the others, linear-lanceolate to subulate, falcate or
   oblique. Fruits few, mostly seedless, caducous.   **4. P. saportae**
3 (1). Leaf rhachis winged; leaflets obtuse, muticous.   **1. P. atlantica**
– Leaf rhachis not winged; leaflets acute to acuminate, often aristate   4
4. Terminal leaflet always present, larger than lateral leaflets; leaflets (1–) 2–4-paired,
   3–10 × 1.5–7 (–8) cm.; leaf rhachis glabrous.   **3. P. khinjuk** var. **glabra**
– Terminal leaflet 0 or reduced to a mucro, or present but smaller than lateral leaflets;
   leaflets (3–) 4–5 (–6–7)-paired, 3–7 × 1.2–2.5 cm.; leaf rhachis crisp-puberulent.
                                                                     2. P. palaestina

1. Pistacia atlantica Desf., Fl. Atl. 2 : 364 (1799); Zoh., Palest. Journ. Bot. Jerusalem ser., 5 : 204 (1952). [Plate 436]

Deciduous tree, 4–20 m. Branches brownish or grey. Leaves ovate or oblong in
outline, imparipinnate; rhachis flattish, winged; leaflets 3–5-paired, 2.5–7 × 0.6–2 cm.,
lanceolate or oblong to broadly oblong, obtuse, muticous. Staminate panicles 3–10 cm.,
compact, later loosening; pistillate panicles 8–15 cm., with branches erect or spreading, loose. Flowers very short-pedicelled. Staminate flowers: stamens about 5(–7),
filaments almost 0. Pistillate flowers: perianth as long as or longer than pistil; pistil
2.5–3 mm., style half as long as ovary. Fruit (5–)6–7(–8) × 5–6 mm., obovoid or
obovoid-globular to globular; exocarp wrinkled when dry; endocarp bony. 2n = 28.
Fl. (February–) March–April.

Var. **atlantica**. *P. mutica* Fisch. et Mey. in Hohenack., Bull. Soc. Nat. Mosc. 11 : 338
(1838) p. min. p. Leaflets lanceolate, about 0.7–1 cm. broad. Fruit obovoid, longitudinally wrinkled.

Hab.: Mostly in semisteppe areas and steppes, solitary or forming scattered stands.
C. Negev, Golan, E. Gilead, Ammon, Edom.

Var. **latifolia** DC., Prodr. 2 : 64 (1825). *P. mutica* Fisch. et Mey. in Hohenack., l.c.
p. max. p.; Boiss., Fl. 2 : 7 (1872) p. max. p. Leaflets oblong to oblong-ovate, up to
2 cm. broad. Fruit reticulately or transversely wrinkled.

Hab.: Usually in the more humid parts of Palestine; occurs as solitary trees or in
pure stands, or as a maquis or forest associate. Acco Plain, Upper and Lower Galilee,
Mt. Carmel, Esdraelon Plain, Samaria, Judean Mts., Dan Valley, Hula Plain, Upper
Jordan Valley. Widespread but not common.

Area of species: Irano-Turanian (mainly Irano-Anatolian, Mesopotamian and N.
African Steppes districts), with extensions into and sporadic occurrences in Caucasia,
Crimea and some E. Mediterranean countries; probably planted sometimes as a shade
tree; also met with in cemeteries.

The differences between the two varieties are unreliable as the characters are inconstant. It seems that under more humid conditions the leaflets are usually broader.

P. atlantica occurs very rarely in typical Mediterranean maquis and is more often an associate of *Quercus ithaburensis* forests; isolated individuals or scattered stands are also met with in the Negev Mts., the E. slopes of the Upper Galilee Mts., E. Gilead, and in some places of E. Ammon and Moav.

This handsome tree sometimes attains a very great age. Though less common in Palestine than other congeneric species, it was probably one of the trees deified and adored by the ancients. The biblical אֵלָה (e.g. Gen. xxxv : 4; Ezek. vi : 13) probably refers to this species.

The fruit of this and the next species is edible and sold in markets; the galls are a source of tannins; the resin is sometimes used in folk medicine.

2. Pistacia palaestina Boiss., Diagn. ser. 1, 9 : 1 (1849) et Fl. 2 : 6 (1872); Zoh., Palest. Journ. Bot. Jerusalem ser., 5 : 209 (1952). *P. terebinthus* L. var. *palaestina* (Boiss.) Engl. in A. et C. DC., Monogr. Phan. 4 : 290 (1883). [Plate 437]

Tree or shrub, 2–6(–10) m. Leaves 10–25 cm., deciduous, petiolate, paripinnate or imparipinnate; rhachis semiterete or angular, not winged, crisp-puberulent; leaflets (3–)4–5(–6–7)-paired, 3–7 ×1.2–2.5 cm., petiolulate or sessile, ovate or oblong to lanceolate, acute to acuminate-aristate; terminal leaflet smaller than the lateral ones or 0 or reduced to a mucro. Staminate panicles 6–10 cm., compact, later loosening; pistillate panicles 8–18 cm., divaricately branched. Staminate flowers : very short-pedicelled; stamens usually 5. Pistillate flowers : pedicels conspicuous, up to 2 mm.; perianth 0.5–1.5 mm.; pistil about 2 mm., style shorter than ovary. Fruit about 5 mm. in diam., ovoid to obovoid-globular, somewhat compressed laterally. Fl. (February–) March–April.

Hab. : Maquis and garigue; mainly in hills and mountains. Sharon Plain, Upper and Lower Galilee, Mt. Carmel, Samaria, Judean Mts., Dan Valley, Hula Plain, Golan, Gilead, Ammon, Moav, Edom. Common.

Area : E. Mediterranean.

The most important associate of the *Quercus calliprinos* – *Pistacia palaestina* maquis association in Palestine, Lebanon, Syria, Turkey and adjacent islands.

3. Pistacia khinjuk Stocks ex Stocks, Hook. Journ. Bot. & Kew Gard. Misc. 4 : 143 (1852) var. **glabra** Schweinf. ex Engl. in A. et C. DC., Monogr. Phan. 4 : 291 (1883); Schweinf. in Sched. (1877). *P. khinjuk* Stocks var. *glaberrima* Schweinf. ex Boiss., Fl. Suppl. 154 (1888); Zoh., Palest. Journ. Bot. Jerusalem ser., 5 : 212 (1952).

Deciduous tree, 3–7 m. Leaves 7–15 cm., firm, imparipinnate; rhachis terete or somewhat angulate, not winged, glabrous; leaflets (1–)2–4-paired, petiolulate, lanceolate, oblique at base, acuminate, glabrous along midrib; terminal leaflet well developed, larger than the lateral leaflets. Staminate panicles 5–12 cm., erect, much branched, loose; pistillate panicles 7–15 cm., loose, with erect or spreading branches. Staminate flowers : almost sessile; stamens 4–5, filaments nearly 0, rudimentary pistil minute. Pistillate flowers : pedicellate; perianth 2.5–3 mm.; pistil 2.5 mm., style very short, stigmas longer than ovary and style. Fruit about 4 mm. in diam., almost globular, apiculate. Fl. spring.

Hab. : Among shrubs. Edom (Petra). Very rare.

Area : Irano-Turanian.

The specimen (Aaronsohn Herb. no. 5820), recorded by Oppenheimer (Bull. Soc. Bot.

Genève ser. 2, 22 : 342, 1931) as *P. khinjuk* Stocks var. *heterophylla* Bornm., should be referred to var. *glabra*. Lastly this variety has been abundantly found in the mountains of southern Sinai.

4. Pistacia × saportae Burnat, Fl. Alp. Marit. 2 : 54 (1896); Zoh., Palest. Journ. Bot. Jerusalem ser., 5 : 203 (1952). *P. lentiscus × terebinthus* (Saporta et Marion) Engl. in A. et C. DC., Monogr. Phan. 4 : 286 (1883). [Plate 438]

Evergreen tree up to 6 m. Leaves persistent, leathery, imparipinnate; rhachis winged; leaflets (3–)4–6(–7)-paired, 2.5–7 × (0.5–)1–2 cm., sessile, oblong or lanceolate to elliptical, acute or often acuminate, mucronate or aristate, sometimes with slightly revolute margins; terminal leaflet smaller, sometimes linear-lanceolate to linear-subulate, falcate and often oblique at base. Staminate inflorescences consisting of a few clustered or spike-like, simple or branching racemes 3–8 cm.; pistillate inflorescences often simple racemes or small branching panicles up to 6(–8) cm. Staminate flowers: short-pedicelled; stamens 4–6(–7), filaments almost 0. Pistillate flowers: almost sessile; perianth 1.5–2 mm.; pistil 1–2 mm., style very short, stigmas often unequal. Fruit 3–4 mm. in diam., ovoid-globular. Fl. March–May.

Hab.: Maquis. Upper and Lower Galilee, Mt. Carmel, Judean Mts. Very rare.

Area: Mediterranean.

A hybrid between *P. lentiscus* L. and *P. palaestina* Boiss.; shows some properties reminiscent of *P. lentiscus* (persistence and consistence of leaves, more condensed inflorescence, winged leaf rhachis) and some of *P. palaestina* (tree habit, shape and number of leaflets). Produces no or few viable seeds.

In view of the widespread and common occurrence of the above parental pairs, the rarity of the hybrid form is rather astonishing.

5. Pistacia lentiscus L., Sp. Pl. 1026 (1753); Boiss., Fl. 2 : 8 (1872); Zoh., Palest. Journ. Bot. Jerusalem ser., 5 : 199 (1952). [Plate 439]

Evergreen shrub (rarely tree), 1(–3) m. Leaves (3–)5–10 cm., persistent, mostly paripinnate, with winged leaf rhachis; Leaflets 2–3 (rarely up to 4)-paired, 1.5–3 × 0.5–1(–1.5) cm., leathery, ovate to oblong-lanceolate or elliptical, obtuse, mucronulate, glabrous. Staminate inflorescences compact spike-like racemes, 1–3 cm.; pistillate inflorescences axillary fascicles of 1–4 spike-like, simple or slightly branched racemes, 1–3 cm. Staminate flowers short-pedicelled, with 4–5 stamens and rudimentary conical pistil. Pistillate flowers: almost sessile; perianth 1.5 mm., about as long as pistil; style shorter than ovary and stigmas. Fruit about 3–4 mm. across, ovoid-globular, somewhat compressed, crowned with a 3-fid style, red or turning black at maturity, reticulate. 2n = 24. Fl. March–April.

Hab.: Maquis and garigue; coast and lower hills usually up to 300 (–500) m. above sea level. Coastal Galilee, Acco Plain, Sharon Plain, Philistean Plain, Upper and Lower Galilee, Mt. Carmel, Mt. Gilboa, Samaria, Judean Mts. Very common.

Area: Mediterranean.

One of the most common components of the maquis. A leading species of the *Ceratonia–Pistacia lentiscus* plant communities.

Often planted as an ornamental; resin used in folk medicine as a diuretic, stimulant and aphrodisiac; the commercial gum — mastic — is derived from the bark of the stems and branches of a particular variety [*P. lentiscus* L. var. *chia* (Desf.) Poir. in Duham., Arb. Arbust. ed. 2, 4 : 72 (1809)] grown in the island of Chios.

2. RHUS L.

Trees or shrubs. Leaves alternate, exstipulate, pinnate or simple, often 3–5-lobed. Flowers hermaphrodite or unisexual (plants then dioecious or polygamous), small, in terminal or axillary panicles. Calyx small, persistent, 4–5-parted; lobes nearly equal, imbricated. Petals 4–6, equal, imbricated, spreading. Stamens 4–6 or 10, free, inserted beneath the annular disk; stamens in pistillate flowers rudimentary. Ovary sessile, 1-celled, ovoid or globular; ovules pendulous from a basal funicle; styles 3, free; stigmas simple or capitate. Fruit drupe-like, small, compressed; stone crustaceous or bony. Seeds with membranous testa; cotyledons flattish, radicle short, hooked.

About 600 species, mainly in temperate regions of Asia, the Mediterranean and N. America.

1. Leaves pinnate with 5–7 pairs of leaflets. Hairy unarmed shrubs.   **1. R. coriaria**
– Leaves not pinnate. Thorny shrubs   2
2. Leaves digitate, 5-foliolate. Fruit subglobular, 3-tuberculate at apex.
                                                                                                          3. R. pentaphylla
– Leaves 3-foliolate or 3-lobed. Fruit globular, not as above.   **2. R. tripartita**

1. Rhus coriaria L., Sp. Pl. 265 (1753); Boiss., Fl. 2 : 4 (1872). [Plate 440]
Polygamous tree or shrub, villose, 2–5 m. Leaves 10–20 cm., deciduous, short-petioled, oblong in outline, imparipinnate; leaflets 5–7-paired, 2–4(–5) × 0.7–2(–2.5) cm., sessile, oblong to ovate, acute or obtuse at apex, coarsely serrate-dentate, villose beneath. Panicles 10–20 cm., terminal or axillary, dense. Flowers 3–4 mm., unisexual or hermaphrodite, greenish-white. Calyx lobes 5, ovate to orbicular, villose. Petals 5, about twice as long as calyx, white, ovate. Stamens 5. Fruit 4–6 mm., globular-reniform, umbilicate, brown, villose and glandular-hairy. Fl. April–May.

Hab.: Neglected places near villages; rarely in maquis. Sharon Plain, Philistean Plain, Upper Galilee, Mt. Carmel, Samaria, Judean Mts., Golan, Gilead, Edom; doubtfully subspontaneous. Locally common.

Area: Presumably Irano-Turanian in origin, widely distributed in the Mediterranean region and elsewhere.

Forms considerable stands in the Golan, where it is associated with other maquis shrubs.
Formerly grown as a tanniferous plant (contains up to 35% tannin); used in folk medicine as an astringent and styptic; fresh fruit toxic.

2. Rhus tripartita (Bernard. da Ucria) Grande, Bull. Ort. Bot. Nap. 5 : 242, 243 (1916; *"tripartitum"*). *R. tripartita* (Bernard. da Ucria) DC., Prodr. 2 : 72 (1825) *pro syn. Rhamnus tripartitus* Bernard. da Ucria, Nuov. Racc. Opusc. Aut. Sicil. 6 : 249 (1793); Bernard. da Ucria in Roem., Arch. 1, 1 : 68 (1796; *"tripartita"*). *Rhus oxyacanthoides* Dum.-Cours., Bot. Cult. 3 : 569 (1802); Boiss., Fl. 2 : 5 (1872). [Plate 441]

Dioecious shrub with twisted and thorny branches, glabrous or almost so, 1–2(–3) m. Leaves up to 2 cm., deciduous, 3-foliolate, glabrous or glabrescent; petiole a little shorter than the leaflets; leaflets 0.4–2 cm., sessile, obovate, cuneate, distinctly or obscurely few-lobed, lobes often dentate. Panicles short, 2–3 cm., axillary or terminal. Flowers minute, green. Calyx about 1 mm.; lobes 5, ovate. Petals 5, 2 mm., greenish, ovate-lanceoelate, obtuse, greenish. Stamens 5. Fruit 5–7 mm., globular, red, glossy, glabrous. Fl. April–May.

Hab.: Rocks in deserts and among shrubs. Sharon Plain, Samaria, Judean Desert, N., C. and S. Negev, Lower Jordan Valley, Gilead, Ammon, Moav. Rather rare.

Area: W. Irano-Turanian (Maghreb Steppes of N. Africa), with extensions into Mediterranean coastal garigue and Saharo-Arabian territories; also recorded from littoral Nubia.

It is, no doubt, a relic of ancient semisteppe vegetation which once covered larger parts of the area.

A codominant associate of the *Retama* — *Rhus tripartita* community on hard limestone rocks of the Judean Desert and the western escarpments of the Ammon district facing the Jordan Valley; also common in some garigue communities of the Sharon Plain.

Bark used for dyeing and tanning.

3. Rhus pentaphylla (Jacq.) Desf., Fl. Atl. 1 : 267, t. 77 (1798; *"pentaphyllum"*). *Rhamnus pentaphyllus* Jacq., Obs. Bot. 2 : 17 (1767); L., Syst. ed. 12, 2 : 179 (1767). [Plate 442]

Thorny, glabrous shrub or shrublet with grey cortex, up to 1 m. Branches and branchlets spiny. Leaves up to 5 cm., deciduous, digitate; petiole as long as or shorter than the leaflets; leaflets 5, 1–2(–3) cm., oblong to lanceolate, entire or few-lobed at apex, glabrous (young leaves hairy). Flowers minute, unisexual (plants dioecious), in slender loose axillary compound racemes. Calyx 5-lobed, one fourth as long as corolla; lobes ovate. Petals 5, about 2 mm., yellowish, ovate. Stamens 5. Fruit about 1 cm., subglobular, with 3 tubercles at apex, red, glabrous. Fl. March–April.

Hab.: Coastal rocks. Coastal Galilee, Acco Plain. Very rare.

Area: S. Mediterranean (also in Sicily).

65. ACERACEAE

Trees or shrubs. Leaves opposite, exstipulate, simple or pinnate. Inflorescences racemose, spicate, paniculate or corymbose. Flowers hermaphrodite or unisexual, actinomorphic or zygomorphic. Sepals 4–5(–12), free or more or less connate, often unequal. Petals as many as sepals, rarely 0. Disk complete or one-sided or reduced. Stamens 4–10(–12), mostly 8, free, inserted around or on the disk. Ovary superior, 2-carpelled, usually 2-celled and 2-lobed, compressed, with the septum along the short axis; ovules 1–2 in each cell, ortho- or anatropous; styles 1–2, free or united below. Fruit a schizocarp of 2–3 mostly 1-seeded samaras. Seeds usually without endosperm, arillate or naked; embryo with flat, folded or convolute cotyledons and long radicle.

Two genera and 150 species in the temperate zones of the N. hemisphere (incl. the Himalayas and C. America).

1. ACER L.

Dioecious or polygamous trees with simple or pinnate leaves. Flowers unisexual or hermaphrodite, actinomorphic, 4–5-merous. Sepals 5, caducous or persistent, free or more or less connate. Petals as many as sepals or 0. Disk annular, sometimes 0. Stamens 8, rarely 4–10; filaments of staminate flowers longer than those of the hermaphrodite ones. Ovary flattened at right angles to septum; cells 2-ovuled; styles 2, filiform. Fruit of 2 winged samaras. Embryo conduplicate; cotyledons irregularly folded.

About 150 species, mostly in the temperate regions of the New and Old World.

1. Acer obtusifolium Sm. in Sibth. et Sm., Fl. Gr. Prodr. 1 : 263 (1809) ssp. **syriacum** (Boiss. et Gaill.) Holmboe ex Zoh. (comb. et stat. nov.); Holmboe, Bergens Mus. Skr. n.r. 1, 2 : 123–124 (1914) *obiter. A. syriacum* Boiss. et Gaill. in Boiss., Diagn. ser. 2, 5 : 72 (1856); Boiss., Fl. 1 : 952 (1867) excl. var. β. [Plate 443]

Evergreen tree or shrub, 3–5 m. Leaves (3–)5–8 × 2–7 cm., obovate, rounded-cuneate or subcordate at base, truncate at apex, usually 3-lobed, glabrous, shining, green on both sides; lobes short, broad, obtuse or acute, entire or undulate; petiole somewhat shorter to somewhat longer than the blade. Inflorescences corymbose. Flowers about 5–7 mm. Sepals and petals obovate to oblong, yellowish-green, the former somewhat shorter than the petals. Ovary sparsely villose; styles much projecting from flower, with long recurved stigmas. Samaras with erect to somewhat divergent wings 2–3 cm. Fl. March–May.

Hab.: In more or less humid maquis; usually on rocky ground. Upper Galilee. Locally fairly common.

Area: E. Mediterranean (Palestine, Lebanon and Syria).

Celastrales

66. SALVADORACEAE

Dioecious or monoecious shrubs or small trees. Leaves opposite, sometimes stipulate, with jointed petiole, more or less leathery, entire. Flowers unisexual or hermaphrodite, actinomorphic, small, in spikes, racemes or panicles, rarely in clusters. Calyx gamosepalous, (2–)4(–5)-lobed. Corolla with 4(–5) slightly connate or free petals alternating with calyx lobes. Disk in the form of small, epipetalous teeth. Stamens 4(–5), alternating with petals; filaments free or connate up to two thirds their length; anthers dorsifixed, 2-celled, opening by longitudinal slits. Ovary superior, free, sessile, 1–2-celled, with 1–2 basal, anatropous ovules in each cell; style short or minute; stigma simple or 2-lobed. Fruit a globular, mostly 1-seeded berry or drupe with a crustaceous or membranous endocarp. Seeds with thick cordate-auriculate cotyledons and no endosperm.

Three genera and 12 species in tropical zones of Africa and Asia.

1. SALVADORA L.

Glaucous trees or shrubs. Leaves thick, with small caducous linear-lanceolate stipules. Flowers usually hermaphrodite or almost unisexual (plants then mostly dioecious), in much branched terminal or axillary spikes or panicles. Bracts minute. Calyx persistent, 4-toothed or -cleft, campanulate. Petals 4, persistent, almost free, imbricate in bud. Stamens 4, inserted on corolla tube; filaments free. Ovary 1-celled, 1-ovuled; style very short or 0; stigma capitate. Fruit a small globular or pyriform berry-like drupe, supported by the slightly enlarged calyx.

Some 5 species in Trop. Africa, Madagascar and S.W. Asia.

1. Salvadora persica L. Sp. Pl. 122 (1753); Boiss., Fl. 4 : 43 (1875). [Plate 444]

Tree or shrub, glabrous, 1–3 m. Branches opposite, repeatedly branched, terete, pendulous, white. Leaves (2–)4–6 ×1.5–3 cm., on petiole 1.5–5 cm., leathery, lanceolate, ovate-oblong, rarely suborbicular, tapering at base, obtuse, sometimes acute, entire, pale green. Racemes axillary or terminal, spike-like, forming diffuse leafy panicles. Pedicels 1–2 mm. Flowers about 3 mm. Calyx campanulate; lobes imbricated. Corolla twice as long as calyx, with imbricated, revolute lobes. Fruit about 4–8 mm., fleshy, globular. Fl. January–April.

Hab.: Hot desert oases; mostly on damp soils, sometimes also on salines. Judean Desert, Lower Jordan Valley, Dead Sea area, Arava Valley, Edom. Uncommon.

Area: Sudanian (up to India).

Fruit edible; shoots and leaves eaten as a salad and also used as fodder; twigs used as toothpicks; leaves, roots, bark and flowers contain oil; diuretic.

Rhamnales

67. RHAMNACEAE

Evergreen or deciduous trees or shrubs, sometimes vines. Leaves alternate or rarely opposite, usually stipulate, simple, 3–5-nerved. Inflorescences mostly cymes arranged in corymbs, or raceme- or panicle-like. Flowers hermaphrodite, sometimes unisexual, actinomorphic, small, green, yellow or whitish. Hypanthium usually present. Sepals 4–5, valvate in bud, caducous. Petals 4–5 or sometimes 0, alternating with sepals, inserted on disk or at throat of hypanthium, often hooded. Disk free or adnate to base of stamens, sometimes obsolete. Stamens 4–5, opposite petals and often enclosed by them; anthers 2-celled, mostly introrsely dehiscent by longitudinal slits. Ovary (1–)2–3 (–4)-celled, free or immersed in disk; ovule mostly 1 in each cell, basal, anatropous; style erect; stigmas 2–4. Fruit a few-celled capsule or a schizocarp, or fruit baccate or drupaceous, sometimes samara-like. Seeds erect, usually with endosperm; embryo straight, cotyledons large and mostly flat, plumule and radicle minute.

About 60 genera and over 900 species in temperate, subtropical and tropical regions.

Literature: K. Süssenguth, Rhamnaceae, in: Engl. & Prantl, *Nat. Pflznfam.* ed. 2, 20d: 7–173, 1953.

1. Branches without stipular spines. Fruit a drupaceous berry, 3–6 mm. in diam.; stones 2–4, seeds solitary.   **1. Rhamnus**
– Branches with stipular spines. Fruit drupe-like, 1-stoned, 0.8–2 cm. in diam. or more; stone usually 2–3-seeded   **2**
2. Fruit dry, discoid with flattened wing-like margin.   **2. Paliurus**
– Fruit fleshy, globular.   **3. Ziziphus**

1. RHAMNUS L.

Shrubs or trees with alternate, rarely subopposite, sometimes spinescent branches. Leaves deciduous or persistent, alternate, opposite or fasciculate, petiolate, entire or dentate, pinnately nerved; stipules caducous, small, subulate. Flowers usually unisexual (plants then dioecious or polygamous), rarely hermaphrodite, small, greenish, in clusters, racemes or cymes, rarely flowers solitary. Hypanthium urceolate or turbinate. Calyx 4–5-fid; sepals erect or spreading, triangular-ovate. Petals 4–5, sometimes 0, inserted at margin of hypanthium, hooded or flat. Disk thin, mostly lining the hypanthium. Stamens 4–5. Ovary superior, free, 2–4-celled; style 2–4-cleft or undivided; stigmas obtuse, papillose. Fruit a drupaceous, fleshy or dry, globular or ovoid berry, with 2–4 leathery or woody 1-seeded stones. Seeds obovoid, smooth or with a groove on the back.

About 150 species in the temperate and subtropical regions of both hemispheres.

Literature: N. Feinbrun, The genus *Rhamnus* in Palestine, *Palest. Journ. Bot. Jerusalem* Ser., 3: 167–169 (1946).

1. Unarmed trees. Leaves 1.5–3.5(–4.5) cm. broad, persistent, glabrous, serrulate.
                                                                               4. R. alaternus
– Shrubs with spinescent branches. Leaves much narrower   **2**
2. Leaves persistent, tomentellous, obovate-oblong or elliptical, margins revolute.
                                                                               3. R. punctatus
– Leaves deciduous, glabrous or sparingly hairy, oblong-cuneate or spatulate, margins not revolute   **3**
3. Leaf margin remotely crenate, with minute glands between teeth.   **2. R. palaestinus**
– Leaf margin entire, glandless.   **1. R. dispermus**

1. Rhamnus dispermus Ehrenb. ex Boiss., Fl. Suppl. 156 (1888; "*disperma*"); Muschl., Man. Fl. Eg. 618 (1912). [Plate 445]

Dioecious or polygamous shrub, 1–1.5 m., with ash-grey bark and twisted stems branched into spinescent twigs. Leaves usually 0.7–1 cm., deciduous, narrowly spatulate to obovate-cuneate, often minutely mucronate, usually entire, at first velvety, later glabrous, minutely pellucid-punctate; petiole 1–4 mm., hairy. Pedicels about twice as long as the flowers or more, capillary. Flowers axillary, 4-merous, clustered. Sepals 2–3 mm., spreading-deflexed, triangular-ovate, yellowish, obsoletely 3-nerved. Petals minute, much shorter than sepals, reddish-yellow, linear. Fruit about 4 mm., dry, subglobular, 2-lobed, brown. Seeds about 3 mm., oblong, yellow. Fl. March–April.

Hab.: Mountains in deserts; stony ground or among rocks. Judean Desert, W. and C. Negev, Moav, Edom. Rare.

Area: E. Saharo-Arabian (Palestine, Sinai, Egypt).

Often associated with *Pistacia atlantica* in deserts.

2. Rhamnus palaestinus Boiss., Diagn. ser. 2, 1 : 119 (1854; "*palaestina*") et Fl. 2 : 16 (1872). *R. oleoides* L., Sp. Pl. ed. 2, 279 (1762) ssp. *graecus* (Boiss. et Reut.) Holmboe, Bergens Mus. Skr. n.r. 1, 2 : 125 (1914); P. H. Davis, Fl. Turk. 2 : 538 (1967). [Plate 446]

Dioecious shrub, 1–2 m. Branches twisted, spinescent, grey to reddish, velvety when young. Leaves 1–2(–2.5) × 0.5–1 cm., deciduous, oblong-cuneate or spatulate to obovate, attenuate at base, often mucronulate, remotely crenate, with minute dark glandules between teeth; petiole 1–4 mm., hairy. Flowers 2–2.5 mm., about as long as the pedicels, axillary, clustered. Sepals 4, rarely 5, spreading, ovate-triangular to ovate-lanceolate, yellowish-green, almost 3-nerved. Corolla 0. Fruit 5–6 mm., dry, obovoid, somewhat compressed, deeply 2-lobed, brown. Seeds 4–5 mm., yellowish, glossy; groove with spongy margin. Fl. March–April.

Hab.: Maquis and garigue, also in semisteppes, on sandy and calcareous ground, often among rocks. Coastal Galilee, Acco Plain, Sharon Plain, Philistean Plain, Upper and Lower Galilee, Mt. Carmel, Mt. Gilboa, Samaria, Judean Mts., Golan, Gilead, Ammon, Moav, Edom. Common.

Area: E. Mediterranean.

A common member of various arboreal plant communities.

3. Rhamnus punctatus Boiss., Diagn. ser. 1, 2 : 4 (1843; "*punctata*") et Fl. 2 : 14 (1872). [Plate 447]

Dioecious or polygamous evergreen shrub, 1–2 m. Branches intricate, rigid, spinescent, hairy, later glabrescent. Leaves 0.7–2(–3) × 0.3–0.8(–1) cm., leathery, obovate-oblong or elliptical, with entire revolute margins, glabrescent above, tomentellous and net-veined beneath; petiole 1–4 mm., hairy. Flowers about 2 mm., axillary, 4-merous, clustered, on tomentellous pedicels as long as or shorter than the flowers. Sepals oblong, yellowish-green, obsoletely 3-nerved. Petals minute, often 0. Fruit about 6 mm., dry, obovoid, 2-lobed, reddish-brown. Seeds 4–5 mm., yellow; groove narrow, with cartilaginous margin. Fl. March–April.

Hab.: Maquis, growing under relatively moist conditions. Upper and Lower Galilee, Mt. Carmel, Judean Mts., Upper Jordan Valley, Ammon (after Dinsmore in Post, Fl. Syr. Pal. Sin. ed. 2, 1 : 290, 1932). Fairly common.

Area: E. Mediterranean.

Var. *angustifolius* Post, Fl. Syr. Pal. Sin. 202 (1883–1896; "*angustifolia*"), which differs from the typical form by its narrower leaflets, can scarcely be retained as a variety.

4. Rhamnus alaternus L., Sp. Pl. 193 (1753); Boiss., Fl. 2 : 14 (1872). [Plate 448]

Dioecious evergreen unarmed glabrous shrub or tree, 2–6 m. Branches ascending. Leaves (2–)3–7 × 1.5–3.5 (–4.5) cm.; petiole about 1 cm., hairy; blade leathery, ovate-elliptical, mucronulate, remotely denticulate-serrulate, glabrous except at the branching points of nerves, upper surface dark green, lower surface light green. Racemes axillary and terminal, short, dense. Flowers 5-merous, about 4 mm. Sepals spreading-deflexed, lanceolate, yellowish-green. Petals 0. Fruit 6–7(–8) mm., berry-like, juicy, obovoid-globular, 2-lobed, black. Seeds 5 mm., yellow, grooved. Fl. February–April.

Hab.: Semihumid maquis. Coastal Galilee, Sharon Plain, Upper Galilee, Mt. Carmel, Samaria, Judean Mts., Dan Valley, Golan. Not rare.

Area: Mediterranean.

Often also grown as an ornamental, especially as a hedge plant; bark laxative; leaves astringent.

2. PALIURUS Mill.

Spiny shrubs or small much branched trees, glabrous or tomentellous. Stipular spines strong, one of them straight, the other curved. Leaves deciduous, alternate, somewhat 2-ranked, petiolate, 3-nerved. Flowers hermaphrodite, in axillary and terminal racemes. Hypanthium broad, obconical. Sepals 5, triangular-ovate, acute. Petals 5, small, inserted on the disk lining the hypanthium, often deflexed, hooded. Stamens 5, included or exserted. Ovary partly immersed in disk, superior to nearly half-inferior, 2–3-celled; style short; stigmas 2–3. Fruit dry, cartilaginous, 1-stoned, hemispherical, expanded into a large, orbicular, entire or lobed wing-like disk. Seeds compressed, obovoid, smooth, with little endosperm.

Some 8 species in S. Europe, W. and E. Asia.

1. Paliurus spina-christi Mill., Gard. Dict. ed. 8 (1768). *Rhamnus paliurus* L., Sp. Pl. 194 (1753). *P. australis* Gaertn., Fruct. 1 : 203, t. 43, f. 5 (1788). *P. aculeatus* Lam., Tabl. Encycl. 1, 2 : 347, t. 210, f. 2 (1792); Boiss., Fl. 2 : 12 (1872). [Plate 449]

Deciduous thorny tree or shrub up to 2 m. or more. Branches alternate, divaricate, often flexuous, grey or reddish. Stipular spines usually unequal, the shorter one curved. Leaves 2–4 × 1.5–3 cm., obliquely ovate, obtuse to somewhat acuminate, 3-nerved, serrate-crenate. Racemes shorter than the leaves, loose. Sepals about 2 mm., half as long as hypanthium. Petals twice as long as calyx, somewhat deflexed, greenish-yellow, ovate. Fruit 1.5–3 cm. in diam., disk-like, reddish, expanded into a broad circular undulate-crenate wing; stone 3-celled, 3-seeded, woody. Seeds 4–5 mm., dark brown, glossy. Fl. April–June.

Hab.: Among shrubs; mostly on alluvial soils. Acco Plain, Sharon Plain (fide Evenari in Opphr. et Evenari, Bull. Soc. Bot. Genève, ser. 2, 31 : 319, 1941), Philistean Plain (fide Rechinger f., Ark. Bot. ser. 2, 2, 5 : 387, 1952), Upper and Lower Galilee, Samaria, Judean Mts. (cult.?), Dan Valley. Rather rare.

Area: N. and E. Mediterranean and W. Irano-Turanian, with extensions into S. Euro-Siberian territories.

Formerly used in medicine as an astringent, tonic, diuretic and anticathartic.

3. ZIZIPHUS Mill.

Evergreen or deciduous shrubs or trees. Stipular spines usually present, unequal, one of them shorter and recurved. Leaves alternate, 2-ranked, petiolate, entire or dentate-crenate, 3–5-nerved. Flowers hermaphrodite, clustered in axillary cymes or solitary, rotate. Hypanthium obconical. Sepals 5, spreading, triangular-ovate, acute, keeled within. Petals 5 (rarely 0), deflexed. Disk lining the hypanthium, flat, 5–10-lobed or -angled. Stamens 5. Ovary partly immersed in and adnate at base to disk but superior, partly or completely 2(–3–4)-celled; style 2(–3–4)-fid; stigmas minute, papillose. Fruit fleshy, drupaceous, globular or ovoid, edible; stone (1–)2(–4)-celled, (1–)2(–3)-seeded, bony. Seeds compressed, ovate to suborbicular, smooth; endosperm 0 or almost so.

About 100 species in tropical and subtropical regions.

1. Leaves hairy to velvety on both sides.   **2. Z. nummularia**
– Leaves glabrous or puberulent at nerves only   **2**
2. A tree with a distinct single stem. Leaves 2–8 cm., mostly persistent. Branches rather straight or slightly flexuous. Drupe 1–1.5 cm.   **1. Z. spina-christi**
– A shrub with intricately branched stems. Leaves 1–2 cm., deciduous. Branches very flexuous. Drupe 0.8–1 cm.   **3. Z. lotus**

1. Ziziphus spina-christi (L.) Desf., Fl. Atl. 1 : 201 (1798); Willd., Sp. Pl. 1 : 1105 (1798; "*Zizyphus*"); Boiss., Fl. 2 : 13 (1872). *Rhamnus spina-christi* L., Sp. Pl. 195 (1753). [Plate 450]

Evergreen tree, 3–8 m., with main stem and almost globular or ovoid crown. Branches ascending and spreading, rather long, greyish-white, glabrous. Stipular spines stout, one straight, about 1 cm. or more, the other recurved, shorter, sometimes spines 0. Leaves 2–8 × 1.5–3 cm., elliptical or ovate to oblong, obtuse or acute, often mucronulate, obsoletely crenate, 3-nerved, glabrous or puberulent at nerves on lower face only; petiole 0.5–1.5 cm. Cymes axillary. Pedicels 3–5 mm. Flowers 4–6 mm. in diam., yellowish-green. Sepals woolly outside. Petals shorter than sepals, yellow, hooded. Disk 5-angled. Fruit 1–1.5 cm., globular or nearly so; mature fruit yellowish. Seeds 5–6 mm., dark brown. Fl. September–April and also in other seasons.

Hab.: Oases in hot deserts, wadi beds, coastal foothills, fields on alluvial soils; usually from 350 m. below to 500 m. above sea level. Acco Plain, Sharon Plain, Philistean Plain, Upper and Lower Galilee, Esdraelon Plain, Samaria, Shefela, Judean Mts., Negev, Dan Valley, Hula Plain, Upper Jordan Valley, Beit Shean Valley, Lower Jordan Valley, Dead Sea area, Arava Valley, Golan, valleys in Moav and Edom.

Area: Sudanian, with extensions into the warmer parts of the Mediterranean, Saharo-Arabian and W. Irano-Turanian territories.

Var. *inermis* Boiss., l.c., can scarcely be maintained as a variety. Records of it probably refer to younger branches of cultivated specimens.

One of the most common trees in the lowlands of Palestine; occurs sometimes as a weed in irrigated crops of the Jordan Valley; attains a great age and large dimensions. Frequently revered by Arabs as a sacred tree; sometimes planted for its shade and edible fruits.

2. Ziziphus nummularia (Burm. f.) Wight et Walk.-Arn., Prodr. 162 (1834; *"Zizyphus"*); Boiss., Fl. 2 : 13 [1872; *"Zizyphus nummularia* (Burm. f.) Walk.-Arn."]. *Rhamnus nummularia* Burm. f., Fl. Ind. 61 (1768). [Plate 451]

Deciduous, thorny, many-stemmed shrub, 1–2 m. Branches many, divaricate, flexuous, hairy to white-tomentose. Stipular spines 0.5–1.5 cm., usually one of them shorter and curved or 0. Leaves 1–1.5 cm., ovate-orbicular, mostly apiculate or mucronate, almost entire, hairy or tomentose on both sides, 3-nerved; petiole 2–5 mm., tomentose. Pedicels 0.5–1 cm. Flowers 3–4 mm., axillary, yellowish-green. Sepals triangular, grey-tomentose. Petals as long as sepals, obovate. Disk 10-lobed. Fruit about 8 mm., almost globular. Seeds 4–5 mm., dark brown. Fl. March–April.

Hab.: Ravines in hot deserts. S. Arava Valley. Very rare.

Area: Sudanian (Nubo-Sindian).

3. Ziziphus lotus (L.) Lam., Encycl. 3 : 317 (1789) et Tabl. Encycl. 1, 1 : 330, t. 185, f. 2 (1792); Boiss., Fl. 2 : 12 (1872; *"Zizyphus"*). *Rhamnus lotus* L., Sp. Pl. 194 (1753); Desf., Mém. Acad. R. Sci. Paris 1788 : 446, t. 21 (1788). [Plate 452]

Deciduous thorny shrub, 1–1.5 m. Stems many, very intricately branched, ash-grey to whitish, glabrous. Stipular spines 0.5–1.2 cm., usually slender, one of them much shorter and curved. Leaves 1–2 cm., ovate-oblong to broadly elliptical, obtuse to acute, crenulate with minute gland at top of each crenule, glabrous, 3-nerved; petiole 1–3 mm. Flowers axillary, 3–4 mm., yellowish-green, solitary or in small clusters, on glabrous pedicels much longer than the calyx. Sepals ovate-triangular, glabrous. Petals obovate, truncate. Disk 10-lobed. Fruit 0.8–1 cm., nearly globular; mature fruit yellowish. Seeds 6 × 4.5 mm., dark brown. Fl. March–April.

Hab.: Stony slopes and alluvial plains, mainly on basalt ground, up to 500 m. above sea level. Acco Plain, Sharon Plain, Upper and Lower Galilee, Mt. Carmel, Esdraelon Plain, Mt. Gilboa, Samaria, Dan Valley, Hula Plain, Upper Jordan Valley, Beit Shean Valley, Lower Jordan Valley, Golan, Gilead. Locally very common.

Area: Mediterranean and Sudanian (Greece, Cyprus, S. Anatolia, W. Syria, Palestine, Socotra, S. Arabia, N. Africa from Libya to Morocco, Spain). Origin probably Trop. Arabia.

The local primary distribution area of this invasive shrub is the Middle Jordan Valley (mainly between Wadi Far'a and Beit Shean); in all other parts of Palestine it is probably secondary, having penetrated into many warm areas where the natural forest or maquis vegetation has been destroyed or devastated. It is a leading plant in a few local semisteppe plant communities. It requires warm winters; propagates vegetatively from subterranean suckers.

Fruit edible, less tasty than that of *Z. spina-christi*.

Malvales

68. TILIACEAE

Trees, shrubs or herbs, often clothed with stellate hairs. Leaves alternate or rarely opposite, undivided or lobed; stipules usually small and caducous, sometimes 0. Inflorescences usually cymose. Flowers hermaphrodite, rarely unisexual (plants then monoecious), actinomorphic. Sepals 4–5, free or united, usually valvate in bud. Petals as many as sepals, free, rarely united, twisted-imbricated in bud, rarely 0. Stamens numerous, rarely 10 or less; filaments free or united into fascicles of 5 or 10; anthers 2-celled; staminodes sometimes present. Ovary usually superior, of 2–10 carpels, 2- to many-celled, each cell with 1 to many anatropous ovules mostly on axile placentae; style 1, lobed or not. Fruit drupaceous or berry- or nut-like or a capsule. Seeds usually with endosperm; embryo straight.

About 45 genera and 400 species widely distributed in temperate and tropical regions.

1. Trees or shrubs. Fruit drupaceous, 8 mm. across. **1. Grewia**
– Annuals. Fruit a siliquose capsule (in ours), 3–10 cm. long. **2. Corchorus**

1. GREWIA L.

Shrubs or small trees. Leaves alternate, frequently 2-ranked, entire or serrate. Flowers hermaphrodite or unisexual, usually arranged in axillary or terminal bracteate cymes or panicles. Sepals 5, free, valvate in bud, somewhat leathery. Petals free, pitted at base, rarely petals 0. Stamens numerous, free, inserted on a short androgynophore; staminodes 0. Ovary 2–4-celled; cells with 2 to many ascending ovules; style subulate; stigma capitate or lobed. Fruit drupe-like, globular, deeply 2–4-lobed, 1–4-stoned, glossy or villose; stones 1–2-seeded. Seeds with or without endosperm.

About 150 species in Trop. Africa, Asia and Australia.

1. Grewia villosa Willd., Neue Schr. Ges. Ñat. Freunde Berlin 4 : 205 (1803). [Plate 453]

Shrub or small tree up to 3 m. Stems brownish-red, young parts covered with long white hairs. Leaves 4–6(–10) cm. across, short-petioled, almost orbicular, mostly cordate at base, rounded and sometimes mucronate at apex, serrate-margined, densely hairy, rugose. Flowers about 1 cm., subsessile in compact axillary cymes. Sepals oblong-lanceolate, acute, villose. Petals shorter than sepals, yellow to reddish, oblong. Fruit about 8 mm. in diam., 4-stoned, almost globular, hard, coppery red, hairy; stones 1–2-seeded. Fl. March–April.

Hab.: Hot valleys; stony ground. Lower Jordan Valley, Dead Sea area, Arava Valley. Very rare (probably locally extinct).

Area: Mainly Sudanian, but also occurring in other tropical regions of the Old World.

2. Corchorus L.

Herbs or shrubs with simple or stellate hairs. Leaves alternate, serrate, pinnately nerved, usually with small stipules. Flowers hermaphrodite, axillary or opposite the leaves, usually small, yellow, 1 or several on short bracteate peduncles. Sepals 5, rarely 4, free, caducous. Petals free, naked at base. Stamens numerous or twice as many as petals, free; staminodes 0. Ovary 2–6-celled, with several ovules in each cell; style short, simple; stigma hollow, crenulate. Capsule either long (siliquose) and smooth, or short and more or less tuberculate, muricate or echinate, dehiscing loculicidally into 2–5 (–6) valves, with several seeds in each cell, rarely transversely septate between seeds. Seeds pendulous or horizontal, without endosperm, usually with curved embryo and leaf-like cotyledons.

About 100 species in tropical regions.

1. Capsule glabrous, 5–10 × 0.3–0.5 cm. Leaves acute to acuminate, usually serrate, the lower teeth with long bristles. Stems glabrous.   **2. C. olitorius**
– Capsule scabrous, 3.5 × 0.2–0.3 cm. Leaves obtuse, crenate-serrate, the lower teeth similar to the others. Stems hairy.   **1. C. trilocularis**

1. Corchorus trilocularis L., Mant. 77 (1767); Boiss., Fl. 1 : 845 (1867). [Plate 454]
Annual, asperulous, 10–35 cm. Stems erect or ascending to procumbent, branched, hairy. Leaves 2–5 × 0.5–2 cm.; stipules setaceous; petiole short; blade oblong-lanceolate or ovate-oblong to elliptical, obtuse, crenate-serrate, glabrous or sparsely hairy below, especially along nerves. Peduncles opposite leaves, 1–3-flowered, shorter than the petioles. Sepals 5, longer than petals, oblong-lanceolate, mucronate. Petals 5–7 mm., yellow, cuneate. Capsule 3–5 × 0.2–0.3 cm., usually 3–4-valved, 3–4-angled, straight or curved, with obtuse beak; valves scabrous, deeply pitted on inner surface. Seeds tetragonous. Fl. June–September.

Hab.: Among irrigated crops. Sharon Plain, Lower Galilee, Esdraelon Plain, Judean Desert, Upper Jordan Valley, Beit Shean Valley, Lower Jordan Valley, Dead Sea area. Uncommon.

Area: Several tropical regions.

Plants edible.

2. Corchorus olitorius L., Sp. Pl. 529 (1753); Boiss., Fl. 1 : 845 (1867). [Plate 455]
Annual, glabrous or glabrescent, 20–80 cm. Stems erect to ascending, branched. Leaves 4–8 × 1–4 cm.; stipules setaceous; petiole 2–5 cm., pilose; blade oblanceolate or ovate-oblong, acute to acuminate at apex, serrate, the lower teeth with long bristles. Peduncles opposite leaves, 1–2 (–3)-flowered, shorter than the petioles. Sepals 5, shorter than or as long as the petals, oblong-lanceolate, mucronate. Petals about 1 cm., yellow, obovate to spatulate. Capsule 5–10 × 0.3–0.5 cm., 5-valved, 10-angled, conical-beaked, glabrous; inner surface of valves transversely septate and pitted. Seeds many, angular, blackish. Fl. May–August.

Hab.: Among irrigated crops. Sharon Plain, Philistean Plain, Lower Galilee, Esdraelon Plain, Dan Valley, Hula Plain, Upper Jordan Valley, Golan. Uncommon. Area: Several tropical regions.

The source of commercially valuable jute fibre; also often cultivated as a pot herb.

69. MALVACEAE

Herbs, shrubs or trees, usually with stellate hairs. Leaves alternate, stipulate, mostly dentate, lobed or divided. Flowers usually hermaphrodite and actinomorphic, mostly axillary, often large, solitary or in terminal inflorescences. Epicalyx of 3 or more free or united bracteoles close to or adnate to the calyx, or epicalyx 0. Sepals 5, rarely 3 or 4, more or less united, usually valvate in bud. Petals 5, free from each other but usually adnate at base to the staminal column, usually contorted in bud, rarely petals 0. Receptacle short or elongated into a central axis. Stamens mostly numerous (very rarely 5), usually connate below and forming a staminal column; anthers often reniform, 1-celled or spuriously divided into 2 cells by a thin septum. Ovary superior, of 2 to many carpels or cells (rarely reduced to a single carpel); placentation axile; ovules 1 or more in each cell; style divided at top into as many or twice as many lobes or stigmas as carpels, rarely style entire and club-shaped. Fruit a loculicidally dehiscing capsule or a schizocarp of few to many mericarps, rarely a berry; mericarps indehiscent, rarely dehiscing into 2 valves. Seeds often hairy, with embryo enclosed in the endosperm.

About 75 genera and 1,000 species, mainly in various tropical and subtropical regions.

1. Flowers without epicalyx.   **2. Abutilon**
− Flowers with epicalyx of free or united bracteoles   2
2. Bracteoles of epicalyx free (in ours)   3
− Bracteoles of epicalyx connate   5
3. Bracteoles of epicalyx more than 3. Fruit a 5-celled capsule; cells 3- or more-seeded.
                                                                                   1. Hibiscus
− Bracteoles of epicalyx 2–3. Fruit a schizocarp; mericarps numerous, 1-seeded   4
4. Petals notched. Mericarps not inflated.   **3. Malva**
− Petals entire. Mericarps inflated.   **4. Malvella**
5 (2). Lobes of epicalyx 3.   **5. Lavatera**
− Lobes of epicalyx more than 3   6
6. Mericarps 1-celled. Central axis of receptacle cylindrical all along. Flowers about
   1–2 cm.   **7. Althaea**
− Mericarps incompletely 2-celled. Central axis of receptacle cylindrical below, dilated
   above into a dentate rim, and ending in a conical body. Flowers 2–6 (–8) cm.
                                                                                    6. Alcea

1. Hibiscus L.

Herbs, shrubs or trees. Leaves undivided or palmately lobed. Flowers hermaphrodite, axillary, mostly solitary. Epicalyx usually of 5 bracteoles or more, free or connate at base. Calyx 5-toothed or 5-fid, sometimes spathe-like and deeply cleft. Petals red, pink, yellow or white, adnate at base to the staminal column. Staminal column truncate or toothed at top; filaments many. Ovary 5-celled, with 3 or more ovules in each cell; lobes of style 5; stigmas capitate. Capsule 5-celled, sometimes 10-celled (by false septa), membranous or leathery. Seeds 1 to several in each cell, ascending, globular, reniform or angular, glabrous, hairy or woolly.

About 300 species, most abundant in the tropical regions of both hemispheres, especially in Africa.

1. Shrubby perennials. Leaves undivided, ovate, acutely dentate. Capsule hirsute, free.
    1. H. micranthus
– Annuals. Leaves 3–5-palmately divided. Capsule villose, included in the inflated, membranous, green- or red-nerved calyx.   **2. H. trionum**

1. Hibiscus micranthus L. f., Suppl. 308 (1781). *H. ovalifolius* sensu Boiss., Fl. 1 : 839 (1867) non *H. ovalifolius* (Forssk.) Vahl, Symb. Bot. 1 : 50 (1790). [Plate 456]

Dwarf shrub, appressed- and stellate-bristly, up to 60 cm. Branches wand-like. Leaves (1.5–)2–2.5 cm., petiolate, ovate to lanceolate, obtuse, acutely dentate; stipules subulate, almost spiny. Pedicels shorter than the subtending leaves, longer than the petiole. Flowers solitary. Epicalyx of free setaceous bracteoles, shorter than the calyx. Calyx lobes 5 mm., triangular-lanceolate, acuminate. Corolla 1–1.5 cm. across; petals about twice as long as calyx, pink or white, obovate-oblong. Capsule about 1 cm., free, ovoid, hirsute; valves dark green above. Seeds numerous, cottony. Fl. January–July.

Hab.: Hot deserts; in wadis or rock fissures. S. Negev, Lower Jordan Valley, Dead Sea area, Arava Valley. Rare.

Area: Widespread in tropical regions of Asia and Africa.

2. Hibiscus trionum L., Sp. Pl. 697 (1753); Boiss., Fl. 1 : 840 (1867). [Plate 457]

Annual, hispid with stellate hairs, 20–60 cm. Stems erect, much branched. Leaves 3–8(–10) cm., long-petioled, the lower leaves orbicular, undivided, the others palmate or 3–5-palmatifid, with obovate to oblong lobulate segments. Pedicels shorter than the leaves, as long as or longer than the petioles. Flowers solitary. Epicalyx of numerous free bracteoles, about 1.2 cm., linear-subulate, hispid. Calyx 1.5 cm., persistent, membranous, inflated, hispid, especially along the red nerves, growing to 2 cm. or more in fruit; lobes as long as the tube, triangular, acute. Petals 2.5–3 cm., yellow with purple spots. Capsule about 1.5 cm., included in the calyx, oblong, obtuse, villose. Seeds reniform, black, tuberculate. Fl. June–August.

Hab.: Among irrigated summer crops. Sharon Plain, Upper and Lower Galilee, Esdraelon Plain, Samaria, Judean Mts., Dan Valley, Hula Plain, Upper Jordan Valley, Golan, Gilead. Not rare.

Area: A widespread weed, especially in the tropical regions of Asia and Africa.

2. ABUTILON Mill.

Herbs or shrubs, tomentose, often with both appressed and patulous hairs. Leaves mostly dentate, sometimes lobed. Flowers axillary, solitary or few in raceme-like flowering branches, rarely in terminal panicles. Epicalyx 0. Calyx 5-cleft; lobes valvate. Petals connate below and adnate to the base of the staminal column. Stamens numerous, filaments free above. Ovary of 5 to numerous carpels, each with 1–3 (–9) ovules; branches of style as many as the carpels, papillose at apex. Fruit a schizocarp; mericarps few to many, 1–3-seeded, beaked, truncate or rounded at apex, separating from the axis and usually splitting lengthwise. Seeds ascending or horizontal.

About 100 species, mainly in tropical regions, some of them weeds.

1. Mericarps truncate or rounded at apex.   **2. A. pannosum**
 – Mericarps beaked, awned, acute or acuminate   2
2. Mericarps about 10 in each fruit. Perennials.   **1. A. fruticosum**
 – Mericarps (13–) 15–30 in each fruit, rarely 10–16 and then plants annual   3
3. Mericarps with long awns. Corolla one and a half times as long as calyx. Leaves entire or very shallowly denticulate. Pedicels thick, shorter than petiole. Green annuals.   **5. A. theophrasti**
 – Mericarps with very short awns or sharp points   4
4. Petals about 1.2 cm. or less, notched. Leaves ovate, long-acuminate.   **4. A. indicum**
 – Petals 1.6 cm. or more, not notched. Leaves broadly ovate to orbicular, apiculate to short-acuminate.   **3. A. hirtum**

1. Abutilon fruticosum Guill. et Perr. in Guill., Perr. et Rich., Fl. Seneg. Tent. 70 (1831); Boiss., Fl. 1 : 836 (1867). *A. denticulatum* (Fresen.) Webb, Fragm. Florul. Aethiop.-Aeg. 51 (1854). *Sida denticulata* Fresen., Mus. Senckenb. 1 : 182 (1834). [Plate 458]

Shrub, appressed- and velvety-canescent (without patulous villi), 1–2 m. Stems many, erect, with numerous erect terete branches. Leaves 2–8 × 2–6 cm., long-petioled; stipules caducous, linear; blade ovate-cordate, coarsely dentate (rarely entire), velvety, lighter beneath. Pedicels longer than the petioles, jointed above the middle. Flowers axillary, often solitary in the axils of short flowering branches. Calyx about 1 cm., broadly campanulate, cleft down to below the middle into ovate-oblong acuminate lobes. Corolla 1.5–2 cm.; petals yellow to yellowish-white, obovate, tapering at base, retuse at apex. Fruit longer than the calyx, short-cylindrical; mericarps 8–11, 8 × 3 mm., united at base and not readily separating, 2–3-seeded, acute at apex, densely stellate-hairy on the back. Seeds about 2 mm., ovoid-reniform, punctulate-papillose. Fl. mainly spring and summer.

Hab.: Wadis and oases in hot deserts. E. and S. Negev, Dead Sea area, Arava Valley. Uncommon.

Area: Mainly Sudanian.

2. Abutilon pannosum (Forst. f.) Schlecht., Bot. Zeit. 9 : 828 (1851); Webb, Fragm. Florul. Aethiop.-Aeg. 52 (1854; *in obs.*). *Sida pannosa* Forst. f., Commentat. Soc. Sci. Gott. ser. 2, 9 (ad ann. 1787): 62 (1789). *A. muticum* (Del. ex DC.) Sweet, Hort.

Brit. ed. 2, 65 (1830); Webb, l.c. 51; Boiss., Fl. 1 : 836 (1867). *A. glaucum* (Cav.) Sweet, Hort. Brit. 54 (1826). [Plate 459]

Shrub, up to 2 m. or more, woolly-canescent with stellate appressed hairs mixed with dense patulous hairs; branchlets and pedicels with short glandular hairs. Stems much branched, terete below, somewhat angulate above. Leaves 5–8 × 4–7 cm., long-petioled; stipules linear, acute to subulate at apex; blade ovate-cordate, acute to acuminate, irregularly and coarsely dentate to slightly lobed, grey to yellowish and stellately tomentose beneath, darker and puberulent above, prominently nerved. Pedicels shorter or longer than the petioles and jointed above the middle. Flowers both axillary and terminal; lowermost flowers solitary; upper flowers in clusters. Calyx about 1.2 × 1.5 cm., campanulate, cleft down to below the middle; each lobe 6–7 mm., broad at base, ovate and abruptly acuminate. Corolla twice as long as calyx or more, yellow or pink; petals obovate, slightly notched. Fruit 0.8–1 × up to 2 cm.; mericarps 25–35, about 8 mm., readily separating, truncate or rounded at apex, stellate-hairy on the back, blackish-brown. Seeds 2 mm., reniform, appressed- and short-bristly. Fl. May–August and also in other seasons.

Hab.: Oases in hot deserts; on cultivated land and near water. Lower Jordan Valley, Dead Sea area (mainly in Ghor es Safi and Arnon River). Rare.

Area: Tropical (mainly Sudanian).

Used in some oriental countries as a fibre plant; seeds eaten by the Bedouins.

3. Abutilon hirtum (Lam.) Sweet, Hort. Brit. 53 (1826). *Sida hirta* Lam., Encycl. 1 : 7 (1783). *A. graveolens* (Roxb. ex Hornem.) Wight et Walk.-Arn. ex Wight, Cat. 13 no. 191 (1833). *S. graveolens* Roxb., Hort. Bengal. 50 (1814) *nom. nud.*; Roxb. ex Hornem., Hort. Hafn. Suppl. 77 (1819). [Plate 460]

Shrub, yellowish-white, tomentose, 1–2 m. Stems many, branching from near base, thick, terete, with long patulous villi and short simple and glandular hairs. Leaves 3–15 × 4–12 cm., very long-petioled; stipules reflexed, linear-lanceolate, often falcate, acute; blade broadly ovate to orbicular, cordate at base, short-acuminate, crenate-dentate, somewhat lighter beneath. Pedicels jointed above the middle, usually shorter than the petioles but the upper ones longer. Flowers axillary, often solitary in the axils of the flowering branches. Calyx 1 cm. in diam., broadly campanulate, cleft down to the middle into ovate-apiculate lobes. Corolla yellow with a darker centre; petals 1.6 cm. or more, obovate, tapering to a short claw. Fruit 1.3 × 1.2 cm.; mericarps 20 or more, 1–1.2 cm., white-membranous, acute or short-acuminate at apex; back densely stellate-hairy or hispidulous. Seeds 2–3 in each carpel, 2 mm., reniform, black, appressed-hirtellous. Fl. almost the whole year round.

Hab.: Wadis and oases in hot deserts. Judean Desert, S. Negev, Lower Jordan Valley, Dead Sea area, Arava Valley, Edom. Uncommon.

Area: Sudanian and other tropical regions of Africa and Asia.

4. Abutilon indicum (L.) Sweet, Hort. Brit. 54 (1826) emend. Hochr., Ann. Cons. Jard. Bot. Genève 6 : 19 (1902). *Sida indica* L., Cent. Pl. 2 : 28 (1756) et Amoen. Acad. 4 : 324 (1759). [Plate 461]

Shrub, velvety-canescent, 1–2 m. Stems many, erect, branched, terete, with long patulous villi and short appressed hairs, the younger twigs somewhat flexuous. Leaves mostly 5–10 × 4–8 cm., long-petioled; stipules linear, acute; blade ovate-cordate, long-acuminate, coarsely and irregularly crenate-dentate, appressed- and short-puberulent and also with longer, simple or forked hairs, lower surface lighter in colour. Pedicels much longer than the petioles, slender, jointed above the middle. Flowers axillary, often appearing together with younger flowering branches. Calyx up to 8 mm., broadly campanulate or cup-shaped, cleft down to below the middle into ovate, apiculate lobes, spreading after flowering. Corolla up to twice as long as calyx, yellow; petals obovate, retuse. Fruit cylindrical, truncate; mericarps 18 or more, 2–3-seeded, oblong, acute, stellate-hairy; apex of mericarp with 2 points, one directed inwards and the other outwards, the latter splitting into 2 at the dehiscence of the mericarp. Seeds about 1 mm., reniform, papillose-tuberculate. Fl. May (but probably also in other seasons).

Hab.: Hot valleys in E. Judean Desert, E. Negev and around the Dead Sea. Rare.

Area: Widespread in the Afro-Asian tropics.

Sometimes used as a fibre plant; also known in folk medicine.

5. Abutilon theophrasti Medik., Künstl. Geschl. Malv.-Fam. 28 (1787). *A. avicennae* Gaertn., Fruct. 2 : 251, t. 135, f. 1 (1791); Boiss., Fl. 1 : 836 (1867). [Plate 462]

Annual, tomentose with short, dense, patulous hairs intermixed with scattered, long villi, 40–60 cm. Stems mostly single, sparingly branched above, terete. Leaves 7–15 × 6–8 cm., long-petioled; stipules linear to filiform, acute; blade ovate-cordate, long-acuminate, entire to shallowly denticulate-crenate, green, sparingly hairy on both sides to glabrescent beneath, prominently nerved. Pedicels shorter than the petioles, thick, jointed above the middle. Lower flowers axillary, solitary; upper flowers clustered in short panicles. Calyx 0.8–1 cm., campanulate, cleft down to below the middle into ovate and apiculate lobes, growing somewhat in fruit. Corolla about one and a half times as long as calyx, yellow; petals obovate, tapering at base, notched at apex. Fruit 1.5–2 cm. in diam.; mericarps usually 10–16, 1–2-seeded, 2-awned; awns erect or spreading, up to 3 mm. Seeds 2–3 mm., ovate-reniform, appressed-bristly. Fl. May–September.

Hab.: Irrigated fields, swamps. Sharon Plain, Philistean Plain. Rare. Introduced recently.

Area: Tropics; also casual in some temperate regions.

3. MALVA L.

Annual or perennial herbs, hairy to glabrescent. Leaves stipulate, usually lobed or divided. Flowers hermaphrodite, axillary, solitary or clustered, sessile or pedicellate. Epicalyx of 3 (rarely 2) free bracteoles arising at base of calyx. Calyx of 5 sepals united below. Petals free, purple, pink or white, emarginate or deeply notched. Staminal column divided above into numerous anther-bearing filaments. Ovary of numerous carpels, each with 1 ovule; branches of style numerous, filiform, stigmatose along their inner faces. Fruit a schizocarp; mericarps many, indehiscent, 1-seeded, whorled around a short or conical receptacle. Seeds ascending.

About 40 species in temperate regions of the N. hemisphere; also in S. America.

1. Petals 3–4 times as long as calyx.   **2. M. sylvestris**
– Petals usually twice as long as calyx or less   2
2. Epicalyx of 2 linear bracteoles. Leaves palmatisect into palmatipartite segments.
                                                                   1. M. aegyptia
– Epicalyx of 3 bracteoles. Leaves not as above   3
3. Bracteoles of epicalyx ovate to oblong, usually broader than 2 mm. Claws of petals
   bearded. Pedicels more or less erect after flowering.   **3. M. nicaeensis**
– Bracteoles of epicalyx linear to linear-oblong, about 1 mm. broad. Claws of petals
   glabrous, or bearded but then pedicels usually deflexed after flowering   4
4. Calyx not accrescent in fruit. Mericarps smooth, pubescent, somewhat rounded at
   margin.   **4. M. neglecta**
– Calyx accrescent in fruit. Mericarps wrinkled, mostly glabrous, angular, crested,
   toothed or winged at margin   5
5. Leaves undivided or 5–7-fid into short, obtuse, crenate or dentate lobes. Fruiting calyx
   lobes broadly ovate to orbicular, apiculate.   **5. M. parviflora**
– Leaves 3–5-fid or -parted; lobes or segments deeply cleft into long, lanceolate, acute,
   entire or 3-fid lobules. Fruiting calyx lobes ovate-triangular, acuminate.
                                                                   6. M. oxyloba

1. Malva aegyptia L., Sp. Pl. 690 (1753); Boiss., Fl. 1 : 818 (1867) p.p. non *M. aegyptia* auct. Fl. Cauc. [Plate 463]

Annual, appressed-hispid, 10–20 cm. Stems many, ascending to erect, moderately branched. Leaves 1–4 cm.; lower leaves long-petioled, uppermost ones subsessile; stipules much shorter than the petiole, ovate to lanceolate, acuminate, setose-ciliate; blade more or less orbicular in outline, palmatisect; segments 0.8–2 cm., palmatifid or -parted into oblong-linear, somewhat cuneate, lobulate lobes. Pedicels longer than the subtending leaves. Flowers axillary and terminal, solitary or clustered. Epicalyx of 2 linear bracteoles, shorter than calyx. Calyx 6–9 mm., accrescent in fruit, with ovate-triangular acuminate ciliate lobes. Petals about as long as calyx, obovate, bluish-violet. Mericarps about 1–1.5 mm., thick, wrinkled. Fl. January–April.

Hab.: Deserts; usually ruderal or segetal on sandy and loess soils. Sharon Plain, Philistean Plain, Judean Mts. (adventive), Judean Desert, W., N. and C. Negev, Ammon, Edom. Locally common.

Area: S. W. Saharo-Arabian, with extensions into adjacent Mediterranean territories.

2. Malva sylvestris L., Sp. Pl. 689 (1753); Boiss., Fl. 1 : 819 (1867). *M. sylvestris* L. var. *mauritiana* (L.) Boiss. et var. *eriocarpa* Boiss., l.c. *M. sylvestris* L. var. *oxyloba* Post, Journ. Linn. Soc. Lond. Bot. 24 : 424 (1888). [Plate 464]

Annual or biennial, hirsute to stellate-pubescent or glabrescent, 20–70 cm. Stems erect to ascending, sometimes procumbent, branched mainly below. Leaves varying in size and shape; petioles shortening towards apex; stipules ovate to oblong or lanceolate, acuminate; blade usually orbicular in outline, cordate or reniform at base, crenate and almost undivided to 5–7-palmatipartite, hairy. Pedicels erect after flowering Flowers axillary, mostly in clusters of 2–3 or more. Epicalyx of 3 oblong-lanceolate bracteoles, two thirds as long as the calyx. Calyx 0.6–1 cm.; lobes connivent, ovate to triangular, often stellate-hairy. Petals 3–4 times as long as calyx, pink to purple with darker veins, obovate-oblong, emarginate, bearded at the cuneate base. Fruit up to 1 cm. in diam.; mericarps 2–2.5 mm., glabrous, rarely pubescent or tomentose, wrinkled. Fl. February–April.

Hab.: Roadsides, waste places, abandoned fields and by fences. Acco Plain, Sharon Plain, Philistean Plain, Mt. Carmel, Judean Mts., Judean Desert, Negev, Lower Jordan Valley, Arava Valley, Ammon, Moav, Edom. Fairly common.

Area: Mediterranean and Euro-Siberian, with extensions into the Irano-Turanian region; adventive in many other regions.

M. sylvestris is rather variable as to indumentum, leaf shape and flower size; it also shows a wide ecological range. Attempts to subdivide this species on the basis of morphological characters have failed so far.

Officinal: (fol., flor. malvae), used as a gargle and mouth wash and to reduce inflammation; leaves and fruit edible; often used as a pot herb.

This or some other species of the genus *Malva* is believed to be the Biblical חַלָּמוּת (Job vi: 6).

3. Malva nicaeensis All., Fl. Ped. 2: 40 (1785); Boiss., Fl. 1: 819 (1867). [Plate 465]

Annual, more or less patulous-hairy to glabrescent, 15–35 (–70) cm. Stems erect, ascending to procumbent, much branched. Leaves 1.5–5 cm.; stipules 3–8 mm., ovate or oblong, acuminate; petiole up to 15 cm.; blade orbicular to reniform in outline, undivided or 5–7-fid into broad crenulate lobes, glabrous or sparingly hairy. Pedicels erect in flower, erect or spreading after flowering. Flowers (1–)2–3 in axillary clusters. Epicalyx of 3 ovate-oblong bracteoles, two thirds as long as the calyx or as long. Calyx 4–5 mm., accrescent in fruit; lobes triangular, acute to acuminate, glabrous, spreading in fruit. Petals 0.7–1.2 cm., purplish, rarely pink or white, cuneate or emarginate; claw bearded. Fruit 0.8–1 cm. in diam.; mericarps glabrous, reticulate-wrinkled and pitted. Fl. February–June.

Hab.: Wastes and roadsides. Sharon Plain, Philistean Plain, Upper and Lower Galilee, Mt. Carmel, Esdraelon Plain, Samaria, Shefela, Judean Mts., N. Negev, Hula Plain, Upper and Lower Jordan Valley, Golan, Gilead, Ammon. Very common.

Area: Mediterranean and Irano-Turanian.

Used as a pot herb.

4. Malva neglecta Wallr., Syll. Pl. Nov. Ratisb. 1: 140 (1824). *M. rotundifolia* auct. non L., Sp. Pl. 688 (1753); Boiss., Fl. 1: 820 (1867). [Plate 466]

Annual, rarely perennial, densely and more or less appressed-hairy, 10–25 cm. Stems many, all procumbent or the central stems ascending. Leaves 0.8–5 cm., long-petioled; stipules 5–8 mm., almost membranous, lanceolate to ovate, ciliate; blade orbicular to reniform in outline or cordate at base, crenate, shallowly lobed, more or less pubescent. Pedicels long, unequal, spreading or deflexed after flowering. Flowers solitary or many in leaf axils. Epicalyx of 3 linear to oblong bracteoles, shorter than the calyx. Calyx about 5 mm.; lobes slightly connivent with reflexed tips, triangular, acute, stellate-hairy, not accrescent in fruit. Petals about 1 cm. (rarely longer), white with lilac veins or pink, obovate, cuneate, deeply emarginate, bearded at base. Fruit

5–7 mm. in diam.; mericarps short-pubescent, smooth (not wrinkled), with rounded margins. Fl. March–April.

Hab.: Weedy places. Negev, Edom. Very rare.

Area: Euro-Siberian, Mediterranean and Irano-Turanian.

A perennial specimen collected in Edom may represent *M. rotundifolia* L. var. *perennans* Post, Fl. Syr. Pal. Sin. 178 (1883–1896). As perennation is a general trend in several species of *Malva,* one can hardly ascribe diagnostic value to this character. Contains tannin; used in folk medicine as a purgative and to reduce inflammation.

5. Malva parviflora L., Demonstr. Pl. Hort. Upsal. 18 (1753), Amoen. Acad. 3 : 416 (1756) et Sp. Pl. ed. 2, 969 (1763); Boiss., Fl. 1 : 820 (1867). *M. parviflora* L. var. *cristata* Boiss., l.c. 821 et var. *cristata* Boiss. f. *hirsuta* Nab., Publ. Fac. Sci. Univ. Masaryk 35 : 54 (1923). *M. parviflora* L. var. *arguta* Post, Fl. Syr. Pal. Sin. 179 (1883–1896) et ed. 2, 1 : 237 (1932). [Plate 467]

Annual, hairy or glabrescent, 5–50(–80) cm. Stems erect to ascending or prostrate. Leaves 1–4(–10) cm.; stipules 3–7 mm., submembranous, oblong-lanceolate to ovate, acuminate, long-ciliate; petiole 5–25 cm.; blade orbicular in outline, cordate to reniform at base, crenate, undivided or 5–7-fid into obtuse lobes. Pedicels 0.3–2.5 cm., spreading to deflexed in fruit. Flowers 2–4 or more in axillary clusters. Epicalyx of 3 linear bracteoles, about one half or two thirds as long as the calyx. Calyx 3–6 mm., growing up to 0.8–1 cm. in fruit; lobes ovate to orbicular, apiculate, spreading in fruit. Petals 5–7(–9) mm., barely exceeding the calyx, pink to purple, sometimes white, obovate, notched. Fruit 4–7(–9) mm. in diam., glabrous, rarely hairy; mericarps reticulately and prominently wrinkled, with sharp, entire or dentate, sometimes elevated and crested margins. Fl. February–May.

Hab.: Roadsides and waste places. Coastal Galilee, Acco Plain, Sharon Plain, Philistean Plain, Mt. Carmel, Esdraelon Plain, Shefela, Judean Mts., Judean Desert, W., N. and C. Negev, Upper Jordan Valley, Beit Shean Valley, Lower Jordan Valley, Dead Sea area, Arava Valley, Golan, Gilead, Ammon, Moav, Edom. Very common.

Area: Mediterranean and Irano-Turanian.

We were unable to divide *M. parviflora* into var. *microcarpa* (Desf.) Paol. in Fiori et Paol., Fl. Anal. Ital. 2 : 268 (1901) and var. *typica* Paol., l.c., on the base of the size of the fruit, as there is continuous variation in this character. For the same reason it was impossible to separate var. *cristata* Boiss., l.c., from the ordinary form. Because of continuous variation we were unable to establish other varieties based on the size and shape of leaves, pedicels, calyx lobes, etc.

Leaves and fruits edible.

6. Malva oxyloba Boiss., Diagn. ser. 1, 8 : 109 (1849) et Fl. 1 : 821 (1867). [Plate 468]

Annual, hairy, 10–40 cm. Stems erect òr procumbent, often much branched from base. Leaves 2–5 cm.; stipules about 3 mm., submembranous, ovate-triangular, acuminate, ciliate; petiole 4–15(–25) cm.; blade broadly ovate to orbicular in outline, cordate at base, 3–5-fid or -parted, glabrous to minutely hairy; segments obovate-cuneate, deeply cleft into lanceolate, long and sharp-pointed, undivided or 3-fid lobules. Flowers usually several (up to 7) in axillary clusters, sessile to long-pedicelled. Epicalyx of 3 linear bracteoles, one half to two thirds as long as the calyx. Calyx 3–6 mm., accrescent and spreading in fruit; lobes ovate-triangular, acuminate. Petals 4–6 mm., pink, obovate-cuneate, retuse. Fruit about 8 mm. in diam.; mericarps glabrous, prominently wrinkled and tuberculate, with dentate and elevated margin. Fl. February–May.

Hab.: Roadsides and weedy places. Coastal Galilee, Sharon Plain, Philistean Plain, Upper Galilee, Mt. Carmel, Esdraelon Plain, Judean Mts. Uncommon.

Area: E. Mediterranean.

4. MALVELLA Jaub. et Sp.

Perennial, prostrate herbs similar in appearance to *Malva*. Leaves undivided. Flowers hermaphrodite, axillary, pedicellate. Epicalyx of 3 free, linear-filiform bracteoles. Calyx 5-fid. Petals entire. Filaments united only at base. Ovary 10–12-carpelled with 1 orthotropous ovule in each carpel; styles distinct; stigmas capitate or club-shaped. Fruit a schizocarp; mericarps numerous, indehiscent, 1-seeded, membranous, inflated, somewhat freely arranged around the very short-winged axis of the receptacle. Seeds erect.

One species, mainly in S.W. Asia.

1. Malvella sherardiana (L.) Jaub. et Sp., Ill. Pl. Or. 5: 47, t. 444 (1855); Boiss., Fl. 1: 834 (1867). *Malva sherardiana* L., Sp. Pl. ed. 2, 1675 (1763). [Plate 469]

Perennial, greyish-woolly and stellate-hairy, 15–60(–80) cm. Stems very short, with long, prostrate, flexuous, densely leafy branches. Leaves 1–3 cm.; stipules caducous, herbaceous, oblong; blade orbicular-cordate or reniform, crenate or obsoletely lobed. Pedicels 2–5 cm. Flowers 1–1.5 cm. in diam., solitary. Epicalyx of free, setaceous bracteoles, half as long as the calyx or shorter. Calyx about 5 mm.; lobes ovate. Petals twice as long as calyx, pink or white, obovate, somewhat hairy outside. Fruit up to 1 cm. in diam.; mericarps 8–15, tomentose. Fl. April–July.

Hab.: Fields; among summer crops. Acco Plain, Sharon Plain, Philistean Plain, Upper and Lower Galilee, Esdraelon Plain, Samaria, Shefela, Judean Mts., N. Negev, Hula Plain, Upper Jordan Valley, Golan, Gilead, Ammon. Fairly common.

Area: E. Mediterranean and W. Irano-Turanian.

5. LAVATERA L.

Herbs or shrubs, mostly stellate-hairy. Leaves usually lobed. Flowers hermaphrodite, solitary or in small pedunculate racemes. Epicalyx of 3 bracteoles connate below. Calyx 5-fid. Petals pink, lilac or violet, adnate at base to the staminal column. Filaments numerous, free above. Ovary of many carpels, each with 1 ovule; styles filiform, inner surface stigmatose. Fruit a schizocarp; mericarps many, separating at maturity from axis; axis conical or cylindrical or variously dilated at apex. Seeds solitary, ascending.

About 20 species in temperate and subtropical regions, especially in the Mediterranean region; also in C. Asia, California and Australia.

1. Axis of receptacle in fruit expanded above into a flat or concave disk, entirely covering the mericarps.   **3. L. trimestris**
 − Axis of receptacle not expanding and not covering the mericarps   2
2. Axis of receptacle depressed above. Flowers (3−) 4 or more in leaf axils. Epicalyx of
   almost free bracteoles.   **4. L. cretica**
 − Axis of receptacle conical at top. Flowers 1−2 in leaf axils. Epicalyx cup-shaped, with
   bracteoles connate to about two thirds of their length   3
3. Flowers predominantly pedicellate; pedicels 2 cm. or more. Stems hairy to almost
   glabrous, never tomentose. Lobes of epicalyx and calyx long-acuminate. Mericarps
   transversely wrinkled. Annuals.   **2. L. punctata**
 − Flowers sessile or pedicellate; pedicels 0.5−1.5 cm. Stems tomentose, at least above.
   Lobes of epicalyx apiculate. Mericarps not wrinkled. Shrubs.   **1. L. bryoniifolia**

1. Lavatera bryoniifolia Mill., Gard. Dict. ed. 8, no. 11 (1768). *L. tomentosa* Dum.-
Cours., Bot. Cult. 3 : 48 (1802) et ed. 2, 5 : 74 (1811). *L. unguiculata* Desf., Tabl. 145
(1804) *nom. nud.;* Desf. ex Pers., Syn. Pl. 2 : 252 (1806); Desf., Hist. Arb. 1 : 471
(1809); Boiss., Fl. 1 : 822 (1867). [Plate 470]

Shrub, tomentose and stellate-hairy, 1.5−3 m. Stems erect, much branched, terete,
tomentose above, glabrous below. Leaves up to 20 cm. or more, long-petioled (except
for the uppermost ones), dentate; lower leaves orbicular-cordate, obsoletely lobed;
middle leaves 3−5-lobed; uppermost leaves hastate or acutely 3-lobed; lobes triangular,
acute, irregularly dentate-crenate. Flowers axillary, solitary or in pairs along the stems,
nearly sessile or with pedicels up to 1.5 cm. Epicalyx somewhat shorter than calyx,
long-connate, striate; lobes very short, triangular, apiculate. Calyx lobes triangular,
acute. Petals 2−3 cm., 2−3 times as long as calyx, pink or violet. Fruit about 1 cm.
in diam.; axis of receptacle ending in a conical, radiately striate body; mericarps 15−
20, not wrinkled, minutely tuberculate, each with a deep longitudinal furrow on the
back. Fl. May−July.

Hab.: Edges of wadis and among maquis. Upper and Lower Galilee, Mt. Carmel,
Golan. Rare.

Area: E. Mediterranean.

2. Lavatera punctata All., Auctuar. Fl. Ped. 26 (1789); Boiss., Fl. 1 : 823 (1867).
[Plate 471]

Annual, densely or loosely hairy, often glabrescent, up to 60 cm. or more. Stems
erect, terete. Branches ascending or spreading, violet, brownish or green, usually with
hairy white spots. Leaves up to 10 cm. (incl. petiole), crenate, hairy, deflexed with
age; lower leaves cordate to reniform; middle leaves 3−5-fid or -lobed, lobes oblong
or oblong-linear and acute; uppermost leaves hastate or lanceolate. Pedicels mostly up
to 8 cm. or more, spreading. Flowers axillary, solitary, rarely in pairs, often together
with young flowering branches. Epicalyx nearly as long as the calyx, growing in fruit,
connate to more than two thirds of its length; lobes broad, semiorbicular, auriculate,
acuminate. Calyx up to 1.5 cm.; lobes triangular, acuminate. Petals about (2−)3 cm.,
pink, cuneate at base, retuse at apex. Fruit 5−8 mm. across; axis of receptacle terminating in a long-conical exserted body; mericarps about 10, with delicate transverse
wrinkles all over. Fl. April−June.

Hab.: Among winter crops, also on roadsides; heavy soils. Coastal Galilee, Sharon Plain, Philistean Plain, Upper and Lower Galilee, Mt. Carmel, Esdraelon Plain, Samaria, Shefela, Judean Mts., Dan Valley, Hula Plain, Upper Jordan Valley, Beit Shean Valley, Dead Sea area, Golan. Rather common.

Area: Mediterranean, extending slightly into adjacent Irano-Turanian territories.

Varies in density of indumentum and in flower size. One small specimen of a perennial form with tomentose leaves and stems has been observed in the Dead Sea area.

3. Lavatera trimestris L., Sp. Pl. 692 (1753); Boiss., Fl. 1 : 823 (1867). [Plate 472]

Annual, hairy or glabrescent, 15–50 cm. Stems erect or ascending, divaricately branched, flexuous, somewhat furrowed, with retrorse hairs. Leaves up to 15 cm. (incl. long petiole), crenate; lower leaves reniform, obtuse; intermediate leaves cordate-ovate, angular; uppermost leaves acutely 3-lobed. Pedicels up to 4 cm. or more, often longer than the petiole. Flowers usually solitary. Epicalyx up to 1 cm., shorter than the calyx, growing considerably in fruit, connate to about half its length; lobes triangular, apiculate, often dentate. Calyx 1 cm. or more; lobes triangular, acuminate. Petals 3.5–5 cm., lilac, cuneate, truncate, irregularly dentate at apex. Fruit 0.8–1.4 cm. in diam.; axis of receptacle expanded at top into a flat or concave disk covering the mericarps; mericarps about 14, white, rounded on the back and at the margin, reticulately and transversely wrinkled. Fl. March–June.

Hab.: Among winter crops; heavy soils. Sharon Plain, Philistean Plain, Upper and Lower Galilee, Mt. Carmel, Esdraelon Plain, Samaria, Shefela, Judean Mts., Dan Valley, Hula Plain, Upper Jordan Valley, Gilead. Locally common.

Area: Mediterranean.

4. Lavatera cretica L., Sp. Pl. 691 (1753); Boiss., Fl. 1 : 822 (1867). [Plate 473]

Annual or biennial, 20–100 cm., often with forked or stellate hairs, especially when young. Stems erect, ascending or rarely prostrate, simple or branched, angular. Leaves 5–12(–20) cm. (incl. the petiole), orbicular or cordate, angular or obscurely (3–)5–7-lobed, dentate at margin, subglabrous or hairy. Pedicels up to 2.5 cm., shorter than the petiole. Flowers in axillary clusters. Epicalyx shorter than the calyx; bracteoles connate at base only, ovate, acute. Calyx 6–8 mm.; lobes ovate, acute or acuminate, hairy. Petals 1.2–2 cm., pink to violet, notched to 2-lobed. Fruit 0.5–1 cm. in diam.; axis of receptacle depressed at top; mericarps 9–12, wrinkled all over the back or only at the margins and lateral faces. Fl. February–April.

Hab.: Roadsides, wastes and abandoned gardens. Coastal Galilee, Acco Plain, Sharon Plain, Philistean Plain, Upper and Lower Galilee, Mt. Carmel, Esdraelon Plain, Samaria, Judean Mts., Dan Valley, Hula Plain, Upper and Lower Jordan Valley, Gilead. Very common.

Area: Mediterranean.

Varies greatly in the indumentum, the stature, the size of the leaves and flowers, and in the sculpture of the mericarps.

6. Alcea L.

Perennial herbs, rarely shrubs, usually tomentose with one or two kinds of hairs, sometimes glabrescent or glabrous. Leaves variously divided or lobed, very often palmately partite, sometimes undivided, often very thick. Flowers hermaphrodite, large, often forming leafless or sparingly leafy racemes. Epicalyx 6–9 (–11)-lobed, much or slightly shorter than calyx. Calyx 5-fid, often accrescent in fruit. Petals pink or purple to yellow and white, rarely mauve or violet, obovate to cuneate, emarginate at apex, with a short bearded claw. Staminal column divided above into numerous filaments; anthers usually yellowish. Ovary many-carpelled; carpels almost 2-celled, i.e. divided by a wall protruding from the pericarp. Fruit large; mericarps many, partitioned in 2 unequal cells of which only the lower bears a single seed, glabrous or hairy, variously wrinkled, with the back plane, concave or winged; central axis of receptacle cylindrical and deeply sulcate below, dilated above into a broad dentate rim, and ending in a conical beak. Seeds ascending.

About 60 species, mainly in S.W. Asia. One of its largest centres of distribution is the highlands of E. Anatolia.

Literature: M. M. Iljin, *Alcea* L., in: *Flora URSS* 15 : 84–127 et Addenda 14 : 675–678, 1949. M. Zohary, Taxonomical studies in *Alcea* of south-western Asia, I, *Bull. Res. Counc. Israel* D, 11 : 210–229 (1963); II, *Israel Journ. Bot.* 12 : 1–26 (1963).

1. Leaves almost undivided or only shallowly lobed (lateral lobes not more than one third the length of the whole blade)   2
   – Leaves, at least the upper ones, deeply palmatipartite (lobes more than one third the length of the whole blade), sometimes divided to base or nearly so   6
2. Plants stemless or with procumbent stems. Petals pink, purple or white. Leaves orbicular or nearly so, usually almost undivided.   **1. A. acaulis**
   – Plants with well-developed, erect stems   3
3. Small desert plants with yellow flowers and glabrous, strongly pitted-wrinkled carpels. Leaves orbicular, regularly crenate.   **2. A. chrysantha**
   – Not as above   4
4. Plants densely or sparsely covered with long, retrorse or patulous, stiff, single or fasciculate bristles. Flowers up to 10 cm. across, purple or lilac.   **6. A. setosa**
   – Plants with a tomentose, mostly appressed cover of hairs, sometimes with additional patulous bristles   5
5. Flowers up to 10 cm. across, white, yellow, pink, violet or crimson, axillary, solitary or in leafless racemes. Epicalyx as long as calyx or almost so.   **8. A. apterocarpa**
   – Flowers less than 10 cm. across, white or cream-coloured, in terminal racemes leafy below. Epicalyx about half as long as calyx or less.   **4. A. striata**
6(1). Flowers white with or without a creamy white centre, very rarely pink and then plants with procumbent stems   7
   – Flowers purple, lilac or mauve   9
7. Mericarps glabrous. Lobes of leaves rounded at apex. Plants mostly with long procumbent stems.   **3. A. galilaea**
   – Mericarps hairy. Leaves and stems not as above   8
8. Uppermost leaves only shallowly 3–5-lobed; terminal lobe triangular.   **4. A. striata**

– Most of the stem leaves deeply 3–5-lobed; terminal lobe ovate-oblong.

5. A. rufescens

9(6). Mature mericarps with deep-canaliculate back; margin extended to form wings on either side. Tall plants, often with glabrous or glabrescent stems and reddish or reddish-tipped epicalyx. **9. A. dissecta**

– Mature mericarps with a convex, plane or very slightly concave back; margins never wing-like 10

10. Epicalyx usually almost as long as calyx. Mericarps tomentose with dense stiff hairs at back. Stems with long, retrorse or patulous, simple or fasciculate setaceous hairs, very rarely stems subglabrous. Leaves shallowly palmatifid to palmatipartite; lobes more or less regularly dentate. **6. A. setosa**

— Epicalyx much shorter than calyx. Mericarps with a loosely hairy back. Stems glabrous or hairy, but hairs not setaceous. Leaves palmatisect almost to base into oblong or linear, irregularly dentate or lobulate segments. **7. A. digitata**

1. Alcea acaulis (Cav.) Alef., Oesterr. Bot. Zeitschr. 12 : 251 (1862). [Plate 474]

Perennial with woody base, tomentose with appressed and patulous stellate hairs, 10–25 cm. Stems almost 0. Branches few or many, procumbent, sparingly ramose. Leaves 2–5 cm. across, reniform to cordate, crenate, green above, greyish-green beneath; petiole much longer than blade; lower leaves almost undivided; upper leaves very shallowly 3–5-lobed. Flowers axillary, solitary, subsessile, usually crowded at base of plant and overtopped by leaves, sometimes arranged along the branches. Epicalyx half as long as the calyx or less, with ovate to oblong lobes. Calyx up to 1.5 cm.; lobes ovate-triangular to lanceolate, striate. Corolla 2–4 times as long as calyx, pink, purple or white. Mericarps numerous, glabrous, the back very prominently wrinkled and slightly canaliculate, the lateral faces prominently wrinkled. Seeds pustulate-punctate. Fl. March–May.

1. Petals 2–2.5 cm., white or pink. var. **brachyantha**
– Petals 3–4 cm. 2
2. Flowers pink or purple. var. **acaulis**
– Flowers white. var. **albiflora**

Var. **acaulis**. *A. acaulis* (Cav.) Alef., l.c.; Boiss., Fl. 1 : 827 (1867). "*Alcea acaulis* Cav.*" var. *longipes* Post, Journ. Linn. Soc. Lond. Bot. 24 : 424 (1888). *Althaea acaulis* Cav., Monad. Class. Dissert. 93, t. 27, f. 3 (1786). Flowers pink or purple.

Hab.: Batha and fallow fields. Acco Plain, Sharon Plain, Philistean Plain, Upper and Lower Galilee, Mt. Carmel, Shefela, Judean Mts., Judean Desert, N. Negev, Hula Plain, Golan. Most common.

Var. **brachyantha** Zoh., Bull. Res. Counc. Israel D, 11 : 221 (1963). Flowers short, 2–2.5 cm., white or pink.

Hab.: Batha and steppes. Lower Galilee, Esdraelon Plain, Judean Desert, Lower Jordan Valley, Gilead, Ammon. Rather rare.

Var. **albiflora** (Post ex Dinsmore) Zoh., l.c. *Althaea acaulis* Cav. var. *albiflora* Post ex Dinsmore, Repert. Sp. Nov. 30 : 127 (1931) et in Post, Fl. Syr. Pal. Sin. ed. 2, 1 : 240 (1932). Flowers white.

Hab.: Batha and fallow fields. Upper Galilee, Esdraelon Plain, Dan Valley, Upper Jordan Valley. Rare.

Area of species: E. Mediterranean, with some extensions into the adjacent Irano-Turanian territories.

2. Alcea chrysantha (Sam.) Zoh., Bull. Res. Counc. Israel D, 11 : 221 (1963). *Althaea chrysantha* Sam., Svensk Bot. Tidskr. 29 : 381 (1935). [Plate 475]

Annual or perennial, subglabrous or sparingly tomentellous, 15–50 cm. Stems solitary or few, erect, almost unbranched. Leaves 4–7 cm. across, diminishing towards apex of plant, long-petioled, orbicular-cordate, crenate, obscurely 3–5-lobed, stellately hairy to glabrescent. Pedicels shorter to longer than the calyx. Flowers axillary, solitary or in groups of 2–3, mostly along the upper part of stem. Epicalyx one third as long as the calyx. Calyx 1.5 cm.; lobes ovate to triangular, stellate-tomentose, prominently striate. Petals 3–4.5 cm., yellow, retuse at apex. Mericarps many, glabrous, with or without winged margins; the back deep-canaliculate and strongly wrinkled, the lateral faces strongly wrinkled. Fl. April–May.

Var. **glabra** Zoh., l.c. 222. Stems glabrous, except for sparse bristles at top.
Hab.: Deserts; stony ground. E. of Ammon. Very rare.
Area: W. Irano-Turanian.

3. Alcea galilaea Zoh., Bull. Res. Counc. Israel D, 11 : 224, f. 2 (1963). [Plate 476]

Perennial, slightly woody at base, appressed-tomentose, 30–60 cm. Stems many, procumbent, rarely ascending, unbranched or sparingly branched, slender. Leaves remote, long-petioled, (2–)3–5 cm. across, 3–5-palmatifid or -partite, greyish-green, with long and short stellate hairs beneath; lobes obovate or oblong, crenulate-dentate, the terminal lobe longer. Flowers short-pedicelled or sessile in a leafy raceme; lower flowers sometimes 2–3 together in a leaf axil. Epicalyx about one fourth to one third as long as the calyx, with 5–8 triangular to lanceolate lobes. Calyx 1.5–2 cm., prominently striate; lobes triangular, with overlapping or auriculate bases. Corolla 3–4 cm., white or pink; petals obovate to oblong, cuneate, notched. Mericarps many, 3–5 mm., glabrous, with a deep furrow on the back and thick pitted-wrinkled margins; lateral faces radially pitted-wrinkled. Fl. April–May.

Var. **galilaea**. Petals white.
Hab.: Batha and fallow fields. Upper Galilee, Dan Valley. Locally quite frequent.

Var. **rosea** Zoh.* Petals pink.
Hab.: Basalt soil. Golan. Rare.
Area of species: E. Mediterranean (endemic in Palestine).

4. Alcea striata (DC.) Alef., Oesterr. Bot. Zeitschr. 12 : 253 (1862); Boiss., Fl. 1 : 829 (1867); Zoh., Bull. Res. Counc. Israel D, 11 : 222 (1963). *Althaea striata* DC., Prodr. 1 : 437 (1824); Baker, Journ. Bot. 28 : 143 (1890). [Plate 477]

---

* See Appendix at end of this volume.

Perennial, whitish, appressed-tomentose, 60–100 cm. Stems erect or ascending, terete, with few or many leaves all along. Leaves long- to short-petioled, crenate-dentate; radical leaves (3–)4–6 cm. across, broad-ovate to orbicular-cordate, undivided; lower cauline leaves rhombic; middle and upper leaves shallowly 3–5-lobed, with triangular terminal lobe much longer than the lateral ones. Inflorescence a raceme, leafy below; lower flowers short- and thick-pedicelled, upper flowers subsessile. Epicalyx about half as long as the calyx or less, cleft to below middle into 6–8 triangular, acute lobes. Calyx 1.8–2 cm., with triangular-ovate and prominently striate lobes. Corolla about 5–6 cm. across, creamy white (in the local variety); petals obovate, cuneate at base, notched at apex. Mericarps many, about 3 mm.; back wrinkled, with a hairy furrow; margins thick, not wing-like; lateral faces radially wrinkled. Fl. March–May.

Hab.: Deserts; wadis and stony hillsides. N. and C. Negev. Rare.

Area: W. Irano-Turanian.

The local specimens belong to the typical variety (var. **striata**). Other varieties with pink or crimson flowers are known from Turkey.

5. Alcea rufescens (Boiss.) Boiss., Fl. 1 : 828 (1867); Zoh., Bull. Res. Counc. Israel D, 11 : 223 (1963). *Althaea rufescens* Boiss., Diagn. ser. 2, 1 : 102 (1854). [Plate 478]

Perennial, greyish-tomentose, 40–60 cm. Stems many, ascending, branched from base, thick, terete. Radical leaves rosulate, long-petioled, with ovate-cordate, crenulate, undivided, yellowish-pannose blades; cauline leaves with gradually shortening petioles and thick, 3–5-palmately lobed, crenulate, stellate-tomentose blades; uppermost leaves palmatipartite, with an ovate-oblong terminal lobe half or two thirds as long as blade. Inflorescence a raceme, leafy below and almost leafless above; flowers many, almost sessile. Epicalyx about half as long as the calyx, with triangular lobes, stellate-canescent, striate. Calyx 2 cm. or more; lobes ovate-triangular, acute, prominently striate. Corolla (in the local variety) white, cream-coloured at centre; petals 4–4.5 × 3 cm., obcordate, strongly nerved. Mericarps 5–6 mm.; back almost plane, tomentose; lateral faces radially wrinkled. Fl. April–June.

Hab.: Hot and dry wadi beds and hillsides facing the Dead Sea. Dead Sea area, Moav. Rare.

Area: Saharo-Arabian.

Our specimens belong to var. **moabitica** Zoh., l.c., distinguished from the typical variety by the deeper lobing of the leaves, the thick indumentum, the white flowers with cream-coloured centre, etc.

Used in folk medicine to treat eye and throat diseases.

6. Alcea setosa (Boiss.) Alef., Oesterr. Bot. Zeitschr. 12 : 255 (1862); Boiss., Fl. 1 : 829 (1867); Zoh., Bull. Res. Counc. Israel D, 11 : 228 (1963). *Althaea setosa* Boiss., Diagn. ser. 1, 8 : 107 (1849). [Plate 479]

Perennial, densely or loosely covered with simple and fasciculate, patulous or retrorse setaceous hairs, sometimes glabrescent, very rarely altogether glabrous, 1–2 m. Stems erect, often purplish with white spots, varying in density of indumentum. Leaves 6–15 cm.; petioles decreasing in length towards apex of stem; blade almost orbicular in outline, cordate at base, undivided to shallowly lobed or (3–)5–7-palmatifid or

-partite; lobes crenate-dentate. Flowers in terminal racemes leafy at base or all along, solitary or in pairs, short-pedicelled. Epicalyx nearly as long as calyx, sometimes much shorter, divided to middle into triangular lobes, stellate-tomentose. Calyx about 2 cm., with a dense stellate-hairy cover often concealing the nerves; lobes oblong-triangular, obtuse. Petals 5–6 cm., purple or lilac, obcordate-cuneate. Mericarps many, about 7–8 mm., back plane, tomentose; lateral faces radially wrinkled. Fl. April–June.

Hab.: Batha and devastated or open maquis; stony ground. Sharon Plain, Upper and Lower Galilee, Mt. Carmel, Mt. Gilboa, Samaria, Shefela, Judean Mts., Judean Desert, Upper Jordan Valley, Ammon. Common.

Area: E. Mediterranean.

Zohary, l.c., distinguishes the following four varieties within this species: 1) Var. **setosa** with spotted stems, shallowly lobed or almost unlobed leaves and a long or short epicalyx. 2) Var. **brachychiton** Zoh. (l.c.) with palmatipartite leaves and a very short epicalyx. 3) Var. **palmata** Zoh. (l.c. 229) with palmatifid or -partite leaves and a long epicalyx. 4) Var. **aegyptiaca** (Boiss.) Zoh. (l.c. 229) with almost glabrous stems, palmatipartite leaves and a long epicalyx. These varieties call for further study as to the constancy of the characters mentioned.

7. Alcea digitata (Boiss.) Alef., Oesterr. Bot. Zeitschr. 12 : 252 (1862); Zoh., Bull. Res. Counc. Israel D, 11 : 226 (1963). [Plate 480]

Perennial, appressed-pilose or -tomentose with stellate hairs, sometimes glabrescent, (0.8–)1–1.5 m. Stems usually solitary, erect, simple or branched from the sometimes brownish base. Leaves (6–)10–15 cm., long-petioled, all 5–9-palmatisect, velvety-pubescent or glabrescent; segments oblong-lanceolate to linear, tapering towards the base, obtuse, irregularly and coarsely dentate-crenate or lobulate. Flowers 6–8 cm. across, axillary, subsessile, forming long and loose leafy racemes. Epicalyx one to two thirds as long as the calyx, appressed-tomentose with stellate hairs or glabrescent; lobes lanceolate or triangular, acute, sometimes greenish. Calyx 1.5–2 cm.; lobes triangular-ovate with slightly auriculate base, acute, stellate-tomentose, prominently striate. Petals 4–5 cm., dark purple, sometimes pale pink to white, obcordate, cuneate. Mericarps many, 4–5 mm.; back plane, stellately hairy, slightly furrowed, transversely wrinkled; lateral faces glabrous, radially wrinkled. Fl. April–June.

Var. **digitata**. *Althaea digitata* Boiss., Diagn. ser. 1, 8 : 106 (1849) non Boiss., Fl. 1 : 828 (1867) *pro syn.* "*Althaea digitata* (Boiss.) Dinsm." var. *pallida* (Post) Dinsmore in Post, Fl. Syr. Pal. Sin. ed. 2, 1 : 241 (1932). "*Alcea lavateraeflora* DC." var. *pallida* Post, Fl. Syr. Pal. Sin. 177 (1883–1896). Tall, tomentose plants, with greyish or rust-brown stem. Leaf segments tapering at base. Epicalyx about half as long as calyx.

Hab.: Hills; stony ground. Upper and Lower Galilee, Mt. Carmel, Samaria, Golan. Uncommon.

Var. **glabrescens** (Boiss.) Zoh., l.c. 227. *Alcea lavateraeflora* (DC.) Alef. var. *glabrescens* Boiss., Fl. 1 : 829 (1867) p.p. Differs from the preceding variety in its brownish, glabrescent or sparingly hairy stems, glabrescent leaves, epicalyx shorter, greenish at tip, etc.

Hab.: As above. Acco Plain. Uncommon.

Area of species: E. Mediterranean.

8. Alcea apterocarpa (Fenzl) Boiss., Fl. 1 : 830 (1867); Zoh., Israel Journ. Bot. 12 : 1 (1963). *Althaea apterocarpa* Fenzl, Del. Sem. Hort. Vindob. 4 (1858). [Plate 481]

Perennial, appressed-tomentose, tomentose-villose or villose, 80–100 cm. Stems solitary or few, erect, poorly branched. Leaves with petiole as long as the blade or somewhat longer; blade ovate-orbicular in outline, slightly lobulate to 3–7-palmatifid; lobes ovate, oblong or ovate-lanceolate, acute, dentate-crenate. Flowers 6–10 cm. across, solitary, axillary below, in leafless racemes above. Epicalyx as long as the calyx or slightly shorter; lobes ovate-triangular, acute, villose, striate. Calyx up to 2 cm.; lobes ovate-triangular. Petals 5–7 cm., white, yellow, pink, violet or crimson, broadly obovate-cuneate.Mericarps with a shallowly canaliculate or furrowed and tomentose back; lateral faces strongly wrinkled, glabrous above, hirsute below. Fl. May-August.

Hab.: Hills; crevices of hard limestone. N. Negev. Very rare.

Area: E. Mediterranean.

9. Alcea dissecta (Baker) Zoh., Israel Journ. Bot. 12 : 16 (1963). [Plate 482]

Perennial, glabrous, glabrescent or tomentose, (1–)2–3 m. Stems solitary or few, erect, branched from base. Radical leaves (7–)10–20 cm., orbicular in outline, cordate, shallowly 7–10-lobed, lobes coarsely dentate-crenate, lower cauline leaves long-petioled; blades palmately 7-fid or -partite or rarely -sect; lobes serrate-crenate, usually with irregular secondary lobules. Flowers 8–10 cm. across, axillary below, in leafless racemes above. Epicalyx one fourth to one half as long as the calyx, with triangular-lanceolate lobes, mostly glabrous or glabrescent and often reddish or brownish at tip or all over (at least in fruit). Calyx about 2 cm.; lobes triangular-lanceolate, prominently striate. Petals (5–)6–8 cm., pink to purple, broadly obcordate-cuneate. Mericarps numerous, 6–7 mm., sparingly hairy, with a deeply canaliculate back and broad, prominently wrinkled wings. Fl. April–July.

Var. **dissecta.** *Althaea dissecta* Baker, Journ. Bot. 28 : 143 (1890). *Alcea octaviae* Reut. in Herb. Boissier, Genève. *Althaea octaviae* (Reut. ex Evenari) Evenari in Opphr. et Evenari, Bull. Soc. Bot. Genève ser. 2, 31 : 322 (1941). *Alcea lavateraeflora* (DC.) Alef. var. *glabrescens* Boiss., Fl. Suppl. 132 (1888) non Boiss., Fl. 1 : 829 (1867). Plants green. Stems and leaves almost glabrous or glabrescent. Epicalyx about half as long as the calyx, glabrescent.

Hab.: Heavy and somewhat damp soil or near watercourses. Dan Valley, Upper Jordan Valley. Locally fairly common.

Var. **microchiton** Zoh., l.c. *Althaea haussknechtii* Boiss. var. *jordanensis* Bornm., Ungar. Bot. Bl. 11, 1/4 : 4 (1912). [Plate 482]. Plants yellowish-tomentose, at least above. Leaves thick, tomentose. Epicalyx one fourth to one third as long as the calyx, tomentose.

Hab.: Stony ground with basalt soil or terra rossa. Upper Galilee, Upper Jordan Valley. Rare.

Area of species : E. Mediterranean.

7. ALTHAEA L.

Annual or perennial herbs. Leaves entire or lobed. Flowers hermaphrodite, not exceeding 2 cm. (in ours), often forming leafy racemes or panicles. Epicalyx of 6–12 linear or lanceolate bracteoles connate below. Calyx campanulate, 5-lobed. Petals and stamens as in *Alcea*. Ovary many-carpelled, carpels 1-ovuled; branches of style as many as carpels, stigmatose on inner surface. Fruit flattened; mericarps 8–25, with a convex back. Seeds ascending. Differs from *Alcea* in its smaller flowers, 1-celled mericarps and the cylindrical, not dilated axis of the receptacle around which the mericarps are inserted.

About 12 species in the Mediterranean region, Europe and S.W. Asia.

1. Mericarps tomentose. Perennial, erect, tomentose swamp plants.   **2. A. officinalis**
 – Mericarps glabrous   2
2. Calyx about 1.5 cm. Erect annuals.   **3. A. hirsuta**
 – Calyx 0.7–1 cm. Prostrate desert perennials (rarely annuals).   **1. A. ludwigii**

1. Althaea ludwigii L., Mant. 98 (1767); Boiss., Fl. 1 : 824 (1867). [Plate 483]

Annual or perennial with thick vertical root, appressed- and sparingly patulous-hirsute, up to 30(–40) cm. Stems many, dense, some short, prostrate or ascending, the others longer, prostrate, branched. Leaves 1–3 cm. across; petioles slender, sparsely hirsute, decreasing in length towards top of stem; stipules 3–6 mm., ovate-triangular, ciliate; blade orbicular in outline, in the lower leaves undivided and crenate, in the upper leaves palmately parted into wedge-shaped, 3–5-lobed segments; ultimate lobes rounded at apex. Pedicels slender, often shorter than the flowers, erect, later spreading or deflexed. Flowers axillary, clustered in leafy, spike-like racemes above. Epicalyx of 8–10, persistent, oblong-linear bracteoles, shorter than to almost as long as the calyx. Calyx 0.7–1 cm., markedly accrescent in fruit; lobes lanceolate in flower, becoming triangular-ovate and acuminate in fruit. Corolla slightly longer than calyx, whitish or pink; petals entire or retuse. Fruit 6–8 mm. across; mericarps 9–10, loose, glabrous, with strongly wrinkled lateral faces and sulcate-concave back; axis of receptacle ending in a hairy conical beak. Seeds lenticular or reniform, brown, smooth. Fl. March–April.

Hab.: Deserts on loamy and gravelly soil; mainly in wadis. C. and S. Negev, Arava Valley. Uncommon.

Area: Saharo-Arabian, with extensions into W. Irano-Turanian and Sudanian territories.

2. Althaea officinalis L., Sp. Pl. 686 (1753); Boiss., Fl. 1 : 825 (1867). [Plate 484]

Perennial, tomentose-canescent, 50–80 cm. Stems few or many, erect, sparingly branched. Leaves (2–)4–10 × 2–7 cm., with petioles usually shorter than blade; stipules 3–5 mm., caducous, lanceolate-subulate; blades irregularly denticulate-crenate, those of the lower leaves broadly ovate to somewhat cordate at base and almost undivided or shallowly 3–5-lobed, those of the middle and upper leaves truncate to cuneate at base and more deeply lobed. Pedicels rather thick, usually shorter than the flowers, later elongating. Flowers 1–3 in an axil, sometimes forming leafy racemes or panicles at the ends of the branches. Epicalyx of 7–12 oblong-lanceolate bracteoles connate at base only, about half as long as the calyx or longer. Calyx 0.8–1 cm.; lobes ovate, acute to acuminate, not or only slightly accrescent. Corolla up to 2 cm. in diam., pink or whitish; petals about 1.4 cm., obovate, broadly cuneate, notched. Fruit 7–9 mm. across; mericarps 15–20, densely covered with stellate hairs, slightly wrinkled. Seeds reniform, brown, almost smooth. Fl. August–November.

Hab.: Swamps and river banks. Sharon Plain, Hula Plain. Very rare.

Area: Euro-Siberian, Irano-Turanian and Mediterranean.

Used as an intestinal demulcent and in cough remedies; the dried root contains up to 35% mucilage.

3. Althaea hirsuta L., Sp. Pl. 687 (1753); Boiss., Fl. 1 : 824 (1867). [Plate 485]

Annual, patulous-hirsute, 15–40 cm. Stems solitary or few, erect, simple or branched from base. Leaves 1–4 × 1.5–3.5 (–4) cm., long-petioled below and almost sessile above; stipules 5–8 mm., ovate-oblong to lanceolate, acuminate, patulous-hairy; blades dentate-crenate, slightly 5–7-lobed in the lower leaves and palmately partite into 3–5 lobes in the upper; lobes oblong, cuneate, crenate to incised or lobulate. Pedicels slender, much longer than the subtending leaves. Flowers axillary, solitary. Epicalyx of 8 bracteoles, shorter than the calyx, lower third connate; lobes lanceolate. Calyx 1.5 cm., 5-lobed; both calyx and epicalyx accrescent, covered with stiff bristles arising from tubercles. Petals as long as calyx to one and a half times as long, pink, white or purple, broadly cuneate, slightly notched at apex. Mericarps 10–15, with rounded margins, glabrous, transversely wrinkled. Fl. April–May.

Hab.: Batha and fallow fields. Upper Galilee, Mt. Carmel, Esdraelon Plain, Samaria, Judean Mts., Dan Valley, Upper Jordan Valley, Gilead, Ammon. Locally fairly common.

Area: Mediterranean and W. Irano-Turanian, with extensions into W. Euro-Siberian territories.

Thymelaeales

70. THYMELAEACEAE

Trees, shrubs or herbs. Leaves usually alternate, rarely opposite, exstipulate, sessile or short-petioled, entire. Flowers hermaphrodite or unisexual, actinomorphic, 4–5-merous (plants then polygamous or dioecious), in racemes, spikes, heads or umbels, rarely flowers solitary. Perianth simple, borne on top of a tubular to funnel-shaped hypanthium usually similar in colour to the perianth; sepals often petaloid, imbricate in bud; petals frequently scale-like or 0. Stamens usually twice as many (sometimes as many) as sepals, inserted on wall of hypanthium or at its throat. Ovary superior, free, mostly 2 (but seemingly 1)-carpelled, mostly 1-celled, with a single, apical, pendulous ovule; style simple or 0; stigma usually capitate. Fruit nut-, drupe- or berry-like, very rarely fruit a capsule. Seeds with a straight embryo and radicle turned towards the hilum; endosperm usually 0.

About 50 genera and 500 species, widely distributed in tropical and temperate regions, especially in the E. hemisphere.

1. Fruit 2–3 mm. Leaves 0.2–2 cm.   **2. Thymelaea**
– Fruit 8 mm. Leaves 3–7 cm.   **1. Daphne**

1. DAPHNE L.

Shrubs or rarely small trees. Leaves alternate, persistent, leathery. Flowers hermaphrodite, terminal or axillary, in short racemes or umbels. Hypanthium caducous, funnel-shaped. Sepals 4. Petals 0. Stamens 8, in 2 rows, 4 of them inserted near the top and 4 in the middle of the hypanthium; filaments very short. Style short, terminal, stigma large, sessile or nearly so, capitate. Fruit fleshy or rather dry, drupe- or nut-like. Seeds with crustaceous coat; endosperm sparse; embryo fleshy.

About 70 species in Europe and Asia.

1. Daphne linearifolia Hart, Trans. R. Irish Acad. 28 : 442 (1885); Post, Fl. Syr. Pal. Sin. 709 (1883–1896) et ed. 2, 2 : 478 (1933). [Plate 486]

Evergreen glabrous shrub, 1–2 m. Stems much branched, slender, leafy, reddish. Leaves 3–7 × 0.2–0.3 cm., sessile or tapering to a petiole, linear to lanceolate, acuminate, glabrous. Pedicels very short, scabridulous to hispid. Flowers 10–15 in terminal or axillary capitate clusters. Hypanthium and perianth pale yellow, densely villose; sepals triangular-lanceolate, mucronulate. Fruit about 8 mm., included in the oblong-ellipsoidal, reddish-brown hypanthium, crowned with persistent sepals. Fl. July–October.

Hab.: High mountains; stony ground. Edom (endemic). Locally quite frequent.
Area: E. Mediterranean.

2. THYMELAEA Mill.

Shrubs or herbs. Leaves deciduous or persistent, alternate, small to scale-like. Flowers hermaphrodite or unisexual, axillary, solitary or in clusters. Hypanthium usually persistent, tubular to funnel-shaped. Sepals 4. Petals 0. Stamens 8, inserted in 2 rows, 4 at the top of the hypanthium and 4 lower down; filaments very short. Style short or almost 0, lateral or sometimes terminal; stigma small, capitate. Fruit a nutlet, included in the hypanthium or naked. Seeds with crustaceous coat; endosperm very sparse or 0.

About 25 species; mainly in the Mediterranean region and in temperate Asia.

1. Shrubs. Stems woolly. Leaves persistent. Flowers yellow.   **1. T. hirsuta**
– Annuals. Leaves and flowers not as above   2
2. Leaves up to 2 cm., glabrous or glabrescent.   **2. T. passerina**
– Leaves 2–8 mm., pubescent.   **3. T. pubescens**

1. Thymelaea hirsuta (L.) Endl., Gen. Suppl. 4, 2 : 65 (1848); Boiss., Fl. 4 : 1054 (1879). *Passerina hirsuta* L., Sp. Pl. 559 (1753). [Plate 487]

Evergreen, usually dioecious shrub, 50–100 cm. or more, with young branches densely white-woolly. Stems many, much branched. Leaves 2–6 mm., densely imbricated, sessile, scale-like, somewhat leathery, ovate to oblong, acute or obtuse at apex, margins usually involute, upper surface deep green, convex and glabrescent, lower surface concave and white-woolly. Flowers usually unisexual, sessile, 5–10 in axillary and terminal bractless clusters on young twigs. Hypanthium 3–4 mm., yellow, campanulate to funnel-shaped, villose outside, glabrous within. Sepals about 1 mm., yellow, ovate-triangular. Staminate flowers with 8 stamens shorter than hypanthium. Pistillate flowers with an ovoid ovary and a sessile stigma shorter than hypanthium. Nutlets 2–3 mm., shorter than the bracts, ovoid, black. Fl. March–July.

Hab.: Steppes and semisteppe batha, rarely Mediterranean batha; sandy, loamy and stony ground. Coastal Galilee, Acco Plain, Sharon Plain, Philistean Plain, Mt. Carmel, S. Judean Mts., W., N. and C. Negev, Hula Plain, Moav, Edom. Common.

Area: Mediterranean and Saharo-Arabian.

This is one of the most common shrubs both in the coastal plain of the Mediterranean territory and in deserts.

It is used by the Bedouins for making ropes.

2. Thymelaea passerina (L.) Coss. et Germ., Syn. Anal. ed. 2, 360 (1859); Lange in Willk. et Lange, Prodr. Fl. Hisp. 1 : 298 (1862). *Stellera passerina* L., Sp. Pl. 559 (1753). *Lygia passerina* (L.) Fas., Att. Accad. Nap. 1787 : 247 (1788; *"Ligia"*); Boiss., Fl. 4 : 1052 (1879). [Plate 488]

Annual, glabrous or glabrescent, 20–50(–100) cm. Stems erect, simple or very strictly branched, green, at first leafy, later naked. Leaves 0.5–2 × 0.2–0.4 cm., sessile, lanceolate-linear, tapering at base, acute, glabrous. Bracts 2–3 mm., lanceolate. Flowers sessile, with a tuft of white hairs at base, usually in clusters of 3, forming long interrupted spikes; the lateral flowers of each cluster pistillate, the middle staminate, rarely hermaphrodite. Hypanthium about 2 mm., greenish, cylindrical, appressed-pubescent. Sepals half as long as hypanthium or less, erect, ovate, obtuse. Staminate flowers with 8 stamens shorter than hypanthium. Pistillate flowers with an ovoid ovary and a short style ending in a capitate stigma. Nutlets about 3 mm., shorter than the bracts, pyriform. Fl. April–September.

Hab.: Fallow fields. Sharon Plain, Philistean Plain, Upper and Lower Galilee, Mt. Carmel, Esdraelon Plain, Samaria, Judean Mts., Judean Desert, N. Negev, Golan, Gilead. Not rare.

Area: Euro-Siberian, Mediterranean and Irano-Turanian.

3. Thymelaea pubescens (L.) Meissn. in DC., Prodr. 14 : 558 (1857). *Daphne pubescens* L., Mant. 66 (1767). *Lygia pubescens* (Guss.) C. A. Mey., Bull. Phys. Math. Acad. Pétersb. 1 : 358 (1843); Boiss., Fl. 4 : 1052 (1879). *Stellera pubescens* Guss., Fl. Sic. Prodr. 1 : 466 (1827). [Plate 489]

Annual, pubescent, 10–30 cm. Stems erect, stiff, with slender leafy branches. Leaves 2–8 × 1–2 mm., dense, sessile, oblong to lanceolate, acute, pubescent. Bracts leaf-like, slightly shorter than the leaves. Flowers hermaphrodite, sessile, 1–3 in a cluster, forming dense leafy spikes. Hypanthium greenish, appressed-pubescent. Sepals half as long as hypanthium, erect, greenish, ovate, obtuse. Nutlets about 2 mm., as long as the bracts, pyriform, tapering at apex. Fl. June–September.

Hab.: Deserts and semideserts. Samaria, Judean Desert, Lower Jordan Valley. Very rare.

Area: W. Irano-Turanian, with extensions into some Mediterranean territories.

71. ELAEAGNACEAE

Shrubs or trees. Branches sometimes spiny. Leaves alternate, opposite or whorled, simple, covered with stellate hairs. Flowers hermaphrodite or unisexual (plants frequently dioecious), actinomorphic, axillary, solitary or in clusters or racemes. Hypanthium more or less tubular. Sepals 4, rarely 2 or 6, forming valvate lobes on rim of hypanthium. Petals 0. Stamens as many or twice as many as sepals. Ovary superior (but seemingly inferior), 1-carpelled, 1-celled, with a solitary anatropous basal ovule; style terminal, oblique, with a unilateral stigma. Fruit drupe-like. Seeds with straight embryo; radicle inferior; endosperm usually 0.

Three genera and about 50 species in N. America and Eurasia as far southwards as Malesia and Australia.

1. ELAEAGNUS L.

Shrubs or trees. Branches unarmed or spinescent. Leaves alternate, pedicellate, entire, lower surface silvery or brownish. Flowers hermaphrodite and sometimes also staminate with abortive pistil (plants then polygamous), in clusters or racemes. Hypanthium campanulate, urceolate or tubular. Sepals 4–6. Stamens as many as sepals and alternating with them; filaments adnate to hypanthium all along; anthers 2-celled. Disk at throat of hypanthium, glandular, surrounding the elongated style. Ovary oblong; stigma club-shaped. Fruit an achene enclosed within the fleshy hypanthium and therefore drupe-like.

About 50 species in the N. hemisphere and Australia.

1. Elaeagnus angustifolia L., Sp. Pl. 121 (1753). *E. hortensis* M.B., Fl. Taur.-Cauc. 1 : 112 (1808) p.p.; Boiss., Fl. 4 : 1056 (1879) p.p. [Plate 490]

Shrub or tree, 5–8 m. Branches often spiny. Leaves 2–5 × 0.6–1.6 cm., short-petioled, lanceolate or lanceolate-linear, light green above, silvery beneath. Flowers 4–8 mm., short-pedicelled, 1–3 in axillary clusters. Hypanthium yellow within. Sepals as long as hypanthium or shorter, triangular. Fruit 2 × 1.5 cm., ovoid, yellowish with silvery scales. Fl. April–June.

Hab.: Cultivated and probably escaped from cultivation, especially on sand dunes of the Coastal Galilee and Acco Plain. Rare.

Area: Mediterranean.

Violales

72. VIOLACEAE

Herbs, shrubs or trees. Leaves alternate, stipulate, entire or pinnatisect. Flowers herm-aphrodite, rarely unisexual (plants then polygamous), actinomorphic or zygomorphic, 5-merous (except for the gynoecium), axillary, solitary or in racemes, spikes or panicles, with or without bracteoles. Sepals mostly persistent. Corolla, when zygomorphic, with a spur on the anterior (lower) petal. Stamens 5, alternating with petals, the 2 lower ones spurred (in zygomorphic flowers); filaments short or 0, connective often elongated; anthers connivent round the ovary, introrse. Ovary superior, 3-, rarely 2–5-carpelled, 1-celled, with parietal placentae bearing 1 to many anatropous ovules; style simple, often curved or thickened above; stigma various. Fruit a 3-valved capsule, rarely a berry, or fruit nut-like. Seeds small, often arillate or winged; endosperm fatty; embryo straight; cotyledons flat.

About 22 genera and 900 species mainly in tropical and subtropical regions; many also in temperate and cold regions.

1. VIOLA L.

Perennial, rarely annual herbs, exceptionally half-shrubs. Leaves undivided, the lower-most often rosulate. Flowers axillary, solitary, pedicellate, bracteolate. Sepals nearly equal, usually with appendages near base. Petals erect or spreading, the lower petal largest, spurred or saccate at base, the rest clawed. Stamens with free, very short filaments and broad, triangular connectives; each of the 2 anterior stamens with a spur-like nectary at base included within the spur of the lower petal. Ovary 3-carpelled, 1-celled; style thickened above, straight or curved. Capsule dehiscing elastically, many-seeded, smooth. Seeds ovoid or globular; endosperm copious; funiculus a short oily body (elaiosome).

About 500 species, mainly in temperate regions.

1. Perennial stoloniferous plants. Flowers 2 cm. across. Leaves cordate, 2–4 cm. across
   or more.   **1. V. odorata**
– Annuals. Flowers and leaves much narrower   2
2. Pedicels bracteolate. Spur of corolla long, protruding beyond base of the calyx   3
– Pedicels ebracteolate. Spur of corolla short, not protruding beyond base of calyx   4
3. Leaves crenate-lobate; stipules digitately divided into 3 or more long lobes.
          2. V. kitaibeliana
– Leaves entire; stipules 2-lobed, one lobe short, the other as long as leaf.
          3. V. pentadactyla
4(2). Stipules undivided or with a single tooth near base.   **5. V. modesta**
– Stipules pinnatipartite or 3-fid.   **4. V. occulta**

1. Viola odorata L., Sp. Pl. 934 (1753).

Perennial, glabrous, 10–15 cm. Stems stoloniferous, somewhat indurated. Leaves 2–4 cm. across; stipules ovate or ovate-lanceolate, fringed; petiole twice as long as the blade or more; blade ovate-orbicular, deeply cordate, usually obtuse, crenate. Pedicels about as long as the leaves, with bracteoles at the middle or above. Flowers about 2 cm. across. Sepals oblong, obtuse, about half as long as petals; appendages spreading. Corolla violet; spur obtuse. Capsule globular, pubescent. Fl. April–May.

Hab.: Woods of C. Palestine and Gilead [after Post, Fl. Syr. Pal. Sin. 119 (1883–1896), under var. *dehnhartii* (Ten.) Boiss., Fl. 1 : 458 (1867)]; damp places, Judean Mts. [Ramallah, after Dinsmore in Post, l.c., ed. 2, 1 : 150 (1932), under var. *maderensis* Lowe ex Dinsmore, l.c.]. There are, however, some doubts as to the indigeneity of this species in Palestine.

Area: Mainly Euro-Siberian and Mediterranean.

2. Viola kitaibeliana Schult. in Roem. et Schult., Syst. Veg. 5 : 383 (1819). *V. tricolor* L. var. *kitaibeliana* (Schult.) Ledeb., Fl. Ross. 1 : 257 (1842); Boiss., Fl. 1 : 466 (1867) p.p. [Plate 491]

Annual, hairy to glabrescent, (5–)10–20 cm. Stems simple or with ascending branches. Leaves (0.5–)1–3 × 0.5–2 cm., long-petioled; stipules 0.8–1.5 cm., digitately divided, lateral lobes linear, terminal lobe oblong-spatulate; blades ovate-orbicular in the lower leaves, oblong in the upper, all crenate-lobate. Pedicels 3–10 cm., bracteolate above the middle or near the flowers. Flowers (1–)1.5–2 × 0.8–1.2 cm. Calyx 0.8–1.2 cm.; sepals linear to oblong-lanceolate, acute. Corolla longer than calyx, mostly yellow or sometimes upper petals bluish; spur longer than appendages of sepals. Capsule 0.7–1 cm., oblong-ovoid, glabrous. Fl. March–April.

Hab.: Batha; on sandy soils. Sharon Plain, Philistean Plain, Upper Galilee. Rare.

Area: Euro-Siberian and Mediterranean.

Our specimens seem to be transitional between the above taxon and *V. hymettia* Boiss. et Heldr. in Boiss., Diagn. ser. 2, 1 : 57 (1854).

3. Viola pentadactyla Fenzl, Pugill. 12 no. 41 (1842); Boiss., Fl. 1 : 467 (1867). [Plate 492]

Annual, retrorsely scabridulous or scabrous, 3–10 cm. Stems erect or ascending, much branched. Leaves 0.5–1.5(–3) × 0.2–0.5 cm., entire, ciliolate-margined; stipules 2-lobed, the inner lobe leaf-like and as long as blade, the other shorter and narrower; lower leaves long-petioled, orbicular; upper leaves almost subsessile, spatulate to oblong-linear. Pedicels 2–3 cm., with 2 small bracteoles above the middle. Flowers about 5 mm. Sepals lanceolate, ciliate. Corolla shorter than calyx to twice as long, blue or white to yellowish; spur somewhat longer than the appendages of the sepals to twice as long. Capsule about 5–8 mm., ellipsoidal, glabrous. Fl. March–April.

Subsp. **hierosolymitana** Zoh.* Corolla shorter than calyx or as long (and not twice as long), white to yellowish (and not blue); spur somewhat longer than the appendages of the sepals (and not twice as long).

* See Appendix at end of this volume.

Hab.: Fields and stony hillsides. Judean Mts., Gilead, Ammon. Very rare.

Area: E. Mediterranean.

4. Viola occulta Lehm., Ind. Sem. Hamb. 1829 (1829); Lehm., Linnaea 5 : Litter. 46 (1830); Boiss., Fl. 1 : 467 (1867). [Plate 493]

Annual, hairy to glabrescent, 5–15 cm. Leaves 0.7–1.5(–2.5) cm., long-petioled, glabrous to scabrous-hairy; stipules one fourth to one half as long as the blade, lanceolate, pinnatipartite or 3-fid; blades ovate to obovate, crenulate in the lower leaves, oblong-spatulate or lanceolate, sparingly dentate or entire in the upper. Pedicels 2.5–7 cm., ebracteolate. Flowers deflexed. Sepals 0.6–1.4 cm., oblong to obovate-lanceolate, accrescent in fruit; appendages half as long as the sepals. Corolla 6–8 mm., usually shorter than calyx, pale yellow; spur about 1.5 mm., concealed by the appendages of the calyx. Capsule 7–9 mm., ellipsoidal. Fl. May.

Hab.: Fields. Samaria (after Barbey, Herbor. Levant 119, 1882), Judean Mts. (after Dinsmore in Post, Fl. Syr. Pal. Sin. ed. 2, 1 : 151, 1932), Golan. Very rare.

Area: Irano-Turanian, with extensions into some Mediterranean mountains.

Not seen by the present author from Palestine. Drawn from an Iranian specimen.

5. Viola modesta Fenzl, Pugill. 12 no. 39 (1842) et in Russegg., Reisen 1, 2 : 934 no. 38 (1843); Boiss., Fl. 1 : 467 (1867). *V. modesta* Fenzl var. *parviflora* Fenzl, Pugill., l.c. *V. ebracteolata* Fenzl in Russegg., l.c. 935 no. 39 (1843); Boiss., l.c. 468. [Plate 494]

Annual, glabrous or minutely scabrous-puberulent, 3–10 cm. Leaves 0.8–2.5 cm., long-petioled, entire or remotely crenulate, with short white hairs; stipules about 5 mm., much shorter than the blade, oblong-linear to lanceolate, entire or with a tooth at each side of base; blades orbicular-ovate in the lowest leaves, oblong to linear-lanceolate, tapering at base to petioles in the upper. Pedicels up to 5 cm., ebracteolate. Flowers (0.7–)1–1.5 cm. Calyx 5–6 mm. Corolla yellow; spur shorter than the appendages of the calyx. Capsule about 5 mm., smooth. Fl. April–May.

Hab.: Fields. Upper Galilee, Judean Mts., Dan Valley, Gilead, Ammon. Rare.

Area: E. Mediterranean and W. Irano-Turanian.

Our specimens are small-flowered and more or less fit that form considered by some as var. *parviflora* Fenzl.

73. CISTACEAE

Shrubs or herbs. Hairs mostly stellate or in bundles, sometimes glandular. Leaves opposite or alternate, stipulate or not, simple and mostly entire. Flowers hermaphrodite, actinomorphic, solitary or in cymose inflorescences, conspicuous. Sepals 3–5, equal or not. Petals usually 5, rarely 3. Stamens numerous, rarely 3–6, inserted on the disk-shaped receptacle. Ovary superior, of 3–5 carpels, rarely more, 1-celled or incompletely septate, with 3–5(–10) parietal placentae; ovules numerous, orthotropous or anatropous; style 1 or 0; stigma simple or divided. Fruit a loculicidally dehiscent capsule. Seeds with copious endosperm and a curved, convolute or folded embryo.

Eight genera with 200 species in the temperate regions of the N. hemisphere, especially in the Mediterranean region; a few species in S. America.

Literature: W. Grosser, Cistaceae, in: *Pflznr.* 14 (IV, 193): 1–161, 1903. E. Janchen, Cistaceae, in: Engl. & Prantl, *Nat. Pflznfam.* ed. 2, 21: 289–313, 1925. E. Guinea, Cistaceas Españolas, *Bol. Minist. Agr. Inst. For. Invest. Exper. Madrid* 71 (An. 25): 1–192 (1954).

1. Capsule of 5–10 valves. Flowers 3–6 cm. in diam., pink or white.	**1. Cistus**
– Capsule of 3 valves. Flowers usually smaller, yellow, rarely pink	2
2. Outer stamens without anthers; filaments moniliform.	**4. Fumana**
– All the stamens anther-bearing	3
3. Stamens in 1 whorl. Flowers bractless, umbellate.	**2. Tuberaria**
– Stamens in many whorls. Flowers in axils of bracts or leaves.	**3. Helianthemum**

1. CISTUS L.

Dwarf shrubs. Leaves deciduous or persistent, opposite, exstipulate, petiolate. Inflorescence a simple or compound cyme, rarely flowers solitary. Calyx of 3 or 5 sepals. Corolla of 5 petals, caducous, contorted in bud. Stamens many, in several rows, all anther-bearing. Ovary incompletely 5–10-celled; placentae protruding inwards, nearly reaching centre of the ovary; ovules orthotropous; style simple, with capitate or obsoletely 5–10-lobed stigma. Capsule splitting down to the middle into 5–10 valves. Seeds minute; embryo spiral; cotyledons narrowly linear.

About 20 species, mainly in the Mediterranean region.

1. Flowers pink. Capsule tapering, rounded at apex, about 1 cm.	**1. C. creticus**
– Flowers white. Capsule depressed-truncate at apex, about 7 mm.	**2. C. salviifolius**

1. Cistus creticus L., Syst. ed. 10, 1077 (1759; "*cretica*") et Sp. Pl. ed. 2, 738 (1762). *C. villosus* L., Sp. Pl. ed. 2, 736 (1762; typ. err. "*pilosus*") corr. L., Mant. Alt. 402 (1771) non *C. pilosus* L., Sp. Pl. 528 (1753) nec ed. 2, 744 (1762); Boiss., Fl. 1 : 436 (1867) [incl. var. *genuinus* Boiss. et var. *creticus* (L.) Boiss., l.c. 437]. *C. villosus* var. *eriocephalus* (Viv.) Grosser, in Pflznr. 14 (IV, 193): 15 (1903). [Plate 495]

Dwarf shrub, tomentose and villose, 30–80 cm. Branches erect or spreading, leafy, branching from older woody stems. Leaves 2–5 × 1–2 cm., decussate, with broad sheathing petioles, ovate to elliptical or oblong to obovate, acute or obtuse to retuse, often mucronulate, entire or more or less undulate, stellately villose and often glandular on both sides. Cymes 3–5 (or more)-flowered, umbel-like, rarely flowers solitary. Pedicels shorter than the calyx. Sepals 5, subequal, ovate, acuminate, silky-villose. Petals 2–3 × 1–2 cm., pink with yellowish base, obovate. Stamens unequal. Ovary globular, silky; style about as long as the stamens; stigma indistinctly 5-lobed. Capsule about 1 cm., ovoid, rounded at apex. Seeds about 1 mm., numerous, angular, brown. 2n = 18. Fl. March–June.

Hab.: Batha, garigue and devastated maquis on sandy clay, calcareous sandstone, terra rossa and rendzina, frequently on stony ground. Costal Galilee, Acco Plain, Sharon Plain, Philistean Plain, Upper and Lower Galilee, Mt. Carmel, Samaria,

Shefela, Judean Mts., Judean Desert, Dan Valley, Golan, Gilead, Ammon, Moav. Very common.

Area: Mediterranean, with slight extensions into the adjacent Euro-Siberian territories.

This species was divided by Grosser, l.c. 14–16, into a series of varieties which can scarcely be maintained since they are based on weak and intergrading characters.

C. creticus is a leading species of a few batha associations which form a long-lasting stage in the successional sere toward the climax of various maquis associations.

2. Cistus salviifolius L., Sp. Pl. 524 (1753; "*salvifolia*"); Boiss., Fl. 1 : 438 (1867; "*salviaefolius*"). [Plate 496]

Dwarf shrub, stellately and subappressed-tomentose, 25–60(–80) cm. Branches erect or spreading, leafy, arising from older woody stems. Leaves mostly 2–4 × 0.5–2 cm., decussate, ovate to oblong-lanceolate, acute to obtuse, undulate to denticulate at margin, green, stellately hairy on both sides to appressed-canescent, strongly wrinkled. Cymes 2–5-flowered. Pedicels shorter than the calyx or as long. Sepals 5, unequal, the outer 3 much longer than the rest, ovate-cordate, green, appressed-hairy. Petals 1.5–2 × 1–1.5 cm., white with yellowish base, obovate-cuneate. Stamens unequal. Ovary globular, silky-hairy; style very short to 0; stigma lobulate or capitate. Capsule 7 × 6–7 mm., obovoid-globular, depressed, truncate at apex. Seeds about 1 mm., angular, brown. 2n = 18. Fl. March–June.

Hab.: Batha, garigue and devastated maquis; sandy clay, calcareous sandstone, terra rossa and rendzina, often stony ground. Coastal Galilee, Acco Plain, Sharon Plain, Philistean Plain, Upper and Lower Galilee, Mt. Carmel, Mt. Gilboa, Samaria, Shefela, Judean Mts., Upper Jordan Valley, Golan, Gilead. Very common.

Area: Mediterranean, slightly extending into the Euxinian province.

Displays slight variation. One of the leading plants of the Mediterranean dwarf-shrub formations.

Herbaceous parts of plant used for tannin; roots used in folk medicine as a styptic and a remedy for bronchitis.

2. TUBERARIA (Dunal) Sp.

Annual or perennial herbs. Radical leaves rosulate and exstipulate, upper cauline leaves stipulate, all 3-nerved. Flowers in terminal monochasia, conspicuous. Sepals 5, the outer 2 smaller than the inner; all accrescent in fruit. Petals 5 (rarely 0). Stamens numerous, all fertile. Ovary incompletely 3-celled; ovules numerous in each cell, orthotropous; style short, erect, obconical or 0; stigma semiglobular, rather 3-lobed. Capsule dehiscing to base into 3 valves. Seeds with an almost globular embryo; cotyledons ovate-oblong.

Eleven species, mainly in the Mediterranean region.

1. Tuberaria guttata (L.) Fourr., Ann. Soc. Linn. Lyon n.s. 16 : 340 (1868). *Cistus guttatus* L., Sp. Pl. 526 (1753). *Helianthemum guttatum* (L.) Mill., Gard. Dict. ed. 8, no. 18 (1768); Boiss., Fl. 1 : 440 (1867). [Plate 497]

Annual, patulous-hairy, 15–40 cm. Stems solitary, rarely few, ascending to erect, sparingly branched above. Leaves 2–7 × 0.3–3 cm., sessile; stipules up to half as long as leaves, subulate or lanceolate; cauline leaves opposite, obovate, lanceolate, oblong or linear, green, hairy on both sides. Inflorescences simple or forked, many-flowered, loose. Pedicels much longer than the calyx, slender, at first erect, later spreading or deflexed. Flowers conspicuous, ebracteolate. Inner sepals 5–7 mm., much broader and longer than outer sepals, ovate, sparingly long-hirsute. Petals longer than sepals, yellow, often blotched at base, obovate. Capsule shorter than the sepals, ovoid, glabrous or puberulent. Seeds ovoid-trigonous, finely granular. 2n = 24. Fl. April–May.

Hab.: Among shrubs; mainly sandy ground. Acco Plain, Sharon Plain, Philistean Plain, Negev, Golan, Gilead. Uncommon.

Area: Euro-Siberian and Mediterranean.

Very variable in the dimensions of leaves and petals. The division of this species into the typical form and var. *plantaginea* (Willd.) Grosser, in Pflznr. 14 (IV, 193): 57 (1903) cannot be retained in our material, because of the continuity of the characters.

3. HELIANTHEMUM Mill.

Dwarf shrubs or perennial or annual herbs. Leaves all opposite, or upper leaves alternate, stipulate. Inflorescences mostly monochasial or dichasial cymes. Flowers conspicuous. Sepals 5, the outer 2 mostly smaller. Petals 5, mostly yellow, rarely pink or purple. Stamens numerous, as long as the style or shorter, all fertile. Ovary 1–3-celled; placentae 2–12-ovuled; ovules orthotropous; stigma capitate. Capsule dehiscing loculicidally almost to base, 3-valved, many- or few-seeded. Seeds with folded, rarely spiral, embryo.

About 100 species, mainly in the Mediterranean region and adjacent territories of the Euro-Siberian and Irano-Turanian regions.

1. Flowers pink or purple (rarely white).   **2. H. vesicarium**
 – Flowers yellow   2
2. Flowers arranged in loose or dense spike-like inflorescences. Bracts minute or much shorter than calyx. Dwarf shrubs or perennials with woody base   3
 – Flowers solitary in the axils of leaves or of bracts which are much longer than calyx. Annuals   9
3. Inflorescence forming a bundle of 3–5 one-sided branches with 8–12 flowers each. Nerves of inner sepals crowded at one side. Capsule half as long as calyx.
                                                                          1. H. syriacum
 – Plant not as above   4
4. Flowers 1.5–2.5 cm. across   5
 – Flowers 0.5–1.2 cm. across   7
5. Flowers sessile, approximate. Calyx and capsule about 7–8 mm.   **6. H. stipulatum**
 – Flowers distinctly pedicellate, remote   6
6. Inner sepals oblong to elliptical, 3 times as long as broad or more. Petals 0.8–1.2 cm. Branches becoming whitish-glossy and spinescent after flowering.
                                                                      5. H. sancti-antonii
 – Inner sepals ovate, scarcely twice as long as broad. Petals up to 1.5 cm. Branches

not becoming whitish-glossy and spinescent after flowering.   **4. H. ventosum**
7(4). Flowers with pedicels half as long as calyx to as long.   **3. H. kahiricum**
– Flowers sessile or subsessile   8
8. Stems intricately branched into spreading and horizontal twigs, becoming spinescent
and white-glossy after flowering. Plants mostly procumbent.   **7. H. lippii**
– Stems sparingly branched. Branches not spinescent, becoming yellowish-grey after
flowering. Plants mostly erect or ascending.   **8. H. sessiliflorum**
9(2). Pedicels deflexed after flowering. Calyx membranous, inflated, with red nerves
12. H. aegyptiacum
– Pedicels erect or horizontal after flowering   10
10. Pedicels horizontal, later bent upwards at apex, much longer than calyx. Fruiting
calyx 5–8 mm.   **11. H. salicifolium**
— Pedicels erect, shorter than calyx to a little longer. Fruiting calyx up to 1 cm. or
more   11
11. Valves of capsule glabrous and ciliate at margins only. Seeds smooth.
9. H. ledifolium
— Valves of capsule hairy throughout. Seeds papillose.   **10. H. lasiocarpum**

1. Helianthemum syriacum (Jacq.) Dum.-Cours., Bot. Cult. 3 : 129 (1802) ssp.
syriacum; Meikle, Israel Journ. Bot. 19 : 253 (1970). *Cistus syriacus* Jacq. in Murr.,
Syst. Veg. ed. 14, 498 (1784), Ic. Pl. Rar. 1 : 10 t. 96 (1784) et Coll. 1 : 33 (1787).
H. fasciculi Greuter in Greuter et Rech. f., Boissiera 13 : 55, f. 2 (1967). *H. lavandu-
lifolium* auct. non Mill., Gard. Dict. ed. 8, no. 13 (1768); "*H. lavandulaefolium*
(Lam.)" Boiss., Fl. 1 : 445 (1867). [Plate 498; under *H. fasciculi* Greuter]

Perennial, appressed-canescent, 20–50 cm. Stems solitary or few, erect, arising from
a woody base and closely branched above, terete. Leaves 1.5–4(–5) × 0.2–1 cm., opposite and with fascicles of younger leaves at axils, oblong to linear, tapering to the
petiole at base, acute, tomentose on both sides, margin revolute; stipules longer than
the petiole, lanceolate to subulate. Inflorescences one-sided, 8–12-flowered, in clusters
of 3–5. Bracts almost 0. Pedicels half as long as calyx to as long, deflexed after flowering. Outer sepals lanceolate, densely hispid; inner sepals about 0.7–1 × 0.4–0.5 cm.,
3–4 times as long as the outer ones, ovate, appressed-pubescent to glabrescent in fruit,
ciliate at margin, with the nerves crowded at one side. Petals as long as calyx or longer,
yellow, patulous or slightly deflexed at anthesis. Capsule about half as long as the
fruiting calyx, few-seeded, ellipsoidal-trigonous, villose at apex. Seeds ovoid, brown,
smooth. 2n = 20. Fl. January–May.

Hab.: Batha; mostly on rendzina and calcareous sandstone. Acco Plain, Sharon
Plain, Philistean Plain, Upper Galilee, Mt. Carmel, Judean Mts., Gilead, Ammon.
Fairly common.

Area : Mediterranean.

2. Helianthemum vesicarium Boiss., Diagn. ser. 1, 8 : 50 (1849). [Plates 499, 499 a]

Perennial herb with woody base, greyish-tomentose, 15–30 cm. Stems procumbent,
rarely ascending or erect, branched. Leaves (1–)2–3(–5) × 0.2–0.4(–0.7) cm., linear
or linear-lanceolate, tapering at base to a short petiole, obtuse, more or less revolute
at margin, appressed-tomentose; stipules one third to one half as long as the blade,

linear-subulate. Inflorescences mostly terminal, one-sided, simple, 3–7 (rarely 12)-flowered. Bracts 0.5–1 cm., linear-subulate. Pedicels 1.5–3 cm., slender, spreading, later deflexed. Sepals prominently nerved, nerves reddish and ciliate, interspaces between nerves appressed-hairy or glabrous; outer sepals oblong, deflexed in fruit; inner sepals up to 8 mm., 3–4 times as long as the outer, broadly obovate. Petals 1.5 cm. or more, 2–3 times as long as calyx, pink to purple (very rarely white). Fruiting calyx 0.8–1 cm., membranous-vesicular. Capsule about 8 mm., globular, densely tomentose or glabrous, somewhat shorter than the fruiting calyx. Seeds 1 mm., flattened, ovoid, brown, finely tuberculate. Fl. January–May.

Var. **vesicarium.** *H. vesicarium* Boiss., l.c. et Fl. 1 : 445 (1867). [Plate 499]. Calyx appressed-hairy between ciliate nerves. Capsule densely tomentose.

Hab. : Batha, semisteppe and desert. Philistean Plain, Shefela, Judean Mts., Judean Desert, Negev, Dead Sea area, Ammon, Moav, Edom. Locally common.

Var. **ciliatum** (Desf.) Zoh. (comb. nov.). *Cistus ciliatus* Desf., Fl. Atl. 1 : 421, t. 109 (1798). *H. ciliatum* (Desf.) Pers., Syn. Pl. 2 : 79 (1806). [Plate 499 a]. Calyx glabrous between the ciliate nerves. Capsule glabrous.

Hab. : As above. Judean Mts., Judean Desert, N. and C. Negev, Ammon, Edom. Rare.

Area of species : W. Irano-Turanian, with extensions into the adjacent Mediterranean coastland.

3. Helianthemum kahiricum Del., Fl. Aeg. Ill. 65 (1813) et Fl. Eg. 93, t. 31, f. 2 (1813); Boiss., Fl. 1 : 442 (1867). *Cistus stipulatus* [var.] β Forssk., Fl. Aeg.-Arab. 101 (1775). [Plate 500]

Dwarf shrub, appressed-canescent, 10–30 cm. Stems many, caespitose, branched from the base and above. Branches erect or ascending. Leaves 0.8–2 × 0.2–0.5 cm., oblong to oblong-lanceolate, appressed-hirsute, tapering at base, revolute-margined; stipules minute, oblong, long-ciliate. Inflorescences one-sided, with 5–12 approximate or remote flowers. Bracts much shorter than the pedicels, linear-subulate. Pedicels slender, as long as or shorter than calyx, deflexed and elongating after flowering. Calyx hairy; outer sepals lanceolate-subulate; inner sepals 4–6 mm., much longer than the outer ones, accrescent in fruit, herbaceous, ovate-oblong, slightly acute. Petals not or only slightly exceeding calyx, yellow, rarely opening (mostly flowers cleistogamous). Capsule shorter than the fruiting calyx, ovoid, hairy. Seeds flattened, ovoid, brown, smooth. 2n = 20. Fl. January–April (–June).

Hab. : Deserts; mainly rocky ground, especially calcareous rocks. Judean Desert, Negev, Lower Jordan Valley, Dead Sea area, Arava Valley, Golan, Ammon Desert, Moav, Edom. Locally fairly common.

Area : E. Saharo-Arabian.

H. kahiricum Del. var. *depauperatum* Post, Fl. Syr. Pal. Sin. 116 (1883–1896) et ed. 2, 1 : 145 (1932) is probably a "hunger form" of the above.

4. Helianthemum ventosum Boiss., Diagn. ser. 1, 8 : 50 (1849) et Fl. 1 : 442 (1867). [Plate 501]

Dwarf shrub, green with young shoots stellately appressed-canescent, 10–30 cm. Stems erect or ascending, richly branched, woody at base. Branches mostly spreading, rigid. Leaves 0.7–2 × 0.2–0.8 cm., petiolate, elliptical, acute, revolute-margined, green, stellately appressed-tomentose on both sides; stipules minute, lanceolate-subulate. Inflorescences one-sided, 2–3(–5)-flowered. Bracts subulate, at some distance from pedicels. Pedicels about half as long as the calyx or shorter, later elongating and deflexed. Sepals acutish, appressed- and stellately hairy, ciliate-margined, prominently nerved; outer sepals linear-subulate; inner sepals up to 8–9 mm., up to twice as long as the outer ones, accrescent in fruit, ovate. Petals large, up to 1–1.5 cm., spreading, yellow, obovate, mucronate. Capsule up to 8 mm., shorter than the fruiting calyx, globular-ovoid, tomentose. Seeds flattened, brown. 2n = 20. Fl. March–May.

Hab.: Steppes; mostly on stony ground. N. and C. Negev, Dead Sea area, Arava Valley, Edom. Locally fairly common.

Area: Saharo-Arabian.

A characteristic plant of the *Artemisia herba-alba* community on stony ground of the C. Negev.

5. **Helianthemum sancti-antonii** Schweinf. ex Boiss., Fl. Suppl. 70 (1888); Schweinf. in Sched. et Schweinf. ex Aschers. et Schweinf., Mém. Inst. Eg. 2 : 45 no. 125 (1887) *nom. nud.* non Aschers. et Schweinf., l.c. 748 (1889). [Plate 502]

Dwarf shrub, canescent above, 15–30 cm. Stems intricately and dichotomously branched, woody at base. Old dry branches persistent and somewhat spinescent, glabrous, glossy, with bark splitting lengthwise. Leaves 0.5–1 (–1.5) × 0.1–0.3 cm., short-petioled, oblong to oblong-linear, strongly revolute-margined, appressed-canescent; stipules somewhat longer than the petiole. Inflorescences very remote, one-sided, with 2–5 flowers. Bracts subulate, at some distance from pedicels. Pedicels shorter than the calyx, later deflexed, hispid. Sepals acute-acuminate, pilose on both sides, with brownish-green nerves; outer sepals subulate; inner sepals 0.7–1 × 0.2–0.3 cm., up to twice as long as the outer ones, oblong to elliptical. Petals somewhat longer than the inner sepals, yellow, obovate. Capsule shorter than the accrescent fruiting calyx, ovoid, tomentose. Seeds flattened, brown. Fl. April.

Hab.: Hot deserts; stony ground. C. Negev, Arava Valley, Moav, Edom. Rare.

Area: Saharo-Arabian.

6. **Helianthemum stipulatum** (Forssk.) Christens., Dansk Bot. Ark. 4, 3 : 20 no. 11 (1922). *Cistus stipulatus* [var.] α Forssk., Fl. Aeg.-Arab. 100 (1775). *H. ellipticum* (Desf.) Pers., Syn. Pl. 2 : 78 (1806). *C. ellipticus* Desf., Fl. Atl. 1 : 418, t. 107 (1798). *H. lippii* (L.) Dum.-Cours. var. *ellipticum* (Desf.) Boiss., Fl. 1 : 443 (1867), var. *macranthum* Bornm., Verh. Zool.-Bot. Ges. Wien 48 : 560 (1898) et var. *philisteum* Bornm., l.c. [Plate 503]

Evergreen dwarf shrub with young branches densely tomentose or appressed- to patulous-hairy, (20–)40–60 cm. Stems woody, intricately branched and leafy above, reddish-brown. Leaves crowded, 1–2.5 × 0.2–0.5(–1) cm., petiolate, oblong-elliptical to ovate-oblong, obtuse, revolute-margined, appressed-hairy on both sides; stipules leaf-like, much shorter than the blade, linear-lanceolate. Inflorescences at the ends of branches, spike-like, 1- or 2-rowed, (5–)7–12(–20)-flowered, at first very dense, later becoming looser. Bracts usually shorter than the calyx, lanceolate. Pedicels very short or 0, deflexed in fruit. Flowers rather large. Calyx woolly-hairy; inner sepals 7(–8) × 4 mm., much longer and broader than the outer ones. Petals up to 1 cm., yellow, dark-veined at base. Capsule almost as long as the prominently nerved fruiting calyx, globular, densely villose. Seeds polyhedric, smooth or obsoletely tuberculate. 2n = 20. Fl. mainly April–August.

Hab.: Batha and steppes; mainly sandy ground. Coastal Galilee, Acco Plain, Sharon Plain, Philistean Plain, Negev, Edom. Locally very common.

Area: Saharo-Arabian, with extensions into adjacent territories of the S.E. Mediterranean area (reaching S. Anatolia) and the Sudanian region.

A leading species of the Mediterranean batha on the calcareous stony hills and the sandy loams of S.W. Palestine.

The record from Gilead (Dinsmore in Post, Fl. Syr. Pal. Sin. ed. 2, 1 : 149, 1932) is doubtful.

7. Helianthemum lippii (L.) Dum.-Cours., Bot. Cult. 3 : 130 (1802); Pers., Syn. Pl. 2 : 78 (1806) excl. syn. [*Cistus lippii* Vahl, Symb. Bot. 1 : 39 (1790) et *C. stipulatus* Forssk., Fl. Aeg.-Arab. 100 (1775)]. *C. lippii* L., Mant. Alt. 245 (1771; "*lippi*"). "*H. lippii* (L.) Willk." var. *micranthum* Boiss., Fl. 1 : 443 (1867) p.p. [Plate 504]

Dwarf shrub, procumbent, white, glossy, canescent, 20–30 cm. Stems many, dichotomously and intricately branched into spreading and horizontal twigs. Older branches with fissured bark, becoming spinescent. Leaves (0.6–)1–1.5 × 0.1–0.2(–0.5) cm., elliptical, ovate-lanceolate or linear-lanceolate to linear, revolute-margined, tomentose; winter leaves soon deciduous, larger than the summer leaves; stipules up to one third as long as the blade. Inflorescences spike-like, one-sided, loosely 3–8-flowered. Bracts much shorter than the calyx, subulate. Flowers subsessile. Calyx hairy; outer sepals linear; inner sepals 3–4 mm., more than twice as long as the outer ones, slightly accrescent in fruit, elliptical or ovate-elliptical. Petals somewhat longer than calyx, yellow or whitish, ovate-oblong. Capsule as long as the fruiting calyx or somewhat shorter, ovoid-oblong, villose. Seeds flattened, angular, brown. Fl. March–April.

Hab.: Deserts. S. Negev, Dead Sea area, Arava Valley, Moav, Edom. Rare.
Area: Saharo-Arabian and E. Sudanian.

8. Helianthemum sessiliflorum (Desf.) Pers., Syn. Pl. 2 : 78 (1806). *Cistus sessiliflorus* Desf., Fl. Atl. 1 : 417, t. 106 (1798). "*H. lippii* (L.) Willk." var. *micranthum* Boiss., Fl. 1 : 443 (1867) p.p. [Plate 505]

Dwarf woody perennial, appressed-canescent to sparingly hairy, 15–35 cm. Stems few, erect, rarely procumbent with a few erect or ascending, more or less rigid, somewhat flexuous branches. Leaves 1–2 × 0.5–0.8 cm., lanceolate to linear-elliptical, tapering into a petiole, obtuse to acute at apex, revolute-margined; stipules one fourth as long as the blade or less, linear; winter leaves deciduous, summer leaves minute to almost 0, scale-like. Inflorescences one-sided, densely 5–10-flowered, becoming loose after flowering. Bracts minute. Flowers very small (the smallest among the local species of the genus), sessile. Sepals white-villose, prominently nerved; outer sepals filiform;

inner sepals 2–3 (–5) mm., much longer than the outer ones, somewhat accrescent in fruit, ovate. Petals as long as or shorter than calyx, yellow, obovate. Capsule as long as the fruiting calyx or shorter or a little longer, ovoid-globular, tomentose. Seeds flattened, angular, brown, smooth. 2n = 20. Fl. March–May.

Hab.: Predominantly in sandy deserts. W., N. and C. Negev, Lower Jordan Valley, Dead Sea area, Arava Valley, Edom. Uncommon.

Area: Saharo-Arabian, with slight extensions into the adjacent Mediterranean coastland.

Roots associated with the edible truffle *Terfezia leonis* Tul. Flowers mostly cleistogamous.

Very near to *H. stipulatum* (Forssk.) Christens. and *H. lippii* (L.) Dum.-Cours. Differs from the former in the minute corolla, which is shorter than the calyx or as long, and from the latter in the sessile flowers and in the branching of the stems (which is not intricate).

9. **Helianthemum ledifolium** (L.) Mill., Gard. Dict. ed. 8, no. 20 (1768). [Plates 506, 506 a]

Annual, appressed-, rarely patulous-, crisp-hairy, 10–40 cm. Stems single or few, erect or decumbent, usually branched, often somewhat flexuous. Branches erect or spreading. Leaves (2–)3–6 × 0.2–0.8(–1.2) cm., short-petioled, elliptical-lanceolate or lanceolate, acute, revolute-margined, often stellate-canescent on both sides; stipules up to half as long as the blade, lanceolate or linear. Pedicels shorter than the calyx or as long, thick, erect. Flowers usually cleistogamous, remote or crowded, solitary in axils of leaves or leaf-like bracts, 3–6(–12) on each branch. Sepals markedly accrescent in fruit, tomentose and hispid or ciliate, especially along the margins and nerves; outer sepals lanceolate-subulate; inner sepals up to (0.6–)0.8–1 × 0.3–0.5 cm., a little longer than the outer ones to twice as long, ovate. Petals shorter than calyx, yellow, cuneate. Ovary glabrous or ciliate at margin of valves. Capsule 0.7–1 cm., about as long as the fruiting calyx or shorter, ovoid-globular, glabrous except for the ciliolate margins of valves. Seeds many, ovoid-tetrahedric, smooth. Fl. February–April.

Var. **ledifolium**. *Cistus ledifolius* L., Sp. Pl. 527 (1753). *H. ledifolium* (L.) Mill. var. *macrocarpum* Willk., Ic. Descr. Pl. 2 : 86, t. 120 (1859). *H. niloticum* (L.) Pers., Syn. Pl. 2 : 78 (1806) non Moench, Meth. 233 (1794); Boiss., Fl. 1 : 441 (1867) p.p. *C. niloticus* L., Mant. Alt. 246 (1771). [Plate 506]. Stems tall, usually simple or strictly branched only above. Mature capsule 0.8–1 × 0.7–0.8 cm., about as long as or longer than calyx.

Hab.: Batha and steppes. Philistean Plain, Upper Galilee, Judean Mts., Judean Desert, Negev, Golan, Gilead, Moav. Fairly common.

Var. **microcarpum** Coss. ex Willk., Ic. Descr. Pl. 2 : 87, t. 121 (1859). *H. niloticum* (L.) Pers. var. *microcarpum* (Coss. ex Willk.) Boiss., l.c. [Plate 506 a]. Stems lower, 10–15 cm., usually branched from the base. Branches spreading. Capsule 6–7 × 3–5 mm., considerably shorter than calyx.

Hab.: Batha and steppes. Sharon Plain, Philistean Plain, Upper Galilee, Samaria, Shefela, Judean Mts., Judean Desert, W., N. and C. Negev, Upper and Lower Jordan Valley, Dead Sea area, Gilead, Ammon, Moav, Edom. Fairly common.

Area of species: Mediterranean, with considerable extensions into Saharo-Arabian and W. Irano-Turanian territories.

10. Helianthemum lasiocarpum Desf. ex Jacques et Herincq, Man. Gén. Pl. 1 : 120 (1847); *H. lasiocarpum* Desf., Cat. Hort. Par. Add. 461 (1832) *nom. nud.;* Desf. ex Sp., Ann. Sci. Nat. Bot. ser. 2, 6 : 361 (1836) *pro syn.;* Desf. ex Willk., Ic. Descr. Pl. 2 : 88, t. 122 (1859). *H. ledifolium* (L.) Mill. var. *lasiocarpum* (Desf.) Bornm., Bot. Jahrb. 59 : 373 (1924). *H. niloticum* (L.) Pers. var. *lasiocarpum* (Desf. ex Willk.) Boiss., Fl. 1 : 441 (1867). [Plate 507]

Annual, crisp- and appressed-canescent, 20–40 cm. Stems single, rarely few, branched above. Leaves 1.5–3(–5) × 0.2–0.5 cm., linear-lanceolate, acute, revolute-margined, appressed-hairy; stipules less than half as long as the blade, lanceolate, acuminate; petiole 2–5 mm. Pedicels as long as the calyx or slightly longer, thick, erect. Flowers crowded below, remote above, solitary in axils of leaves or leaf-like bracts, 3–6(–10) on each branch. Sepals tomentose; outer sepals lanceolate, tapering at both ends; inner sepals 0.8 cm., slightly longer than the outer ones, up to 1.2 cm. in fruit, ovate-lanceolate, acuminate. Petals shorter to slightly longer than calyx, yellow, cuneate. Ovary tomentose. Capsule up to 1 cm., as long as the fruiting calyx, ovoid, densely pubescent throughout. Seeds roughly papillose. Fl. March–May.

Hab.: Batha. Acco Plain, Sharon Plain, Philistean Plain, Upper and Lower Galilee, Mt. Carmel, Samaria, Judean Mts., N. Negev, Dan Valley, Upper Jordan Valley. Fairly common.

Area: Mediterranean, with extensions into the adjacent northern borderlands.

11. Helianthemum salicifolium (L.) Mill., Gard. Dict. ed. 8, no. 21 (1768); Boiss., Fl. 1 : 441 (1867). *Cistus salicifolius* L., Sp. Pl. 527 (1753). [Plate 508]

Annual, appressed- and crispulous-pubescent, 10–40 cm. Stems few, erect or ascending, branched from base. Leaves 1.5–4 × 0.5–1(–1.5) cm., petiolate, green, lower leaves ovate-oblong, upper ones lanceolate or elliptical, sometimes revolute-margined; stipules linear-lanceolate to subulate. Pedicels about 1 cm. or more, longer than the flowers, subtended by a large ovate leaf-like bract, horizontally spreading, later turned upwards at apex. Flowers solitary in axils, several on each branch. Sepals tomentose, especially along the prominent nerves; outer sepals linear-lanceolate, inner sepals 5–8 mm., about twice as long as the outer ones, ovate-lanceolate, acute. Petals as long as or shorter or slightly longer than calyx, yellow, often flowers remaining closed. Capsule 3–7 mm., ovoid-globular, glabrous. Seeds flattened, ovoid, brown, minutely tuberculate. 2n = 20. Fl. January–April.

Hab.: Batha, fallow fields, steppes and semideserts. Coastal Galilee, Acco Plain, Sharon Plain, Philistean Plain, Upper and Lower Galilee, Mt. Carmel, Esdraelon Plain, Samaria, Shefela, Judean Mts., Judean Desert, W., N. and C. Negev, Dan Valley, Hula Plain, Upper and Lower Jordan Valley, Gilead, Ammon, Moav, Edom. Very common.

Area: Mediterranean, Euro-Siberian and W. Irano-Turanian.

The most common species of *Helianthemum* in the region.

The varieties: var. *macrocarpum* Willk., Ic. Descr. Pl. 2 : 90 (1859) and var. *micro-*

carpum Willk., l.c. 91, recorded by Dinsmore (in Post, Fl. Syr. Pal. Sin. ed. 2, 1 : 144, 1932) are scarcely discernible from one another.

12. Helianthemum aegyptiacum (L.) Mill., Gard. Dict. ed. 8, no. 23 (1768); Boiss., Fl. 1 : 442 (1867). *Cistus aegyptiacus* L., Sp. Pl. 527 (1753). [Plate 509]

Annual, more or less appressed-pilose, 15–25 cm. Stems solitary or few, erect, sparsely branched above, terete. Leaves 1.5–3 × 0.2–0.5(–0.7) cm., petiolate, linear-oblong, obtuse, revolute-margined; stipules longer than the petiole, linear, acuminate. Bracts as long as the pedicels or shorter. Pedicels about 1 cm., filiform, at first erect, later deflexed and elongating. Flowers remote, solitary in axils, 3–9 on each branch. Sepals hispid along the red nerves; inner sepals up to 1 cm., 3 times as long as the outer ones and much broader, accrescent in fruit, scarious, ovate, mucronate. Petals shorter than the inner sepals, yellow (very often remaining within the closed calyx). Capsule about 1 cm., ovoid-trigonous, pubescent, enclosed in the inflated-vesicular fruiting calyx. Seeds polyhedric, densely tuberculate. Fl. February–April.

Hab.: Batha, steppes and semideserts. Acco Plain, Sharon Plain, Philistean Plain, Upper and Lower Galilee, Mt. Carmel, Esdraelon Plain, Samaria, Judean Mts., Judean Desert, N. and C. Negev, Upper and Lower Jordan Valley, Gilead, Ammon. Fairly common.

Area: Mediterranean and W. Irano-Turanian.

4. FUMANA (Dunal) Sp.

Dwarf shrubs, caespitose or diffuse, richly branched. Leaves alternate or rarely opposite, with or without stipules, small, mostly linear to lanceolate. Inflorescences cymose, few- to many-flowered. Flowers conspicuous, mostly long-pedicelled. Sepals 5, scarious between nerves and at margin; the 2 outer sepals minute. Petals 5, exceeding the calyx, yellow. Stamens 20–40, the outer ones without anthers, moniliform, shorter than the anther-bearing inner ones. Ovary globular, 3-carpelled, 1-celled, with (3–)6(–12) pendulous, anatropous or semianatropous ovules; style as long as the stamens, geniculate at base, thickened at apex; stigma 3-lobed. Capsule dehiscing to base into 3 spreading valves. Seeds with spiral or curved embryo and linear curved cotyledons.

Fifteen species, mainly Mediterranean.

Literature: E. Janchen, Die systematische Gliederung der Gattung *Fumana*, *Oesterr. Bot. Zeitschr.* 69 : 1–30 (1920).

1. Leaves alternate, more or less equal all along the flowering stem, scarcely revolute at margin. Flowers (2–)2.5–3 cm. in diam. Capsule 6–8 mm.   **1. F. arabica**
- Leaves at least partly opposite, the floral ones smaller, bract-like, strongly revolute at margin. Flowers 1–1.5 cm. in diam. Capsule 4–5 mm.   **2. F. thymifolia**
   Natural hybrids and introgressants between these two species are fairly common.

1. Fumana arabica (L.) Sp., Ann. Sci. Nat. Bot. ser. 2, 6 : 359 (1836) et Hist. Nat. Vég. Phan. 6 : 10 (1838). [Plate 510]

Dwarf shrub, green, patulous-pubescent and glandular-viscid especially above, 20–

30(–50) cm. Stems many, procumbent or ascending, diffuse, moderately branched, leafy. Leaves (0.8–)1–2(–3) × 0.1–0.4(–0.6) cm., all alternate, sessile to short-petioled, linear to oblong-lanceolate, obtuse to acute, rarely with revolute margins, hairy or hairy-glandular on both sides or glabrescent above; stipules leaf-like, much smaller than the blade, oblong. Flowers (2–)2.5–3 cm., scattered in the upper part of branches on pedicels much longer than the calyx, deflexed in bud, later spreading or ascending, ebracteolate. Sepals glandular-hairy, membranous between nerves and at margin; outer sepals linear-lanceolate; inner sepals 0.6–0.8(–1) cm., twice as long as the outer ones, accrescent in fruit, ovate-oblong, acuminate. Petals 1–1.5 cm., short-clawed, obovate. Style geniculate below, straight above. Capsule 6–8 mm., globular-ovoid. Seeds triquetrous, brown, reticulate-wrinkled. 2n = 32. Fl. March–May.

Var. **arabica.** *F. arabica* (L.) Sp., l.c.; Boiss., Fl. 1 : 449 (1867). *Cistus arabicus* L., Cent. Pl. 1 : 14 (1755), Amoen. Acad. 4 : 275 (1759) et Sp. Pl. ed. 2, 745 (1762). Plants green. Leaves 1–3 × 0.2–0.6 cm.
   Hab.: Batha and garigue on sandy loams, calcareous sandstone, terra rossa and rendzina, from sea level to 1,200 m. Acco Plain, Sharon Plain, Philistean Plain, Upper and Lower Galilee, Mt. Carmel, Mt. Gilboa, Samaria, Judean Mts., Judean Desert, Upper Jordan Valley, Gilead, Ammon, Moav. Common.

Var. **incanescens** Hausskn., Mitt. Thür. Bot. Ver. N.F. 5 : 43 (1893). Plants (at least younger shoots and leaves) white-canescent. Leaves smaller.
   Hab.: As above. Sharon Plain, Philistean Plain, Upper Galilee, Judean Mts., Gilead. Rare.
   Area of species: Mediterranean, with extensions into W. Irano-Turanian border-lands.

2. Fumana thymifolia (L.) Sp., Ann. Sci. Nat. Bot. ser. 2, 6 : 271 (1836; expl. t. 16, f. 1–5). [Plate 511]
   Dwarf shrub, patulous- and glandular-hairy above, 15–30 cm. Stems many, much branched. Branches intricate, erect or ascending, sometimes procumbent, the young branches brownish. Leaves 0.3–1.5(–2.5) cm., opposite, decreasing in size towards upper part of stem, linear to subulate, acute to cuspidate, entire with revolute margins; stipules one third to one half as long as the blade, subulate. Pedicels long, 2–3 times as long as the oblong bracts, patulous, velvety-glandular. Flowers 3–8 in raceme-like cymes at ends of young branches. Sepals appressed-hairy and viscid; inner sepals 3–6(–7) mm., 2 or 3 times as long as the outer ones and much broader, ovate. Petals 5–8 mm., obovate. Capsule 4–5 mm., globular-ovoid, glabrous. Seeds 1 mm., tri-angular, brown, slightly tuberculate. 2n = 32. Fl. March–July.

Var. **thymifolia.** *F. thymifolia* (L.) Sp., l.c.; Webb, It. Hisp. 69 (1838). *Cistus thymifolius* L., Sp. Pl. 528 (1753); Boiss., Fl. 1 : 449 (1867) *pro syn. F. glutinosa* (L.) Boiss., Fl. 1 : 449 (1867) p.p. *F. viscida* Sp. var. *thymifolia* (L.) Sp., Ann. Sci. Nat. Bot. ser. 2, 6 : 359 (1836) p.p. et Hist. Nat. Vég. Phan. 6 : 12 (1838) p.p. Leaves small, dark green; youngest leaves glandular-pubescent. All parts of the plant densely pubescent and glandular.

Var. **laevis** (Cav.) Grosser, in Pflznr. 14 (IV, 193): 130 (1903). *C. laevis* Cav., Ic. 2: 35, t. 145, f. 1 (1793). *Helianthemum glutinosum* (L.) Pers. var. *laeve* (Cav.) Benth., Cat. Pyr. 85 (1826) et var. *juniperinum* (Lag. ex Dun.) Benth., l.c. excl. syn. [*H. barrelieri* Ten.]. *F. glutinosa* (L.) Boiss. var. *viridis* (Ten.) Boiss., l.c. Leaves light green or glaucous, not at all viscid or only slightly so; young leaves more or less glabrous, the margins sometimes setose.

Intermediates between these varieties have been observed.

Hab. of species: Batha and garigue; mostly stony ground, sandy loam, calcareous sandstone, terra rossa and rendzina. Acco Plain, Sharon Plain, Philistean Plain, Upper and Lower Galilee, Mt. Carmel, Mt. Gilboa, Samaria, Judean Mts., Judean Desert, Upper Jordan Valley, Gilead, Ammon, Edom. Common.

Area of species: Mediterranean.

F. thymifolia and *F. arabica* are important constituents in the dwarf-shrub vegetation of Palestine. They are the pioneers in the earlier stages of revegetation on soils with truncate profiles in the Mediterranean hill and mountain zones.

74. TAMARICACEAE

Trees or shrubs. Leaves persistent, alternate, exstipulate, mostly sessile, small, mostly scale-like, or ericoid, herbaceous or fleshy, mostly bearing salt-secreting glands. Inflorescences racemose or paniculate, rarely flowers solitary. Flowers mostly hermaphrodite, actinomorphic, 4–5(–6)-merous. Sepals and petals free or sometimes connate at base. Disk often fleshy, nectariferous. Stamens 4, 5 or many, often free, rarely connate at base; anthers versatile, 2-celled, opening by longitudinal slits. Ovary superior, 1-celled, rarely septate; carpels 2–5; placentae parietal, rarely basal-parietal; ovules numerous or rarely few, anatropous, ascending, borne on short funiculi; styles as many as carpels or 0, free, sometimes connate; stigmas capitate, sometimes sessile. Fruit a many-seeded loculicidal capsule. Seeds hairy all around or crowned with a tuft of hairs, with or without endosperm; embryo straight.

Four genera and about 120 species, mostly in steppes and deserts of the Old World.

1. Dwarf shrubs with flowers usually exceeding 8 mm. in length, each subtended by a whorl of many bracts. Sepals connate at lower part. Stamens numerous.

   1. Reaumuria
 – Shrubs or trees with flowers not exceeding 8 mm. in length, each subtended by a single bract. Sepals free. Stamens 4–5, rarely up to 12.   **2. Tamarix**

Trib. REAUMURIEAE. Flowers solitary. Seeds covered with hairs.

1. REAUMURIA Hasselq. ex L.

Much-branched, glaucous dwarf shrubs, glabrous to hirsute. Leaves leathery or fleshy, flat or cylindrical-linear, frequently dotted. Bracts 5–10, imbricated. Flowers hermaphrodite, terminal or axillary, solitary or arranged in interrupted spikes. Calyx of 5 sepals, mostly connate at base, sometimes free. Petals 5, free, squamate on both sides; scales mostly oblong, entire or dentate to fringed. Stamens numerous, more or less connate at base, generally in 5 groups opposite petals; filaments inserted on a fleshy disk. Ovary mostly 5-carpelled, 1-celled, globular or pentagonous; placentae 5 or less, basal-parietal, 4–10-ovuled, forming spurious partitions; styles 5, with simple stigmas. Capsule cartilaginous, dehiscing by 5 valves which become recurved. Seeds few, fleshy, densely covered with hairs; endosperm mealy or almost fleshy.

About 20 species in N. Africa, and S.W. and C. Asia.

Literature : E. G. Bobrov, A review of the genus *Reaumuria* L., etc., *Bot. Zhurn.* 51 : 1057–1072 (1966). M. Zohary & A. Danin, The genus *Reaumuria* in the Near East, *Israel Journ. Bot.* 19 : 305–313 (1970).

1. Leaves and bracts thin, flat, elliptical or lanceolate to linear, up to 2 cm. long and 0.3 cm. broad, acute; leaves, bracts and sepals acute or acute-mucronate.
          3. R. alternifolia
– Leaves and bracts succulent and obtuse; sepals also obtuse   **2**
2. Glabrous plants with cylindrical leaves. Sepals with entire margins.
          1. R. negevensis
– Hirsute or puberulent to glabrescent plants with flat or semicylindrical leaves. Sepals with irregularly denticulate margins.   **2. R. hirtella**

1. Reaumuria negevensis Zoh. et Danin, Israel Journ. Bot. 19 : 309, f. 3 (1970). [Plate 512]

Dwarf shrub, glabrous, 15–20 cm. Stems many, ascending, diffuse, branching mainly below, whitish. Branches rather divergent and forming an angle of 30°–40° with the stem, sparingly leafy. Leaves cylindrical with a somewhat flattened upper surface, sessile, slightly clasping, glabrous; winter leaves 5–6 × 1 mm., obtuse and rounded at apex; summer leaves 2–3 × 1 mm., crowded into sparse bud-like clusters. Bracts many, leaf-like, much shorter than the calyx, mostly erect, cylindrical, glabrous. Flowers 0.8–1 cm. across, sessile or subsessile, in interrupted spikes (on the stronger branches) or solitary and terminal (on the weaker branches). Calyx 4 mm.; sepals connate up to about half their length, free part ovate, not apiculate, with entire membranous margin. Corolla nearly twice as long as calyx, pink to white; petals elliptical, unilaterally eroded, squamate at base; scales fringed. Filaments usually uniform, not dentate, only a few dilated at base. Ovary 3 mm., as long as style, subconical. Capsule 4–5 mm., ovoid. Seeds 2 mm., long-hairy. Fl. May–June.

Hab. : Chalky ground and rock crevices of harder limestone. C. and S. Negev (endemic). Rare.

Area : Saharo-Arabian.

2. Reaumuria hirtella Jaub. et Sp., Ill. Pl. Or. 3 : 54, 55, t. 244 (1848). [Plates 513, 514]

Dwarf shrub, hirtellous to hirsute, 15–40 cm. Stems many, diffuse, profusely branched. Branches ascending to erect. Leaves flattish or semiterete, linear, obtuse; winter leaves 0.5–2 × 0.1–0.2 cm., summer leaves 0.3–0.4 × 0.1 cm., fleshier, crowded into bud-like clusters. Bracts many, leaf-like, shorter to longer than the calyx, obtuse, hairy. Flowers 0.8–1.6 cm. across, short-pedicelled, arranged along the leafy branches and forming interrupted spikes. Calyx 0.5–1 cm., hirtellous; sepals connate up to one fourth or one third their length, free part oblong or triangular-lanceolate to ovate, with a triangular, obtuse tip or a long horn at apex and a dentate membranous margin. Petals 0.7–1.3 cm., white or pinkish, obovate-oblong to oblong, elliptical, obliquely eroded at apex, squamate at base; scales 2, ciliate-fringed. Filaments many, almost all with broadened, mostly undulate-denticulate base. Ovary obconical. Capsule 4–6 mm., ellipsoidal-conical. Seeds usually long-hairy and with a glabrous club-shaped appendage at apex. Fl. March–July.

1. Stems and often also leaves and bracts hirsute. var. **hirtella**
 - Stems glabrescent to minutely puberulent 2
2. Bracts as long as or longer than calyx, deflexed or somewhat spreading.
 var. **palaestina**
 – Bracts shorter than calyx and usually appressed to it. var. **brachylepis**

Var. **hirtella**. *R. hirtella* Jaub. et Sp., l.c.; Boiss., Fl. 1 : 760 (1867). [Plate 513]. Stems, leaves and bracts hirsute. Winter leaves 6–8 × 2 mm., flattish, summer leaves fleshier. Bracts very dense, 4–5 mm., shorter than and appressed to the calyx. Flowers up to 1.2 cm. across. Sepals connate up to one third their length, free part oblong, ending in a short triangular tip. Petals obovate-oblong. Fl. June–July.

Hab.: Deserts; wadi beds, rocky ground. N. Sinai (Paran Desert), near the border of, and probably also within, the Negev; recorded from the Dead Sea area and from Edom by Nabelek (after Dinsmore in Post, Fl. Syr. Pal. Sin. ed. 2, 1 : 221, 1932) and by Dinsmore (after Rech. f., Ark. Bot. ser. 2, 2, 5 : 389, 1952).

Var. **palaestina** (Boiss.) Zoh. et Danin, Israel Journ. Bot. 19 : 309, f. 2 (1970). *R. palaestina* Boiss., Diagn. ser. 1, 10 : 10 (1849) et Fl. 1 : 760 (1867). [Plate 514]. Stems glabrescent to minutely puberulent, 15–40 cm. Winter leaves 0.5–2 × 0.1–0.2 cm., fleshy, semiterete, summer leaves 3 × 1 mm. Bracts about 6–7 mm., as long as the calyx or longer, spreading or recurved. Flowers up to 1.6 cm. across. Sepals connate up to one fourth their length, free part triangular-lanceolate to ovate, ending in a long, obtuse horn. Petals oblong-elliptical. Fl. March–May(–June).

Hab.: Steppes and deserts; stony or marly ground. Judean Mts., Judean Desert, W. Negev, Lower Jordan Valley, Dead Sea area, Arava Valley, Moav. Locally fairly common.

Var. **brachylepis** Zoh. et Danin, Israel Journ. Bot. 19 : 309 (1970). Bracts 4–5 mm., shorter than and usually appressed to the calyx. Flowers up to 1 cm. across. Other characteristics as in var. *palaestina*.

Hab.: As above. Judean Desert, W. Negev. Rare.

Area of species: E. Saharo-Arabian and W. Irano-Turanian.

Reaumuria hirtella var. *palaestina* is the leading plant of the "*Reaumuria palaestina*" community in the Judean Desert, the Negev and the Sinai Peninsula. It is highly salt-tolerant and is covered rather thickly with exuded salt crystals.

3. Reaumuria alternifolia (Labill.) Britten, Journ. Bot. 54 : 110 (1916); Grande, Bull. Ort. Bot. Napoli 8 : 112 (1925); Bobr., Bot. Zhurn. 51 : 1068 (1966). *Hypericum alternifolium* Labill., Ic. Pl. Syr. Dec. 2 : 17, t. 10 (1791). *R. billardieri* Jaub. et Sp., Ann. Sci. Nat. Bot. ser. 3, 8 : 381 (1847); Boiss., Fl. 1 : 762 (1867). [Plate 515]

Dwarf shrub, glabrous to scabridulous, 10–30 cm. Stems many, erect, branched from base, leafy. Branches paniculate, ascending to erect. Leaves flat, not succulent; winter leaves 0.7–2 × 0.1–0.3 cm., subsessile, elliptical or lanceolate to nearly linear, tapering at base, acute, pitted-punctate; summer leaves minute. Bracts almost as long as the calyx or longer, erect, linear, mucronate. Flowers terminal, up to 1.3 cm. across. Calyx 6–7 mm.; sepals connate up to one fourth their length, free part ovate-lanceolate, mucronate-acuminate. Petals 0.9–1.1 cm., pink, obliquely truncate, squamate at base; scales 2, unequal, ciliate-dentate at apex. Filaments with dilated, obscurely crenate-dentate base. Capsule shorter than the calyx. Seeds long-hairy. Fl. May–July.

Hab.: Deserts. Edom. Rare.

Area: Irano-Turanian.

Trib. TAMARICEAE. Flowers in more or less dense racemes or spikes. Seeds with tufts of hairs at apex only.

2. TAMARIX L.

Trees or shrubs, mostly with distinct stems, profusely branched. Young branches glabrous or hairy. Leaves small, scale-like, sessile, amplexicaul or sheathing, glabrous or papillose, rarely hairy, mostly with salt-exuding glands; blade distinct, rarely reduced. Inflorescences simple or compound spike-like racemes on previous- (vernal) or current-year (aestival) branches or both. Flowers hermaphrodite, rarely unisexual (plants then dioecious), with 4–5(–6)-merous calyx and corolla, mostly pedicellate, bracteate. Calyx herbaceous or membranous; sepals free or slightly connate at base, entire or slightly dentate, glabrous, rarely papillose or hairy. Petals caducous or persistent, free or slightly connate at base, erect or deflexed, white, pink or reddish, entire or emarginate. Disk variously formed, usually with 4–5 entire or emarginate lobes, sometimes almost 0. Androecium mostly haplostemonous; stamens episepalous, constantly or predominantly 4 or 5 or 4 to 5 (in the various flowers of the same raceme); sometimes androecium diplostemonous and then the inner whorl of 1–10 epipetalous stamens usually somewhat shorter than the episepalous stamens of the outer whorl; filaments arising from the top of lobes of the disk or from the sinuses between the lobes. Ovary 3–4-carpelled, 1-celled, many-ovuled; placentae basal-parietal, short; styles 3 or 4, very rarely 2–5; stigmas short, capitate. Capsule many-seeded, conical, pyramidal or pyriform, loculicidally dehiscent. Seeds with a sessile apical pappus of unicellular hairs.

About 90 species, mostly in the deserts of temperate and subtropical regions of the Old World, also introduced into the New World.

Literature : A. v. Bunge, *Tentamen generis Tamaricum Species accuratius definiendi*, 1–85, Dorpat, 1852. P. E. Boissier, *Tamarix* L., in : *Flora Orientalis* 1 : 763–779, 1867. F. Niedenzu, De Genere Tamarice, *Index lectionum in Lyceo regio Hosiano Brunsbergensi par hiem 1895 / 6*, Inst. Braunsberg, 1–11 (1895). F. Niedenzu, Tamaricaceae, in : Engl. & Prantl, *Nat. Pflznfam.* ed. 2, 21 : 282–289, 1925. M. Zohary, The genus *Tamarix* in Israel, *Trop. Woods* 104 : 24–60 (1956). B. Baum, On the Vernales-Aestivales character in *Tamarix* and its diagnostic value, *Israel Journ. Bot.* 13 : 30–35 (1964). B. Baum, *A Monograph of the Genus Tamarix* (MS.).

Many species of *Tamarix* are useful as dune binders and as forest trees in deserts and salines. Some of them are wind- and salt-resistant and may grow well on seashores.

The Biblical name אֵשֶׁל (Gen. xxi : 33 and elsewhere) should probably be referred to *T. aphylla* (L.) Karst. which is a handsome tree very often cultivated for shade in Arab villages.

Some species produce galls containing 40% tannin. Others are used for carpentry and building construction.

The genus *Tamarix* has long been subject to general and regional revisions. There has always been much disagreement between the authors as to the delimitation and the grouping of the species. The recent monograph of B. Baum (inedit.) has removed many of the difficulties involved in the taxonomy of this genus, but has left a number of problems open for discussion and further study.

In presenting the local species of *Tamarix,* the author retained most of the names recorded in his previous study on this genus (Zohary, l.c.). Some names were corrected according to Baum (l.c.).

For introducing the reader to the local species of *Tamarix,* the following remarks may be of some help. The local species can be divided into the following groups :

1. Pleiandrae : Flowers with 6–15 stamens, 3 styles and a 5-merous perianth. The three local species of this group are *T. passerinoides, T. amplexicaulis* and *T. aravensis*.

2. Tetrandrae : Flowers with 4 stamens, 3–4 styles, 4(–5)-merous perianth (in some cases the number of stamens may be 5 or more but the number of styles remains constantly 4). The local species of this group are *T. tetragyna* (incl. varieties) and *T. parviflora*.

3. Pentandrae : This group can be divided into the following two subgroups :

(1) Xeropetalae. Flowers with a persistent corolla (remaining long after spring or summer flowering). The two species of this group are *T. jordanis* and *T. chinensis,* the latter a pink-flowered, cultivated or subspontaneous ornamental.

(2) Piptopetalae. Flowers shedding the petals soon after anthesis. There are six species in this group : *T. aphylla* with leaves almost entirely reduced to sheaths, so that the branches appear to be articulate; *T. nilotica* with stout, short or long racemes, mostly not over 5 cm., in panicles, usually mainly aestival; *T. hampeana* with short thick vernal racemes and white flowers; of the remaining species, *T. negevensis* and *T. gennessarensis* have dense and thick racemes, pink flowers with deflexed petals, long-exserted stamens, and relatively long styles, while *T. palaestina* has very slender, long, and usually interrupted racemes, and minute white flowers with erect petals and short- or non-exserted stamens.

1. Stamens (5–6–)7–15. Styles 3. Disk 0   2
– Stamens 4–5, very rarely 6–8 but then styles 4. Disk with 4–5 entire or 2-fid lobes   4
2. Leaves sessile, narrower at base, not amplexicaul, with erect or incurved apex. Racemes very loose, interrupted. Petals pink, deflexed.   **13. T. aravensis**

– Leaves amplexicaul or semiamplexicaul with broad, cordate base and short, mostly spreading apex. Racemes usually· spike-like, compact. Petals white or pink, erect or spreading, never deflexed   3

3. Flowers 1.5–2 mm., almost sessile, in very compact spike-like racemes 3 × 0.3 cm. Petals about 1.5–2 × 0.7 mm. Filaments about 1(–2) mm. Capsule up to 6 mm.
                                                                                11. T. amplexicaulis

– Flowers up to 5(–7) mm., with pedicels up to 1.5 mm. Racemes longer, broader and less compact than above. Petals 3–5(–6) mm. Filaments longer than above. Capsule mostly 0.7–1.2 cm.   **12. T. passerinoides**

4(1). All or most of the flowers in each raceme with 4 styles   5
– All or most· of the flowers in each raceme with 3 styles   6

5. Calyx and corolla 5-merous or predominantly so. Stamens 5, rarely 6 or more, very rarely 4. Racemes 6–10 cm.   **9. T. tetragyna**

– Calyx and corolla predominantly 4-merous. Stamens mostly 4 in each flower.
                                                                                9. T. tetragyna

6(4). Stamens 4.   **10. T. parviflora**
– Stamens 5   7

7. Leaves sheath-like (without blade). Branches articulate in appearance. Trees flowering in autumn.   **7. T. aphylla**
– Leaves with free and distinct blades   8

8. Petals of all racemes or at least of those appearing in late spring or summer persisting after flowering and sometimes also at fruiting stage   9
– Petals falling off soon after flowering   10

9. Petals pink. Racemes in all phases of flowering up to 6 cm., slender, linear to filiform. Cultivated or subspontaneous ornamentals.   **5. T. chinensis**

– Petals white. Racemes of late spring and summer short, usually 2–3(–4) × 0.5–0.7 cm. Fresh-water plants.   **4. T. jordanis**

10(8). Flowers pink. Petals deflexed. Bracts linear, 1.5–3 mm., much longer than pedicels   11
–– Flowers white. Petals erect or slightly spreading (not deflexed). Bracts more or less triangular   12

11. Racemes up to 10 cm. long and up to 8 mm. thick. Bracts 2–3 × 0.6 mm., deflexed. Ovary (incl. styles) 3 mm. Filaments arising from the sinuses of the disk; anthers apiculate.   **2. T. gennessarensis**

–– Racemes much shorter. Bracts 1.5 mm., not deflexed. Ovary (incl. styles) 1.5 mm. Filaments arising on top of lobes of disk; anthers muticous.   **1. T. negevensis**

12(10). Inflorescences compound, paniculate, borne on the young, current-year branches. Plants flowering mainly in late spring and summer. Ultimate racemes of panicle on branches of third or fourth order. Leaves mostly glaucous or greyish.
                                                                                6. T. nilotica

–– Inflorescences of racemes arranged mainly or exclusively along simple lignified branches of the previous year   13

13. Racemes slender, loose, usually up to 6 or 8 cm., usually not exceeding 3–4 mm. in width. Petals connivent, about 1.3 mm. Leaves deep green, linear-subulate, sessile (not amplexicaul). Anthers apiculate. Disk of 5 deeply 2-lobulate lobes; filaments arising from sinuses between the main lobes.   **3. T. palaestina**

–– Racemes thick, usually 2–5 × 0.6–0.7 cm. Petals erect or somewhat divergent, usually 2.5 mm. Leaves semiamplexicaul, deltoid. Anthers muticous. Disk 5-lobed, lobes entire or crenate; filaments arising from top of lobe.   **8. T. hampeana**

1. Tamarix negevensis Zoh., Trop. Woods 104 : 38 (1956). [Plate 516]

Tree, green, glabrous, up to 3–4 m. Branches elongated, with greyish-brown bark. Leaves green-glaucous, sessile, not amplexicaul, appressed to somewhat divergent, ovate-oblong to oblong, with inflexed, acute-acuminate tip, cartilaginous at margin and apex. Peduncles 1–1.5 cm., loosely covered with leaf-like scales. Inflorescences racemose (not paniculate) with lateral racemes on the previous year's branches, (3–4–)6–7 × 0.4–0.5 cm.; flowers rather remote. Bracts 1.5 mm., oblong-lanceolate to linear. Pedicels 1–1.2 mm. Flower buds obovoid. Sepals (4–) 5, 1.3 × 0.7 mm., ovate-rhombic, green with membranous margins. Petals 5 (very rarely 4 or 6), 2 × 1 mm., pink, elliptical, with deflexed upper part. Stamens 5; filaments 2.5 mm., not dilated at base, arising from top of disk lobes; anthers muticous. Styles 3, half as long as ovary, spatulate to club-shaped. Capsule about 8 mm. or more, pyramidal. Fl. March–May.

Hab. : Wet salines. Arava Valley (Eilat, Ein Yahav and probably elsewhere in the Arava Valley) (endemic). Uncommon.

Area : Saharo-Arabian.

A handsome tree, very striking in its green foliage and its pink, deflexed petals. It is readily distinguished from its nearest species (*T. gennessarensis*) by its much shorter racemes, smaller flowers, stamens and styles, erect bracts and by the epilophic insertion of the filaments.

2. Tamarix gennessarensis Zoh., Trop. Woods 104 : 36 (1956). [Plate 517]

Tree, green, glabrous, up to 6 m. Branches loose, spreading, elongated, brown. Leaves 2.5 mm., distinct (not imbricated) also in younger branches, sessile with narrow decurrent base, oblong-lanceolate, acute to acuminate with incurved apex, narrowly scarious-margined. Inflorescences simple lateral racemes arising from the previous year's branches, flowering in winter; aestival inflorescences 0 or unknown; racemes 6–8(–10) × 0.5–0.6(–0.8) cm., lower part covered with sterile bracts. Bracts 3–3 × 0.6 mm., over twice as long as the pedicels, deflexed, linear to subulate-linear. Sepals 5, 1.5 × 0.8 mm., ovate or rhombic, acutish. Petals 5, up to 3 × 1.5 mm., pink, obovate-oblong, slightly clawed, at first erect, later deflexed. Stamens 5; filaments very long-exserted, not broadened at base, arising from the sinuses between the very broad entire or retuse lobes of the disk; anthers cordate, apiculate. Ovary 2 mm., pitcher-shaped; styles 3, more than half as long as ovary, club-shaped. Capsule about 1 cm., pyramidal. Fl. March.

Hab. : By water. Upper Jordan Valley (banks of the Sea of Galilee; endemic). Rare.

Area : E. Mediterranean.

A stately tree of which only a few specimens have so far been observed.

3. Tamarix palaestina Bertol., Misc. Bot. 14 : 16, t. 1, f. 4 (1853) non sensu Baum, Monogr. Tamarix (MS.). *T. jordanis* auct. non Boiss., Fl. 1 : 771 (1867). *T. maris-mortui* Gutm., Palest. Journ. Bot. Jerusalem ser., 4 : 50 (1947) p. max. p. *T. jordanis* Boiss. var. *typica* Zoh., Trop. Woods 104 : 41 (1956). [Plate 518]

Tree or shrub, with brown or reddish-brown bark, glabrous all over, 2–6(–8) m.

Leaves 1.5–5 mm., sessile with narrow base, those of young branches with long-acuminate spreading apex. Inflorescences almost exclusively vernal, with lateral racemes arising from the previous year's branches, mostly 5–10 × about 0.3 cm., slender and almost filiform, very loosely and interruptedly flowered, some often deflexed; aestival (late spring) racemes, or rarely paniculate and similar to the vernal racemes in shape though often somewhat shorter. Bracts much longer than the pedicels, oblong to narrowly triangular and long-acuminate. Pedicels often exceeding calyces in length. Sepals 5, about 1 mm., the outer 2 more acute than the inner, all appressed to the corolla. Corolla caducous, white (very rarely pale pink); petals 5, 1.25–1.75 mm., erect, elliptical to narrowly elliptical, becoming boat-shaped. Stamens 5; filaments slightly exserted, arising from the deeper sinuses of the disk; anthers apiculate. Styles 3, half as long as ovary or longer, club-shaped. Capsule 3–4 mm., pyramidal. Fl. February–April.

Hab. : By water containing a high percentage of chlorides. Upper and Lower Jordan Valley, Dead Sea area (endemic). Locally common.

Area : Saharo-Arabian.

Together with *Populus euphratica* forms the riverine thickets of the Jordan River; well preserved near Jisr Damia and elsewhere. In its vernal racemes it greatly resembles *T. jordanis,* but in the latter the corolla of the ovoid-oblong aestival racemes is semipersistent. Within the array of varieties of *T. nilotica* there is one which strongly resembles *T. palaestina* and may even be intermediate between the two; it is, however, well recognizable by the grey branches, the glaucous leaves, the shorter bracts, the spreading calyces, etc.

4. Tamarix jordanis Boiss., Fl. 1 : 771 (1867). *T. jordanis* Boiss. ssp. *xeropetala* Gutm., Palest. Journ. Bot. Jerusalem ser., 4 : 49 (1947). *T. jordanis* Boiss. var. *brachystachys* Zoh., Trop. Woods 104 : 41 (1956). [Plate 519]

Tree or shrub with reddish-brown to brown bark, glabrous, 2.5–4 (–6) m. Leaves 2–2.5 mm., sessile with narrow base, oblong-lanceolate, acute with more or less divergent apex, membranous at margin. Racemes of vernal inflorescences 4.5–6 × 0.3–0.5 cm., linear to filiform, in racemose branches; racemes of aestival inflorescences 2–4 (–5) × 0.5–0.7 cm., ovoid or oblong, in racemose or paniculate branches; aestival inflorescences occurring immediately after the vernal (sometimes both types occurring together). Lower sterile bracts longer than the pedicels, oblong, acute to acuminate, the fertile ones triangular-ovate, somewhat denticulate. Pedicels shorter than the calyx. Sepals 5, 1–1.5 mm., rhombic-ovate to ovate, somewhat denticulate or eroded at apex. Corolla of aestival flowers semipersistent, i.e. remaining entirely or partly until the fruit is mature; petals 5, 2–2.25 mm., erect, white, obovate to elliptical, keeled in their lower half. Stamens 5; filaments arising from the sinuses of the disk; anthers apiculate. Styles 3. Capsule about 3 mm., narrowly pyramidal. Fl. March–August.

Hab.: Mainly by streams and other fresh water bodies. Dan Valley, Hula Plain, Upper (and rarely Lower) Jordan Valley, Golan, Moav. Locally common.

Area: E. Mediterranean (Palestine, Syria, Lebanon).

The specimens identified by the present author as *T. jordanis* have been referred by Baum (Monogr. Tamarix, MS. 47) to *T. smyrnensis* Bge., Tent. 53 (1852). To judge from the specimens of *T. smyrnensis* collected by us in the locus classicus and from the description of Bunge, there is a whole series of differences between our specimens and what has been considered as *T. smyrnensis* by Bunge. Here are some of them :

T. jordanis. Three types of inflorescences : vernal — with long, linear or filiform, interrupted racemes up to 6 × 0.3–0.5 cm.; aestival — with 2–4 × 0.5–0.7 cm. racemes; and intermediate ones. The vernal racemes are loose and borne on bracteate, conspicuous peduncles; bracts 2 mm. or more, triangular-ovate; pedicels 1 mm. or more; sepals 1 mm. or more, rhombic, with a green middle nerve; corolla semipersistent, falling off at maturity of the capsule, petals about 2 mm., obovate; disk with 5 crenate lobes.

In *T. smyrnensis* all racemes are alike, 1–2.5 cm., compact, almost sessile; bracts about 1 mm., as long as the sepals and appressed to them, triangular-subulate; flowers subsessile; sepals about 1 mm., ovate-triangular, white; corolla persisting long after maturity of the capsule, petals ovate-orbicular with a gibbous dorsal protuberance below; disk with 5 entire lobes. Such plants do not occur at all in Palestine.

T. jordanis has long been misinterpreted. The type specimen of Boissier collected by Kotschy (No. 432, sub. *T. pallasii*), which I have examined and which has been referred by Baum, l.c. 40, to *T. palaestina* Bertol., Misc. Bot. 14 : 16, t. 1, f. 4 (1853), includes two forms of inflorescence, and is identical with the plants growing abundantly in the Upper Jordan Valley (referred by Baum, l.c. 47, to *T. smyrnensis* Bge., l.c.), but also occurring near the northern Dead Sea foreshore, where *T. jordanis* Boiss. ssp. *xeropetala* Gutm. (also referred by Baum to *T. smyrnensis*) was found and where the above type specimen of *T. jordanis* was collected. Besides, the latter cannot be referred to *T. palaestina* Bertol., l.c. (as done by Baum, l.c. 40), also since *T. palaestina* has slender, long ("bi–tri-pollicares") racemes almost exclusively vernal and flowers with caducous (and not semi-persistent) corollas.

5. Tamarix chinensis Lour., Fl. Cochinch. 1 : 182 (1790). *T. (gallica) chinensis* (Lour.) Ehrenb., Linnaea 2 : 267 (1827). [Plate 520]

Shrub or tree, glabrous, 3–6 m. Branches erect, spreading, with brown bark. Leaves 1–2.5 mm., subappressed, sessile with narrow base, ovate-oblong, with incurved acuminate apex. Racemes vernal, 2–6 × up to 0.6 cm., rather loose; base of raceme naked or with a few bracts. Bracts shorter than the pedicels, oblong, acuminate. Pedicels as long as the calyx or longer. Sepals 5, about 3–4 mm., ovate-rhombic, acute. Petals 5, about 2 mm., persistent, pink, obovate to elliptical, usually keeled at base. Disk with entire or 2-fid lobes. Stamens 5, slightly exserted; filaments inserted at the sinuses of the disk or beneath them. Styles 3. Capsule pyramidal. Fl. March–November.

Hab. : Grown as an ornamental; sometimes escaped from cultivation (e.g. Hula Plain).

Area : Sino-Japanese.

6. Tamarix nilotica (Ehrenb.) Bge., Tent. 54 (1852). [Plates 521, 521 a, b]

Tree or shrub with reddish-brown to brown bark, younger parts glabrous or slightly papillose, 2–4(–10) m. Leaves 1–3 mm., ovate-deltoid, subauriculate or semiamplexicaul. Racemes many, 1–6 × 0.4–0.6 cm., erect or spreading, mostly arranged in a richly branched, paniculate, aestival inflorescence. Bracts as long as the pedicels or slightly longer, erect, triangular-lanceolate to subulate. Pedicels mostly somewhat shorter than the calyx or as long. Sepals 5, about 1 mm., deltoid-ovate, more or less acute, entire or subentire. Corolla caducous; petals 5, 1.5–2(–2.5) mm., usually erect or slightly diverging, white, elliptical to obovate, flat to boat-shaped. Stamens 5; all or some of the filaments arising from the sinuses between the lobes or from the top of the lobes of the disk. Styles 3. Capsule (1.5–2.5–)3–4(–5) mm., pyramidal. Fl. mainly March–December.

T. nilotica is the most critical species among the local representatives of the genus. It comprises a whole series of E. Mediterranean and E. Saharo-Arabian forms and is an eastern counterpart of *T. gallica*. Ehrenberg, the author of this taxon, considering it as a variety of *T. gallica* L., has named it *T. (gallica) nilotica*. Actually Ehrenberg has published in his article (Linnaea 2 : 265, 1827), under *T. gallica*, three varieties : *T. (gallica) nilotica* Ehrenb., *T. (gallica) mannifera* Ehrenb. and *T. (gallica) arborea* Sieb. ex Ehrenb. However, in a note on these taxa, Ehrenberg (l.c., p. 265) writes as follows : "Durch eine grosse Zahl an sehr verschiedenen Orten in Nordafrica und Arabien von uns gesammelter Exemplare der *T. gallica*, habe ich so viel Abänderungen ... verschiedene Extreme vor mir liegen, dass ich weder wage, die Manna gebende von der saftlosen, noch beide von der europäischen als Art zu trennen. Spitzere stumpfere, längere kürzere, ansitzende halbumfassende, einfarbige weissgerandete, anliegende abstehende ... Blätter, können allein nicht Spezial-Charakter in dieser Abtheilung geben. Eben so wenig constant sind lange order kurze, End- oder Seiten-Trauben, aufrechte oder sparrige Zweige. Das Bracteenverhältniss ist bei allen mir bekannten Formen zu unbedeutend verschieden".

For the three above varieties concerned here, Ehrenberg uses as differential characters mainly the nature of lobing of the disk. This character is reliable in a number of species, but in many cases the form of the disk varies greatly, as emphatically evidenced by Rusanov (Tamarisks of Central Asia, Tashkent Akad. Nauk Uzbek. USSR, 1949, in Russian); in others, the forms of the disk are not clearly distinguishable. The use of the disk configuration as a key character has, therefore, rightly been avoided by many students of the genus, such as Niedenzu (1895, 1925), Gorschkova (Southwest. Natural. 2 : 48–73, 1957), Schiman-Czeika (in Rech. f., Fl. Iranica, Contrib. 4 : 5–15, 1964), Zohary (1956) and others. Even Bunge has attributed to this character only a secondary importance. Boissier (Fl. 1 : 776) also expresses his doubts on the independence of the three species under discussion.

To the three above-mentioned binomials of the *nilotica* group, a fourth has been added by Bunge, *T. arabica* (Bge., l.c. 55), which is also based on extremely obscure characters.

Extensive examination of the material concerned has led the present author to include *T. mannifera* (Ehrenb.) Bge., *T. arborea* (Sieb. ex Ehrenb.) Bge., and *T. arabica* Bge. within *T. nilotica* (Ehrenb.) Bge. In fact, neither Bunge (l.c.) nor Baum (Monogr. Tamarix, MS.) were able to give a clear-cut delimitation of these binomials. To base species on the character of the disk, even when proved constant, is absolutely inadequate, the more so when this character is rather versatile, as proved by Rusanov.

Nonetheless, within *T. nilotica*, as conceived here, a number of other forms could perhaps be differentiated by various macromorphological characters. Some of them could match var. *arborea*; others more or less fit the original descriptions of *T. (gallica) nilotica* Ehrenb. and *T. (gallica) mannifera* Ehrenb. Unfortunately, there is no hope of comparing our forms with the authentic material, since Ehrenberg's type specimens of the taxa concerned were lost during World War II. A reassessment of the whole complex of forms around *T. nilotica* can perhaps be arrived at by future experimental studies.

The varieties of *T. nilotica* recorded here have mostly been published by Zohary (l.c.). Some of those fell into synonyms, others appear as new combinations. All the varieties should be looked upon as tentative.

1. Filaments arising from sinuses between the entire, crenate or 2-partite lobes of disk;
   base of filaments mostly not dilated   2
 – Filaments arising fro..u top of the entire or 2-fid lobes of disk; base of filaments mostly
   dilated   6
2. Racemes mainly lateral, 1–2 cm. (even in fruit), divaricate; panicles sparsely branched.
                                                                              var. **brevispica**
 – Racemes usually much longer   3
3. Capsules (even the fully mature ones) 1.5–2.5 mm.   4
 – Capsule longer   5
4. Leaves spreading. Bracts triangular-lanceolate.   var. **microcarpa**
 – Leaves appressed. Bracts deltoid.   var. **micrantha**
5(3). Racemes 2–3 cm., fruiting racemes strongly divarica`- and remote. Leaves greyish-
   white, pulverulent, appressed.   var. **divergens**
 – Racemes not as above. Leaves green, erect-spreading, rarely appressed.   var. **nilotica**
6(1). Branches capillary (the thinnest in the local species). Flowers long-pedicelled, arranged in very loose racemes. Stately trees flowering in late summer.   var. **tenuior**
 – Not as above   7
7. Stamens often 6–7. Racemes short, loose.   var. **anisandra**
 – Stamens constantly 5   8
8. Leaves and branches densely covered with salt grains. Racemes few, short and narrow, compact, erect. Flowers about 1 mm. Flowering in late summer.   var. **eilatensis**
 – Leaves not as above. Racemes many, usually longer and up to 6 mm. broad, variously
   directed. Flowers about 1.5 mm. Flowering in spring.   var. **arborea**

Var. **nilotica**. *T. nilotica* (Ehrenb.) Bge., l.c.; Boiss., Fl. 1 : 775 (1867). *T. (gallica)*
nilotica Ehrenb., Linnaea 2 : 269 (1827) p.p. *T. arabica* Bge., l.c. 55. *T. mannifera*
(Ehrenb.) Decne., Ann. Sci. Nat. Bot. ser. 2, 3 : 261 (1835) *obiter, comb. inval.*;
T. mannifera (Ehrenb.) Bge., l.c. 63; Boiss., l.c. *T. (gallica) mannifera* Ehrenb., l.c.
270. *T. gallica* L. var. *maris-mortui* (Gutm.) Zoh., Trop. Woods 104 : 44 (1956); var.
longispica Zoh., l.c. 45; var. *abiadensis* Zoh., l.c. 46; var. *erythrocarpa* Zoh., l.c. 48;
var. *ascalonica* Zoh., l.c. 48; var. *subpatens* Zoh., l.c. 49. [Plate 521]. Branches leafy.
Leaves erect-spreading, rarely appressed, mostly green. Panicles richly and divaricately
branched with racemes 2.5–5 cm. Disk 5-lobed. Filaments arising from sinuses between
disk lobes.

Hab.: Sandy soil of coastal plain, stony and sandy dry wadi beds, marshes and
near saline springs. Coastal Galilee, Acco Plain, Sharon Plain, Philistean Plain, Shefela,
Judean Mts., Negev, Upper and Lower Jordan Valley, Dead S.u area, Arava Valley,
Edom.

Var. **brevispica** (Zoh.) Zoh. (comb. nov.). *T. gallica* L. var. *brevispica* Zoh., l.c. 46.
Plants glaucous or white-pulverulent. Leaves very short, deltoid, semiamplexicaul.
Panicles sparsely branched or inflorescences racemose with lateral, very short (1–2 cm.),
divaricate racemes.

Hab.: Saline soils. Negev, Arava Valley.

Var. **micrantha** (Zoh.) Zoh. (comb. nov.). *T. gallica* L. var. *micrantha* Zoh., l.c. 48.
[Plate 521 a]. Branchlets thick, erect. Leaves fleshy, ovate-deltoid, short-decurrent at
base, acute. Inflorescences almost simple; racemes 1.5–4 × 0.3–0.35 cm. Bracts deltoid,

acute. Flowers subsessile, 1.5 mm. before anthesis. Capsule 1.5–2.5 mm.

Hab.: Sand dunes. Acco Plain, Sharon Plain.

Var. **microcarpa** (Zoh.) Zoh. (comb. nov.). *T. gallica* L. var. *microcarpa* Zoh., l.c. 47. Leaves semiamplexicaul, upper part spreading, lanceolate-acuminate. Panicles rather dense; racemes slender, 3–6 cm. Bracts triangular-lanceolate. Capsule minute, 2.5 mm. at maturity.

Hab.: Wadis. Arava Valley.

Var. **divergens** (Zoh.) Zoh. (comb. nov.). *T. gallica* L. var. *divergens* Zoh., l.c. 47. Leaves appressed, ovate-deltoid, acute, greyish-white, pulverulent. Panicles rather loose; racemes 2–3 × 0.4–0.6 cm., pedunculate, rigid; fruiting panicles divaricate and remote.

Hab.: Sands of coastal plain, wadis. Acco Plain, Sharon Plain, Philistean Plain, Negev, Dead Sea area, Arava Valley.

Var. **arborea** (Sieb. ex Ehrenb.) Zoh. (comb. nov.). *T. arborea* (Sieb. ex Ehrenb.) Bge., Tent. 67 (1852). *T. (gallica) arborea* Sieb. ex Ehrenb., Linnaea 2 : 269 (1827). *T. jordanis* Boiss. var. *negevensis* Zoh. et var. *sodomensis* Zoh., l.c. 42. *T. gallica* L. var. *pachybotrys* Zoh., l.c. 47. Branches brown to greyish. Inflorescences paniculate, richly branched, sometimes also simple, lateral (vernal); racemes 3–6 × 0.4–0.6 cm., long-peduncled. Bracts 1.5 mm., oblong-lanceolate. Pedicels about 1 mm. Petals 1.5 mm., erect, boat-shaped. Disk 5-angled or with 5 simple or confluent lobes. Filaments long-exserted.

Hab.: Sandy and gravelly wadis, also on saline ground. Negev, Dead Sea area, Arava Valley.

Var. **tenuior** (Zoh.) Zoh. (comb. nov.). *T. gallica* L. var. *tenuior* Zoh., l.c. 49. Green tree flowering mainly in late summer. Branchlets diffuse, very slender, elongated. Leaves deltoid-lanceolate, acute-acuminate, membranous at margin and apex. Racemes 2–4 cm., loose. Bracts lanceolate-subulate. Pedicels 2 mm. Petals connivent, keel-shaped. Filaments scarcely exserted, arising at top of lobes.

Hab.: Sandy soil. Acco Plain, Sharon Plain.

Also cultivated as an ornamental tree attaining a great age.

Var. **anisandra** (Zoh.) Zoh. (comb. nov.). *T. gallica* L. var. *anisandra* Zoh., l.c. 45. Flowering branches erect. Leaves semiamplexicaul. Racemes rather short, loose. Bracts 1–1.5 mm. Petals diverging after anthesis. Stamens 6–7; filaments arising from top of lobes.

Hab.: Saline soil. Arava Valley.

Var. **eilatensis** (Zoh.) Zoh. (comb. nov.). *T. gallica* L. var. *eilathensis* Zoh., l.c. 46. [Plate 521 b]. Plants flowering in late summer. Branches strictly erect, rather white-puberulent. Leaves somewhat fleshy, semiamplexicaul, with somewhat divergent tip. Racemes 3–4(–5) cm., compact, rigid. Filaments arising between each 2 confluent disk lobes.

Hab.: Salines. Arava Valley.

Area of species: Saharo-Arabian, with penetrations into adjacent Sudanian and Mediterranean territories.

7. **Tamarix aphylla** (L.) Karst., Deutschl. Fl. 641 (1882). *Thuja aphylla* L., Cent. Pl. 1 : 35 (1755) p.p. et Amoen. Acad. 4 : 295 (1759) p.p. excl. syn. Shaw. *Tamarix orientalis* Forssk., Fl. Aeg.-Arab. 206 (1775). *Tamarix articulata* Vahl, Symb. Bot. 2 : 48, t. 32 (1791) *subs. illegit.* [Plate 522]

Tree or high shrub, glabrous, with reddish-brown to grey bark, 4–12 m. Branches jointed, green. Leaves about 2 mm., sheath-like, with an abruptly short-pointed apex. Inflorescences usually aestival, paniculate; racemes 3–6 × 0.4–0.5 cm. Bracts longer than the pedicels, triangular to broadly triangular, somewhat clasping, with sheathing lower and divaricate acuminate upper part. Pedicels much shorter than the calyx. Sepals 5, about 1.5 mm., obtuse, entire, the outer 2 somewhat smaller and broadly ovate to broadly elliptical; the inner somewhat larger, broadly elliptical to suborbicular. Corolla semipersistent to caducous; petals 5, about 2 mm., oblong, elliptical-oblong to obovate. Stamens 5; filaments inserted in the deeper sinuses of the disk. Styles 3. Capsule about 3 mm., pyriform. Fl. August–November.

Hab.: Sandy plains and dunes, salty deserts and wadi beds. Negev, Dead Sea area, Arava Valley. Fairly common. Spontaneous in wadis of hot deserts only.

Area : Sudanian, with penetrations into the Saharo-Arabian region.

Widely grown as a shade and afforestation tree, especially in desert regions. Propagates readily by cuttings. Requires large amounts of moisture and transpires intensively.

8. **Tamarix hampeana** Boiss. et Heldr. in Boiss., Diagn. ser. 1, 10 : 8 (1849) emend. Boiss., Fl. 1 : 767 (1867) var. **philistaea** (Zoh.) Zoh. (comb. nov.). *T. hexandra* Hampe, Flora 25 : 62 (1842) *nom. nud. T. africana* Poir. var. *philistaea* Zoh., Trop. Woods 104 : 39 (1956). [Plate 523]

Small tree with brown to greyish-brown bark, glabrous, 3–5 m. Leaves 1.5–3 mm., imbricated, appressed, ovate-oblong or deltoid, semiamplexicaul, acuminate, with entire scarious margin. Inflorescences solitary racemes 2–5 (–10) × 0.6–0.7 (–1) cm., mainly vernal. Bracts usually shorter than the pedicels, membranous, ovate-triangular to oblong, somewhat boat-shaped, subamplexicaul, acute, those of the upper part of raceme as long as or longer than the pedicels. Pedicels longer than the calyx. Sepals (in ours) 5, 1–2 mm., deltoid-ovate, obtuse; margin broad, membranous, slightly denticulate. Corolla caducous, white, campanulate; petals (in ours) 5, (2–)2.5–3 mm., erect, oblong-spatulate. Stamens 5, slightly exserted; filaments arising from top of disk lobes. Styles (in ours) 3, less than half as long as the ovary, club-shaped. Fl. April–May.

Hab.: Maritime sands. Philistean Plain. Very rare.

Area of species : N. Mediterranean.

Our plants differ from the typical form (as described by Boissier and Heldreich, l.c.) in their vernal racemes, the exclusively 5-merous perianth, the membranous bracts and calyces, the relatively longer petals, and the 3-gynous ovary.

9. **Tamarix tetragyna** Ehrenb., Linnaea 2 : 257, 258 (1827); Boiss., Fl. 1 : 768 (1867). [Plates 524, 524 a]

Small tree or shrub with purple to blackish-brown bark, papillose to glabrous, 1.5–4 m. Leaves 1.5–6 mm., sessile, oblong-subulate, not amplexicaul. Vernal inflorescences solitary lateral racemes, 4–10 × (0.4–)0.8–1.2 cm.; aestival inflorescences 0, rarely present and then shorter and narrower; all with papillose rhachis. Bracts oblong to linear-oblong, the lowest truncate with a short obtuse point, the upper acuminate; all longer than the pedicels and calyces and sometimes equalling the flowers in length. Pedicels somewhat longer to shorter than the calyx. Calyx urceolate; sepals 4–5, ovate to elliptical, mostly with a few teeth at apex, the outer 2 acute, about 2 mm.; the inner ones somewhat shorter, obtuse. Corolla caducous, rarely subpersistent; petals 4–5, 3.5–5 mm., spreading to deflexed, white, narrowly obovate to elliptical, tapering or short-clawed at base. Stamens 4–5, episepalous, rarely with 1–3 additional epipetalous stamens; filaments arising at the top of the entire or retuse disk lobes. Styles 4. Capsule 3–5 × 1.5–2 mm., pyramidal. Fl. mainly December–April.

1. Sepals, petals and stamens predominantly 5 (rarely stamens 6–8). var. **tetragyna**
– Sepals, petals and stamens predominantly 4 2
2. Vernal racemes up to 10 × 0.4–0.8 cm., more or less loose. Styles spatulate, shorter than 1 mm. var. **deserti**
– Vernal racemes shorter, 4–6 × 0.9–1.2 cm. Styles club-shaped, about 1 mm.
var. **meyeri**

Var. **tetragyna**. [Plate 524]. Racemes slender, up to 10 × 0.8 cm. Calyx and corolla predominantly 5-merous. Stamens (4–)5(–6–8); anthers exapiculate.

Hab.: Saline and brackish swamps. C. Negev, Lower Jordan Valley, Dead Sea area. Rare.

Var. **deserti** (Boiss.) Zoh. (comb. nov.). *T. deserti* Boiss., Diagn. ser. 1, 10:9 (1849); Zoh., Trop. Woods 104:33 (1956). [Plate 524]. Racemes slender, up to 10 × 0.8 cm. Calyx and corolla predominantly 4-merous. Stamens predominantly 4, as long as corolla.

Hab.: As above. Negev, Dead Sea area. Rare.

Var. **meyeri** (Boiss.) Boiss., Fl. 1:768 (1867). *T. meyeri* Boiss., Diagn. ser. 1, 10:9 (1849). [Plate 524 a]. Racemes thick, compact, usually shorter and broader than above. Calyx, corolla and stamens as in var. *deserti;* differs from var. *deserti* in its apiculate anthers and club-shaped styles.

Hab.: As above. Acco Plain, Sharon Plain, N. Negev, Upper Jordan Valley. Common.

Area of species: E. Mediterranean and Saharo-Arabian.

10. Tamarix parviflora DC., Prodr. 3:97 (1828). [Plate 525]

Low tree or shrub with brown to purple bark, glabrous, 2–3 m. Leaves 2–2.5 mm., sessile with narrow base, slightly divergent, oblong, acute to acuminate. Inflorescences mainly vernal, simple; racemes 1.5–3 × 0.3–0.5 cm., dense. Bracts longer than the pedicels, triangular-acuminate, boat-shaped, broadly membranous-margined, upper part mostly spreading. Pedicels much shorter than the calyx. Sepals 4, 1.25–1.5 mm., connate at base, eroded-denticulate, herbaceous or broadly membranous at margin; the outer 2 deltoid-ovate, acute; the inner ovate, obtuse. Corolla subpersistent or caducous, campanulate; petals 4, 2 mm., white, ovate-elliptical, at first erect, later deflexed. Stamens 4; filaments arising from the top of the lobes of the disk. Styles 3 (–4). Capsule about 5 mm., narrowly pyramidal. Fl. March–June.

Var. **parviflora**. *T. parviflora* DC., l.c.; Boiss., Fl. 1 : 769 (1867); Zoh., Trop. Woods 104 : 35 (1956). Sepals green, not membranous. Petals subpersistent. Filaments broadened at base.

Hab. : Near river banks. Sharon Plain (cultivated), Hula Plain (probably indigenous). Rare.

Area : E. Mediterranean.

Var. **sodomensis** (Zoh.) Zoh. (comb. nov.). *T. sodomensis* Zoh., l.c., f. 5. Sepals with broad membranous margin. Petals caducous. Filaments not broadened at base.

Hab. : Salines. Dead Sea area.

Area : Saharo-Arabian.

T. sodomensis was described from a single specimen. Astonishingly, Baum (Monogr. Tamarix, MS. 50) has included it within *T. arborea* (Sieb. ex Ehrenb.) Bge., Tent. 67 (1852), despite its predominantly 4-merous flowers.

11. Tamarix amplexicaulis Ehrenb., Linnaea 2 : 275 (1827); Bge., Tent. 76 (1852); Boiss., Fl. 1 : 778 (1867). [Plate 526]

Shrub with brownish-red bark, glabrous, densely beset with salt grains, 1–1.5 m. Leaves 1–2 mm., amplexicaul to semiamplexicaul, ovate-deltoid, cordate at base, with acute-acuminate spreading apex, densely punctate, not scarious-margined. Lower part of peduncle with leaf-like scales. Inflorescences simple, spicate, compact, 3 × 0.3 cm. Bracts almost as long as the calyx, leaf-like, almost horizontal, acute-acuminate. Flowers almost sessile. Sepals 5, about 1 mm., broadly ovate, acutish. Petals 5, about 1.5–2 × 0.7 mm., erect or connivent, white, oblong-elliptical. Disk 0. Stamens 8–10, scarcely exserted; filaments up to 2 mm., broadened at base; anthers apiculate. Styles 3, club-shaped. Capsule 5–6 mm., long-pyramidal. Fl. March–December.

Hab. : Saline soil. Dead Sea area, Arava Valley. Uncommon.

Area : Saharo-Arabian and E. Sudanian.

Our specimens agree well with the description of this species as amplified by Bunge, except for the leaves which vary from amplexicaul to semiamplexicaul. This species is readily distinguished from all other species of this group by its small flowers arranged in very short compact spikes not more than 3 cm. long and 3 mm. broad. The pedicels do not usually exceed 1 mm., even in fruit. The petals do not exceed 2 mm., and they are always white and erect. The fruits are the smallest among the local representatives of the Pleiandrae group.

12. Tamarix passerinoides Del. ex Desv., Ann. Sci. Nat. 4 : 349 (1824). [Plate 527]

Shrub with dark brown to purple bark and papillose younger parts, 1–2 m. Leaves 1–2.5 mm., amplexicaul to semiamplexicaul, with spreading apex. Inflorescences mainly aestival, simple to slightly paniculate; racemes usually 3–5 × 0.4–0.8 cm., fairly dense. Bracts shorter to longer than the pedicels, amplexicaul to semiamplexicaul. Pedicels as long as the calyx. Sepals broadly ovate, acute or obtuse, the outer ones often denticulate. Corolla usually campanulate; petals 3–5(–6) mm., spreading, often pale pink, broadly elliptical to slightly ovate. Stamens 6–15, usually 8–13 in 2 slightly discernible whorls, the outer of 5, the inner of 1 or more stamens; filaments not arising from disk. Styles 3, club-shaped. Capsule 0.6–1.3 cm., ovoid-pyramidal. Fl. April–November (mainly).

Var. **passerinoides**. *T. passerinoides* Del. ex Desv., l.c.; Del., Fl. Aeg. Ill. 58 no. 352 (1813) *nom. nud.*; Boiss., Fl. 1 : 778 (1867). Stamens usually 10–13. Capsule 6–7 mm. Sepals often acute.

Var. **macrocarpa** Ehrenb., Linnaea 2 : 276 (1827). *T. macrocarpa* (Ehrenb.) Bge., Tent. 80 (1852); Boiss., l.c. 779. Stamens up to 10 (usually less). Capsule up to 1.3 cm. Sepals usually obtuse.

Hab. of species : Salines in warm deserts. Dead Sea area, Arava Valley, deserts E. of Amman. Uncommon.

Area of species : E. Saharo-Arabian and E. Sudanian.

According to Burtt and Lewis, Kew Bull. 1954 : 390 (1954) there is no reason to separate the large-fruited form from *T. passerinoides* as a distinct species and not even as a variety.

13. Tamarix aravensis Zoh., Trop. Woods 104 : 50, f. 11 (1956). [Plate 528]

Shrub or small tree with brown to grey-brown bark, younger parts often papillose, 1.5–3 m. Leaves 2–4 mm., sessile with narrow base, ovate to oblong, auriculate, not amplexicaul, acute to acuminate, incurved at apex, with rather scarious margin. Inflorescences usually simple; racemes 5–8 × 1 cm., arising from the previous year's branches, pedunculate, very loose, bearing scale-like sterile bracts below. Bracts 3 mm., triangular-lanceolate with narrow base, acuminate. Pedicels 2 mm., about as long as the calyx. Sepals (4–)5, 2–3 × 1.3–1.8 mm., obovate-rhombic, obtuse; outer sepals slightly keeled. Corolla subpersistent; petals (4–)5, 2.5–4 mm., deflexed, pink, obovate to elliptical. Stamens (5–7–)8–10, the longer 5 episepalous, the rest epipetalous; filaments 2.5 mm., broadened at base, long-exserted, arising from centre of flower (with no true disk). Styles 3, spatulate. Capsule 7–9 × 2.5–3 mm., pyramidal. Fl. March–December.

Hab. : Salines. Dead Sea area, Arava Valley. Uncommon.

Area : E. Saharo-Arabian and E. Sudanian.

The author disagrees with Baum (Monogr. Tamarix, MS. 143), who includes this species within *T. macrocarpa* (Ehrenb.) Bge. which can be kept only very doubtfully even as a variety of *T. passerinoides* Del. ex Desv. *T. aravensis* is readily distinguishable from *T. passerinoides* and its var. *macrocarpa* Ehrenb. by its sessile (not amplexicaul) leaves, its long racemes, deflexed petals, etc. It has recently been recorded by Schiman-Czeika (in Rech. f., Fl. Iranica, Contrib. 4 : 15, 1964) from Iran and Afghanistan. Forms with smaller flowers (var. *micrantha* Zoh., l.c. 52) and divergent leaves (var. *patentissima* Zoh., l.c. 52) grow together with the typical form, and are clearly distinguishable.

T. aravensis is a handsome shrub, worth introducing as an ornamental on saline ground.

All the records from Palestine on *T. pentandra* Pall., Fl. Ross. 1, 2 : 72 (1789) *subs. illegit.* [= *T. ramosissima* Ledeb., Fl. Alt. 1 : 424 (1829); fide Baum, l.c. 42] and on *T. pallasii* Desv., Ann. Sci. Nat. 4 : 349 (1824) [= *T. laxa* Willd., Abh. Akad. Berl. Phys. 1812–1813 : 82 (1816); fide Baum, l.c. 89] are erroneous.

75. FRANKENIACEAE

Annual or perennial herbs or half-shrubs. Leaves small, opposite or whorled, entire; petiole more or less membranous-winged at side or at base, wings (stipules ?) ciliate, united to a sheath at base. Flowers small, hermaphrodite or rarely unisexual, actinomorphic, solitary or in cymes. Sepals 4–7, persistent, connate for more than half their length. Petals as many as sepals, imbricated in bud, free or connate below, clawed with a scale adherent to inner side of claw, pink or flesh-coloured. Stamens 3–6 or numerous, free or connate at base; anthers versatile, 2-celled, opening by 2 longitudinal slits. Ovary superior, free, 2–4-carpelled, 1-celled, with parietal placentae; ovules numerous, usually anatropous, on long, ascending funiculi; style filiform, divided above into as many branches as carpels; stigmas terminal and capitate or decurrent on the inner side of the stylar branches. Fruit a loculicidal capsule, enclosed in the calyx, opening by 2–4 valves. Seeds oblong or ovoid with crustaceous coat; endosperm mealy; embryo straight.

Five genera with about 90 species, mostly in salt marshes and deserts of temperate and subtropical regions.

1. FRANKENIA L.

Annual or perennial herbs or half-shrubs. Leaves opposite or whorled. Flowers nearly always hermaphrodite, in axillary or terminal dichasia. Calyx tubular, (4–)5-lobed. Petals (4–)5, small, pink. Stamens usually 6, free, in 2 whorls; filaments broadened at base. Ovary usually of 3 carpels; style filiform, parted into 3–4 linear, club-shaped lobes stigmatose along their inner face. Capsule 1-celled, dehiscing usually by 3 valves.

About 80 species, mostly in salt marshes and salt deserts in temperate and subtropical regions.

Literature: F. Niedenzu, Frankeniaceae, in: Engl. & Prantl, *Nat. Pflznfam.* ed. 2, 21 : 276–281, 1925. R. Nègre, Les Frankenia du Maroc, *Trav. Inst. Sci. Chérif. Bot.* 12 : 1–56 (1957).

1. Annuals. Leaves obovate, flat, mostly mealy and puberulent beneath. Flowers mostly
   solitary.   **2. F. pulverulenta**
 – Perennials. Leaves linear or linear-oblong, revolute-margined, hirsute or ciliate. Flowers
   few in clusters.   **1. F. hirsuta**

1. Frankenia hirsuta L., Sp. Pl. 331 (1753). *F. hirsuta* L. var. *hispida* Boiss., Fl. 1 : 780 (1867) p.p. [Plate 529]
Perennial with woody base, puberulent or white-hirsute, up to 25 cm. Stems procumbent, densely branched, leafy. Leaves (2–)3–7 × 0.5–2 mm., whorled, sessile or tapering to a petiole, linear or linear-oblong, often revolute-margined, often with spreading white-ciliate hairs at base. Flowers in dense corymbose terminal clusters. Calyx 4–5 mm., sparingly hirsute. Corolla purplish or pink; petals 4–6 mm., obovate, long-

clawed, finely denticulate above. Stamens 6. Capsule 2.5–3 mm., 3-valved, ovoid or oblong-ovoid. Seeds minute, oblong-ellipsoidal. Fl. March–June.

Hab.: Maritime and inland salines. Coastal Galilee, Acco Plain, Sharon Plain, Philistean Plain, W. Negev, Dead Sea area. Locally common.

Area: Mediterranean and Euro-Siberian, with extensions towards Irano-Turanian territories.

2. Frankenia pulverulenta L., Sp. Pl. 332 (1753); Boiss., Fl. 1 : 779 (1867). [Plate 530]

Annual, mealy and puberulent, 5–30 cm. Stems ascending or procumbent, much branched. Leaves usually in whorls of 4, 2–5 × 1–2.5 mm., flat, obovate to oblong, tapering to a petiole, obtuse to retuse at apex. Flowers 4–5 mm., solitary or in pairs, in short axillary or terminal spikes. Calyx about 2.5–4 mm., cylindrical; lobes lanceolate-linear. Petals 3.5–5 mm., pale or deep violet, oblong to obovate, somewhat clawed at base, minutely denticulate at apex. Stamens 6. Capsule 2.5–3 mm., 3-valved, ovoid or oblong-ovoid. Seeds oblong. Fl. April–August.

Hab.: Salines. Coastal Galilee, Acco Plain, Sharon Plain, Philistean Plain, Judean Desert, Negev, Upper and Lower Jordan Valley, Dead Sea area, Arava Valley, Ammon, Moav. Locally fairly common.

Area: Euro-Siberian, Mediterranean and Irano-Turanian.

76. ELATINACEAE

Tiny annual or perennial herbs, mostly aquatic or paludinal. Leaves opposite or whorled, undivided, with tapering base and small stipules. Flowers small, hermaphrodite, usually actinomorphic, 2–5(–6)-merous, axillary, solitary on in small cymes, with or without bracteoles. Sepals as many or twice as many as petals, free or connate at base. Petals free, imbricated in bud. Stamens as many as or twice as many as petals; anthers versatile, 2-celled, opening introrsely by longitudinal slits. Ovary superior, 2–5(–6)-carpelled, 2–5(–6)-celled, with axile placentation; ovules numerous, anatropous; styles free, mostly club-shaped. Fruit a septicidal capsule. Seeds straight or curved, with crustaceous coat; endosperm 0 or very thin.

Two genera and about 40 species, in temperate and tropical regions of both hemispheres.

Literature: F. Niedenzu, Elatinaceae, in: Engl. & Prantl, *Nat. Pflznfam.* ed. 2, 21 : 270–276, 1925.

1. Leaves denticulate, hairy. Flowers (in ours) 5-merous. **1. Bergia**
– Leaves entire, glabrous. Flowers 2–4-merous. **2. Elatine**

1. BERGIA L.

Annual or perennial herbs, hairy or glandular-hairy, rarely glabrous. Leaves opposite, dentate. Flowers small, 5-merous (rarely 3-merous), in axillary clusters or umbels, rarely solitary, mostly with bracteoles. Sepals and petals mostly free. Stamens 10 (rarely 5), sometimes more. Ovary 5 (3–6)-celled, globular or ovoid; styles as many as the cells; stigmas usually capitate. Capsule dehiscent, corky. Seeds numerous, small, smooth or wrinkled.

About 20 species, mainly in tropical regions.

1. Bergia ammannioides Heyne ex Roth, Nov. Pl. Sp. 219 (1821); *B. ammannioides* Roxb., Hort. Bengal. 34 (1814) *nom. nud.*; Boiss., Fl. 1 : 782 (1867). *B. pentandra* Guill. et Perr. in Guill., Perr. et Rich., Fl. Seneg. Tent. 42, t. 12 (1831). [Plate 531]

Annual, more or less patulous-hairy, 15–25 cm. Stems many, erect to ascending, branched from base. Leaves 1–3 × 0.5–1 cm., opposite, sessile or tapering to a petiole, elliptical-lanceolate to oblanceolate, acute, acutely serrate especially above, hairy or glandular-hairy, prominently nerved beneath; stipules 3–4 mm., membranous, linear-subulate. Flowers in axillary clusters or rarely solitary, pedicellate. Sepals 5, 1.2–1.5 mm., lanceolate, acuminate, membranous-margined, hairy or glandular-hairy. Petals 5, shorter than sepals, pinkish, lanceolate, acute. Stamens 5, as long as petals. Ovary usually 5-celled, globular-ovoid or oblong. Capsule 1.2 mm.; valves with recurved apex, separating from a central axis. Seeds numerous, 0.2–0.3 mm., ovoid to oblong, brown, wrinkled. Fl. August–September.

Hab.: Swampy places; sandy ground. Sharon Plain. Rare.

Area: Mediterranean and Irano-Turanian. Tropical in origin.

2. ELATINE L.

Tiny glabrous annuals, aquatic or paludinal. Leaves opposite or whorled, entire. Flowers minute, 2-, 3- or 4-merous, pedicellate or sessile, solitary or rarely whorled, ebracteolate. Sepals persistent, connate at base. Petals caducous, white or pink. Stamens 3–4 or 6 or 8, free. Ovary depressed-globular or ellipsoidal with concave apex; styles 3–4, free, short; stigmas club-shaped. Fruit a globular or somewhat depressed-globular, membranous capsule, with 3–4 many-seeded cells. Seeds cylindrical, straight or curved, mostly pitted or wrinkled.

About 20 species, widespread in various regions.

1. Stamens 4. Leaves linear to oblong-elliptical. Seeds straight or very slightly curved.
   1. E. hydropiper
 – Stamens 8. Leaves obovate to oblong-spatulate. Seeds semicircular.
   2. E. macropoda

1. Elatine hydropiper L., Sp. Pl. 367 (1753). *E. major* A. Br., Syll. Pl. Nov. Ratisb. 1 : 83 (1824); Litard. in Briq., Prodr. Fl. Corse 2,2 : 154 (1935). [Plate 532]

Annual, glabrous, 5–10 cm. Stems tufted, creeping, rooting from nodes, with many erect branches. Leaves 1 × 0.1–0.15 cm., opposite, linear to oblong-elliptical. Pedicels 0.3–1 cm., sometimes longer or 0. Flowers axillary and terminal, solitary, sometimes in pairs, 4-merous. Sepals about 1 mm., ovate-oblong. Petals twice as long as sepals, white or pink, ovate-oblong. Stamens 4–8 (4 in ours). Capsule 4-celled, depressed-globular. Seeds straight or very slightly curved, wrinkled. Fl. March.

Hab.: Small puddles on rocks. Sharon Plain, Shefela. Rare.

Area: Euro-Siberian, extending to Mediterranean territories.

2. Elatine macropoda Guss., Fl. Sic. Prodr. 1 : 475 (1827). *E. campylosperma* Seub. in Walp., Repert. Bot. Syst. 1 : 284 (1842) et Nov. Act. Acad. Leop.-Carol. 21, 1 : 49 (1845); Boiss., Fl. 1 : 781 (1867). [Plate 533]

Annual, glabrous, 2–10 cm. Stems tufted, prostrate, rooting from nodes and branched all along. Leaves 0.5–1 × 0.1–0.2 cm., opposite, obovate to oblong-spatulate. Pedicels up to 1.5 cm., longer than the leaves, axillary and terminal. Flowers solitary, 4-merous. Sepals about 2 mm., with ovate obtuse lobes. Petals much shorter than sepals, whitish, broadly ovate, obtuse. Stamens 8, in 2 whorls. Capsule 4-celled, depressed-globular. Seeds semicircular, prominently wrinkled. Fl. February–April.

Hab.: Small puddles on stony or silty ground. Sharon Plain, Upper and Lower Galilee, Shefela. Rare.

Area: Mediterranean and S.W. Euro-Siberian.

Myrtiflorae

77. LYTHRACEAE

Herbs or shrubs, rarely trees. Stems often 4-angled. Leaves opposite, alternate, rarely in whorls; stipules minute or 0. Flowers hermaphrodite, actinomorphic or zygomorphic, usually (3–)4–6-merous, in axillary or terminal spike-like cymes or panicles, sometimes solitary or whorled. Hypanthium ("calyx") persistent, tubular or campanulate; margin of hypanthium with (3–)4–6(–8) valvate sepals ("inner calyx teeth or lobes") and often with epicalyx segments ("additional or outer calyx teeth or lobes") alternating with the sepals. Petals as many as sepals ("inner teeth or lobes"), crumpled in bud, inserted near the top of hypanthium; sometimes petals 0; stamens 2–8(–12) or numerous, inserted below the petals; anthers versatile, 2-celled, splitting longitudinally. Ovary superior (but appearing half-inferior within the perigynous perianth), usually 2–6-celled; placentation axile, rarely parietal; ovules numerous, anatropous; style simple; stigma capitate. Capsule usually dehiscent septicidally, sometimes 1-celled by abortion of septa and opening by a lid or irregularly torn. Seeds without endosperm and with a straight embryo.

Some 25 genera and about 550 species, predominantly in tropical and subtropical regions, especially in Trop. America.

Literature: E. Koehne, Lythraceae, in: *Pflznr.* 17 (IV, 216): 1–326, 1903.

1. Flowers in axillary, sessile or pedunculate clusters. Leaves opposite. Petals 0 or present and 0.5–1 mm. Fruiting hypanthium globular or hemispherical. **1. Ammannia**
– Flowers solitary and axillary or in terminal spikes. Petals present and much larger than above. Fruiting hypanthium cylindrical to campanulate. **2. Lythrum**

1. AMMANNIA L.

Annual glabrous herbs. Branches often 4-angled. Leaves opposite or whorled, sessile, exstipulate, entire, 1-nerved. Flowers small, actinomorphic, 4-merous, axillary, 2-bracteolate, subsessile, solitary or in small cymes. Hypanthium campanulate or tubular-campanulate, later becoming hemispherical or globular. Epicalyx (outer teeth) present or 0. Sepals (inner lobes or teeth) 4. Petals 4 or 0, small, inserted between the sepals. Stamens (2–)4 or 8, inserted on the hypanthium. Ovary sessile, enclosed in the hypanthium, incompletely 2–5-, rarely 1-celled, the septa very thin; placentae axile; style filiform, short, sometimes 0; stigma capitate. Capsule usually irregularly torn. Seeds minute, with leathery coat.

About 30 species, widespread mainly in tropical and subtropical regions of both hemispheres; some of them mainly weeds in summer crops of the temperate regions.

1. Styles 0.3 mm. or less. Cymes glomerate, compact. Flowers subsessile.
　　　　　　　　　　　　　　　　　　　　　　　　　　　　　1. A. aegyptiaca
– Styles longer than 0.3 mm. Cymes loose. Flowers distinctly pedicellate.
　　　　　　　　　　　　　　　　　　　　　　　　　　　　　2. A. prieureana

1. Ammannia aegyptiaca Willd., Hort. Berol. 1 : 6, t. 6 (1803) et Enum. Pl. Hort. Berol. 167 (1809). *A. auriculata* Willd. var. *subsessilis* Boiss., Fl. 2 : 743 (1872). *A. verticillata* auct. Fl. Palaest. non Lam., Tabl. Encycl. 1, 2 : 311 no. 1554 (1792). [Plate 534]

Annual, glaucescent, up to 60 cm. or more. Stems erect, simple or oppositely branched, terete below, 4-angled or slightly winged above. Leaves 1–5 × 0.3–0.8 cm., opposite, oblong or oblanceolate, tapering or broadened and auriculate-cordate at base, acute. Cymes umbellate, small, forming compact clusters in the axils of leaves. Pedicels up to 1–2 mm. Flowers about 2 mm. Hypanthium 1–2 mm., growing somewhat in fruit, broadly campanulate, green, glabrous; sepals (inner lobes) spreading, triangular, acute, with or without smaller outer additional teeth (epicalyx segments) alternating with the lobes. Petals often 0. Stamens 4. Style 0.3 mm. or less. Capsule 2–3 mm., almost globular, reddish, enclosed in the coriaceous, hemispherical, brown fruiting hypanthium. Seeds angular-ovoid, brown. Fl. May–August.

Hab.: Swampy ground. Sharon Plain, Philistean Plain, Hula Plain, Upper and Lower Jordan Valley. Rare.

Area: Tropics; pluriregional.

2. Ammannia prieureana Guill. et Perr. in Guill., Perr. et Rich., Fl. Seneg. Tent. 303 (1833); Koehne, in Pflznr. 17 (IV, 216): 48 (1903). [Plate 535]

Annual, 20–60 cm. Stems erect or ascending, with opposite branches, 4-angled, winged above. Leaves 1.5–6 × 0.4–0.8 cm., opposite, oblong or oblanceolate, broadened to auriculate at base, acute. Cymes umbellate, small, loose. Pedicels half to twice as long as the flower. Flowers 2–2.5 mm. Hypanthium 1–1.5 mm., campanulate, prominently ribbed, hirtellous along ribs; fruiting hypanthium widened up to 3 mm.; sepals (inner teeth) half as long as hypanthium or less, broadly triangular, apiculate, with minute, horn-shaped outer additional teeth (epicalyx segments) alternating with the inner teeth. Petals much exserted from calyx, pink. Stamens 4, slightly exserted. Style about 1 mm., exserted. Capsule about 2 mm., almost globular, included in the fruiting hypanthium. Seeds many, 0.3–0.5 mm., angular, brown, glossy. Fl. July–August.

Hab.: Borders of swamps; sandy soil. Sharon Plain. Rare.

Area: Trop. Africa.

2. Lythrum L.

Herbs or small shrubs. Stems usually 4-angled, at least when young. Leaves opposite, alternate or whorled, entire. Flowers somewhat zygomorphic, axillary, 2-bracteolate, solitary or in small cymes or spikes, purple or pink. Hypanthium tubular or tubular-campanulate, straight, 8–12-ribbed; outer teeth or lobes (epicalyx segments) 4–6, alternating with the 4–6 inner teeth or lobes (sepals). Petals usually 4–6, inserted on upper part of hypanthium. Stamens 2–12, in 1 or 2 whorls, inserted at the bottom or middle of hypanthium. Ovary sessile, 2-celled; style filiform, with capitate stigma. Flowers often heterostylous. Capsule 2-celled, many-seeded, mostly dehiscing by 2 valves.

About 35 species widely distributed in many regions of both hemispheres.

1. Leaves ovate or obovate, usually almost as long as broad, opposite except for the upper ones. Very low annuals. **1. L. borysthenicum**
- Leaves linear to oblong or lanceolate, much longer than broad, usually alternate, but if opposite or whorled then plants perennial and tall 2
2. Hairy, tall perennials with long terminal spike-like inflorescences. **6. L. salicaria**
- Glabrous or glabrescent plants. Flowers usually solitary or in pairs in the axils of leaves 3
3. Stamens 12, exserted. Flowers 1–1.5 cm. **5. L. junceum**
- Stamens 2–6, included. Flowers much smaller than above 4
4. Sepals (inner teeth) 0.5 mm., sometimes almost obsolete, the outer additional teeth usually as long as the former, triangular, obtuse. Flowers approximate along leafy branches. Petals about 2 (–3) mm. **2. L. tribracteatum**
- Sepals (inner teeth) longer than above 5
5. Sepals (inner teeth) subulate, as long as the outer additional teeth or somewhat shorter. Stamens usually 5–6. Stems erect. **3. L. hyssopifolia**
- Sepals (inner teeth) broadly ovate, apiculate, much shorter than the outer additional teeth. Stamens usually 2. Stems prostrate or procumbent. **4. L. thymifolia**

1. Lythrum borysthenicum (Schrank) Litv. in Maevskiy, Fl. Sred. Ross. ed. 5, 209 (1917; "Spreng." *pro auctore basionymi*); D. A. Webb in Heywood, Repert. Sp. Nov. 74: 11 (1967). *Peplis borysthenica* M.B. ex Bess., Enum. Pl. Volh. 81 (1822) *nom. nud.*; M.B. ex Spreng., Syst. Veg. 2: 135 (1825); *P. borysthenica* Schrank, Flora 5: 643 (1822). *P. erecta* Requien ex Benth., Cat. Pyr. 111 (1826) *nom. nud.*; Boiss., Fl. 2: 742 (1872). [Plate 536]

Annual, glabrous or scabrous-hirtellous, up to 15 cm. Stems erect, branched from base, striate to 4-angled. Leaves 0.8–1.5 × 0.4–0.8 cm., opposite except for the uppermost ones, subsessile, obovate, somewhat cuneate at base, minutely serrulate, ciliate. Bracteoles much shorter than the hypanthium, scarious, filiform. Flowers 4 mm., solitary, rarely in pairs. Hypanthium 2–3 mm. in flower, ovoid-campanulate; outer teeth 6, subulate, reflexed, usually hairy along nerves; inner teeth 6, as long as or shorter than the outer, triangular. Petals 6 or 0, as long as hypanthium or slightly exserted, white or purple, obovate. Stamens (5–)6, included. Capsule somewhat shorter than hypanthium, hardly dehiscent, many-seeded, membranous, ovoid to globular. Fl. April–May.

Hab.: Damp places. Sharon Plain. Rare.

Area: Mediterranean and Saharo-Arabian.

2. Lythrum tribracteatum Salzm. ex Spreng., Syst. Veg. 4, 2 (Cur. Post.): 190 (1827); Salzm. ex Benth., Cat. Pyr. 98 (1826; *"tribracteata"*) *nom. nud. L. bibracteatum* Salzm. ex DC., Prodr. 3: 81 (1828) *pro syn.*; Boiss., Fl. 2: 740 (1872). [Plate 537]

Annual, glabrous, 10–50 cm. Stems erect, ascending or prostrate, branched from base, often with short axillary branchlets. Leaves 0.5–2 × 0.1–0.5 cm., alternate or opposite, sessile, linear-oblong to linear, tapering at base, obtuse at apex. Bracteoles as long as the hypanthium or much shorter, oblong or elliptical, acute, green, usually serrulate. Flowers about 5 mm., solitary along the main leafy branches and also crowded on the short lateral branches. Hypanthium about 4 mm., elongating in fruit, cylindrical, 10–12-striate; teeth 8–12, very short, almost equal in length, often almost obsolete, outer teeth triangular, obtuse. Petals one third to one half as long as hypanthium, violet, obovate-oblong. Stamens 4–6, included. Capsule narrow, enclosed within the hypanthium, cylindrical, brown, glabrous. 2n = 10 *. Fl. February–August.

Hab.: Damp places. Coastal Galilee, Acco Plain, Sharon Plain, Philistean Plain, Mt. Carmel, Samaria, Hula Plain, Upper Jordan Valley, Dead Sea area. Uncommon.

Area: Euro-Siberian, Mediterranean and Irano-Turanian.

3. Lythrum hyssopifolia L., Sp. Pl. 447 (1753); Boiss., Fl. 2: 739 (1872). [Plate 538]

Annual, rarely perennial, glabrous, up to 50 cm. Stems erect or ascending, simple or sometimes diffusely branched, densely leafy. Leaves 1–2.5 × 0.2–0.8 cm., alternate, the lower ones oblong to linear-oblong, the others linear-lanceolate to oblong. Flowers about 8 mm., solitary, subsessile, with 2 minute, persistent, membranous, subulate bracteoles. Hypanthium about 5 mm., somewhat elongating in fruit, tubular; teeth 10, subulate, the outer ones 1–1.5 mm., the inner shorter. Petals shorter than hypanthium, pink, obovate-oblong, obtuse. Stamens 4–6, included. Capsule enclosed within the hypanthium, cylindrical. 2n = 20. Fl. February–August.

Hab.: Swampy and seasonally flooded ground. Acco Plain, Sharon Plain, Philistean Plain, Upper and Lower Galilee, Judean Mts., Hula Plain, Upper and Lower Jordan Valley, Ammon. Uncommon.

Area: Pluriregional.

---

* Chromosome numbers in this and the subsequent species of the genus *Lythrum* have been taken from R. Dulberger, Israel Journ. Bot. 17: 179–183 (1968).

4. Lythrum thymifolia L., Sp. Pl. 447 (1753); Boiss., Fl. 2 : 740 (1872). [Plate 539]

Annual, glabrous, 10–30 cm. Stems prostrate or procumbent, slender, angular. Leaves 0.6–2 × 0.15–0.3 cm., alternate, linear, the lower ones oblong-lanceolate; margin scabridulous. Bracteoles half as long as the hypanthium or shorter, caducous, linear-lanceolate. Flowers 5–7 mm., 4(–5)-merous, solitary, nearly sessile. Hypanthium 4–5 mm., cylindrical, 8-nerved; teeth 8, the outer ones triangular-lanceolate, acute, the inner shorter, broadly ovate, apiculate. Petals 1–3 mm., pinkish-violet to white, obovate-oblong. Stamens 2, opposite, not exceeding the hypanthium tube. Capsule enclosed within the hypanthium, oblong. Fl. May–July.

Hab.: Damp places. Philistean Plain, Judean Mts. Rare.

Area: Euro-Siberian, Mediterranean and Irano-Turanian.

5. Lythrum junceum Banks et Sol. in Russ., Nat. Hist. Aleppo ed. 2, 2 : 253 (1794). *L. graefferi* Ten., Prodr. Fl. Nap. Suppl. 2 : LXVIII (1811–1815); Boiss., Fl. 2 : 739 (1872). *L. flexuosum* auct. non Lag., Gen. et Sp. Nov. 16 (1816). [Plate 540]

Perennial, glabrous, 30–60 cm. Stems erect to ascending, usually diffuse, branched from base, angular. Leaves 1–4 × 0.2–1 cm., usually alternate, the lower ones elliptical-oblong, sometimes cordate at base, the upper linear-lanceolate to linear. Bracteoles minute, membranous, subulate. Flowers 1–1.5 cm., heterostylous, remote, solitary, nearly sessile. Hypanthium 5–7(–9) mm., cylindrical-obconical, 10–12-nerved, sometimes with purple spots at middle; teeth 12, triangular, the outer ones with blackish tips, the inner somewhat shorter than the outer ones or as long. Petals up to 1 cm., pink to purplish, obovate. Stamens 12, 6 of them long-exserted, the others not exceeding the throat of hypanthium. Capsule enclosed within the hypanthium, cylindrical. 2n = 10. Fl. March–June.

Hab.: Swamps, ditches and other damp places. Acco Plain, Sharon Plain, Philistean Plain, Upper and Lower Galilee, Mt. Carmel, Esdraelon Plain, Shefela, Judean Mts., Dan Valley, Hula Plain, Upper Jordan Valley, Dead Sea area, Gilead, Edom. Locally fairly common.

Area: Mainly Mediterranean, with extensions to S.W. Euro-Siberian territories.

6. Lythrum salicaria L., Sp. Pl. 446 (1753); Boiss., Fl. 2 : 738 (1872). *L. salicaria* L. var. *tomentosum* DC., Cat. Hort. Monsp. 123 (1813); Boiss., l.c. *L. tomentosum* Mill., Gard. Dict. ed. 8, no. 2 (1768). [Plate 541]

Perennial, shrubby, densely pubescent to subglabrous, 1–3 m. Stems erect, stout, with short, slender branches, 4-angled. Leaves 2–7(–10) × 0.4–0.8(–2) cm., usually opposite or whorled, sessile, lanceolate or oblong or sometimes ovate, often cordate or semiamplexicaul at base, usually acute. Pedicels 1–2 mm. Bracteoles about as long as the hypanthium, linear-subulate, often coloured. Flowers 1.2–2 cm., heterotristylous, in dense cymes in the axils of large bracts and congested into a terminal spike-like inflorescence 10–30 cm. long. Hypanthium 0.5–0.8(–1) cm., cylindrical, hairy, 12-nerved; teeth 12, the outer ones longer, subulate, the inner triangular. Petals 0.8–1.2 cm., purple, oblong-elliptical to oblong-obovate. Stamens 12, some or all exserted, in 2 whorls. Capsule enclosed within the hypanthium, oblong-ovoid. 2n = 30. Fl. June–November.

Hab. : River banks and swamps. Acco Plain, Sharon Plain, Philistean Plain, Upper and Lower Galilee, Mt. Carmel, Esdraelon Plain, Dan Valley, Hula Plain, Upper and Lower Jordan Valley, Golan. Locally fairly common.

Area : Pluriregional.

The young leafy shoots are eaten as vegetables; the flowering branches are used in folk medicine to prepare astringents, tonics and styptics.

78. MYRTACEAE

Trees or shrubs, rarely herbs. Leaves mostly containing aromatic oil, mostly opposite, petiolate, simple, mostly entire, generally leathery and dotted with pellucid glands; stipules 0 or very small, caducous. Inflorescences mostly paniculate, more rarely racemose or dichasial. Flowers hermaphrodite, actinomorphic, very rarely zygomorphic. Sepals 4–5 (–6), rarely more, persistent, usually imbricated, free or connate at base. Petals as many as sepals, imbricated, free or rarely connate, rarely petals 0. Stamens usually many, in several rows, free or grouped in bundles; anthers usually versatile, 2-celled, dehiscing lengthwise or by apical pores. Ovary inferior or half-inferior, crowned with a fleshy disk, (1–)2- to many-celled; placentae parietal and strongly protruding into the cell, or more frequently axile; each placenta with 1 or more anatropous or campylotropous ovules; style and stigma 1. Fruit a berry, capsule or nutlet. Seeds without or with a sparse endosperm.

About 100 genera and 3,000 species, mainly in tropical regions, especially of America and Australia.

1. MYRTUS L.

Evergreen aromatic shrubs. Leaves opposite or in whorls, leathery, glabrous. Flowers actinomorphic, axillary, solitary or in short cymes. Sepals 5, somewhat connate at base. Petals 5, spreading. Stamens numerous, free, in several rows; connective usually gland-tipped. Ovary inferior, with 2–3 cells almost or completely separated; ovules numerous in each cell, campylotropous; style filiform; stigma mostly small. Fruit a 2–3-celled berry, crowned with the persistent calyx lobes. Seeds reniform.

About 100 species, mainly in S. America, Australia; only 1 species in the Mediterranean region.

1. Myrtus communis L., Sp. Pl. 471 (1753); Boiss., Fl. 2 : 736 (1872). [Plate 542]

Evergreen aromatic shrub, glabrous, 0.5–2 m. Stems numerous, branched. Twigs 4-angled, leafy. Leaves 1–4 × 0.7–2 cm., opposite or whorled, short-petioled, leathery, ovate-lanceolate to elliptical, acuminate, pellucid-dotted; stipules caducous. Bracteoles 2, caducous, linear. Flowers about 1.5 cm. in diam., solitary, long-pedicelled. Sepals 2–3 mm., ovate, acute. Petals nearly 3 times as long as sepals, white, obovate to orbicular, concave. Berry 0.8–1 cm., broadly ellipsoidal to subglobular, blackish-blue, crowned by the persistent calyx lobes. Fl. May–August.

Hab.: Maquis and riverine thickets. Upper Galilee, Mt. Carmel, Dan Valley, Upper Jordan Valley, Golan. Uncommon.

Area: Mediterranean with extensions into S.W. territories of the Irano-Turanian and Euro-Siberian regions.

Varies considerably in size of flowers and fruits. The Biblical names הֲדַס (Is. xli : 19 and elsewhere) and עֵץ עָבֹת (Lev. xxiii : 40 and elsewhere) are referred to this species.

Known in medicine as oleum, folia et fructus myrti; also used in the perfume industry. Fruit edible.

79. ONAGRACEAE

Herbs, rarely shrubs or trees. Leaves opposite, alternate or whorled, undivided, entire or toothed, with caducous stipules or exstipulate. Flowers hermaphrodite, actinomorphic or somewhat zygomorphic, mostly axillary and solitary or in spikes or racemes at the end of the branches. Hypanthium cup- or tube-like, adnate to and often prolonged much above the ovary as a "hypanthial tube". Sepals 2 or 4–5. Petals as many as sepals and alternating with them, contorted in bud, rarely petals 0. Stamens usually 8, in 2 whorls, rarely 1, 2, 4, 5, 10, emerging from or near hypanthium margin; anthers usually 2-celled, opening longitudinally. Ovary inferior, 1- to many-celled, often 4-celled; placentation axile (septa sometimes incomplete); ovules 1 to many, anatropous; style 1, cylindrical or subulate; stigma capitate or nearly 2-lobed or 4-fid. Fruit a loculicidal capsule or a nutlet or a berry, 1- or several-celled, 1- or many-seeded. Seeds without endosperm.

About 20 genera and 650 species in temperate and subtropical regions; a few in tropical regions.

1. Petals pink to purplish or violet. Flowers arranged in racemes.   **2. Epilobium**
  – Petals yellow or 0. Flowers solitary   2
2. Leaves and stems glabrous. Aquatic plants.   **1. Ludwigia**
  – Leaves and stems hairy. Terrestrial plants.   **3. Oenothera**

1. Ludwigia L. ("*Ludvigia*") corr. L.

Perennial aquatic herbs, often creeping or free-floating. Leaves alternate or opposite, mostly entire; stipules very small or 0. Flowers actinomorphic, usually 4-merous, axillary, usually 2-bracteolate, solitary or clustered or in head- or spike-like inflorescences. Hypanthium not prolonged above ovary. Sepals 4–5, semipersistent. Petals as many as sepals or 0, caducous, showy, spreading. Stamens as many or twice as many as petals. Ovary 4–5-celled; ovules many; stigma capitate, slightly 4-lobed. Capsule linear, terete or angular, 8–10-ribbed, crowned by the sepals, dehiscing irregularly by a terminal pore or septicidally by valves separating from the placentae. Seeds many, without a tuft of hairs, free or embedded in endocarp.

About 75 species, predominantly in tropical regions.

Literature: P. H. Raven, The Old World species of *Ludwigia* (including *Jussiaea*), etc., *Reinwardtia* 6: 327–427 (1963).

1. Petals large, yellow. Leaves alternate.   **1. L. stolonifera**
- Petals 0. Leaves opposite.   **2. L. palustris**

1. Ludwigia stolonifera (Guill. et Perr.) Raven, Reinwardtia 6: 390 (1963). *Jussiaea stolonifera* Guill. et Perr. in Guill., Perr. et Rich., Fl. Seneg. Tent. 292 (1833). *J. diffusa* Forssk., Fl. Aeg.-Arab. 210 (1775). *L. diffusa* (Forssk.) Greene, Fl. Francisc. 1: 227 (1891) non Buch.-Ham., Trans. Linn. Soc. Lond. 14: 301 (1824). *J. repens* L. var. *diffusa* (Forssk.) Brenan, Kew Bull. 1953: 171 (1953). *J. repens* sensu Boiss., Fl. 2: 751 (1872) non L., Sp. Pl. 388 (1753). [Plate 543]

Perennial aquatic. Stems creeping or floating, glabrous, furnished with vesicular and fibrous roots at base and nodes. Leaves 1.5–9 × 0.7–1.6 cm., alternate, petiolate, narrowly elliptical to lanceolate, tapering at base, acute or obtuse at apex. Flowers solitary, pedicellate. Hypanthium about 1 cm., elongating in fruit, cylindrical, tapering at base, hirtellous. Sepals 5, 1–1.5 cm., lanceolate-acuminate. Petals 5, 1–1.8 cm., yellow, obovate. Stamens 8–10, shorter than sepals. Capsule about 3–4 cm., terete or angular, pilose or glabrous, crowned by the persistent calyx. Seeds about 1.3 mm., pale brown. Fl. April–November.

Hab.: In stagnant and permanent water bodies. Acco Plain, Sharon Plain, Philistean Plain, Esdraelon Plain, Dan Valley, Hula Plain, Upper Jordan Valley, Golan. Rare.

Area: Trop. Africa, extending into the adjacent Mediterranean territories.

2. Ludwigia palustris (L.) Elliott, Sketch Fl. S. Carol. Georg. 1: 211 (1817); Boiss., Fl. 2: 752 (1872). *Isnardia palustris* L., Sp. Pl. 120 (1753). [Plate 544]

Perennial aquatic herb, glabrous, (10–)20–60 cm. Stems prostrate or ascending, rooting from nodes, simple or branched, 4-angled, reddish. Leaves 1–5 × 1.2 cm., opposite, decussate, obovate to broadly elliptical, tapering at base to a long petiole, obtuse and shortly acuminate at apex, entire, glaucous. Bracteoles minute or 0, lanceolate. Flowers axillary, solitary, subsessile. Hypanthium about 3 mm., campanulate or tubular, finely striate. Sepals 4, 1–2 mm., triangular, acute. Petals 0. Stamens 4, shorter than sepals. Capsule 3–4 mm., longer than broad, many-seeded, obovoid, crowned by the persistent calyx. Seeds ovoid-cuneate. Fl. May.

Hab.: Swamps and irrigated crops. Hula Plain. Very rare.

Area: Pluriregional, especially in the tropical and subtropical parts of the globe.

2. EPILOBIUM L.

Annuals or perennials, rarely suffruticose. Leaves opposite, alternate or whorled. Flowers hermaphrodite, actinomorphic or slightly zygomorphic, axillary, white or pink or purple, solitary or often in racemes or spikes. Hypanthial tube short or 0. Sepals 4, caducous. Petals 4. Stamens 8, 4 of them longer than the rest. Ovary erect; style filiform; stigmas 4, often spreading or sometimes coalescent into a knob. Capsule

4-celled, elongated, linear, 4-angled, dehiscing loculicidally from apex to base by 4 valves, leaving seed-bearing column in the centre. Seeds many, with a chalazal tuft of long hairs.

About 200 species in most temperate regions of the globe.

Literature: K. Haussknecht, *Monographie der Gattung Epilobium,* Jena, 1884. H. Léveillé, Monographie synthétique et iconographique du genre *Epilobium, Bull. Acad. Inst. Géogr. Bot.* 16: 241–305 (1907).

1. Stems with 2–4 elevated longitudinal ribs. Capsule glabrous. **3. E. tournefortii**
− Stems furrowed or striate. Capsule hairy   **2**
2. Flowers about 2 cm. in diam.   **1. E. hirsutum**
− Flowers about 1 cm. in diam.   **2. E. parviflorum**

1. Epilobium hirsutum L., Sp. Pl. 347 (1753); Boiss., Fl. 2: 746 (1872). *E. hirsutum* L. var. *tomentosum* (Vent.) Boiss., l.c. [Plate 545]

Perennial rhizomatous herb, villose, 0.6–2 m. Stems erect, branched above, terete. Leaves (2–)3–9 × 1–2.5 cm., opposite, sessile, oblong or ovate-oblong to lanceolate, semiamplexicaul, acute, serrulate, hirsute on both sides with longer hairs along nerves; upper leaves sometimes alternate. Flowers 1.5–2.3 cm. in diam., in leafy terminal racemes. Sepals 0.6–0.8(–1) cm., lanceolate, apiculate. Petals (0.6–)1–2 cm., pink to purplish, broadly obovate, notched. Stigma 4-lobed, exceeding the 4 outer stamens. Capsule 4–8 cm., linear, pubescent with soft patulous or antrorse hairs. Seeds 1–1.5 mm., oblong-obovoid, brownish, papillose. Fl. May–December.

Hab.: Swamps and river banks. Acco Plain, Sharon Plain, Philistean Plain, Upper and Lower Galilee, Esdraelon Plain, Samaria, Shefela, Judean Mts., Dan Valley, Hula Plain, Upper Jordan Valley, Beit Shean Valley, Lower Jordan Valley, Dead Sea area, Gilead, Moav. Locally fairly common.

Area: Euro-Siberian, Mediterranean and Irano-Turanian, also occurring in E. and S. Africa.

2. Epilobium parviflorum Schreb., Spic. Fl. Lips. 146, no. 1164, 155 Consp. no. 314 (1771); DC., Prodr. 3: 43 (1828); Boiss., Fl. 2: 746 (1872). [Plate 546]

Perennial rhizomatous herb, villose throughout and often glandular-pubescent above, 30–70 cm. Stems erect, poorly branched, terete. Basal leaves sometimes rosulate; cauline leaves opposite, 3–8 × 1–3 cm., sessile or short-petioled; uppermost leaves alternate, oblong to lanceolate, acute, denticulate. Flowers 0.5–1 cm. in diam., in terminal leafy racemes. Sepals 4–6 mm., lanceolate, acute. Petals 4–9 mm., purplish-pink (sometimes white), obovate, deeply notched. Stigma with patulous lobes, not exceeding stamens. Capsule 6–8 cm., hirsute. Seeds about 1 mm., obovoid, brownish, papillose. Fl. June–October.

Hab.: River banks. Upper Galilee, Dan Valley. Rare.

Area: Euro-Siberian and Mediterranean.

3. Epilobium tournefortii Michal., Bull. Soc. Bot. Fr. 2: 731 (1855); Boiss., Fl. 2: 748 (1872). *E. salzmannii* Boiss. et Reut. ex Nym., Consp. 247 (1879) *pro syn. E. tetra-gonum* L. var. *tournefortii* (Michal.) Post, Fl. Syr. Pal. Sin. 322 (1883–1896). [Plate 547]

Perennial rhizomatous herb, glabrous below and sparingly pubescent above, 30–80 cm. Stems erect, much branched, rigid, often with 2–4 elevated longitudinal ribs. Leaves 2–7 × 0.5–1.5 cm., sessile, oblong-lanceolate, irregularly denticulate; lower leaves opposite, upper ones alternate. Flowers 1–1.5 cm. in diam., erect, in terminal leafy racemes. Sepals somewhat shorter than petals, lanceolate, acute, hirsute. Petals 0.8–1 cm., purple or violet, obovate, notched. Capsule 5–9 cm., glabrous (when mature), linear. Seeds 1–1.2 mm., oblong, tuberculate. Fl. July–September.

Hab.: By water. Dan Valley. Rare.

Area: Mediterranean.

3. OENOTHERA L.

Annual or perennial herbs. Leaves alternate. Flowers actinomorphic, axillary, solitary, sometimes forming a leafy terminal spike, showy. Hypanthial tube conspicuous. Sepals 4, often caducous, usually strongly reflexed. Petals 4, yellow, rarely white or pink, obovate or obcordate, with or without a short claw. Stamens 8, equal or the inner ones shorter. Ovary 4-celled, cylindrical; stigma deeply 4-cleft into linear lobes or rarely capitate. Capsule splitting loculicidally into 4 valves. Seeds without a tuft of hairs.

About 80 species, mainly in S. America.

1. Oenothera drummondii Hook., Bot. Mag. 3361 (1834). [Plate 548]

Perennial pubescent herb, shrubby, up to 60(–80) cm. Stems many, erect or procumbent, much branched all along. Leaves 3–6 × 1–2 cm., lanceolate-oblong or oblanceolate, tapering gradually or abruptly to a short petiole, acute or obtuse, entire or slightly toothed, densely soft-pubescent. Flowers 5–7 cm. across, opening in the evening. Sepals 2–3 cm., reflexed, linear-lanceolate. Petals about 3 cm., bright yellow, broadly obovate. Stigma deeply 4-cleft. Capsule 2.5–5 cm., obtusely 4-angled, with numerous fusiform seeds. $2n = 14$. Fl. mainly April–September.

Hab.: Sand dunes and sandy loams. Acco Plain, Sharon Plain, Philistean Plain; recently also found on damp soils of the Hula Plain. Locally very common.

Area: S. America.

Casually introduced at the end of the last century; at present occupies primary and man-made habitats of the coastal plain. Competes strongly with *Ammophila arenaria* in mobile sand dunes.

80. HALORAGACEAE

Aquatic or subaquatic herbs or half-shrubs. Leaves opposite or whorled, sometimes alternate, stipulate or exstipulate. Flowers usually unisexual, actinomorphic, minute, axillary, sessile, solitary or in terminal spikes, racemes or panicles. Sepals 4, rarely 3, 2 or 0, small. Petals as many as sepals or 0, caducous, free. Stamens 2–8, free; anthers 2-celled. Ovary inferior, 2–4-carpelled, 1–4-celled, each cell with 1 anatropous ovule; placentation axile or (when ovary 1-celled) parietal; styles 1–4, often very short; stigmas 1–4, feathery or coarsely papillose. Fruit nut-like or drupaceous, or fruit a schizocarp separating into 1-seeded nutlets. Seeds with oily endosperm and straight embryo.

Some 6 genera and 120 species; cosmopolitan but with larger concentration in the southern hemisphere.

1. MYRIOPHYLLUM L.

Perennial aquatic herbs, free-floating or with creeping rhizomes attached to the substrate, monoecious, dioecious or polygamous. Shoots submerged except for the inflorescence, very leafy. Leaves whorled, opposite or alternate, dentate or pinnatisect; aerial leaves and bracts sometimes simple, toothed or entire. Flowers usually unisexual, whorled in the axils of leaves or bracts, forming leafy or bracteate terminal spikes; upper flowers commonly staminate, the lower ones pistillate. Staminate flowers: sepals 4 or 0, caducous; petals 4 or 0, caducous; stamens 8, sometimes 4 or 6. Pistillate flowers: sepals small; petals minute, deflexed; ovary 4-celled, stigmas 4, persistent, villose. Fruit dry, separating into 4 nutlets.

Forty-five species almost all over the globe.

1. Myriophyllum spicatum L., Sp. Pl. 992 (1753); Boiss., Fl. 2 : 755 (1872). [Plate 549]

Perennial glabrous herb with creeping rhizomes and branched leafy shoots up to 2 m. in length. Leaves 1–2 cm., about equalling the internodes in length, whorled, pinnatisect into setaceous segments. Spikes 3–10 cm., terminal, naked at apex. Staminate flowers in the upper whorls of spike subtended by 3 entire bracts one third as long as the calyx; petals 5, about 3 mm., caducous, dull red, elliptical; stamens 8. Pistillate flowers in the lower whorls of the spike subtended by 3 bracts; the lowest bracts pectinate, shorter than flowers; petals very small. Fruit about 2 mm., ovoid, of 4 dry 1-seeded nutlets. Fl. July–August.

Hab.: Pools and streams. Hula Plain, Upper Jordan Valley, Golan, Gilead. Rare.
Area: Euro-Siberian, Mediterranean and Irano-Turanian.

81. THELIGONACEAE

Flaccid annual herbs, monoecious. Leaves opposite (or the upper often alternate due to the abortion of one leaf of the pair), petiolate, simple, entire; stipules almost sheathing base of leaf, membranous to fleshy. Flowers unisexual, axillary, 1 to 3 in a cluster. Staminate flowers: 2–3 in upper axils, ebracteolate; perianth 2–5-lobed, lobes membranous, later becoming revolute; stamens 6–28, filaments free, filiform, anthers 2-celled, linear. Pistillate flowers: 1–3 in lower axils, 2-bracteolate; perianth minute, caducous, more or less funnel-shaped, 2–4-dentate, membranous, accrescent; ovary inferior, 1-celled, included in the short perianth, with 1 basal campylotropous ovule; style lateral, linear to club-shaped, papillose from middle, caducous in fruit. Fruit a short-stalked subglobular nut-like drupe; pericarp somewhat fleshy, beset with small whitish warts. Seeds with a thin testa, a horseshoe-shaped embryo and a mealy endosperm.

One genus of 3 species in the Mediterranean region, C. and E. Asia.

1. THELIGONUM L.

Description as for family.

1. Theligonum cynocrambe L., Sp. Pl. 993 (1753). *Cynocrambe prostrata* Gaertn., Fruct. 1 : 362, t. 75, f. 9 (1788); Boiss., Fl. 4 : 897 (1879). [Plate 550]

Annual herb, somewhat puberulent, 5–40 cm. Stems prostrate to ascending, with a long hypocotyl. Leaves 1–3.5 × 0.5–2.5 cm., opposite below, alternate above, petiolate, ovate, more or less cuneate at base, obtuse to acutish at apex, scabrous at margins; stipules connate or clasping in alternate leaves, entire or dentate. Flowers small, sessile, greenish. Staminate flowers : twinned, opposite the alternate leaves; perianth 2-lobed, membranous, rolled back; stamens 7–20, exserted; filaments filiform, bearing long, narrowly linear anthers. Fruit about 2 mm. in diam., more or less globular, with hyaline-crystalline warts. Fl. January–April.

Hab. : Shady and stony places, frequently on screes and fences. Sharon Plain, Philistean Plain, Upper and Lower Galilee, Mt. Carmel, Esdraelon Plain, Samaria, Judean Mts., Judean Desert, Hula Plain, Upper and Lower Jordan Valley, Dead Sea area, Gilead, Ammon, Moav, Edom. Common.

Area : Mediterranean, with extensions into territories of adjacent regions.

Umbelliflorae

82. ARALIACEAE

Herbs, shrubs, trees or woody climbers. Leaves usually alternate, simple or compound, usually stipulate. Flowers hermaphrodite or unisexual, actinomorphic, usually 5-merous, small, in heads, umbels, racemes or spikes, often forming compound inflorescences. Calyx cupuliform, adnate to ovary, with small or obsolete lobes. Petals 5–10 (rarely 3), valvate or imbricated, caducous. Stamens as many as petals and alternating with them; anthers 2-celled, dehiscing longitudinally. Disk flat or conical or otherwise swollen, covering top of ovary. Ovary usually inferior, 2- to many (sometimes 1)-carpelled, 1- to many-celled, with 1 anatropous ovule in each cell; placentation axile; styles as many as the cells, free or more or less connate. Fruit berry- or drupe-like with hard endocarp, usually 5-celled, or endocarp divided into crustaceous, 1-seeded pyrenes or mericarps. Seeds pendulous, with a copious endosperm; embryo small.

About 55 genera and 700 species mainly in the tropical regions of Asia, America and Australia; some in temperate, mainly E. Asian, regions.

1. HEDERA L.

Evergreen woody climbers with tufts of clinging rootlets on the aerial branches. Leaves alternate, petiolate, simple, leathery; stipules 0. Flowers pedicellate, in terminal umbels often arranged in a panicle. Calyx with 5 small lobes. Petals 5, free, valvate, with a broad base. Stamens 5. Ovary inferior, usually 5-celled, with a conspicuous domed disk at apex terminating in a single short style. Fruit berry-like, 5-celled, crowned with the scars of the calyx lobes; pyrenes ovoid-triquetrous. Seed solitary in each pyrene, pendulous.

Some 15 species in the N. temperate regions of the Old World.

1. Hedera helix L., Sp. Pl. 202 (1753); Boiss., Fl. 2 : 1090 (1872). [Plate 551]

Perennial climbing shrub. Stems woody and thick, diffusely or very densely branched. Twigs with clinging roots; young twigs pubescent. Leaves long-petioled; blades (2–)3.5–12 × 1.5–6 cm., cuneate or cordate or rounded at base, dark green above, glossy, hairy when young, often with pale veins; blades of lower leaves 3–5-lobed with more or less triangular entire lobes, those of upper leaves entire, ovate to rhombic, acuminate or sometimes obtuse. Peduncles and pedicels stellately tomentose. Flowers in subglobular umbels often arranged in a terminal panicle. Calyx lobes 2 mm., deltoid. Petals 3–4 mm., yellowish-green, triangular-ovate, somewhat hooded at apex. Fruit 5–8 mm., turbinate to globular, black. Fl. October–February.

Hab.: Rocks and maquis. Upper Galilee, Edom. Very rare.

Area: Euro-Siberian and Mediterranean.

Widely grown as an ornamental; the fruit (toxic to children) is emeto-cathartic and sudorific.

83. UMBELLIFERAE

Annual or perennial herbs, rarely shrubs or tree-like plants. Leaves alternate, very rarely opposite, mostly exstipulate, with sheathing petioles, usually pinnately or palmately divided, rarely leaves undivided. Inflorescence an umbel, usually compound, rarely simple, sometimes capitate; umbel of few or many rays, subtended by an involucre of 1 or more involucral leaves (bracts), rays terminating in umbellets provided with 1 or many involucellar leaves (bracteoles); sometimes involucre or involucel 0. Flowers hermaphrodite or sometimes partly or entirely unisexual (plants then monoecious or rarely dioecious), actinomorphic. Calyx mostly inconspicuous, adnate to the ovary, with or without 5 lobes or teeth. Corolla of 5 distinct equal or unequal petals valvate in bud; petals usually notched with inflexed apex, outer petals mostly larger (radiating). Stamens 5, inflexed in bud, alternating with the petals; anthers 2-celled, basi- or dorsifixed, dehiscing longitudinally. Ovary inferior, 2-carpelled, 2-celled (rarely 1-celled by reduction), with axile placentation; ovules solitary in each cell, anatropous, with 1 integument; styles 2, divergent, very often broadened at base and forming an epigynous disk – the stylopodium; stigma short-capitate or obsolete. Fruit a schizocarp composed of 2 connate mericarps later dehiscing along their adjacent faces (commissures); mericarps flattened either dorsally (i.e., parallel to the commissure) or laterally (i.e., at right angles to the commissure), or mericarps semicylindrical; each mericarp has usually 5 primary ribs (3 dorsal and 2 lateral) and sometimes also 4 secondary ribs between the primary ones; oil ducts (vittae) generally present in the furrows between the ribs, or under the secondary ribs, and at the commissural face; mature mericarps 1-seeded and usually suspended at dehiscence on a slender stalk (carpophore). Seeds adnate to pericarp, rarely free, with a copious endosperm and a small embryo.

About 275 genera and 2,850 species, mainly in the temperate and subtropical regions of the N. and S. hemispheres, from the seashore to the high mountain zones.

Literature: O. Drude, Umbelliferae, in: Engl. & Prantl, *Nat. Pflznfam.* III, 8 : 63–250, 1898. H. Wolff, Umbelliferae — Apioideae — *Bupleurum, Trinia* et reliquae Ammineae heteroclitae, in: *Pflznr.* 43 (IV. 228): 1–214, 1910; Umbelliferae — Saniculoideae, in: *Pflznr.* 61 (IV. 228): 1–305, 1913; Umbelliferae — Apioideae — Ammineae — Carinae, Ammineae novemjugatae et genuinae, in: *Pflznr.* 90 (IV. 228): 1–398, 1927. E. Janchen & H. Neumayer, 98. Umbelliferae, in: Beiträge zur Benennung, Bewertung und Verbreitung der Farn- und Blütenpflanzen Deutschlands, *Oesterr. Bot. Zeitschr.* 91 : 264–267 (1942).

1. Involucre of indurated, spiny bracts   2
 – Involucre not spiny or 0   3
2. Leaves spiny. Umbels simple, head-like or spike-like. Teeth of calyx conspicuous, mostly sharp.   **2. Eryngium**
 – Leaves not spiny. Umbels compound. Teeth of calyx obsolete.   **50. Exoacantha**
3(1). Leaves all undivided, entire or toothed, very rarely lobed (in aquatic plants). Fruits all alike   4
 – All or some of the leaves variously pinnatifid to pinnatisect or otherwise divided, rarely leaves undivided and then fruits of two forms   5
4. Leaves ovate, lanceolate or linear, entire.   **25. Bupleurum**
 – Leaves orbicular or orbicular-cordate, dentate or lobed.   **1. Hydrocotyle**
5(3). Fruit linear, rarely conical, (1.5–)2–7 cm. long (incl. beak) and 0.1–0.2(–0.3) cm. broad; beak as long as the seed-bearing part or several times as long.   **7. Scandix**
 – Fruit usually not linear, rarely linear and then not beaked and less than 1.5 cm. long   6
6. Fruit consisting of a single mericarp. Calyx teeth large, pinnatisect.   **3. Lagoecia**
 – Fruit usually of 2 mericarps. Calyx teeth (if present) never pinnatisect   7
7. Fruits (all or most) dorsally flattened into a disk-like, lenticular or elliptical to ellipsoidal body; mericarps with a thickened, inflated or wing-like margin   8
 – Fruits not dorsally flattened; mericarps usually without wing-like or thickened margin   21
8. Flowers white, pinkish or greenish-white   9
 – Flowers yellow or yellowish-green   16
9. Mericarps 1 cm. in diam. or more, with broad wings cut into obovate-spatulate lobes.
                                                                          51. Artedia
 – Mericarps not as above, not winged or wings not cut into obovate-spatulate lobes   10
10. Ribs of mericarp armed with 1 or more rows of long, stout prickles   11
 — Ribs of mericarp not armed with prickles   12
11. Ribs of mericarp each with 1 row of prickles hooked at apex; fruit usually more

than 1 cm. Batha plants.   **12. Orlaya**

—   Ribs of mericarp with 2–3 rows of prickles not hooked at apex but glochidiate; fruit
    usually less than 1 cm. Littoral plants.   **13. Pseudorlaya**

12(10). Fruits dimorphic, or all alike and then at least the lower leaves undivided   13

—   Fruits all alike. All leaves 1–3-pinnatisect, very rarely the uppermost leaves 2-fid
    or divided   14

13. Discoid fruits 0.8–1 cm., or less and then stem leaves 2–3 pinnatisect, with small,
    narrow, oblong ultimate lobes.   **45. Tordylium**

—   Discoid fruits 2–7 mm. Stem leaves not 2–3-pinnatisect, all or some leaves with large,
    broad orbicular-cordate blades or segments.   **46. Ainsworthia**

14(12). Leaves 1-pinnatisect, rarely the uppermost leaves 2-fid or undivided; segments 1–
    3 cm. broad. Plants up to 100 cm. tall or more.   **47. Synelcosciadium**

—   Leaves 2–3-pinnatisect; ultimate segments 1–2 mm. broad. Plants 20–50 cm. tall   15

15. Petals glabrous. Mericarps ellipsoidal, with thick dorsal ribs transversely wrinkled-
    tuberculate. Annuals.   **41. Capnophyllum**

—   Petals hairy. Mericarps orbicular or almost so; dorsal ribs thin, not tuberculate.
    Perennials.   **48. Zosima**

16(8). Mericarps (in ours) with dorsal wings usually unequal in number, one mericarp
    with 1–2, the other with 2–3 dorsal wings; fruit twice as long as broad or more.

                                                                          24. Heptaptera

—   Mericarps without or with equal dorsal wings; fruit not or very rarely as long as
    above   17

17. Rays of umbel 2–5(–8), very unequal in length. Fruit 3–7 mm. Tall (1–2 m.), almost
    leafless, divaricately branched perennials, flowering in summer.   **44. Peucedanum**

—   Rays of umbel equal, or plants differing in other characters   18

18. Middle and upper cauline leaves 1-pinnatisect; segments crenate-dentate, 1 cm. broad
    or more.   **49. Malabaila**

—   All leaves 2–3-pinnatisect; segments dissected into filiform or oblong lobes   19

19. Involucre of 5 or more bracts.   **43. Ferulago**

—   Involucre 0 or of 1–2 bracts   20

20. Annuals. Lateral wings of mericarp not inflated. Sheaths of leaves not inflated.
                                                                             40. Anethum

—   Perennials. Lateral wings of mericarp inflated. Sheaths of leaves mostly inflated.
                                                                               42. Ferula

21(7). Umbellets with heteromorphic flowers and fruits: the central flowers sessile and
    fertile, some of the others fertile, others sterile. Fruiting umbellets becoming detached
    from plant together with their broad leathery bracteoles. Calyx teeth persistent in
    fruit. Very rare prostrate desert annuals.   **4. Anisosciadium**

—   Not as above   22

22. Fruit hairy, prickly or spiny   23

—   Fruit glabrous and unarmed (smooth or wrinkled)   33

23. Mericarps armed with 1–3(–4–7) stout spines in each rib. Annuals with strongly
    radiating petals.   **14. Lisaea**

—   Mericarps hairy or prickly, not spiny   24

24. Mericarps irregularly beset with bristles 4–6 times as long as the diameter of the
    seed-bearing part.   **8. Chaetosciadium**

—   Mericarps with hairs or prickles much shorter than above   25

25. Mericarps with 4 equal secondary ribs, each extended to a wing cleft into 1 row
    of prickles usually glochidiate at tip; primary ribs filiform, short-setulose. Involucre

of pinnatisect or 3-fid, rarely of entire bracts. **52. Daucus**

— Mericarps not as above, or as above and then involucre 0 or of 1 bract 26

26. Fruit 0.8–1.5 cm. 27

— Fruit much smaller 29

27. Stems strongly inflated at joints. Fruit about 4 mm. broad (incl. prickles).

5. Myrrhoides

— Stems not inflated as above. Fruit 8 mm. broad or more 28

28. Perennials. Mericarps with 5 very broad corky ribs, each muricate or prickly all over. Involucre almost 0. **21. Lecokia**

— Annuals. Mericarps with 7 dorsal ribs, each with 2–3 rows of prickles (lateral ribs with only 1 row of prickles). Involucre usually of 5 bracts. **11. Turgenia**

29(26). Desert perennials, woody at base, 30–100 cm. high, almost leafless at time of flowering. Fruit 1–3 mm., hirsute (not prickly). Petals mostly hairy.

33. Pituranthos

— Not as above 30

30. Mericarps with distinct ribs armed with patulous or ascending prickles mostly glochidiate at tip 31

— Mericarps hairy all over 32

31. Each of the 4 secondary ribs of mericarp with only 1 row of prickles. **10. Caucalis**

— Each of the 4 secondary ribs of mericarp with 2–3 rows of prickles. **9. Torilis**

32(30). Involucre 0 or of 1, rarely of 3–5 bracts and then plants perennial, often with woody base. **34. Pimpinella**

— Involucre usually of 5 bracts. Annuals with herbaceous stems.

27. Trachyspermum

33(22). Flowers white, rarely pink or greenish-white 34

— Flowers yellow, rarely yellowish-green 48

34. Leaves, at least most of them, 2–3-pinnatisect or 2–3-ternatisect 35

— Leaves, at least most of them, 1-pinnatisect or 1-ternatisect, very rarely submerged leaves of water plants 3–4-pinnatisect; segments about 1 cm. broad or more 45

35. Involucre of pinnatisect bracts. **28. Ammi**

— Involucre (if present) of undivided bracts 36

36. Calyx teeth conspicuous. Fruit globular, hardly separating into mericarps. Plants with heavy odour. **15. Coriandrum**

— Calyx teeth obsolete. Fruit separating into mericarps; mericarps frequently almost globular 37

37. Mericarps densely beset with papillae or tubercles. Shrub-like plants, 30–50 cm., di- or trichotomously branched from base. **34. Pimpinella**

— Mericarps not beset with papillae or tubercles. Herbaceous annuals or perennials, not branched from base 38

38. Mericarps globular or almost so. Umbels usually 2–3-rayed. Annuals with heavy odour. **16. Bifora**

— Mericarps not as above. Plants not as above 39

39. Ribs of mericarp transversely wrinkled-tuberculate; fruit ellipsoidal, with dorsally compressed mericarps. Annuals. **41. Capnophyllum**

— Ribs of mericarp not transversely wrinkled-tuberculate 40

40. Fruit globular or subglobular 41

— Fruit neither globular nor subglobular 42

41. Involucre 0 or of 1–2 bracts. Roots rhizomatous, fusiform. **35. Scaligeria**

— Involucre of 5 or more bracts. Roots bulbiferous. **17. Astoma**

42(40). Fruit at least twice as long as broad, cylindrical, prismatic or oblong. Pedicel
as long as or longer than the fruit   43
— Fruit less than twice as long as broad, obconical or obovoid, rarely cylindrical and
then pedicel much shorter than the fruit   44
43. Fruit short-beaked, glossy; ribs scarcely visible. Petals strongly radiating.
                                                                          6. Anthriscus
— Fruit not beaked, not glossy; ribs prominent. Petals scarcely or not at all radiating.
                                                                          32. Bunium

44(42). Involucre of 5 or more bracts. Pedicel usually longer than fruit. Fruit readily
separating into somewhat arcuate mericarps; ribs mostly wavy. Styles not indurated.
Roots fusiform.   **20. Conium**
— Involucre 0 or of 1–2(–3) bracts, rarely of 3–5 bracts and then pedicel much shorter
than the fruit. Fruit not readily separating into mericarps; mericarps not arcuate;
ribs not wavy. Styles indurated. Roots fibrous.   **38. Oenanthe**
45(34). Involucre 0, rarely of 1–2 bracts. Aquatic plants.   **26. Apium**
— Involucre of 4–5 or more bracts   46
46. Leaves ternately divided; segments broad, leathery. Calyx teeth conspicuous.
                                                                          30. Falcaria
— Leaves pinnately divided. Segments and calyx not as above   47
47. Stems almost naked, 1–2 m. Leaves mainly radical. Rays of umbel 1–1.5 cm. Maquis
plants.   **31. Sison**
— Stems leafy all along, 30–60(–100) cm. Rays of umbel 2–5 cm. Aquatic plants, mostly
rooting from nodes.   **36. Berula**
48(33). Littoral shrubby perennials with succulent leaves divided into lobes up to 1–
2 cm. broad. Umbels (8–)10–20(–30)-rayed, with fleshy involucre.   **37. Crithmum**
— Not as above   49
49. Leaves, at least some of them, ternately divided or 1-pinnatisect into large, broad,
oblong to ovate segments with ultimate lobes not linear, or often some of the leaves
undivided and connate   50
— Leaves 2–4-pinnatisect into narrow, linear to filiform segments; leaves never
connate   51
50. Cauline leaves opposite, or connate-perfoliate and forming broad basin-shaped
structures.   **18. Smyrnium**
— Cauline leaves pinnatisect, neither opposite nor connate-perfoliate.   **19. Smyrniopsis**
51(49). Fruit 1 cm. or more; pericarp spongy; ribs prominent or expanded into wings.
                                                                          23. Prangos
— Fruit much smaller   52
52. Ribs of mericarp with transverse scales or warts; fruit transversely ovoid to depressed-globular. Shrubby perennial herbs.   **22. Hippomarathrum**
— Ribs of mericarp not warty. Annuals, or perennials and then plants with 1–2 tall
stems   53
53. Annual winter weeds. Fruit 1.5–2 mm. Pedicel 3–4 times as long as the fruit.
                                                                          29. Ridolfia
— Perennial summer plants, not weeds. Fruit 4–6(–8) mm., about as long as or longer
than the pedicel.   **39. Foeniculum**

Subfam. HYDROCOTYLOIDEAE. Fruit with lignified endocarp, without free carpophore; oil ducts 0 or immersed in the primary ribs, absent from the furrows between
the ribs.

Trib. HYDROCOTYLEAE. Fruit laterally compressed, with a very narrow commissure; mericarps 2.

1. HYDROCOTYLE L.

Annual or perennial aquatic herbs with prostrate or erect stems rooting from the nodes. Leaves with membranous stipules and entire, dentate or lobed blades. Umbels spike-like or head-like, mostly simple, arranged in axils or opposite the leaves. Bracts small, caducous. Flowers hermaphrodite. Calyx teeth obsolete. Petals ovate, acute, entire; apex not incurved. Stylopodium flat; styles filiform. Fruit laterally compressed; carpophore undivided; the middle dorsal rib of mericarp usually prominently keeled and wing-like, the others frequently obsolete; oil ducts 0. Seeds laterally compressed, keeled.

About 100 species in many regions, mainly in the S. hemisphere.

1. Leaves peltate. Flowers in remote clusters along the peduncle.   **1. H. vulgaris**
- Leaves reniform to cordate at base, not peltate. Flowers in head-like umbels at the end of the peduncle   2
2. Mericarps with marginal wings.   **2. H. ranunculoides**
- Mericarps not winged.   **3. H. sibthorpioides**

1. Hydrocotyle vulgaris L., Sp. Pl. 234 (1753); Boiss., Fl. 2 : 820 (1872). [Plate 552]
Perennial, creeping, glabrous or glabrescent, with slender stems rooting at nodes. Leaves erect, long-petioled, peltate, with more or less orbicular, undivided, usually crenate blade, 1–4 cm. across; stipules small. Peduncles axillary, solitary, shorter than the subtending leaves, bearing 1–3 distinct clusters of short-pedicelled flowers. Petals about 1 mm., longer than filaments, ovate. Fruit about 2 mm., broader than long, notched at base; mericarps hemispherical, with the middle dorsal rib dilated into a wing. Fl. April–July.
Hab.: Swamps and stagnant brooks. Sharon Plain, Hula Plain. Very rare; probably extinct.
Area: Euro-Siberian and N. Mediterranean; elsewhere introduced.

2. Hydrocotyle ranunculoides L.f., Suppl. 177 (1781); Boiss., Fl. Suppl. 251 (1888). *H. natans* Cyr., Pl. Rar. Neap. 1 : 20, t. 6B (1788). [Plate 553]
Perennial, creeping, glabrous. Stems prostrate, slender, rooting at the nodes. Leaves erect, long-petioled; stipules fairly conspicuous; blade 2–10 cm. across, orbicular in outline, reniform to cordate at base, slightly lobed and crenate. Peduncles much shorter than the subtending leaves, axillary, solitary, becoming incurved. Inflorescences head-like, of 4–15 flowers. Petals 1–1.5 mm. Fruiting pedicels up to 4 mm. Fruit about 2 mm. broad, broader than long, laterally compressed; mericarps subhemispherical; ribs dilated into wings. Fl. March–July.
Hab.: Swamps and stagnant brooks. Sharon Plain, Samaria, Hula Plain, Golan. On the verge of extinction.
Area: Pluriregional (subtropical and tropical).

3. Hydrocotyle sibthorpioides Lam., Encycl. 3 : 153 (1789). [Plate 554]

Glabrous perennial. Stems creeping, caespitose, rooting from nodes, terete. Leaves erect; petiole 2–10 cm.; stipules 1–2 cm.; blade 0.5–2.5 cm., orbicular in outline, deeply cordate to reniform at base, 3–5-lobed with crenate to entire segments. Peduncles 2–6 cm., much shorter than the subtending leaves, axillary, solitary or 2–4 together, deflexed in fruit. Inflorescences terminal, head-like, 3–8-flowered. Pedicels very short, deflexed in fruit. Petals 0.5–1 mm., ovate, acute. Fruit 1.5–3 mm., broader than long, laterally compressed; mericarps hemispherical, with obsolete dorsal ribs, turning brown in fruit, sometimes red-punctulate. Fl. June–July.

Hab.: Swampy soil and puddles. Hula Plain. Rare.

Area: Many tropical regions.

Subfam. SANICULOIDEAE. Fruit mostly covered with scales or bristles; endocarp soft-parenchymatous. Styles long, with capitate stigmas; stylopodium annular or discoid. Oil ducts various.

Trib. SANICULEAE. Ovary 2-celled, 2-ovuled. Fruit with broad commissure; mericarps 2; oil ducts mostly present.

2. ERYNGIUM L.

Perennial herbs, mostly spiny. Leaves undivided to 3-pinnatisect, with margin usually prickly-ciliate or -toothed. Umbels simple, head-like or spike-like, surrounded by an involucre of several large, mostly spiny, bracts. Flowers hermaphrodite, sessile, subtended by lanceolate spiny bracteoles. Calyx teeth conspicuous, rigid, sharp. Petals white to purple, erect, connivent, emarginate with a long inflexed apex. Stylopodium dilated, with margin elevated around the filiform styles. Fruit obovoid or terete, covered with white scales or tubercles; carpophore adnate to mericarps; ribs of mericarp mostly obsolete; commissure mostly broad; oil ducts 0 or numerous beneath the primary ribs. Inner face of seeds somewhat concave or somewhat keeled.

About 230 species in most of the warm and temperate regions of both hemispheres.

Literature: H. Wolff, *Eryngium* L., in: *Pflznr*. 61 (IV. 228): 106–271, 1913.

1. Bracts rhombic to ovate. Heads 2–3 cm. Maritime plants.   **5. E. maritimum**
   – Bracts lanceolate or subulate. Heads usually shorter than above   2
2. Bracteoles all (2–)3(–5)-toothed at apex. Heads 0.7–1.2 cm. across. Stems and leaves
   bluish.   **4. E. creticum**
   – Bracteoles, at least the central ones, not toothed at apex   3
3. All the leaves (except the uppermost ones) 2–3-pinnatisect, with sheathing petiole.
   Bracteoles all entire.   **2. E. glomeratum**
   – Lower leaves undivided   4
4. Bracts 2–3 times as long as bracteoles.   **3. E. falcatum**
   – Bracts as long as bracteoles.   **1. E. barrelieri**

1. Eryngium barrelieri Boiss., Ann. Sci. Nat. Bot. ser. 3, 1 : 125 (1844) et Fl. 2 : 821 (1872). [Plate 555]

Annual or perennial, glabrous, 7–30 cm. Stems simple, striate, dichotomously branched from base or above. Leaves 3–9 × 0.6–1.5 cm.; basal leaves rosulate, with sheathing petiole, membranous, oblong-lanceolate to oblanceolate, obtuse or acute, spinulose-dentate to serrate; upper leaves sessile, 3-partite or -sect, prickly-dentate. Inflorescences simple or sparingly branched; heads small, 2 cm. (incl. bracts and bracteoles), sessile. Bracts 1–2 cm., coriaceous, linear-lanceolate, triquetrous, spiny with sharp prickles at base. Bracteoles similar to the bracts and as long, dilated at base into membranous auricles with or without 1–2 spines. Calyx teeth 2–2.5 mm., erect, ovate, obtuse, aristate. Fruit flattened, densely covered with scales and crowned with calyx teeth. Fl. July.

Hab.: By water and swamps. Golan. Rare.

Area: Mediterranean.

2. Eryngium glomeratum Lam., Encycl. 4 : 755 (1798); Boiss., Fl. 2 : 823 (1872). [Plate 556]

Perennial, stout and spiny, glabrous, up to 80 cm. Stems many, erect, sparingly branched, strongly ribbed, glaucous-green. Leaves up to 15 × 12 cm., alternate, with sheathing, prominently nerved petioles; blade ovate in outline, 2–3-pinnatisect; lobes linear-lanceolate, spiny- or prickly-toothed; rhachis of leaf remotely prickly-toothed; blades soon drying up in lower leaves, persistent, coriaceous, recurved in upper leaves. Inflorescences of many cymose branches, forming a more or less contracted panicle; heads 1 cm. in diam. or less. Bracts mostly 5, 2–3 (–5) times as long as the head, very rigid, subulate, carinate, almost entire. Bracteoles almost as long as the flower, broadened at base, entire. Calyx teeth 2–3 mm., erect, ovate, prickly-mucronate. Fruit flattened, covered with scales and crowned with calyx teeth. Fl. May–September.

Hab.: Rocky places, batha and semisteppe. Upper Galilee, Esdraelon Plain, Samaria, Judean Mts., Judean Desert, Hula Plain, Upper Jordan Valley, Golan, Gilead, Ammon, Moav, Edom. Fairly common.

Area: E. Mediterranean, with slight extensions into the adjacent Irano-Turanian territories.

3. Eryngium falcatum Laroche, Eryng. Hist. 40, t. 13 (1808); Boiss., Fl. 2 : 827 (1872). [Plate 557]

Perennial, glabrous, 50–80 cm. Stems erect, single or few, dichotomously or corymbosely branched, smooth, green, glossy. Leaves simple or divided; basal leaves 10–15 cm., long-petioled, membranous, ovate, cordate, crenate, undivided; cauline leaves 4–8 cm., sessile, coriaceous, 3–6-palmatisect, segments unequal, lanceolate or linear, prickly-serrate, deflexed-falcate. Inflorescences simple or sparingly branched; heads few, 1.2–1.6 cm. Bracts 5–6, 2–5 times as long as the head, broadly lanceolate, canaliculate, prickly at margin and apex. Bracteoles somewhat exceeding the flower, the outer ones 3-cuspidate, the others entire. Calyx teeth 2.5–3 mm., oblong-lanceolate, abruptly mucronate. Fruit 5-ribbed; ribs broad, scaly. Fl. May–August.

Hab.: Batha and maquis; especially in shady sites. Acco Plain, Upper and Lower Galilee, Mt. Carmel, Esdraelon Plain, Samaria, Judean Mts., Upper Jordan Valley, Golan. Locally fairly common.

Area: E. Mediterranean.

4. Eryngium creticum Lam., Encycl. 4 : 754 (1798); Boiss., Fl. 2 : 827 (1872). [Plate 558]

Perennial or biennial, glaucous, glabrous, 20–50 cm. Stems divaricately much branched from below. Branches ribbed or angular, bluish. Basal leaves 5–10 cm., withering early, herbaceous, petiole flat, longer than the blade, blade oblong to ovate, crenate to lobulate, bluish; lower leaves sessile, rigid, pinnatipartite into entire or prickly-toothed lobes; upper leaves 3–8-palmatisect, segments cut or prickly-toothed. Inflorescences forked repeatedly; heads 0.7–0.8(–1.2) cm. Bracts mostly 5, 2–5 times as long as the head, spreading, linear-subulate, keeled, prickly at base or along margin. Flowers overtopped by the 3-cuspidate, rarely 2–5-toothed bracteoles. Calyx teeth 2–3 mm., ovate, mucronate, narrowly scarious-margined. Fruit scaly-bristly, obscurely ribbed. Fl. May–August.

Hab.: Fallow fields and roadsides. Coastal Galilee, Acco Plain, Sharon Plain, Philistean Plain, Upper and Lower Galilee, Mt. Carmel, Esdraelon Plain, Samaria, Shefela, Judean Mts., Judean Desert, N. Negev, Dan Valley, Lower Jordan Valley, Golan, Ammon, Edom. Very common.

Area: E. Mediterranean, with slight extensions into W. Irano-Turanian territories.

Used as a pot herb (young leaves).

5. Eryngium maritimum L., Sp. Pl. 233 (1753); Boiss., Fl. 2 : 829 (1872). [Plate 559]

Perennial, glaucous, glabrous, 20–50 cm., mostly forming globular tufts. Stems thick, prominently ribbed, much branched. Leaves leathery, thick and whitish, prickly-lobed, copiously nerved; basal leaves 5–10 × 5–15 cm., long-petioled, suborbicular to truncate or cordate-reniform at base, undivided or palmately lobed, coarsely dentate or lobulate at margin; upper leaves 3–8 cm. long and broad, clasping, palmately lobed, lobes triangular and terminating in long sharp spines. Inflorescences repeatedly di- or trichotomous-branched; heads many-flowered, usually 2–3 × 0.8–1.5(–2) cm. Bracts 3–5(–7), 2–5 × 1–3 cm., broadly rhombic to ovate, usually with 3–5 spiny lobes. Bracteoles about 1 cm., longer than the flowers, narrowly lanceolate, 3-cuspidate. Calyx teeth 4–5 mm., elliptical to lanceolate, aristate, broadly scarious-margined. Fruit about 1 cm., spongy, densely scaly-prickly, crowned with the spreading calyx teeth. Fl. April–August.

Hab.: Sandy and shingly beaches. Coastal Galilee, Acco Plain, Coast of Carmel, Sharon Plain, Philistean Plain. Uncommon.

Area: Mediterranean.

Sometimes grown as an ornamental; known in folk medicine as a diuretic and laxative.

Trib. LAGOECIEAE. Ovary 1-celled, 1-ovuled, rarely 2-celled. Fruit with 1 mericarp; oil ducts obsolete.

3. LAGOECIA L.

Annuals, erect, little branched. Leaves 1-pinnatisect. Umbels pedunculate, many-flowered, globular; umbellets 1-flowered. Bracts, bracteoles and calyx teeth large, leaf-like, pinnatisect. Flowers hermaphrodite. Petals notched, with obtuse grooved inflexed apex and with 2 long straight bristles. Stylopodium shorter than the single style, semiglobular, inflated on one side. Fruit of 1 ovoid somewhat compressed mericarp crowned with the calyx; carpophore 0; ribs filiform, hardly visible; oil ducts 0. Seeds nearly terete, with flattish inner face.

One species. N. and E. Mediterranean countries.

1. Lagoecia cuminoides L., Sp. Pl. 203 (1753); Boiss., Fl. 2 : 833 (1872). [Plate 560]

Annual, slender, glabrous herb, 15–60 cm. Stems erect, mostly simple, corymbose above, grooved. Leaves 5–15 × 0.5–1.5 cm., oblong-linear in outline, pinnatisect; segments up to 1 cm., sessile, opposite, ovate, dentate or cut into ovate to oblong, serrate lobes. Peduncles 1.4 cm. Umbels head-like, 1–1.5 cm. across, nodding before flowering. Bracts many, 0.6–1.5 cm., oblong to ovate, pinnatipartite; lobes oblong, 2–3-cleft, aristate. Bracteoles 4–5, pectinate, pubescent. Flowers enclosed in involucel, pedicellate. Petals 1–1.5 mm., white. Mericarps 2 mm., glandular-hairy, crowned with the pectinate calyx teeth. Fl. March–April.

Hab.: Batha and fields. Coastal Galilee, Acco Plain, Sharon Plain, Philistean Plain, Upper and Lower Galilee, Mt. Carmel, Esdraelon Plain, Samaria, Shefela, Judean Mts., Judean Desert, N. Negev, Hula Plain, Upper Jordan Valley, Beit Shean Valley, Lower Jordan Valley, Dead Sea area, Gilead, Ammon. Common.

Area: Mainly E. Mediterranean, extending somewhat towards W. Irano-Turanian territories.

Subfam. APIOIDEAE. Fruit with soft, parenchymatous, sometimes indurated endocarp. Styles on the top of the stylopodium. Fruit not covered with scales; oil ducts at first in the furrows, later variously located.

Trib. ECHINOPHOREAE. Umbellets with 1 or few sessile hermaphrodite or pistillate (fertile) flowers and many or few pedicellate staminate (sterile) flowers. Inner face of seed deeply sulcate.

4. ANISOSCIADIUM DC.

Low desert annuals, hairy or scabrous, with diffuse stems and pinnatisect leaves resembling those of *Scandix*. Umbels few- to many-rayed, with conspicuous, persistent, leaf-like bracts and bracteoles. The central flowers (usually only 1) of each umbellet hermaphrodite and fertile, surrounded by 1–3 sterile staminate flowers (with reduced ovary); the outer 2–3 flowers hermaphrodite. Calyx teeth 0 in central flowers, 5 in outer flowers, outer teeth large. Petals radiating, obovate, notched with inflexed apex. Stylopodium conical; styles very long in the central flower, obsolete in the others. Fruits 1-seeded, of two forms: the central one oblong, free or adnate to the adjacent pedicels; the outer fruits cylindrical, adnate at base to the broad, leathery bracteole; carpophore undivided; mericarps of central fruit membranous, those of the outer fruits crustaceous;

ribs obsolete; oil ducts solitary in the furrows. Inner face of seed deeply grooved.

Two to three species, all in the deserts of the Middle East.

1. Anisosciadium isosciadium Bornm., Repert. Sp. Nov. 10 : 468 (1912). [Plate 561]

Prostrate annual, hirtellous, 10–20 cm. Central stem very short, terminating in a short-peduncled umbel; lateral stems dichotomously or trichotomously branched, leafy. Basal leaves 5–10 cm., long-petioled, ovate-oblong in outline, 2-pinnatisect; stem leaves short-petioled, oblong in outline, with 3–5 pairs of segments; segments 2–3-fid into short linear lobes. Umbels (except the basal ones) opposite the leaves, long-peduncled, 3–6-rayed. Bracts unequal, leathery, lanceolate, finally deflexed. Umbellets polygamous. Bracteoles ovate, white-margined, pinnately nerved, finally indurated and spreading but not deflexed. Calyx of all marginal flowers with 2 (–3) leaf-like, leathery, ovate, mucronate lobes. Petals about 2 mm., radiating, white. Stylopodium depressed; styles long, thick and erect. Fruiting umbellets with their thickened peduncles separating from the plants as dispersal units. Fruit 2–3 mm., oblong to cylindrical, hirsute. Fl. March–April.

Var. **idumaeum** Zoh.* Outer flowers all fertile, sessile, each with 2–3 broad, leaf-like calyx teeth at outer side; central flower fertile, with no calyx teeth, free and not adnate to adjacent sterile flowers.

Hab.: Deserts; pebbly ground. Edom. Rare.

Area: E. Saharo-Arabian.

Our specimens occupy an intermediate position between *A. orientale* DC., Coll. Mém. 5 : 63, t. 15 (1829) and *A. isosciadium,* so that the new variety could equally well be referred to either species. This was also the reason why this taxon has been identified (Zohary, Palest. Journ. Bot. Jerusalem ser., 2 : 170, 1941) as *A. orientale.* In its radiating petals and lack of broadened calyx teeth in the central flower it closely approaches *A. orientale,* but in shape, size and direction of the bracts and bracteoles it is nearer *A. isosciadium;* nor are the calyx teeth in our specimens hooked, as they are in *A. orientale.*

Trib. SCANDICEAE. All flowers of umbellets hermaphrodite, or some staminate but not surrounding the fertile flowers. Seeds deeply sulcate at commissural face. Fruit cylindrical or ovoid to depressed-globular, beaked or not, glabrous, bristly or prickly (mainly along ribs); fruit with a crystalline layer in the parenchyma around the carpophore.

5. MYRRHOIDES Heist. ex Fabr.

Annual herbs, branched. Stems hollow, inflated at nodes. Leaves 2-pinnatisect. Umbels few-rayed, few-flowered. Flowers hermaphrodite, minute. Calyx teeth obsolete. Petals white, obovate, obcordate with inflexed apex. Stigmas sessile on the top of the conical stylopodium. Fruit laterally compressed, ovoid to subconical with a broad base, covered

---

* See Appendix at end of this volume.

with antrorse bristles emerging from a tubercle; carpophore 2-fid; mericarps almost semiorbicular in cross section; primary ribs of mericarp 5, flattened, obtuse, the 2 lateral ribs marginal; oil ducts solitary in each furrow. Inner face of seed deeply grooved.

One species in the Mediterranean region and adjacent countries of S. Europe and Asia.

1. Myrrhoides nodosa (L.) Cannon in Heywood, Repert. Sp. Nov. 79 : 65 (1968). *Scandix nodosa* L., Sp. Pl. 257 (1753). *Physocaulis nodosus* (L.) Tausch, Flora 17 : 342 (1834); Koch, Syn. Fl. Germ. Helv. ed. 2, 348 (1843); Boiss., Fl. 2 : 909 (1872; *"Physocaulos"*). [Plate 562]

Annual, strigose-hirsute, 20–100 cm. Stems dichotomously branched above, hollow, striate, inflated below the joints. Lower leaves hirsute, 2-pinnatisect into ovate-oblong, obtuse, pinnatipartite or incised or dentate segments; upper leaves reduced. Umbels 2–3(–5)-rayed; rays 1–4 cm., stiff, angular, hispid, thickened in fruit. Involucre 0, rarely of 1–2 bracts. Umbellets 5–10-flowered. Involucel usually of 5 triangular-lanceolate or linear bracteoles. Petals sparsely setulose outside. Fruit 0.8–1.5 cm., setose-pustulate. Fl. April–June.

Hab.: Among rocks and shrubs. Upper and Lower Galilee, Mt. Carmel, Gilead (after Boiss., l.c.). Rare.

Area: Mediterranean and adjacent northern and eastern borderlands.

6. ANTHRISCUS Pers.

Annuals, biennials or perennials. Leaves 2–3-pinnatisect, with sheathing petioles. Umbels terminal or axillary. Involucre mostly 0. Involucel of several bracteoles, usually deflexed. Flowers mostly hermaphrodite, some staminate. Calyx teeth obsolete. Petals radiating, white, yellow or whitish-green, obovate, entire or notched with inflexed apex. Stylopodium usually conical; styles erect or deflexed. Fruit laterally compressed, mostly cylindrical or conical, beaked; carpophore undivided or 2-fid; mericarps almost orbicular or semiorbicular in cross section; ribs obsolete below, prominent only at apex; furrows each with 1 inconspicuous oil duct. Inner face of seed deeply grooved.

About 20 species in Europe, temperate Asia and N. Africa.

1. Anthriscus lamprocarpus Boiss., Ann. Sci. Nat. Bot. ser. 3, 2 : 59 (1844) et Fl. 2 : 912 (1872). [Plate 563]

Biennial or perennial, glabrous all over or hirsute below, 50–100 cm. Roots fusiform. Stems divaricately branched, hollow, furrowed. Leaves 5–25 cm., tender; lower leaves broadly ovate in outline, 2–3-pinnatisect; primary and secondary segments with rather long petiolule-like stalks, hairy at base; ultimate segments ovate-oblong, mucronate, incised-dentate, usually glabrous. Umbels borne on long peduncles, 4–8-rayed; rays 2–6 cm., filiform. Bracts 0. Bracteoles 5, oblong, acuminate, woolly or ciliate at margin, deflexed in fruit. Flowers hermaphrodite and staminate in each umbel. Petals radiating, white; outer petals 5 mm. or more. Styles scarcely longer than the divergent parts of the stylopodium. Fruit (0.8–)1–1.2 × 0.3 cm., oblong, smooth, glossy; beak short. Fl. April–May.

Hab.: Shady places in maquis, among rocks and by hedges. Philistean Plain, Upper and Lower Galilee, Mt. Carmel, Samaria, Judean Mts., Upper Jordan Valley, Golan, Gilead, Ammon, Moav. Locally fairly common.

Area: E. Mediterranean.

7. SCANDIX L.

Annuals. Leaves 2–3-pinnatisect; ultimate lobes linear to filiform. Umbels terminal or axillary, long-peduncled, few-rayed. Involucre mostly 0. Involucel of 2-lobed or incised bracteoles, mostly scarious-margined and ciliate. Flowers hermaphrodite; a few staminate flowers in the centre of the umbel. Calyx teeth minute or 0. Petals white, obovate, shallowly notched with short inflexed apex, the outer ones sometimes larger and more deeply notched. Stylopodium as long as the styles or much shorter, depressed-obconical. Fruits oblong-linear, long-beaked, all fertile, rarely central fruit sterile; carpophore setaceous, undivided or 2-fid at apex; seed-bearing part laterally compressed; beak often dorsally compressed, tapering, with bristly nerves and margins; mericarps mostly separating at maturity; primary ribs of mericarp 5, broad, obtuse, prominent; oil ducts 1–3 in each furrow, obscure. Inner face of seed deeply grooved.

About 20 species, mainly Mediterranean; also in other parts of Europe.

Literature: A. Thellung, *Scandix* L. emend. Adanson, in: Hegi, *Ill. Fl. Mitteleur.* 5, 2: 1032–1041, 1926.

1. Central fruit of umbellets sessile, much thicker than the others, up to 4 mm. across, not separating into mericarps, with beak as long as the seed.   **5. S. palaestina**
– All the fruits alike   2
2. Beak of fruit about as long as the seed-bearing part, not clearly discernible from it; fruit (incl. beak) 2–2.5 cm., falcate, covered with stiff bristles all over.   **3. S. falcata**
– Beak much longer than the seed-bearing part of the fruit   3
3. Fruit (incl. beak) 1.5–2.5 cm.   **4. S. stellata**
– Fruit 4–6 cm.   4
4. Styles 2–3 times as long as the stylopodium. Outer petals slightly radiating.
                                                                                          1. S. pecten-veneris
– Styles 5–7 times as long as the stylopodium. Outer petals strongly radiating.
                                                                                                     2. S. iberica

Sect. SCANDIX. Sect. *Pecten* (Lam.) Duby, Bot. Gall. 240 (1828). Beak of fruit more or less compressed dorsally, bristly or scabrous only along margin. Styles 2–7 times as long as the stylopodium.

1. Scandix pecten-veneris L., Sp. Pl. 256 (1753); Boiss., Fl. 2: 914 (1872). [Plate 564]
  Annual, hairy to glabrescent, 15–30 cm. Stems erect or ascending, branched from base, furrowed. Leaves ovate in outline, 2–4-pinnatisect, ultimate lobes crowded, 3–5 mm., linear, acute, mucronate, often setulose at margin; lower leaves long-petioled, the upper short-petioled or sessile. Umbels long-peduncled, 2(–3)-rayed; rays equal, 1–3 cm., thickened after flowering. Involucre 0. Umbellets 4–7-flowered. Bracteoles

ovate-oblong, often 2–3(–5)-fid at apex, ciliate at margin. Flowers mostly hermaphrodite, some staminate. Petals slightly radiating, white, obovate, notched. Styles 2–3 times as long as the stylopodium, erect. Fruit (incl. beak) 4–6 cm., short-bristly to scabrous at margin; beak 3–4 times as long as the seed-bearing part, dorsally compressed; ribs of mericarp prominent, brighter in colour than the dark brown furrows. Fl. March–April.

Hab.: Batha and fields. Coastal Galilee, Sharon Plain, Philistean Plain, Upper and Lower Galilee, Mt. Carmel, Esdraelon Plain, Samaria, Shefela, Judean Mts., Judean Desert, N. Negev, Hula Plain, Upper Jordan Valley, Golan, Gilead, Ammon, Edom. Fairly common.

Area: Euro-Siberian, Mediterranean and Irano-Turanian; elsewhere adventive.

Var. *brevirostris* Boiss., l.c., recorded by Dinsmore (in Post, Fl. Syr. Pal. Sin. ed. 2, 1 : 531, 1932) from Gilead, has not been observed by others.

2. Scandix iberica M.B., Fl. Taur.-Cauc. 1 : 230, 425 (1808), 3 : 236 (1819); Boiss., Fl. 2 : 915 (1872). [Plate 565]

Annual, erect, patulous-pubescent, 15–30 cm. Stems erect or ascending, branched from base. Leaves, except for the uppermost ones, long-petioled, ovate-oblong in outline, 2–3-pinnatisect with short, oblong-linear, setulose or glabrous, simple or 2-fid ultimate lobes. Umbels usually 2–5-rayed; rays 1–3 cm., sparsely patulous-pubescent. Bracts 1 or 0, linear to filiform. Umbellets many-flowered. Bracteoles deflexed, ovate to oblong, entire or mostly 2-fid, ciliate or woolly at margin. Petals strongly radiating, white, obovate, notched. Styles erect, 5–7 times as long as the stylopodium. Fruit 4–5 cm. (incl. beak), bristly at margin; beak (3–)4–5 times as long as the seed-bearing part, dorsally compressed, bristly; ribs of mericarp broad, prominent, scabrous. Fl. March–April.

Hab.: Fields. Sharon Plain, Upper and Lower Galilee, Mt. Carmel, Esdraelon Plain, Mt. Gilboa, Samaria, Shefela, Judean Mts., Hula Plain, Upper Jordan Valley, Beit Shean Valley, Golan, Edom. Fairly common.

Area: E. Mediterranean and W. Irano-Turanian.

Sect. WYLIA (Hoffm.) Duby, Bot. Gall. 240 (1828). Beak of fruit not or very slightly compressed laterally, not readily discernible from the seed-bearing part, covered all over with stiff bristles. Styles 3–5(–6) times as long as the stylopodium. Bracteoles ovate to elliptical, entire, membranous-margined. Petals strongly radiating.

3. Scandix falcata Lond., Mém. Soc. Nat. Mosc. 1 : 58 (1806) et ser. 2, 1 : 32, t. 5 (1811). [Plate 566]

Annual, patulous-hispid or -villose, 10–20 cm. Stems few, ascending, divaricately branched, furrowed. Leaves, except for the upper ones, long-petioled, ovate-oblong in outline, 2–3-pinnatisect; ultimate lobes 0.4–1 cm., linear or filiform, entire or 2-fid, obtuse. Umbels long-peduncled, 4–7-rayed; rays nearly equal, 2.5–3 cm., scabrous or hispidulous. Involucre 0. Umbellets 4–10-flowered. Bracteoles 4–6, about 3 mm., ovate, entire, broadly membranous-margined, villose. Staminate flowers few, in the centre of the umbellets and also in separate axillary umbels. Petals strongly radiating (the outer 2–3 times as long as the inner), white, obovate to obcordate. Styles 5–6 times as long as the depressed, somewhat undulate stylopodium. Fruit 2–2.5 cm., almost cylindrical or slightly compressed laterally, falcate, tapering into a beak as long as the seed-bearing part or shorter; mericarps with 5 prominent ribs, hispidulous all over. Fl. May.

Hab. : Near rivers; sandy soil. Acco Plain. Very rare.

Area : E. Mediterranean and W. Irano-Turanian.

The above description and plate were prepared from the two specimens found near the Kishon River in the Acco Plain. Our specimens deviate markedly from the original description of *S. falcata* in the proportions of the beak. It is not improbable that our specimens should accordingly be considered a distinct variety.

Sect. SCANDICIUM (C. Koch) Walp., Repert. Bot. Syst. 2 : 421 (1843). Subgen. *Scandicium* C. Koch, Linnaea 16 : 363 (1842). Beak of fruit dorsally compressed; ribs scabrous or hispidulous. Styles as long as the stylopodium or shorter. Bracteoles (in ours) pinnatifid. Petals not radiating or only very slightly so.

4. Scandix stellata Banks et Sol. in Russ., Nat. Hist. Aleppo ed. 2, 2 : 249 (1794). *Scandicium stellatum* (Banks et Sol.) Thell., Repert. Sp. Nov. 16 : 16 (1919). *Scandix pinnatifida* Vent., Descr. Pl. Jard. Cels t. 14 (1800–1801); Boiss., Fl. 2 : 916 (1872). [Plate 567]

Annual, tender, hairy or glabrous, 5–25 cm. Stems erect or procumbent, sparingly and dichotomously branched above, terete, striate. Leaves ovate in outline, 2–3-pinnatisect with linear or setaceous acute ultimate lobes; upper leaves sessile, with filiform lobes 0.5–1.5 cm. long. Umbels 1- or 2–3-rayed; rays short, thickened. Involucre 0. Umbellets many-flowered. Bracteoles divided into 3–5 linear lobes. Flowers minute, staminate flowers very few or 0. Petals weakly radiating, white, obovate, notched. Styles minute, about as long as the stylopodium. Fruit 1.5–2.5 cm. (incl. beak), sessile, scabridulous; beak 2–3 times as long as the seed-bearing part, dorsally compressed, scabrous; ribs filiform, with broad dark furrows. Fl. April–May.

Hab. : Semisteppe batha and steppe; stony ground. Gilead, Ammon, Moav, Edom. Rather rare.

Area : Irano-Turanian, with extensions into the Mediterranean and the S.W. Euro-Siberian territories.

Very polymorphic. The following forms, distinguished in the local populations by Zohary (Palest. Journ. Bot. Jerusalem ser., 2 : 168, 1941, under *Scandicium*) : var. *velutinum* (Coss.) Thell., l.c. 17, var. *hebecarpum* Thell., l.c. 18, var. *vulgare* Thell., l.c. 18, are not clearly discernible, since the occurrence of intermediate forms obscures the limits of these varieties. Similarly, var. *pinnatifidum* (Vent.) Thell., l.c. 18, discerned by Thellung, is not clearly delimited.

Sect. CYCLOTAXIS (Boiss.) Boiss., Fl. 2 : 918 (1872). Gen. *Cyclotaxis* Boiss., Diagn. ser. 1, 10 : 48 (1849). Beak of fruit cylindrical-subulate, as long or twice as long as the seed-bearing part; central fruit of umbellet sessile, the others pedicellate.

5. Scandix palaestina (Boiss.) Boiss., Fl. 2 : 918 (1872). *Cyclotaxis palaestina* Boiss., Diagn. ser. 1, 10 : 49 (1849). [Plate 568]

Annual, glabrous or somewhat scabrous or tomentellous, 10–40 cm. Stems solitary or few, erect, branched especially above, striate to angular. Leaves oblong in outline, 2–3-pinnatisect; lobes 0.3–1 cm., divergent, linear or filiform. Umbels terminal and axillary, (3–)5–12-rayed; rays 2–3 cm. thick, more or less equal. Involucre 0. Umbellets many-flowered. Bracteoles many, oblong-linear, simple or 2-fid, ciliate. Petals minute, almost equal, oblong. Styles 2–3 times as long as the undulate stylopodium. Central fruit of umbellet sessile, indehiscent, spongy, thickened, ovoid-conical and tapering into an awl-shaped beak about as long as the seed-bearing part; outer fruits very slender, 2–2.5 cm., on glabrous or scabrous thickened pedicels, tapering to a subulate beak one and a half times to twice as long as the seed-bearing part; central fruit glabrous or hispid, with prominent ribs; outer fruits scabrous or glabrous with less prominent ribs and narrower furrows. Fl. March–April.

Hab.: Fields. Coast of Carmel, Sharon Plain, Philistean Plain, Upper and Lower Galilee, Esdraelon Plain, Upper Jordan Valley, Golan, Gilead, Ammon. Uncommon.

Area : E. Mediterranean.

8. CHAETOSCIADIUM Boiss.

Annual herbs, glabrous or setulose. Leaves 2–3-pinnatisect. Umbels long-peduncled; rays few. Involucre 0. Involucel of subulate bracteoles. Flowers all hermaphrodite, or some staminate. Calyx teeth subulate. Petals minute, slightly radiating, pinkish to white, obovate, notched with inflexed apex. Fruit somewhat compressed dorsally, oblong, apex narrowed into a disk-like stylopodium terminating in very long styles; carpophore filiform, 2-parted; mericarps all irregularly covered with very long bristles; ribs and furrows obsolete; oil ducts obscure, 4 dorsal and 2 commissural. Inner face of seed concave.

One species endemic to Palestine and Syria.

Should probably be included within the genus *Torilis,* but differs from the latter in its obsolete ribs and the irregular insertion of the bristles.

1. Chaetosciadium trichospermum (L.) Boiss., Fl. 2 : 1078 (1872). *Scandix trichosperma* L., Mant. 57 (1767). [Plate 569]

Annual, sparingly setulose, 10–60 cm. Stems dichotomously branched from base. Leaves oblong to ovate in outline, 3-pinnatisect, ultimate segments parted into oblong or ovate, acute, entire, dentate or lobulate lobes. Umbels long-peduncled; rays 3–6. Bracts 0. Bracteoles many, 3–8 mm., longer than the pedicels, subulate. Fruiting umbellets 0.8–1.5 cm. across, more or less globular. Mericarps covered with long, weak, purple or white scabrous bristles 3–5 times as long as the diameter of the seed-bearing part. Fl. March–April.

Hab.: Batha and among rocks. Acco Plain, Sharon Plain, Philistean Plain, Upper and Lower Galilee, Mt. Carmel, Esdraelon Plain, Mt. Gilboa, Samaria, Shefela, Judean Mts., Judean Desert, W., N. and C. Negev, Hula Plain, Upper and Lower

Jordan Valley, Dead Sea area, Arava Valley, Golan, Gilead, Ammon, Moav, Edom. Common.

Area: E. Mediterranean (Palestine to Syria).

9. Torilis Adans.

Annual herbs, hairy. Leaves 1–3-pinnatisect. Umbels subsessile to long-peduncled. Bracts several, 1 or 0. Bracteoles several, mostly subulate. Flowers hermaphrodite and staminate. Calyx teeth persistent, triangular-lanceolate. Petals often radiating, white or pinkish, obovate, with inflexed apex. Stylopodium short, thick; styles persistent, varying in length. Fruit somewhat compressed laterally, ovoid or oblong; carpophore more or less 2-fid; mericarps with 5 narrow setulose primary ribs concealed by the numerous rows of prickles which occupy the furrows, and with 4 secondary ribs armed with several rows of prickles or rarely of tubercles; the prickles of the two mericarps sometimes unequal in length; oil ducts solitary under each secondary rib. Seeds flattened, with concave inner face.

About 15 species in Eurasia and N. Africa.

1. Bracts 4–6(–12). Rays of umbel 5–12. Petals strongly radiating.   **1. T. japonica**
– Bracts 0–2   2
2. Umbels long-peduncled, often terminal   3
– Umbels subsessile or short-peduncled, axillary or opposite the leaves   4
3. Fruit 3–5 mm.; prickles of mericarp scabrous, as long as the width of the seed-bearing part.   **2. T. arvensis**
– Fruit 7–8 mm.; prickles of mericarp smooth, 4–5 times as long as the width of the seed-bearing part.   **3. T. gaillardotii**
4(2). Fruit 3–5 mm.; mericarps strikingly heteromorphic, the outer with long prickles, the inner with tubercles.   **5. T. nodosa**
– Fruit 7–8 mm.; mericarps homomorphic (all alike).   **4. T. leptophylla**

1. Torilis japonica (Houtt.) DC., Prodr. 4 : 219 (1830). *T. anthriscus* (L.) C. C. Gmel., Fl. Bad. 1 : 615 (1805) non Gaertn., Fruct. 1 : 83, t. 20 (1788) nec Bernh., Syst. Verz. Erf. 167 (1800); Boiss., Fl. 2 : 1081 (1872). *Caucalis japonica* Houtt., Nat. Hist. 2, 8 : 42, t. 45, f. 1 (1777). [Plate 570]

Annual, sparsely appressed-setulose, 10–100 cm. Stems erect, dichotomously branched above, solid, striate-angular. Leaves 1–3-pinnatisect; segments 1–4 cm., ovate to lanceolate, acute, pinnatifid to serrate. Umbels 5–12-rayed; rays unequal, 1–4 cm. Bracts 4–6(–12), shorter than the rays, unequal, linear-subulate. Bracteoles about as long as the pedicels. Flowers 2–3 mm. across. Petals radiating, pinkish or purplish-white. Styles twice as long as the conical stylopodium or more. Fruit 2–4 mm., ovoid; secondary ribs with 2–3 rows of prickles; prickles about half as long as the width of the seed-bearing part, incurved, scabrous, not glochidiate. Fl. July–August.

Hab.: Roadsides. Golan, Ammon (after Dinsmore in Post, Fl. Syr. Pal. Sin. ed. 2, 1 : 569, 1932).

Area: Euro-Siberian and Mediterranean.

2. Torilis arvensis (Huds.) Link, Enum. Hort. Berol. Alt. 1 : 265 (1821). [Plate 571]
Annual, hispid or almost glabrous, (10–)40–80(–100) cm. Stems erect, sparingly branched, terete, furrowed or striate. Leaves sparsely appressed-hairy, 1–2-pinnatisect; segments 1–4 cm., broadly lanceolate or linear-subulate, serrate, incised or lobed. Umbels long-peduncled, 2–12-rayed; rays 1–3 cm. Bracts 0 or 1. Bracteoles 3 or more, nearly as long as the pedicels, hispid. Flowers 2 mm. Petals radiating, white or pinkish. Styles as long or 2–6 times as long as the stylopodium; stylopodium becoming conical. Fruit 3–5 mm., ovoid to ellipsoidal; secondary ribs with 2–3 rows of erect or spreading, scabrous, glochidiate prickles, length of prickles often different in the two mericarps. Fl. April.

The following subspecies have been observed :
1. Umbels of 4–12 rays.   ssp. **arvensis**
– Umbels of 2–3(–4) rays   2
2. Upper leaves smaller than the basal and middle stem leaves but similar in form.
                                                              ssp. **elongata**
– Upper leaves entire or ternately dissected into linear or lanceolate segments; terminal segment very long; basal and middle stem leaves pinnatisect.   ssp. **heterophylla**

Subsp. **arvensis**. *Caucalis arvensis* Huds., Fl. Angl. 98 (1762). *T. arvensis* (Huds.) Link var. *occulta* (Post) Dinsmore in Post, Fl. Syr. Pal. Sin. ed. 2, 1 : 569 (1932). Leaves gradually decreasing in size, more or less homomorphic, the lower ones pinnatisect into 2–3 pairs of pinnatisect or -partite or -fid segments; the upper leaves ternatisect into pinnatifid or dentate segments. Rays of umbel (3–)4–12. Petals radiating, pink or white. Styles 2–3 times as long as the stylopodium. Fruit often heteromericarpous, i.e. the prickles of the two mericarps unequal in length; prickles directed somewhat upwards.
Hab. : Fields and garigue. Coastal Galilee, Sharon Plain, Philistean Plain, Upper and Lower Galilee, Mt. Carmel, Dan Valley, Hula Plain, Upper Jordan Valley, Dead Sea area, Golan, Edom. Common.

Subsp. **heterophylla** (Guss.) Thell. in Hegi, Ill. Fl. Mitteleur. 5, 2 : 1057 (1926). *T. infesta* Hoffm. ssp. *heterophylla* (Guss.) Bonnier, Fl. Fr. Suiss. Belg. 4 : 84, t. 210, f. 1129 b (1921). *C. infesta* (L.) Curt. ssp. *heterophylla* (Guss.) Ball, Journ. Linn. Soc. Lond. Bot. 16 : 479 (1878). *T. heterophylla* Guss., Fl. Sic. Prodr. 1 : 326 (1827; "*Torylis*"); Boiss., Fl. 2 : 1082 (1872). *T. arvensis* (Huds.) Link ssp. *purpurea* (Ten.) Hay., Prodr. Fl. Pen. Balc. 1 : 1057 (1927). *T. helvetica* (Jacq.) C. C. Gmel. ssp. *purpurea* (Ten.) Nym., Consp. 281 (1879). *C. purpurea* Ten., Corso Bot. Lez. 4 : 209 (1822) emend. Caruel in Parl., Fl. Ital. 8 : 559 (1889). *T. purpurea* (Ten.) Guss., Fl. Sic. Prodr. 1 : 325 (1827); Boiss., l.c. *pro syn.* [Plate 571]. Leaves more or less heteromorphic, the lower and middle ones as in the former variety, the upper ones undivided or ternatisect into lanceolate or linear segments, with the terminal segment very long, serrate or incised. Umbels of 2–4 rays. Petals scarcely radiating, mostly pink. Styles as long as the stylopodium. Prickles of mericarp long and more or less horizontal.
Hab. : As above. Upper and Lower Galilee, Mt. Carmel, Esdraelon Plain, Judean Mts., Judean Desert, Hula Plain. Common.

Subsp. **elongata** (Hoffmanns. et Link) Cannon in Heywood, Repert. Sp. Nov. 79 : 61 (1968). *C. elongata* Hoffmanns. et Link, Fl. Port. 2 : 392 (1834 ?). Var. *purpurea* (Ten.) Paol. in Fiori et Paol., Fl. Anal. It. 2 : 194 (1900) excl. f. *heterophylla. T. homophylla* Stapf et Wettst. ex Stapf, Denkschr. Akad. Wiss. Wien 51 : 372 (1886) [incl. var. *tetractis* (Post) Dinsmore in Post, Fl. Syr. Pal. Sin. ed. 2, 1 : 570 (1932)]. Leaves as in ssp. *arvensis.* Umbels generally 2- or 4 (–5)-rayed. Petals generally pink, scarcely radiating. Styles almost twice as long as the stylopodium. Prickles of mericarp almost horizontal.

Hab. : As above. Coastal Galilee, Acco Plain, Sharon Plain, Philistean Plain, Upper and Lower Galilee, Mt. Carmel, Esdraelon Plain, Samaria, Judean Mts., Judean Desert, Gilead, Ammon. Common.

Area of species : Mediterranean, W. Irano-Turanian and S. Euro-Siberian.

Within the last subspecies a few forms can be distinguished, e.g. : f. *brevispina* Zoh. (f. nov.), with prickles reduced to thick and short tubercles; f. *longiradiata* Zoh. (f. nov.), with some of the rays longer than 4 cm.

The records of *T. radiata* Moench, Meth. 103 (1794) (as *T. neglecta* Spreng. ex Schult. in Roem. et Schult., Syst. Veg. 6 : 484, 1820) from Palestine have not been confirmed.

3. Torilis gaillardotii (Boiss.) Drude in Engl. et Prantl, Nat. Pflznfam. III, 8 : 156 (1898). *Caucalis gaillardotii* Boiss., Fl. 2 : 1085 (1872).

Annual, appressed-setulose, 20–40 cm. Stems dichotomously branched, slender. Leaves lanceolate in outline, pinnatisect; segments 3–4 pairs, remote, short, each cut into oblong-linear lobes. Umbels long-peduncled, 2–3-rayed. Bracts 1 or 0. Bracteoles as long as the flowers, linear. Styles as long as the stylopodium. Fruit 7–8 × 5 mm. (incl. prickles), oblong-linear, crowned by long, acuminate calyx teeth; secondary ribs with 2 rows of smooth, subulate prickles, 4–5 times as long as the diameter of the seed-bearing part, minutely glochidiate at tip. Fl. April–May.

Hab. : Stony places. Dan Valley (after Post, Fl. Syr. Pal. Sin. 375, 1883–1896 et ed. 2, 1 : 572, 1932), Golan. Rare.

Area : E. Mediterranean (Palestine-Syria).

4. Torilis leptophylla (L.) Reichb. f. in Reichb., Ic. Fl. Germ. 21 : 83, t. 169, ff. 1–9 (1866). *Caucalis leptophylla* L., Sp. Pl. 242 (1753); Boiss., Fl. 2 : 1084 (1872). [Plate 572]

Annual, appressed-setulose, 10–40 cm. Stems dichotomously branched from base, furrowed. Leaves oblong in outline, 2–3-pinnatisect; ultimate lobes linear, acute. Peduncles 1–3 (–4–5) cm. Umbels borne along stems and branches and spuriously opposite the leaves; rays 2–4, 1–2 cm., thickened, spreading. Bracts 1 or 0. Bracteoles 3 or more, linear-lanceolate, broadly membranous-margined. Petals white or purple, scarcely radiating. Styles shorter than the conical stylopodium. Fruit 7–8 × 3–4 mm. (incl. prickles), linear to oblong, crowned with calyx teeth; secondary ribs with 2– 3 rows of prickles somewhat longer than the diameter of the seed-bearing part to twice as long, scabrous, yellowish, greyish or purplish-black, glochidiate at tip. Fl. March–May.

Var. **leptophylla.** Petals white. Prickles on secondary ribs of mericarp in 3 rows, twice as long as the diameter of the seed-bearing part, yellowish or greyish.

Hab.: Fields, batha and roadsides. Sharon Plain, Philistean Plain, Upper and Lower Galilee, Mt. Carmel, Esdraelon Plain, Samaria, Shefela, Judean Mts., Judean Desert, N. Negev, Dan Valley, Upper Jordan Valley, Dead Sea area, Golan, Gilead, Ammon, Moav, Edom. Fairly common.

Var. **erythrotricha** (Reichb. f.) Zoh. (comb. et stat. nov.). *T. erythrotricha* Reichb. f., l.c. 84. *C. erythrotricha* Boiss. et Hausskn. ex Reichb. f., l.c. *pro syn.*; *C. erythrotricha* (Reichb. f.) Boiss. et Hausskn. in Boiss., l.c. 1085. Petals purple. Prickles on secondary ribs of mericarp in 2 rows, a little longer than the diameter of the seed-bearing part, purplish-black.

Hab.: As above. Philistean Plain, Upper Galilee, Mt. Carmel, Esdraelon Plain, Shefela, Judean Mts., Hula Plain, Upper Jordan Valley, Ammon, Moav. Fairly common.

Area of species: Mediterranean and W. Irano-Turanian extending into some parts of the Euro-Siberian region.

5. Torilis nodosa (L.) Gaertn., Fruct. 1 : 82, t. 20, f. 6 (1788); Boiss., Fl. 2 : 1083 (1872). *Tordylium nodosum* L., Sp. Pl. 240 (1753). [Plate 573]

Annual, sparsely appressed-hispid to scabridulous, 10–40 cm. Stems erect to prostrate, terete, striate. Leaves 2-pinnatisect with segments 1–3 cm. long, incised to pinnatipartite into oblong acute lobes. Peduncles 0 or up to 1 cm. or so. Umbels along stems and branches and spuriously opposite the leaves; rays 2–3, 0–0.5 cm. Bracts 0. Bracteoles few, subulate, exceeding umbellets in length. Flowers minute. Petals scarcely radiating, pinkish. Styles very short, erect. Fruit 3–5 mm., subsessile, shortly ovoid, hetero-mericarpous, i.e. outer mericarp with 2–3 rows of spreading, scabrous, apically glochidiate prickles, inner mericarp covered with tubercles. Fl. March–May.

Hab.: Roadsides, waste places and fields. Acco Plain, Sharon Plain, Philistean Plain, Upper Galilee, Mt. Carmel, Esdraelon Plain, Samaria, Judean Mts., Upper and Lower Jordan Valley, Golan, Gilead, Ammon, Moav. Common.

Area: Mediterranean, Irano-Turanian and Euro-Siberian.

10. CAUCALIS L.

Annuals, often appressed-setose. Leaves 2–3-pinnatisect. Umbels terminal or axillary, few- to many-rayed. Bracts few or 0. Bracteoles numerous. Flowers hermaphrodite and staminate in each umbel. Calyx teeth minute or obsolete. Petals equal or radiating, white or reddish, cuneate or obovate, notched with an inflexed apex. Stylopodium short; styles shorter and often indistinct. Fruit laterally compressed; carpophore undivided or 2-fid; 5 primary ribs of mericarp filiform, bristly; 4 secondary ribs more prominent, each furnished with 1 row of prickles; oil ducts solitary under the secondary ribs. Inner face of seed involute-grooved.

Some 4 species in N. temperate zones.

1. Caucalis tenella Del., Fl. Aeg. Ill. 58 (1813) et Fl. Eg. 58, t. 21, f. 3 (1813); Boiss., Fl. 2 : 1084 (1872). [Plate 574]

Annual, sparingly setulose, 10–30(–50) cm. Stems erect, little branched, especially above, more or less furrowed. Leaves oblong in outline, 2–3-pinnatisect with linear ultimate lobes. Umbels more or less long-peduncled, with 5–10(–15) mostly unequal rays. Involucre 0. Bracteoles lanceolate-subulate. Calyx teeth 0.5 mm. Styles shorter than the conical stylopodium. Fruit 4–7 × 2–3 mm. (including prickles), mostly longer than the pedicel, oblong in outline; prickles on secondary ribs 3 times as long as the diameter of the seed-bearing part, scabrous, minutely glochidiate. Fl. February–May.

Hab. : Fields, grassy places, batha and maquis. Coastal Galilee, Acco Plain, Coast of Carmel, Sharon Plain, Philistean Plain, Upper and Lower Galilee, Mt. Carmel, Esdraelon Plain, Mt. Gilboa, Samaria, Shefela, Judean Mts., Judean Desert, N. and C. Negev, Hula Plain, Upper and Lower Jordan Valley, Dead Sea area, Golan, Gilead, Ammon, Moav. Very common.

Area : E. Mediterranean and W. Irano-Turanian.

One of the most common plants of the country, occurring in several plant communities.

11. TURGENIA Hoffm.

Annual herbs, hispid or strigulose. Leaves 1-pinnatisect. Umbels pedunculate, few-rayed. Involucre and involucel of several bracts or bracteoles. Flowers hermaphrodite and staminate in each umbel. Calyx teeth triangular. Petals radiating, white or purplish, obovate, notched with inflexed apex; outer petals 2-lobed. Stylopodium conical; styles short-conical. Fruit laterally compressed, with narrowed commissural face; carpophore undivided; mericarps almost orbicular in cross section, with 5 primary and 4 secondary ribs, the 2 lateral ribs tuberculate or armed with a single row of prickles, the 7 dorsal ones each armed with 2–3 rows of nearly equal prickles, the latter shorter or longer than the width of the seed-bearing part; oil ducts solitary under each secondary rib, commissural ducts 2. Inner face of seed involute-grooved.

One species in the Mediterranean region and W. Asia.

1. Turgenia latifolia (L.) Hoffm., Gen. Umb. 59 (1814); Boiss., Fl. 2 : 1087 (1872). [Plate 575]

Annual, hispid or scabrous, 15–40 cm. Stems erect or procumbent, dichotomously branched, furrowed-angular. Leaves ovate or oblong in outline, usually 1-pinnatisect; segments 2–6 cm., oblong-lanceolate, incised-serrate or lobed. Umbels long-peduncled, with 2–4 somewhat spreading hispid or scabrous rays. Bracts and bracteoles usually 5, ovate to oblong, obtuse, scarious-margined. Fruit (0.8–)1–1.5 × 0.8 cm. (incl. prickles), usually ovoid, tapering at apex, crowned with the lanceolate-subulate calyx teeth; dorsal ribs with 2–3 rows of scabrous prickles broadened at base and glochidiate at apex. Fl. March. Fr. April–May.

Var. **latifolia.** *Turgenia latifolia* (L.) Hoffm., l.c. *Tordylium latifolium* L., Sp. Pl. 240 (1753). *Caucalis latifolia* L., Syst. ed. 12, 2 : 205 (1767). *Turgenia latifolia* (L.) Hoffm.

var. *genuina* Godr. in Gren. et Godr., Fl. Fr. 1 : 673 (1848–1849); Boiss., l.c. Prickles on lateral ribs of mericarp well developed.

Hab. : Fields and waste places. Upper Galilee, Esdraelon Plain, Judean Mts., Negev, Upper Jordan Valley, Golan, Gilean, Edom. Fairly common.

Var. **tuberculata** (Boiss.) Godr. in Gren. et Godr., l.c.; Boiss., l.c. *Turgenia tuberculata* Boiss., Ann. Sci. Nat. Bot. ser. 3, 2 : 52 (1844). Prickles on lateral ribs of mericarp reduced to tubercles.

Hab. : As above. Philistean Plain. Uncommon.

Area of species : Mediterranean, Irano-Turanian and Euro-Siberian.

12. ORLAYA Hoffm.

Annuals, glabrous or sparingly setulose-hirsute. Leaves 2–3-pinnatisect. Umbels pedunculate, few-rayed. Involucre and involucel present. Flowers many, hermaphrodite and staminate in each umbel. Teeth of calyx subulate. Petals radiating, white, obovate-oblong, notched with inflexed apex; outer petals of peripheral flowers 5–10 times as long as the inner ones, 2-lobed. Stylopodium conical; styles filiform. Fruit dorsally compressed, ovoid-ellipsoidal; carpophore strong, 2-fid; the 5 primary ribs of mericarp slender, setulose, the 4 secondary ribs wing-like, each with 1–2 rows of long equal prickles hooked but not glochidiate at apex and broadly connate at base; oil ducts solitary in each furrow, commissural ducts 2. Inner face of seed plane.

Some 5 species in the Mediterranean countries and Eurasia.

1. Orlaya daucoides (L.) Greuter in Greuter et Rech. f., Boissiera 13 : 92 (1967). *Caucalis daucoides* L., Sp. Pl. 241 (1753) non L., Syst. ed. 12, 2 : 205 (1767). *O. platycarpos* (L.) Koch, Nov. Act. Acad. Leop.-Carol. 12, 1 : 79 (1824); "*O. platycarpos* (L.) Hoffm., Umb. 79" err. Boiss., Fl. 2 : 1071 (1872). [Plate 576]

Annual, glabrous or hirsute or scabrous, 15–30 cm. Stems procumbent or erect, branched from base, angular, furrowed. Leaves 2–3-pinnatisect, sparsely or densely bristly; ultimate lobes small, oblong to lanceolate, acute, short-mucronate. Umbels long-peduncled, (1–)2–3-rayed; rays 0.5–2 cm. Bracts shorter than the rays, oblong-lanceolate, acuminate, narrowly scarious-margined (rarely 2-fid). Bracteoles shorter and broader, as long as or longer than the flowers. Calyx teeth up to 1 mm. Fruit 1 cm. long or more and 0.8–1 cm. broad (incl. prickles). Fl. April–May.

Hab. : Batha; stony ground. Upper Galilee, Mt. Carmel, Esdraelon Plain, Judean Mts., Gilead, Ammon. Uncommon.

Area : Mediterranean, with extensions into the W. Irano-Turanian territories.

13. PSEUDORLAYA (Murb.) Murb.

Annuals, velvety, procumbent, much branched. Leaves 2–3-pinnatisect. Umbels unequally few-rayed. Involucre and involucel present. Flowers small, hermaphrodite and staminate in the same umbel. Calyx teeth distinct. Petals somewhat radiating, white or purplish, obovate, notched with inflexed apex. Stylopodium conical; style short. Fruit dorsally compressed, lenticular-elliptical in cross section; carpophore very slender, filiform, setaceous; primary ribs 5, filiform, hairy; secondary ribs 4, stouter, those at the margin much more prominent than the dorsal ones; prickles in 2–3 more or less distinct rows, glochidiate, at least in some of the secondary ribs; oil ducts solitary under the secondary ribs, elliptical in cross section. Seeds plane at inner face.

Three species in the Mediterranean countries.

1. Pseudorlaya pumila (L.) Grande, Nuov. Giorn. Bot. It. n.s., 32 : 86 (1925). *Caucalis pumila* L., Syst. ed. 10, 955 (1759). *Orlaya maritima* (Gouan) Koch, Nov. Act. Acad. Leop.-Carol. 12, 1 : 79 (1824) *nom. illegit.*; Boiss., Fl. 2 : 1071 (1872). *C. maritima* Gouan, Hort. Monsp. 135 (1762) *nom. illegit. O. pumila* (L.) Hal., Consp. Fl. Gr. 1 : 622 (1901). [Plate 577]

Annual, mostly grey-velvety, 10–30 cm. Stems procumbent, branched from base, hollow, striate. Leaves 5–10 cm., ovate-oblong in outline, 2–3-pinnatisect; ultimate lobes small, ovate-oblong, obtuse, bristly. Umbels 2–4(–5)-rayed; rays 2–3 cm., unequal. Bracts 1–1.2 cm., linear, simple or 2–3-fid. Bracteoles shorter, much longer than the fruiting pedicels. Fruit 0.8–1.2 × 0.5–0.8 cm. (incl. prickles), lenticular-elliptical; prickles in 2–3 rows in all or some of the secondary ribs, straight (not hooked), glochidiate at tip, the marginal prickles longer, more connate at base than the dorsal ones. Fl. March–May.

Var. **pumila.** Fruit 1–1.2 cm.; prickles as long as or somewhat shorter than the diameter of the seed-bearing part.

Hab.: Maritime sand and sandy inland deserts. Coastal Galilee, Acco Plain, Coast of Carmel, Sharon Plain, Philistean Plain, Negev, Moav. Locally fairly common.

Var. **breviaculeata** (Boiss.) V. Täckh., Stud. Fl. Eg. 204 [1956; "var. *breviaculeata* (Boiss. et Heldr.) Täckh."]. *O. maritima* (Gouan) Koch var. *breviaculeata* Boiss., Fl. 2 : 1071 (1872). "*O. maritima* (Gaertn.) Koch" var. *breviaculeata* Boiss. et Heldr. ex Raul., Act. Soc. Linn. Bordeaux 24 : 461 (1869) *nom. nud.* This is a desertic form with smaller fruits and much shorter prickles than in the typical form.

Hab.: As above. Philistean Plain, C. Negev, Edom. Rare.

Area of species: Mediterranean and Saharo-Arabian.

14. Lisaea Boiss.

Annual herbs, hairy or scabrous. Leaves 1-pinnatisect. Umbels pedunculate, usually few-rayed. Involucre and involucel present. Calyx teeth membranous, lanceolate. Petals strongly radiating, white, obovate, with an inflexed apex; outer petals deeply cleft into obovate lobes. Stylopodium small; styles short, erect. Fruit somewhat compressed laterally, constricted at commissure; carpophore adnate to mericarps; primary ribs 5, the 2 lateral ribs obsolete or with a row of appressed prickles or tubercles, the 3 dorsal ribs mostly dilated at base and usually forming a crest, each with 1 row of prickles; secondary ribs 0 or in the form of prickly crests similar to the primary ones, sometimes reduced to tubercles; oil ducts obsolete under secondary ribs. Inner face of seed concave.

Three to five species in S.W. Asia.

1. Lisaea strigosa (Banks et Sol.) Eig, Journ. Bot. Lond. 75 : 189 (1937). *Caucalis strigosa* Banks et Sol. in Russ., Nat. Hist. Aleppo ed. 2, 2 : 248 (1794). *L. syriaca* Boiss., Ann. Sci. Nat. Bot. ser. 3, 2 : 55 (1844) et Fl. 2 : 1088 (1872). [Plate 578]

Annual, patulous-hirsute to strigose, 20–40 cm. Stems erect or ascending, moderately and dichotomously branched, terete, furrowed, with ordinary hairs intermixed with long, scabrous, glochidiate bristles. Leaves 6–12 cm., ovate-oblong in outline, 1-pinnatisect; segments 4–6 pairs, oblong-lanceolate, incised-dentate or pinnatipartite, appressed-pubescent. Umbels terminal, long-peduncled, with 5–8 rays densely covered with long stiff bristles. Bracts and bracteoles usually 5, 0.8–1 cm., oblong, cuspidate, broadly membranous-margined. Flowers hermaphrodite and staminate in each umbel. Outer petals 0.7–1 cm., broadly obovate and obcordate. Stylopodium broad-conical. Fruit 6–8 mm. across, ovoid-globular, separating at maturity into 2 equal or unequal mericarps, with 3 dorsal primary ribs; each rib extended to a crest, on each crest 1–4 or 6–7 * long or short spiny prickles; secondary ribs obsolete or tuberculate. Fl. April–May.

Hab.: Fields. Judean Mts., Judean Desert, Golan, Gilead. Very rare.

Area : W. Irano-Turanian.

Trib. CORIANDREAE. Flowers and seeds as in the preceding tribe, but crystalline layer in fruit parenchyma 0; mericarps with ligneous layers under epidermis.

15. CORIANDRUM L.

Annual or biennial glabrous herbs with heavy scent. Leaves 1–3-pinnatisect. Umbels terminal and opposite the leaves; rays many. Bracts 0 or 1. Involucel of few small bracteoles. Flowers hermaphrodite and staminate in each umbel. Calyx teeth persistent, unequal, conspicuous. Petals radiating, white or reddish, notched or 2-lobed with inflexed apex. Stylopodium conical; styles long. Fruit slightly compressed laterally, ovoid to globular; carpophore 2-fid above; mericarps not separating at maturity, hemispherical; primary ribs 5, wavy, secondary ribs 4, more prominent; dorsal oil ducts obsolete, commissural ducts 2. Inner face of seed concave.

Two species in the E. Mediterranean countries.

1. Coriandrum sativum L., Sp. Pl. 256 (1753); Boiss., Fl. 2 : 920 (1872). [Plate 579]

Glabrous annual, 20–50 cm. Stems erect, dichotomously branched from base, terete, striate, leafy. Leaves glossy, of three kinds : the basal ones marcescent, long-petioled, undivided or 3-lobed or ternatisect; lower cauline leaves pinnatisect into 2–4 pairs of

---

* All the specimens so far observed by us have mericarps with 1–3 stout spines on each rib. They should probably be considered as a distinct variety of the above species.

ovate-cuneate, incised-dentate segments; upper leaves sessile, 2–3-pinnatisect with linear to filiform ultimate lobes. Umbels usually long-peduncled, 3–5 (rarely more)-rayed; rays 1–4 cm. Bracts 1, minute or 0. Umbellets 3–8-rayed. Bracteoles 3 or more, incurved, linear-subulate, cuspidate. Fruit 2.5–3.5 (–5) mm. across, crowned with the prominent unequal calyx teeth and the long horizontal or deflexed styles. Fl. March–June.

Hab.: Among winter crops; sometimes also cultivated. Philistean Plain, Upper and Lower Galilee, Mt. Carmel, Esdraelon Plain, Samaria, Shefela, Judean Mts., Hula Plain, Upper Jordan Valley, Golan, Gilead, Ammon. Uncommon.

Area: E. Mediterranean and W. Irano-Turanian.

Cultivated as a condiment; known in medicine as oleum and fructus coriandri.

The Biblical name גד (Exod. xvi : 31) is usually referred to this species.

16. BIFORA Hoffm.

Glabrous annual herbs with heavy odour. Leaves 2–3-pinnatisect. Umbels with few short rays, and usually without involucre and involucel or with only 1 (–2–3) bracts and bracteoles. Flowers all hermaphrodite or some also staminate in each umbellet. Calyx teeth obsolete. Petals equal or unequal, white, notched or retuse with inflexed apex. Stylopodium minute, conical; styles very short. Fruit laterally compressed, much broader than long; carpophore 2-fid; mericarps subglobular with perforated commissural face, inconspicuous ribs and tuberculate-wrinkled furrows; oil ducts disappearing in mature fruits. Seeds almost globular, concave at inner surface.

Two species, mainly in the Mediterranean and in some S.W. Asian countries.

1. Bifora testiculata (L.) Spreng. ex Schult. in Roem. et Schult., Syst. Veg. 6 : XXXVIII, 448 (1820; *"Biforis"*) excl. syn. [*Bifora radians* M.B., Fl. Taur.-Cauc. 3 : 233 (1819)]; *B. testiculata* (L.) Roth, Enum. 1 : 888 (1827; *"Biforis"*); *B. testiculata* (L.) DC., Prodr. 4 : 249 (1830); Boiss., Fl. 2 : 921 (1872). [Plate 580]

Glabrous annual, 15–30 cm. Stems erect, richly branched from base, angular. Leaves (1–)2–3-pinnatisect, the basal and lower ones with long petioles and oblong-cuneate, incised-dentate ultimate segments; middle and upper cauline leaves 3–5 × 2 cm., ovate-oblong in outline, with short sheathing petioles and 2-pinnatisect blades with narrow linear lobes. Umbels 2–3-, very rarely 1- or 5-rayed; umbellets 2–6-flowered. Bracts and bracteoles 0 or 1(–3), setaceous. Flowers all hermaphrodite. Petals 0.5–1 mm., scarcely radiating. Styles short, as long as the stylopodium or shorter, recurved. Fruit 2–4 × 4–6(–7–8) mm., notched at base; mericarps apiculate, strongly wrinkled. Fl. March–April.

Var. **testiculata**. *Coriandrum testiculatum* L., Sp. Pl. 256 (1753). Fruit 3–4 × 7–8 mm.

Hab.: Fields. Judean Mts., Ammon (after Dinsmore in Post, Fl. Syr. Pal. Sin. ed. 2, 1 : 534, 1932).

Var. **microcarpa** Boiss., l.c. 922. [Plate 580]. Fruit about 2–3 × 5 mm.

Hab.: Fields; among winter crops. Sharon Plain, Philistean Plain, Upper and

Lower Galilee, Mt. Carmel, Samaria, Shefela, Judean Mts., Judean Desert, Upper Jordan Valley, Gilead, Ammon, Moav, Edom. Uncommon.

Area of species: Mainly Mediterranean, with slight extensions into adjacent W. Irano-Turanian territories.

17. ASTOMA DC.

Perennial herbs with tuberous roots. Leaves 2-pinnatisect. Umbels terminal, many-rayed. Involucre and involucel present, the former caducous. Flowers hermaphrodite and staminate, minute. Calyx teeth obsolete. Petals not radiating, white, obovate, notched with inflexed apex. Stylopodium depressed, almost disk-like, located in the sinus between the two mericarps; styles long, deflexed. Fruit laterally compressed, much broader than long; carpophore 2-fid, short; mericarps almost globular, with concave inner face; commissure narrow; ribs distinct; oil ducts 2 in each furrow. Seeds grooved at inner face.

One species in Palestine and Syria.

1. Astoma seselifolium DC., Coll. Mém. 5 : 71, t. 17 (1829); Boiss., Fl. 2 : 919 (1872). [Plate 581]

Glabrous perennial, 15–50 cm. Stems much branched. Basal and lower leaves long-petioled with petioles broadly sheathing at base; blades ovate in outline, 2-pinnatisect, with ovate-oblong segments, pinnatipartite into oblong-lanceolate to linear mucronate lobes; upper cauline leaves sessile on short sheaths, with few, long, setaceous or linear segments. Umbels long-peduncled, usually 8–12-rayed; rays (2–)3–6 cm.; staminate umbels lateral, beneath the main fertile one and mostly overtopping it. Bracts and bracteoles 4–6, 0.4–1.5 cm., linear-setaceous. Fruit up to 1.5 × about 2 mm.; mericarps black with 5 white ribs. Fl. March–May.

Hab.: Cultivated and fallow fields; among winter crops; also on rocks and in semi-steppe batha. Upper and Lower Galilee, Mt. Carmel, Esdraelon Plain, Samaria, Judean Mts., Judean Desert, N. Negev, Upper and Lower Jordan Valley, Arava Valley, Gilead, Ammon. Locally fairly common.

Area: E. Mediterranean and W. Irano-Turanian.

One of the obligatory weeds of the E. Mediterranean region that have their home of origin in the adjacent steppes.

Subterranean tubers roasted and eaten by villagers.

Trib. SMYRNIEAE. Flowers and seeds as in the preceding tribe. Crystalline layer in fruit parenchyma 0; fruit laterally compressed; mericarps with very narrow commissural face; back strongly convex, with obsolete or prominent primary ribs.

18. SMYRNIUM L.

Biennial or perennial herbs, erect, glabrous. Basal leaves ternately divided into broad segments, upper leaves frequently undivided. Umbels few- to many-rayed. Bracts and bracteoles small or 0. Flowers all hermaphrodite or some of them staminate. Calyx teeth minute or obsolete. Petals yellow or yellowish-green, oblong, acute, almost entire with inflexed apex. Stylopodium conical; styles spreading. Fruit laterally compressed, ovoid or subglobular, glabrous; carpophore divided to over half its length; mericarps blackish; commissure narrow; ribs 0 or only the 3 dorsal ones prominent; oil ducts many in each furrow. Inner face of seed concave.

About 8 species, mainly in the Mediterranean and Middle-Eastern countries.

1. Mericarps globular or nearly so, 5–6 mm. Upper leaves undivided, connate at base to form a basin-like structure.   **2. S. connatum**
–   Mericarps hemispherical, 8 mm. Upper leaves ternately divided, not connate at base, opposite.   **1. S. olusatrum**

1. Smyrnium olusatrum L., Sp. Pl. 262 (1753); Boiss., Fl. 2 : 927 (1872). [Plate 582]

Tall and stout biennial, glabrous, much branched, 0.5–1.5 m., with thick roots. Stems branched from base, furrowed-angular. Upper branches often opposite. Leaves large, green, glossy above and opaque beneath; basal leaves 20–50 cm., alternate, 2–3-ternatisect, segments 3–8 cm., petiolulate, ovate, crenate, often 3-lobed; upper cauline leaves much shorter, often opposite, 1-ternatisect, with broad sheaths at base. Umbels many, long-peduncled, (3–)5–15(–18)-rayed; rays 3–8 cm., furrowed-angular, becoming thickened. Bracts and bracteoles 0 or few, caducous. Petals yellowish-green. Styles somewhat longer than the stylopodium. Fruit 8 × 6–8 mm., broadly ovoid, black; mericarps hemispherical, with acute prominent dorsal ribs. Fl. March–May.

Hab.: Shady waste places. Sharon Plain, Philistean Plain, Upper and Lower Galilee, Mt. Carmel, Samaria, Judean Mts., Dan Valley, Hula Plain, Upper Jordan Valley, Golan, Gilead, Ammon. Uncommon.

Area: Mediterranean, with extensions towards S. and W. Euro-Siberian territories.

Young shoots eaten like those of asparagus; known in folk medicine as an anti-scorbutic.

2. Smyrnium connatum Boiss. et Ky. ex Ky. in Ung. et Ky., Ins. Cyp. 309 (1865); Boiss., Fl. 2 : 926 (1872). [Plate 583]

Biennial, glabrous or glabrescent, 0.8–1.5 m. Stems erect, branched, terete, striate. Upper branches opposite. Basal leaves often 25–40 cm., long-petioled, 2–3-subternately pinnatisect into ovate, subcordate, obtusely dentate segments; lower cauline leaves sessile, auriculate at base, pinnatisect into 3–5 ovate segments or undivided; upper leaves opposite, connate into ovate basin-like structures slightly dentate or lobed. Umbels 8–20-rayed; rays 2–5 cm., angular. Bracts and bracteoles minute or 0. Styles longer than the stylopodium. Fruit 3 × 5–7 mm., transversely ovoid, black; mericarps almost globular; all the ribs, or only the lateral ones, obsolete. Fl. March–May.

Hab.: Stony ground and batha. Upper and Lower Galilee, Samaria, Judean Mts., Upper Jordan Valley. Rare.

Area: E. Mediterranean, with extensions into W. Irano-Turanian territories.

19. SMYRNIOPSIS Boiss.

Large, glabrous, much-branched perennial herbs. Leaves 1-pinnatisect with a few large, oblong, ovate or obovate segments. Umbels terminal, many-rayed, subtended by 3–5 or more large leaf-like bracts; umbellets large, many-rayed, bracteolate. Flowers large, hermaphrodite and staminate. Calyx teeth obsolete. Petals yellow, oblong, acute, almost entire with inflexed apex. Fruit laterally compressed, crowned with flattened stylopodium and styles often longer than the stylopodium; carpophore 2-fid; mericarps prismatic, 5-angled, with 5 prominent, thin, almost wing-like ribs; oil ducts broad, 1–2 or more in each furrow. Inner face of seed concave.

Four species from Palestine to Iran.

1. Smyrniopsis cachroides Boiss., Fl. 2 : 928 (1872). *Colladonia syriaca* Boiss., Ann. Sci. Nat. Bot. ser. 3, 2 : 86 (1844) non *S. syriaca* Boiss., Diagn. ser. 1, 10 : 51 (1849) nec Boiss., Fl. l.c. *sp. alt.* [Plate 584]

Perennial shrub-like herb, bright green, glabrous and leafy, 40–60 cm. Stems erect, usually branched from base, terete below and almost angular above. Basal leaves mostly undivided and oblong, the rest with inflated, sheath-like petiole 3–8 cm. long and blade up to 20 cm. long, ovate in outline, pinnatisect into 2–3 pairs of decurrent, broadly oblong, crenate, undivided or 2-lobed segments; upper cauline leaves with progressively more inflated sheaths and fewer segments; uppermost leaves reduced to sheaths. Umbels rather short-peduncled; rays numerous, 10–15 cm., equal, thick and angular; staminate umbels beneath the main umbel and overtopping it. Bracts few or many, 1–3 cm., leaf-like. Bracteoles 0.8–1.5 cm., oblong-linear. Pedicels 5–8 cm., angular, somewhat thickened above. Styles horizontal, somewhat longer than the diameter of the flat, undulate stylopodium. Fruit 1–1.2 × 0.7–0.9 cm., ellipsoidal; mericarps with expanded wing-like ribs. Fl. April–May.

Hab. : Fields, steppes. Gilead. Rare. (Tumble weed).

Area : W. Irano-Turanian.

20. CONIUM L.

Biennial or perennial herbs, tall, glabrous. Stems branched above, hollow, mostly spotted. Leaves 2–4-pinnatisect. Umbels several- to many-rayed. Bracts and bracteoles 3–6, small. Flowers hermaphrodite, or some staminate. Calyx teeth obsolete. Petals white, obcordate, notched with inflexed short apex. Stylopodium conical; styles filiform, deflexed in fruit. Fruit laterally compressed, broadly ovoid; carpophore 2-fid; mericarps with 5 prominent, often somewhat wavy, primary ribs and broad, many-striate furrows; commissure narrow; oil ducts obsolete. Inner face of seed grooved.

Four species in N. temperate regions and S. Africa.

1. Conium maculatum L., Sp. Pl. 243 (1753); Boiss., Fl. 2 : 922 (1872). [Plate 585]

Biennial or perennial, tall, glabrous, 0.6–1.5 m. Roots fusiform. Stems erect, branched especially above, hollow, furrowed, mostly spotted. Branches often opposite or whorled. Lower leaves 20–40 × 5–10 cm., long-petioled, broadly triangular in outline, (2–)3(–4)-

pinnatisect into ovate or oblong pinnatifid or pinnatipartite segments with oblong, acute to mucronate lobules; upper leaves subsessile, 2-pinnatisect with oblong to linear segments. Umbels opposite leaves and terminal, long-peduncled, 8–20-rayed. Bracts usually 4–5, caducous, deflexed, lanceolate, acuminate. Umbellets 12–20-rayed. Bracteoles 3–6, 2–6 mm., much shorter than the fruiting pedicel, one-sided. Fruit 2.5–4 × 2–3 mm., broadly ovoid; mericarps somewhat arcuate when ripe; ribs very prominent, often wavy. Fl. April–June.

Hab.: Waste and weedy places, roadsides and by fences and walls. Sharon Plain, Philistean Plain, Upper and Lower Galilee, Mt. Carmel, Esdraelon Plain, Mt. Gilboa, Samaria, Judean Mts., Hula Plain, Golan, Gilead. Fairly common.

Area: Euro-Siberian and Mediterranean, with extensions into some Irano-Turanian territories.

The Biblical name ראש (Deut. xxxii : 32–33) has often been referred to this plant.

Poisonous; dried unripe fruit contains the alkaloid coniine, and has been used medicinally as an antispasmodic and sedative. A decoction of the young fruits of this plant is believed to have been the poison given to Socrates.

The form with smooth ribs [var. *leiocarpum* Boiss. ex Reichb. f., in Reichb., Ic. Fl. Germ. 21 : 94, t. 191 (2032) f. V (1867); Boiss., l.c.], recorded in Post (Fl. Syr. Pal. Sin. 335, 1883–1896 et ed. 2, 1 : 535, 1932), has not been observed by others.

21. Lecokia DC.

Perennial glabrous herbs with fusiform roots and leafy stems. Leaves 1–2-pinnatisect into large dentate or divided segments. Umbels terminal, few- to many-rayed. Bracts almost 0. Central umbellets short, staminate. Bracteoles few to many. Calyx teeth short. Petals white, obovate, notched with inflexed apex. Styles equalling the conical stylopodium. Fruit laterally compressed, oblong-ovoid, narrowed at commissure; carpophore deeply 2-fid; ribs of mericarp 5, thick, corky, obtuse, muricate throughout; furrows deep; oil ducts numerous under the pericarp and adherent to the seed. Inner face of seed concave.

One species, from Crete to Persia.

1. Lecokia cretica (Lam.) DC., Coll. Mém. 5 : 67, 75, t. 2, f. L (1829); Boiss., Fl. 2 : 931 (1872). *Cachrys cretica* Lam., Encycl. 1 : 259 (1783). [Plate 586]

Perennial, glabrous, 40–100 cm. Stems single, erect, somewhat corymbosely branched above, angular, striate. Lower leaves broadly triangular in outline, long-petioled, subternately 2-pinnatisect; segments 5–8 × 1–3 cm., oblong, usually cuneate at base, acuminate, acutely dentate, sometimes 3–5-fid; upper leaves smaller, 1-pinnatisect. Umbels 5–10-rayed; rays 5–8 cm., rigid, angular. Bracts usually 0. Bracteoles subulate. Stylopodium long-conical. Fruit 1.2–1.5 cm., longer or shorter than the pedicel, ovoid, muricate. Fl. April–May.

Hab.: Maquis. Golan, Gilead. Rare.

Area: E. Mediterranean, with extensions into the adjacent Hyrcanian province.

22. HIPPOMARATHRUM Link * non P. G. Gaertn., B. Mey. et Scherb.

Perennial herbs. Leaves 3–4-pinnatisect into linear or filiform segments. Umbels terminal or axillary. Bracts and bracteoles numerous, linear. Flowers hermaphrodite and staminate. Calyx teeth minute. Petals yellow, ovate, entire with inflexed apex. Fruit somewhat compressed laterally, ovoid to globular, crowned with a broad cup-shaped disk, a smaller undulate stylopodium in the centre, and short spreading styles; carpophore 2-parted; mericarps with prominent, smooth or transversely tuberculate or crested ribs; pericarp hard, crustaceous; oil ducts numerous, slender, often irregularly spread. Inner face of seed concave.

Some 12 species, mainly in S.W. Asia.

1. Hippomarathrum boissieri Reut. et Hausskn. in Boiss., Fl. 2 : 933 (1872). [Plate 587]

A shrubby perennial, glabrescent to scabrous or hispidulous, sometimes woody at base, 30–80 cm. Roots thick, fusiform. Stems divaricately much branched from the fibrous base, stout, striate. Basal leaves 20–40 cm. across, 3–4-pinnatisect, segments 1–4 cm., rigid, somewhat divaricate, filiform, scabrous; upper leaves ternately pinnatisect. Umbels long-peduncled, 4–8-rayed; rays 3–8 cm., angular; lateral staminate umbels beneath each fertile one. Petals usually sparsely hairy at outer face. Fruit 5–6 × 6–8 mm., transversely ovoid to depressed-globular, with 5 thick ribs densely covered with transverse scale-like warts. Fl. March–June.

Hab.: Batha. Acco Plain, Sharon Plain, Philistean Plain, Upper and Lower Galilee, Mt. Carmel, Esdraelon Plain, Mt. Gilboa, Samaria, Shefela, Golan, Gilead, Ammon. Locally fairly common.

Area : E. Mediterranean and W. Irano-Turanian.

A leading plant of some dwarf-shrub communities in the sandy-calcareous hills of the coastal plain and in the Golan.

The record of *H. crispum* (Pers.) Koch, Nov. Act. Acad. Leop.-Carol. 12, 1 : 136 (1824) by Decaisne (after Dinsmore in Post, Fl. Syr. Pal. Sin. ed. 2, 1 : 537, 1932) from near Gaza is probably erroneous.

23. PRANGOS Lindl.

Perennial herbs, much branched. Leaves 2–4-pinnatisect; ultimate lobes linear or filiform, acute. Umbels several- to many-rayed. Bracts and bracteoles many. Flowers hermaphrodite and staminate. Calyx teeth obsolete. Petals yellow, broad, ovate, almost entire with inflexed apex. Stylopodium disk-like, with wavy margin; styles longer than the stylopodium. Fruit laterally compressed, terete, globular or ovoid, with spongy pericarp; carpophore 2-parted; ribs of mericarp 5, mostly dilated into thick ridges or plane or wavy membranous wings; oil ducts numerous, adherent to the seed along the thin endocarp. Seeds deeply grooved at inner face, groove with involute margins.

* Proposed for conservation; if this proposal is not accepted, *Cachrys* L. should be used as the generic name, and a new specific combination is required.

About 30 species mainly in S.W. Asia.

Future studies may lead to the fusion of *Prangos* with the Linnaean genus *Cachrys*. These genera differ from one another mainly in the nature of the ribs of mericarp. *P. goniocarpa* recorded below presents a clear transitional link between the two genera.

1. Ribs of mericarp not or slightly dilated into narrow, not wavy, wings.
                                                                        1. P. goniocarpa
– Ribs of mericarp dilated into undulate wings as broad as or broader than the diameter of the seed-bearing part.   **2. P. asperula**

1. Prangos goniocarpa (Boiss.) Zoh. (comb. nov.). *Cachrys goniocarpa* Boiss., Diagn. ser. 1, 10 : 53 (1849) et Fl. 2 : 935 (1872). [Plate 588]

Perennial herb, glabrous to papillose, 30–60 cm. Roots vertical, very thick and long. Stems branched from base, terete, grooved. Lower leaves 15–40 cm., often as long as the stem, sometimes overtopping it; base broadly sheathed; petiole flattish; blade 3-pinnatisect; ultimate lobes divaricate, linear or filiform, acute or mucronate, prominently ribbed and mostly papillose; upper leaves 2–3-pinnatisect with longer and more slender lobes. Umbels usually terminal, usually 6–15-rayed, outer umbels on long and strongly grooved peduncles, central umbels short-peduncled; umbellets 3- to many-rayed, rays 2–5 cm. in fruit, often papillose at tip. Bracts and bracteoles 1–3 cm., linear-setaceous, the latter about half as long as the rays. Petals hirtellous beneath, becoming glabrescent. Fruit 1–2 × 0.6–1.5 cm., varying in size and shape, turgid, spongy, with 5 prominent ribs often dilated into narrow, not wavy, wings. Fl. February–April.

Var. **goniocarpa**. *C. goniocarpa* Boiss., l.c. Ribs of mericarp not dilated into wings.

Hab.: Fields; alluvial soils. Philistean Plain, Mt. Carmel, Upper Jordan Valley. Rather rare.

Var. **stenoptera** (Boiss.) Zoh. (comb. nov.). *P. asperula* Boiss. var. *stenoptera* Boiss., Fl. 2 : 942 (1872) et var. *judaica* Sam. ex Rech. f., Ark. Bot. ser. 2, 2, 5 : 396 (1952). [Plate 588]. Mericarps with narrow, plane or obsoletely undulate wings. Transitional forms between the two varieties are more common than the typical ones.

Hab.: Fields. Sharon Plain, Philistean Plain, Upper and Lower Galilee, Mt. Carmel, Esdraelon Plain, Mt. Gilboa, Shefela, Judean Mts., Judean Desert, Upper Jordan Valley, Golan. Locally common.

Area of species: E. Mediterranean.

Very common as a weed on heavy soils (Tumble weed).

The *P. ferulacea* (L.) Lindl., Quart. Journ. Sci. 19 : 7 (1825) recorded tentatively from Palestine by Zohary, Palest. Journ. Bot. Jerusalem ser., 2 : 168 (1941) has not been observed again.

2. Prangos asperula Boiss., Diagn. ser. 1, 10 : 54 (1849) et Fl. 2 : 942 (1872). *P. asperula* Boiss. var. *leiopetala* Post, Fl. Syr. Pal. Sin. 338 (1883–1896) et ed. 2, 1 : 539 (1932). [Plate 589]

Perennial herb, 80–100 cm. Stems angular. Branches many, opposite, spreading to divaricate. Leaves up to 60 cm., triangular in outline, papillose, 3–4-pinnatisect;

ultimate lobes 1–1.5 cm. long, filiform, acute. Peduncles long, papillose. Umbels 10–20-rayed, some bearing staminate flowers. Bracts up to 2.5 cm., filiform, papillose. Bracteoles shorter. Petals hirsute beneath or glabrescent. Fruit 1.5–2 × 1–1.4 cm., oblong to ovoid, often reddish, with undulate wings as broad as or broader than the diameter of the seed-bearing part. Fl. May–June.

Hab.: Fields. Philistean Plain (after Post, l.c.), S. Judean Desert. Very rare.

Area: E. Mediterranean (Israel-Lebanon).

Var. *stenoptera* of the preceding species should be regarded as a connecting link between the two species.

24. HEPTAPTERA Marg. et Reut.

Perennial herbs, sparingly branched, glabrous. Leaves mostly 1-pinnatisect with ultimate lobes ovate-lanceolate. Umbels many-rayed. Bracts and bracteoles many. Flowers mostly hermaphrodite, some staminate. Calyx teeth short. Petals yellow, oblong, entire with an inflexed apex. Stylopodium broad, depressed, cupuliform; styles as long as the stylopodium. Fruit slightly compressed dorsally, with spongy pericarp; mericarps with 5 ribs, all or only the lateral ribs dilated into wings, rarely 1 or 2 of the dorsal ribs obsolete in one of the mericarps; oil ducts numerous, adherent to the thin endocarp and to the seed. Inner face of seed deeply grooved.

A few species in the E. Mediterranean countries.

1. Heptaptera crenata (Fenzl) Tutin in Heywood, Repert. Sp. Nov. 74: 34 (1967). [Plates 590, 591]

Perennial, 40–70 cm. Roots fusiform. Stems branched mainly above, grooved. Basal leaves often undivided, broadly elliptical to oblong, cordate or cuneate at base, crenate; cauline leaves ovate in outline, the longest ones 20(–40) × 15(–25) cm., 1-pinnatisect; rhachis somewhat winged; segments 5–10 cm., sessile or petiolulate, ovate-oblong, undivided, with crenate margin, or the lower segments 2-parted or pinnatipartite into oblong to elliptical lobes. Umbels more or less equally 8–22-rayed; rays (5–)10–20 cm. in fruit; staminate umbels 2 or more, arising below the fertile umbels. Bracts and bracteoles lanceolate, acuminate, scarious-margined. Stylopodium depressed-conical; styles longer than the width of the stylopodium. Fruit about (1.5–)1.8 × 0.5–0.7 cm., subequal to pedicels, dorsally compressed, linear-ellipsoidal to ellipsoidal, sometimes tapering at base; mericarps usually unequal, one with 1–2, the other with 2–3 dorsal wings or ribs as long as or one third to one half as long as the seed-bearing part, wings or ribs gently or abruptly disappearing towards base. Seeds half as long as mericarp. Fl. April–May.

Var. **crenata.** *H. crenata* (Fenzl) Tutin, l.c. *Anisopleura crenata* Fenzl, Flora 26: 459 (1843). *Colladonia crenata* (Fenzl) Boiss., Fl. 2: 946 (1872). *C. crenata* (Fenzl) Boiss. var. *brachyptera* et var. *carmeli* Zoh., Palest. Journ. Bot. Jerusalem ser., 2: 169 (1941). *H. anisoptera* (DC.) Tutin in Heywood, l.c. 33 *nom. illegit. Prangos anisoptera* DC., Prodr. 4: 240 (1830; err. "*anisopetala*") *nom. confus.* *Meliocarpus anisopterus*

* Based on the organs of plants belonging to two different genera — inflorescence (and fruit) of *Heptaptera* and leaves resembling *Prangos*.

(DC.) Boiss., Ann. Sci. Nat. Bot. ser. 3, 2 : 85 (1844). *C. anisoptera* (DC.) Boiss., Fl. 2 : 946 (1872). *C. crenata* (Fenzl) Boiss. var. *anisoptera* (Boiss.) Zoh., l.c. *nom. illegit.* [Plate 590]. Mericarps rather broad-ellipsoidal and unequal as to the number of dorsal ribs or wings; the latter about as long as mericarp though gently or abruptly attenuating towards base.

Hab.: Batha and maquis. Upper and Lower Galilee, Mt. Carmel, Samaria, Judean Mts., Golan. Uncommon.

Var. **subalata** (Zoh.) Zoh. et Fertig (comb. nov.). "*C. anatolica* Boiss." var. *subalata* Zoh., l.c. *H. anatolica* (Boiss.) Tutin in Heywood, l.c. 33. *M. anatolicus* Boiss., Ann. Sci. Nat. Bot. ser. 3, 2 : 84 (1844). *C. anatolica* (Boiss.) Boiss., Fl. 2 : 945 (1872). [Plate 591; under *H. crenata* (Fenzl) Tutin var. *anatolica* (Boiss.) Zoh.]. Mericarps oblong-ellipsoidal to cuneate at base; dorsal ribs or wings about half as long as mericarp or shorter.

Hab.: Batha, maquis and fallow fields. Sharon Plain, Philistean Plain, Upper and Lower Galilee, Judean Mts., Hula Plain, Upper Jordan Valley. Uncommon.

Area of species: E. Mediterranean.

Trib. APIEAE. Flowers as in the preceding tribe. Crystalline layers in fruit parenchyma 0; fruit usually compressed laterally, sometimes terete or globular; all ribs of mericarps usually alike. Seeds plane at commissural face and semiorbicular in cross section.

25. BUPLEURUM L.

Annual or perennial herbs or dwarf shrubs. Leaves entire, usually sessile. Umbels usually compact; rays few to several (in ours), erect to divaricate. Bracts and bracteoles leaf-like, sometimes bracts 0. Flowers hermaphrodite. Calyx teeth obsolete. Petals mostly equal, yellow to yellowish-green, sometimes reddish or brownish, orbicular or ovate, entire or sometimes serrulate at the inflexed apex; outer face keeled along nerve. Stylopodium flat or depressed, rarely conical, entire; styles very short, divaricate. Fruit more or less compressed laterally, mostly ovoid, ellipsoidal or oblong; carpophore usually 2-parted; mericarps with 5 equal, filiform or thick, primary ribs, the lateral ribs marginal; secondary ribs 0; oil ducts (1–)2–3(–5) in each furrow, commissural ducts 2–10. Seeds semicylindrical with plane inner face.

About 150 species of cold and temperate (rarely tropical) regions (mostly of the N. hemisphere).

Literature: H. Wolff, *Bupleurum* L., in: *Pflznr.* 43 (IV, 288) : 36–173, 1910.

1. Leaves, at least the upper ones, ovate to lanceolate, perfoliate. Involucre 0. Bracteoles orbicular or ovate. **1. B. lancifolium**
− Leaves all linear or linear-lanceolate, not perfoliate   2
2. Fruiting umbellets entirely enclosed in the involucel. Bracteoles 3–5-nerved   3
− Fruiting umbellets not enclosed in the involucel. Bracteoles 1–3 nerved   5
3. Bracts overtopping at least part of the umbel. Bracteoles prominently 3-nerved, translucent between nerves, nerves not pinnately veined. **3. B. nodiflorum**

– Bracts shorter than the long rays of the umbel. Bracteoles 3–5-nerved   4
4. Bracteoles translucent between pinnately veined nerves.   **2. B. odontites**
– Bracteoles opaque between nerves, nerves not pinnately veined.   **4. B. brevicaule**
5(2). Mericarps tuberculate or muricate between the ribs   6
– Mericarps smooth between the ribs   7
6. Desert plants, 5–15 cm. Bracteoles 4–5 mm. Inflorescences dichotomously corymbose.
    8. B. semicompositum
– Salt-marsh plants, usually 30–70 cm. Bracteoles 2–3 mm. Inflorescences dichotomous
above, monochasial below.   **7. B. tenuissimum**
7(5). Umbels 3–7(–8)-rayed; rays slender but not filiform; umbellets usually 5–7-flowered.
    5. B. gerardii
– Umbels 2–3(–4)-rayed; rays filiform; umbellets usually 2–4-flowered.   **6. B. boissieri**

Sect. BUPLEURUM. Sect. *Perfoliata* Godr. in Gren. et Godr., Fl. Fr. 1 : 717 (1848–1849). Leaves, at least the upper ones, perfoliate. Involucre 0. Annuals.

1. Bupleurum lancifolium Hornem., Hort. Hafn. 267 (1813). [Plate 592]
Annual, glabrous, 10–60 cm. Stems divaricately branched from base, striate. Basal leaves 5–15 × 1–4 cm., oblong-lanceolate to linear-lanceolate, acuminate, tapering at base, 5–9-nerved; cauline leaves perfoliate, ovate to ovate-oblong or lanceolate, with rounded base. Umbels terminal and axillary, pedunculate, (2–)3(–5)-rayed. Bracts 0. Bracteoles 5(–6), 0.5–1.5 × 0.3–1 cm., connate at base, patulous, ovate to orbicular, mucronate, 5–7-nerved, 3–4 times as long as the pedicellate flowers. Petals ovate, with truncate or emarginate inflexed apex. Styles spreading, shorter than the stylopodium. Fruiting pedicels thickened, much shorter than the fruit; fruit 2–5 mm., ovoid. Fruiting umbellets head-like. Mericarps dark brown, prominently ribbed, densely tuberculate in the furrows. Fl. March–June.

1. Fruits 3–5 mm., compact in each umbellet, not separating into mericarps. Plants caulescent with stems usually 30–60 cm.   var. **lancifolium**
– Fruits about 2 mm., loose; mericarps separating   2
2. Plants stemless or almost so.   var. **subacaule**
– Plants with stem 10–20 cm.   var. **heterophyllum**

Var. **lancifolium**. *B. subovatum* Link ex Spreng., Sp. Umb. 19 (1818) p.p. *B. protractum* Hoffmanns. et Link, Fl. Port. 2 : 387 (1834); Boiss., Fl. 2 : 836 (1872). Plant 30–60 cm. Upper leaves ovate to oblong. Bracteoles orbicular-ovate, about 1–1.5 cm.

Hab.: Fields; among winter crops. Acco Plain, Sharon Plain, Philistean Plain, Upper and Lower Galilee, Mt. Carmel, Esdraelon Plain, Samaria, Shefela, Judean Mts., Judean Desert, N. Negev, Dan Valley, Hula Plain, Upper Jordan Valley, Beit Shean Valley, Lower Jordan Valley, Golan, Gilead, Ammon, Moav. Very common.

Var. **heterophyllum** (Link) Maire in Jah. et Maire, Cat. Pl. Maroc (2): 530 (1932). *B. heterophyllum* Link, Enum. Hort. Berol. Alt. 1 : 262 (1821); Boiss., Fl. Suppl. 251 (1888). *B. protractum* Hoffmanns. et Link var. *heterophyllum* (Link) Boiss., Fl. 2 : 836 (1872). Plant 10–20 cm. Upper leaves 2–5 mm. broad, narrowly lanceolate-linear, sometimes grass-like. Bracteoles often 5–7 mm., ovate, abruptly acuminate.

Hab.: Fields and steppes. Coast of Carmel, Philistean Plain, Judean Mts., Judean Desert, N. and C. Negev, Dead Sea area, Gilead, Ammon, Moav. Locally fairly common.

Var. **subacaule** (Wolff) Zoh. (comb. et stat. nov.). *B. subovatum* Link ex Spreng. var. *heterophyllum* (Link) Wolff f. *subacaule* Wolff, in Pflznr. 43 (IV, 228): 49 (1910). Plant stemless or almost so; in other characters intermediate between var. *heterophyllum* and var. *lancifolium*.

Hab.: Steppes and batha. Judean Mts., Judean Desert, Negev, Lower Jordan Valley. Rare.

Area of species: Mediterranean and W. Irano-Turanian.

The two last-mentioned varieties differ from the typical form also in their smaller fruit which readily splits into mericarps at maturity (in var. *lancifolium* the two mericarps do not separate from one another), in the persistence of the whole fruiting umbel, and in their "wild" habitats (var. *lancifolium* is exclusively segetal).

Sect. GLUMACEA Boiss., Fl. 2: 835 (1872). Leaves linear or lanceolate. Bracteoles membranous, glume-shaped, ovate or elliptical-lanceolate, exceeding the flowers. Fruit smooth. Annuals.

2. Bupleurum odontites L., Sp. Pl. 237 (1753) excl. syn. Columnae et hab.; Boiss., Fl. 2: 839 (1872); Thell. in Hegi, Ill. Fl. Mitteleur. 5(2): 1100 (1926). [Plate 593]

Annual, glabrous, 10–40 cm. Stems erect, dichotomously branched almost from the base. Branches thin, finely grooved. Leaves 2–10 × 0.3–0.5 cm., linear-lanceolate, acuminate, (3–)5–7-nerved. Umbels terminal and axillary, pedunculate, with about 5 unequal rays. Bracts 5–6, shorter than the longer rays; bracts and bracteoles lanceolate, acute, cuspidate, usually 3-nerved, translucent between the pinnately veined nerves; lateral nerves very near the margin. Flowers unequally long-pedicelled. Petals broadly ovate to obovate, with inflexed 2-lobed apex. Fruits 1–1.5 mm., ovoid-ellipsoidal, included in the indurated, closed fruiting involucel; mericarps obscurely ribbed, smooth. Fl. March–April.

Var. **odontites**. Flowering umbels 3–7 cm.; umbellets loose.

Hab.: Fields and batha. Sharon Plain, Philistean Plain, Upper and Lower Galilee, Mt. Carmel, Esdraelon Plain, Samaria, Shefela, Judean Mts., Hula Plain, Gilead. Uncommon.

Var. **condensatum** Post, Fl. Syr. Pal. Sin. 341 (1883–1896). *B. fontanesii* Guss. var. *condensatum* (Post) Dinsmore in Post, l.c. ed. 2, 1: 510 (1932). Flowering umbels much shorter and more densely crowded.

Hab.: As above. Philistean Plain, Mt. Carmel, Esdraelon Plain. Rare.

Area of species: Mediterranean.

B. odontites has not been properly understood by the many botanists who have replaced this name by *B. fontanesii* Guss., Ind. Sem. Hort. R. Boccadifalci 1825: 3 (1825–1826) *nom. nud.*; Guss. ex Guss., Fl. Sic. Prodr. 1: 313 (1827). This is, however, unplausible, since *B. odontites* can readily be typified, especially because in the Linnaean Herbarium the name on both sheets, nos. 335/11 and 335/12, is given in Linnaeus's own hand-writing. Thellung, l.c. thus rightly retains the name *B. odontites*.

3. Bupleurum nodiflorum Sm. in Sibth. et Sm., Fl. Gr. Prodr. 1 : 177 (1806) et Fl. Gr. 3 : 54, t. 260 (1821); Boiss., Fl. 2 : 840 (1872). [Plate 594]

Annual, glabrous, 5–20 cm. Stems procumbent or ascending, di- or trichotomously branched from the base, angular or often with prominent ribs, grooved. Branches unequally long, divaricate. Leaves 2–7(–9) × 0.2–0.4(–1) cm., linear-lanceolate, acute, narrowly membranous-margined, 3–5-nerved. Umbels axillary along the branches and terminal, head-like, sessile or pedunculate; rays 5–12, unequal, most shorter than the bracts and some longer. Bracts 3–5, unequal, oblong-lanceolate, acute, mucronate, scarious-margined, very prominently 3-nerved. Bracteoles ovate-lanceolate, long-acu-minate, cuspidate, with 3 thick prominent nerves, middle nerve keeled; interspaces between nerves translucent. Flowers unequally pedicelled. Petals ovate, upper margin obscurely 3-lobed; middle lobe long, inflexed, divaricately 2-lobulate. Fruiting umbel-lets hidden in the indurated, closed, conical involucel. Fruit 1.5–2 mm., oblong, brown; mericarps prominently ribbed. Fl. March–May.

Hab.: Fields and batha throughout the Mediterranean territory. Sharon Plain, Philistean Plain, Upper and Lower Galilee, Mt. Carmel, Esdraelon Plain, Samaria, Judean Mts., Judean Desert, S. Negev, Dan Valley, Upper Jordan Valley, Beit Shean Valley, Golan, Gilead, Ammon, Moav. Common among winter crops.

Area : E. Mediterranean.

4. Bupleurum brevicaule Schlecht., Linnaea 17 : 124 (1843); Boiss., Fl. 2 : 840 (1872). *B. brevicaule* Schlecht. var. *trinervium* Opphr., Bull. Soc. Bot. Genève ser. 2, 22 : 346 (1931). [Plate 595]

Annual, glabrous, 15–30 cm. Stems procumbent to ascending, divaricately and di- or trichotomously branched from near the base. Branches somewhat angular and some-times slightly scabridulous at the angles. Leaves 3–6 × 0.3–0.5 cm., caducous, lanceolate to linear-lanceolate, acute, obscurely 5-nerved. Umbels terminal and axillary, peduncu-late or sessile, very unequally 2–5-rayed; rays becoming indurated and tightly con-tracted in fruit, forming a kind of spike. Bracts 5–7, shorter than or as long as the longer rays, 5-nerved. Bracteoles mostly 4, equal, lanceolate-acuminate, somewhat scarious-margined, 3–5-nerved, opaque between nerves, not pinnately veined, becoming leathery in fruit. Flowers unequally pedicelled. Petals with prominent red nerve, ovate, with slightly inflexed and obsoletely denticulate tip. Fruiting umbellets entirely en-closed in the involucel. Fruit 1.5–3 mm., ellipsoidal-oblong; mericarps prominently ribbed. Fl. March–May.

Hab.: Fields. Upper and Lower Galilee, Esdraelon Plain, Samaria, Golan, Gilead, Ammon. Rather rare.

Area : E. Mediterranean.

Sect. GRAMINEA Boiss., Fl. 2 : 835 (1872). Leaves linear or oblong-lanceolate. Bracteoles herbaceous, narrowly linear, not concealing the flowers.

5. Bupleurum gerardii All., Auct. Syn. Meth. Stirp. Hort. Taurin. 29 (1773; "*gerardi*") et Misc. Taur. 5 (Mélanges Phil.-Math. Soc. Turin): 81 (1774–1776); Boiss., Fl. 2 : 845 (1872) p.p. [Plate 596]

Annual, green, glabrous, (10–)20–50 cm. Stems erect, dichotomously or corymbosely branched from about the middle, slender, almost capillary, angular, furrowed. Leaves 3–10 × 0.3–0.5 cm., linear-lanceolate, acuminate, 3–5-nerved. Umbels terminal and axillary, long-peduncled, unequally 3–7(–8)-rayed. Bracts 3–5, unequal, much shorter than the longer rays, linear-subulate, cuspidate, 1–3-nerved. Bracteoles 5, the longest somewhat longer than to twice as long as umbellets, 1–3-nerved. Flowers short-pedicelled. Fruit 1.5–3 mm., shorter than to as long as pedicel, oblong-prismatic; mericarps prominently ribbed. Fl. March–July.

Hab.: Batha and maquis. Upper Galilee, Golan (very common), Gilead, Ammon, Edom. Rare.

Area: Mediterranean, S. W. Euro-Siberian and W. Irano-Turanian.

Erroneously recorded by Eig, Bull. Inst. Agr. Nat. Hist. 6 : 32 (1927) as *B. dichotomum* Boiss., Diagn. ser. 1, 10 : 28 (1849).

Var. *patens* Reichb., Ic. Bot. 2 : 56, t. 165, f. 296 (1824; "*B. gerardi* Jacq. var. *patens*")= *B. australe* Jord., Pugill. Pl. Nov. 72 (1852), seems to represent a very slight deviation from the typical form, displaying involucels a little longer than flowers.

6. Bupleurum boissieri Post ex Boiss., Fl. Suppl. 251 (1888) et Post, Journ. Linn. Soc. Lond. Bot. 24 : 426 (1888). [Plate 597]

Annual, slender, glabrous, up to 50 cm. Stems erect, subdichotomously branched from below. Branches very slender, ascending; branchlets filiform, more or less contracted. Lower leaves 4–10 × 0.3–0.8 cm., more or less spreading, linear-lanceolate, tapering towards base, acuminate, cuspidate, 5-nerved at base, 3-nerved above; upper leaves much shorter and narrower. Terminal umbels 2–3(–4)-rayed, axillary umbels mostly 1–2-rayed; rays up to 2.5 cm., very unequal, filiform, angular. Bracts 2–3, 4–6 mm., equal, very narrow to almost subulate, cuspidate, 3-nerved. Umbellets minute, 3–4(–6)-flowered. Bracteoles similar to bracts, but shorter, obsoletely 3-nerved. Pedicels longer than the flowers, sometimes as long. Petals with inflexed 2-toothed apex. Fruit (immature) about 2 mm., prismatic-cylindrical. Fl. July.

Hab.: Maquis; basalt soil. Golan. Rare.

Area: E. Mediterranean.

7. Bupleurum tenuissimum L., Sp. Pl. 238 (1753). [Plate 598]

Annual, slender, glaucescent, glabrous, (20–)30–70 cm. Stems erect to ascending, dichotomously branched from base and above, furrowed-angular. Leaves 1–5 × 0.2–0.3 cm., sparse, linear to linear-lanceolate, acuminate, 3(–5)-nerved. Umbels terminal and axillary, mostly of 2–3 unequal rays, rarely of 1 ray only. Bracts 1–3(–5), much shorter than the short rays, 1(–3)-nerved, linear-subulate. Bracteoles mostly 5, subulate, filiform, obscurely 3-nerved, as long as the 3–5(–8), very short-pedicelled flowers, or longer. Stylopodium depressed, discoid, broader than the styles. Petals minute, with narrow inflexed tip. Fruit 1.5–2 mm., ovoid-globular to ellipsoidal, densely covered with whitish granules along and between the ribs. Fl. June–August.

Subsp. **tenuissimum.** Ssp. *eutenuissimum* Wolff, in Pflznr. 43 (IV, 228): 102 (1910). *B. tenuissimum* L., l.c.; Boiss., Fl. 2: 841 (1872). *B. tenuissimum* L. var. *brevibracteatum* (Wolff) Dinsmore in Post, Fl. Syr. Pal. Sin. ed. 2, 1: 511 (1932). Rays of umbel unequal. Bracteoles about twice as long as the flowers.

Hab.: Salines and flooded places. Coast of Carmel, Sharon Plain, Philistean Plain, Hula Plain, Beit Shean Valley. Rare.

Subsp. **gracile** (M.B.) Wolff, l.c. 104. *Odontites gracilis* M.B. in Hoffm., Gen. Umb. ed. 2, 209 (1816) et Fl. Taur.-Cauc. 3: 198 (1819). *B. gracile* (M.B.) DC., Prodr. 4: 128 (1830) *nom. illegit.* non Urv., Mém. Soc. Linn. Paris 1: 286 (1822). *B. marschallianum* C.A. Mey., Verz. Pfl. Cauc. 123 (1831); Boiss., l.c. 842. Rays of umbel nearly equal. Bracteoles about equalling the flowers.

Hab.: As above. Acco Plain. Very rare.

Area of species: Euro-Siberian, Mediterranean and Irano-Turanian.

8. Bupleurum semicompositum L., Demonstr. Pl. Hort. Upsal. 12 (1753) et Amoen. Acad. 3: 405 (1756). *B. semicompositum* L. var. *glaucum* (Rob. et Cast. ex DC.) Paol. in Fiori et Paol., Fl. Anal. It. 2: 155 (1900). *B. glaucum* Rob. et Cast. ex DC. in Lam. et DC., Fl. Fr. ed. 3, 5: 515 (1815); Boiss., Fl. 2: 842 (1872). [Plate 599]

Dwarf annual, glaucous, glabrous, 5–15 cm. Stems dichotomously branched from base, angular. Leaves 1–6 × 0.1–0.3 cm., lanceolate-subulate or oblong-subulate, semi-amplexicaul, acute, 3–5-nerved. Umbels terminal and axillary, unequally 3–6-rayed. Bracts shorter than the longer rays, opaque, lanceolate, scabridulous, prominently 3-nerved. Bracteoles almost twice as long as the flowering umbellets, lanceolate to linear-lanceolate, aristate, 3-nerved, mostly scabridulous along nerves. Flowers unequally pedicelled. Stylopodium depressed, discoid, narrower than the styles. Petals yellowish or brownish-green with a narrow inflexed tip. Fruit 1–1.5 mm., ovoid-globular, blackish, densely white-granulate to -tuberculate; ribs obsolete. Fl. February–April.

Hab.: Steppes. Judean Desert, Negev, Lower Jordan Valley, Dead Sea area, Ammon, Moav. Uncommon.

Area: Mediterranean, W. Irano-Turanian and E. Saharo-Arabian.

26. APIUM L. emend. Benth.

Annual or perennial glabrous herbs. Leaves pinnately or ternately divided. Umbels terminal or axillary and opposite the leaves. Involucre and involucel 0 or fairly conspicuous. Flowers usually hermaphrodite. Calyx teeth obsolete. Petals white to greenish-white or reddish, mostly entire, sometimes with inflexed apex. Stylopodium short-conical; styles short. Fruit slightly compressed laterally, broadly ovoid or ellipsoidal to subglobular; carpophore undivided or somewhat 2-fid at the apex; commissure narrow; ribs of mericarp prominent, filiform; oil ducts 1 (–2–3) in each furrow, commissural ducts 2. Seeds mostly with a rounded back and plane inner face.

About 20 species, widespread mainly in aquatic and paludinal habitats.

Literature: H. Wolff, *Apium* L. emend., in: *Pflznr.* 90 (IV, 228): 26–58, 1927.

1. Cauline leaves ternately divided. Bracteoles 0.   **1. A. graveolens**
   – All leaves pinnately divided. Bracteoles 5 or more.   **2. A. nodiflorum**

1. Apium graveolens L., Sp. Pl. 264 (1753); Boiss., Fl. 2 : 856 (1872). [Plate 600]

Annual or biennial, glabrous, strongly aromatic, 30–100 cm. Roots fusiform. Stems erect or ascending, divaricately branched, often hollow, grooved-angular. Leaves often somewhat fleshy; basal leaves petiolate, 1-pinnatisect, segments 5, 1–3 cm., deltoid to rhombic, incised-dentate; cauline leaves short-petioled or sessile, ternately divided, segments rhombic to lanceolate. Umbels mostly axillary, short-peduncled or sessile; rays of umbel few to many, almost equal; rays of umbellets short. Involucre and involucel 0. Flowers 0.5 mm. Petals white or greenish-white, elliptical, subcordate at base. Styles much longer than the stylopodium. Fruit about 1.5 × 1.5–2 mm., shorter than the pedicel, broadly ovoid; mericarps semicircular in cross section, with 5 prominent ribs. Fl. mainly May–September.

Hab.: Swampy places, brooks and ditches. Acco Plain, Sharon Plain, Philistean Plain, Upper Galilee, Mt. Carmel, Esdraelon Plain, Samaria, Judean Mts., C. Negev, Upper Jordan Valley, Beit Shean Valley, Dead Sea area, Golan, Edom. Locally common.

Area: Pluriregional (temperate and tropical).

Leaves and roots edible; used in folk medicine as a diuretic, carminative, tonic, etc.

2. Apium nodiflorum (L.) Lag., Amen. Nat. Españ. 1, 2 : 101 (1821). *Helosciadium nodiflorum* (L.) Koch, Nov. Act. Acad. Leop.-Carol. 12, 1 : 126 (1824); Boiss., Fl. 2 : 856 (1872). *Sium nodiflorum* L., Sp. Pl. 251 (1753). [Plate 601]

Perennial, glabrous, 30–100 cm. Roots fusiform. Stems procumbent or ascending, hollow, furrowed, rooting at lower nodes. Leaves petiolate, 1-pinnatisect; segments 2–6 pairs, 1–4 cm., sessile with oblique base, lanceolate to ovate, serrate or crenate. Umbels opposite the leaves, sessile or short-peduncled; rays few, unequal, spreading or recurved. Bracts usually 0. Bracteoles about 5 or more, usually longer than the pedicels, lanceolate or oblong, membranous-margined, 3-nerved. Flowers 0.5–1 mm. Petals white, broadly ovate. Styles longer than the stylopodium, deflexed. Fruit 1.5–2 mm., ovoid-oblong, with 5 prominent and thick ribs. Fl. April–October.

Hab.: By brooks, ditches and ponds. Sharon Plain, Philistean Plain, Upper Galilee, Esdraelon Plain, Samaria, Shefela, Judean Mts., Dan Valley, Hula Plain, Upper and Lower Jordan Valley, Golan, Gilead, Edom. Locally common.

Area: Pluriregional (temperate and tropical).

27. TRACHYSPERMUM Link

Annual herbs, much branched. Leaves 2–4-pinnatisect into linear or filiform lobes, rarely leaves ternately divided with broader segments. Umbels usually many-rayed. Involucre and involucel usually present. Flowers hermaphrodite. Calyx teeth inconspicuous or 0. Petals white, ovate, 2-lobed, with inflexed, obtuse apex. Styles becoming spreading or recurved, somewhat longer than the conical stylopodium. Fruit laterally compressed, ovoid, hispid or covered with short or papillose hairs; carpophore divided to base; mericarps 5-angled; ribs prominent; oil ducts solitary in each furrow, commissural ducts 2. Seeds with rounded back and plane inner face.

About 20 species of E. India and Trop. Africa.

1. Trachyspermum ammi (L.) Sprague, Kew Bull. 1929 : 228 (1929). *Sison ammi* L., Sp. Pl. 252 (1753). *T. copticum* (L.) Link, Enum. Hort. Berol. Alt. 1 : 267 (1821). *Ammi copticum* L., Mant. 56 (1767); Boiss., Fl. 2 : 891 (1872). [Plate 602]

Annual, glabrous or minutely puberulent, 10–20(–90) cm. Stems much branched, furrowed-angular. Lower leaves long-petioled, 2–3-pinnatisect, lobes linear or filiform, 1–2.5 cm.; upper or all leaves ternately divided, with linear lobes. Umbels terminal and axillary, long-peduncled; rays 8–20, 1–2(–6) cm. Bracts 5 or less, very rarely 0, one half to one third as long as the rays, linear to linear-lanceolate. Bracteoles 3–6, shorter than the unequal pedicels. Petals 1 mm., hirsute at outer surface. Styles longer than the stylopodium, deflexed. Fruit 1.5–2 mm., slightly compressed laterally, ovoid, densely covered with granular grey papillae or hairs; ribs of mericarp prominent. Fl. May.

Hab.: Stony ground. Judean Mts. (Jerusalem; very rare, probably adventive).

Area: Known only as a cultivated plant, mainly in the Middle-Eastern countries.

Our (single!) specimen differs from typical *T. ammi* in its exclusively ternately divided leaves, its low habit (5–15 cm.) and its shorter pedicels.

Grown for its aromatic seeds and used in folk medicine.

28. AMMI L.

Annuals or biennials, much branched. Leaves 1–3-pinnatisect into filiform or lanceolate segments. Umbels terminal and axillary, pedunculate; rays numerous. Bracts numerous, mostly divided. Bracteoles numerous, shorter or longer than the pedicels, entire. Flowers hermaphrodite. Calyx teeth obsolete. Petals partly radiating, white, obovate, 2-lobed, with inflexed apex. Stylopodium depressed, shorter than the deflexed styles. Fruit laterally compressed, ovoid or oblong; carpophore entire or 2-parted; ribs of mericarp 5, filiform; oil ducts solitary in each furrow, commissural ducts 2. Seeds with convex back and concave inner face.

Some 10 species in the Mediterranean region, Trop. Africa and Macaronesia.

1. Ultimate lobes of all or at least of the lower leaves oblong or lanceolate, acutely serrulate. Fruiting rays divergent, forming an open umbel.   **1. A. majus**
－ Ultimate lobes of all the leaves linear or filiform, not serrulate. Fruiting rays con-
   vergent, forming a nest-like umbel.   **2. A. visnaga**

1. Ammi majus L., Sp. Pl. 243 (1753); Boiss., Fl. 2 : 891 (1872). [Plate 603]

Annual, glabrous, 30–70 cm. Stems erect, much branched especially above, stiff, furrowed. Leaves up to 10 cm. or more, green-glaucescent, ovate in outline; lower leaves long-petioled, ternately and pinnately divided, segments oblong to lanceolate, acutely serrulate; upper leaves less divided, segments cuneate or linear, serrulate or entire. Umbels long-peduncled; flowering umbels up to 10 cm. across, fruiting umbels open, with diffuse rays; rays elongating in fruit, not forming a nest-like structure. Bracts much shorter than the rays, 3–5-partite into linear or filiform segments. Bracteoles subulate. Pedicels much longer than the flowers and fruit. Petals not radiating. Styles longer than the short-conical stylopodium, divaricate. Fruit 1.5–2 mm., oblong or ovoid, smooth; ribs slender, prominent. Fl. (March–) June–August (–September).

Hab.: Roadsides and fields; heavy alluvial soil. Coastal Galilee, Acco Plain, Coast of Carmel, Sharon Plain, Philistean Plain, Upper and Lower Galilee, Esdraelon Plain, Mt. Gilboa, Samaria, Shefela, N. Negev, Dan Valley, Hula Plain, Upper Jordan Valley, Beit Shean Valley, Lower Jordan Valley, Dead Sea area, Golan, Gilead, Ammon. Locally very common.

Area: Mediterranean, with slight extensions into the adjacent W. Irano-Turanian and Euro-Siberian territories.

The seeds contain thymol and are used in folk medicine as a carminative and antispasmodic.

2. Ammi visnaga (L.) Lam., Fl. Fr. 3 : 462 (1778). [Plate 604]

Annual, glabrous, 50–80 cm. Stems erect, much branched, terete, furrowed, very leafy. Leaves ovate in outline; basal leaves 1-pinnatisect, deep green; cauline leaves 3-pinnatisect, ultimate lobes 1–3 × 0.05–0.1 cm., divaricate, linear or filiform, cuspidate, entire. Umbels mainly terminal, long-peduncled, open and flat in flower, 8–13 cm. across, contracted in fruit; rays thick, rigid, the outer ones 3–7 cm. Bracts as long as or longer than the rays, 3–5-partite into setaceous-filiform lobes, later deflexed. Umbellets many-flowered. Bracteoles entire, setaceous. Pedicels much longer than the flowers and fruits. Petals not radiating. Styles long, deflexed. Fruiting umbels closed, globular, nest-like, opening only after being moistened by rains. Fruit 1.5–2 mm., ovoid to obovoid-oblong, glabrous; ribs rather thick. Fl. April–August.

Var. **visnaga.** *A. visnaga* (L.) Lam., l.c.; Boiss., Fl. 2 : 892 (1872). *Daucus visnaga* L., Sp. Pl. 242 (1753). Umbels and umbellets longer than involucre and involucel respectively.

Hab.: Heavy, alluvial soils; field borders, fallow fields and also swamps. Acco Plain, Sharon Plain, Philistean Plain, Upper and Lower Galilee, Mt. Carmel, Esdraelon Plain, Shefela, Hula Plain, Upper Jordan Valley, Golan. Locally very common.

Var. **longibracteatum** Zoh.* Umbels and umbellets overtopped by involucre and involucel.

Hab.: Among rocks. Hula Plain. Very rare.

Area of species: Mediterranean, extending towards W. Irano-Turanian borderlands.

Seeds used medicinally as a principal source of khellin, a vasodilator of the coronary circulation; seeds diuretic and emmenagoguic; fruiting pedicels sold as toothpicks; the plant is used in Iraq as a source of red dye.

---

* See Appendix at end of this volume.

29. RIDOLFIA Moris

Annual herbs, branched, glabrous. Stems erect. Leaves 3–4-pinnatisect into filiform lobes. Umbels axillary and terminal, many-rayed. Involucre and involucel 0. Flowers hermaphrodite. Calyx teeth obsolete. Petals yellow, ovate, truncate-notched with inflexed apex. Stylopodium depressed, flattened into a broad disk; styles short, recurved. Fruit slightly compressed laterally, oblong-prismatic; carpophore 2-parted; mericarps with 5 filiform, almost obsolete ribs; oil ducts solitary in each furrow. Inner face of seed somewhat concave.

One species in the Mediterranean countries.

1. Ridolfia segetum (L.) Moris, Enum. Sem. Hort. Taur. 1841 : 43 (1841) et Fl. Sard. 2 : 212, t. 75 (1840–1843); Boiss., Fl. 2 : 858 (1872). *Anethum segetum* L., Mant. Alt. 219 (1771) p.p. quoad syn. et herb. Tourn. et syn. C. Bauh., excl. descr.; Thell. in Hegi, Ill. Fl. Mitteleur. 5(2) : 1161 (1926). [Plate 605]

Annual, glabrous, 0.3–0.8(–1.2) m. Stems erect, dichotomously branched above, furrowed. Lower leaves 20–30 cm., long-petioled, ovate in outline with broad sheathing base, 3-pinnatisect into crowded filiform lobes, the ultimate lobes 1 cm. or more; upper leaves sessile, with short sheaths and blades ternately dissected into long filiform lobes; the uppermost leaves sheath-like, undivided. Umbels long-peduncled; rays slender, 3–8 cm.; umbellets many-flowered. Pedicels unequal, the longer ones 3–4 times as long as the fruit. Fruit 1.5–2 mm., oblong to prismatic, glabrous. 2n = 22. Fl. April–June.

Hab. : Fields; heavy soils. Acco Plain, Sharon Plain, Philistean Plain, Upper Galilee, Mt. Carmel, Esdraelon Plain, Samaria, Judean Mts., N. Coastal Negev, Dan Valley, Hula Plain, Upper and Lower Jordan Valley, Golan, Gilead. Locally very common.

Area : Mediterranean, with slight extensions into adjacent S. Euro-Siberian borderlands.

The basionym of Linnaeus is retained here because Linnaeus's binomial is based on Tournefort's phrase-name and herbarium specimen. The identity of the latter with *R. segetum* has been confirmed by Gussone (fide Moris, l.c. et Thell., l.c.).

One of the most noxious weeds among winter crops.

Aromatic plant used as a substitute for fennel in pickles; also used as a source of green dye.

30. FALCARIA Fabr.

Biennial or perennial herbs with fusiform roots. Stems erect, spreadingly branched. Leaves ternately to pinnately dissected, with serrate or acutely dentate segments. Umbels terminal and axillary, diffuse, many-rayed. Bracts and bracteoles conspicuous, entire. Flowers hermaphrodite and staminate. Calyx teeth persistent, conspicuous. Petals white, obovate or obcordate, notched with broad inflexed apex. Stylopodium small, conical, on a dilated, obsoletely undulate disk; styles short, deflexed. Fruit laterally compressed, oblong-prismatic, with a narrow commissure; carpophore free, 2-parted;

ribs of mericarp 5, thick, the lateral ribs at margin; oil ducts 1(–3–4) in each furrow, commissural ducts 2(–8). Inner face of seed flattish.

Four species in Europe, the Mediterranean region, S.W. and C. Asia and W. Siberia.

1. Falcaria vulgaris Bernh., Syst. Verz. Erf. 176 (1800). *Sium falcaria* L., Sp. Pl. 252 (1753). *F. sioides* (Wibel) Aschers., Fl. Prov. Brandenb. 1 : 241 (1860) *nom. illegit. Drepanophyllum sioides* Wibel, Prim. Fl. Werthem. 196 (1799) *subs. illegit. F. rivini* Host, Fl. Austr. 1 : 381 (1827); Boiss., Fl. 2 : 892 (1872). [Plate 606]

Biennial or perennial, glaucescent, glabrous or slightly puberulent, 30–50 cm. Stems erect, divaricately branched from base, flexuous, terete, finely striate-grooved. Leaves somewhat leathery, acutely serrulate; basal leaves long-petioled, undivided or ternately divided; cauline leaves 1–3-ternately divided, ultimate segments 4–20 cm., 2–3-fid, lobes linear-lanceolate, often falcate; uppermost leaves with very reduced blades. Umbels long-peduncled, 5–15(–18)-rayed; rays 2–5 cm.; umbellets few-flowered. Bracts and bracteoles 4–8(–10), linear-subulate to filiform, deflexed in fruit. Flowers long-pedicelled. Calyx teeth triangular-subulate. Petals broadly obovate. Stylopodium depressed-conical; styles accrescent in fruit, divergent. Fruit 3–5 mm., shorter than the filiform pedicel, oblong-linear; carpophore splitting to base; mericarps 5-angled, with primary ribs only; oil ducts solitary in each furrow, commissural ducts 2. Fl. May–July.

Hab.: Fallow fields, along field borders and roadsides. Upper and Lower Galilee, Esdraelon Plain, Samaria, Judean Mts., Judean Desert, Upper and Lower Jordan Valley, Golan, Ammon, Edom. Frequent.

Area : Euro-Siberian, Mediterranean and Irano-Turanian.

31. SISON L.

Tall biennials or perennials with erect, branched, glabrous stems. Leaves long-petioled, 1-pinnatisect. Umbels terminal or axillary, unequally few-rayed. Involucre and involucel present. Flowers hermaphrodite. Calyx teeth obsolete. Petals white, orbicular, deeply notched with inflexed apex. Stylopodium short-conical, with entire margin; styles short, almost erect. Fruit somewhat compressed laterally, short-ovoid, with narrow commissure; carpophore 2-parted; mericarps with prominent filiform ribs; oil ducts solitary in each furrow, attaining half the length of the mericarp and almost club-shaped, commissural ducts 2. Inner face of seed plane.

Two species, one in Europe, the other in the E. Mediterranean countries.

1. Sison exaltatum Boiss., Diagn. ser. 1, 10 : 21 (1849) et Fl. 2 : 893 (1872). [Plate 607]

Biennial, tall, glabrous, 1–2 m. Roots thick, fusiform. Stems erect, grooved or angular, upper part sparingly branched, almost leafless, green. Lower leaves 20–25 × 3–6 cm., oblong to lanceolate in outline, blade 1-pinnatisect, segments 12–20, 1–3 cm., ovate-oblong, coarsely dentate or incised with mucronate teeth, undivided or unequally 2-fid; cauline leaves almost sessile, reduced, divided into linear segments.

Umbels long-peduncled, 5–7-rayed; rays 1–1.5 cm., unequal. Bracts and bracteoles 5–6, lanceolate. Styles about as long as the stylopodium. Fruit 1.5–2 mm., laterally compressed, broadly ovoid; oil ducts broad, red, occupying the entire furrow. Fl. July–August.

Hab.: Maquis. Upper Galilee. Very rare.

Area: E. Mediterranean.

32. BUNIUM L.

Annual or perennial herbs, rather glabrous. Roots bulbiferous. Leaves 2–3-pinnatisect. Umbels usually terminal, with or without involucre; umbellets with involucels of 5 or more bracteoles. Flowers hermaphrodite or polygamous. Calyx teeth 0 or minute. Petals white or reddish, obcordate, notched with inflexed apex. Stylopodium depressed or conical; styles longer than the stylopodium, divaricate or deflexed in fruit. Fruit laterally compressed, oblong, ovoid or prismatic, with 5 filiform, prominent ribs and 1–3 oil ducts in each furrow; carpophore 2-parted or rarely obsolete. Inner face of seed plane. Seedling with a single cotyledon.

About 40 species, mainly in the Mediterranean, C. European, S.W. Asian and C. Asian countries.

Literature: H. Wolff, *Bunium L.*, in: *Pflznr.* 90 (IV, 228): 186–212 (1927).

1. Oil ducts 2 or 3 in each furrow. Involucre 0 or of 1 bract. Pedicel usually shorter than the fruit. **3. B. pestalozzae**
- Oil ducts solitary in each furrow. Involucre of few to several bracts. Pedicel usually longer than the fruit   2
2. Fruiting pedicels stellately divaricate, thick. Styles somewhat longer than the stylopodium. **1. B. ferulaceum**
- Fruiting pedicels erect, slender. Styles 3 times as long as the stylopodium or longer. **2. B. elegans**

1. Bunium ferulaceum Sm. in Sibth. et Sm., Fl. Gr. Prodr. 1: 186 (1806). *Carum ferulaceum* (Sm.) Arcang., Comp. Fl. It. 273 (1882). *C. ferulaefolium* (Desf.) Boiss., Diagn. ser. 1, 10: 22 (1849) et Fl. 2: 886 (1872). *B. ferulaefolium* Desf., Ann. Mus. Nation. Hist. Nat. Paris 11: 275, t. 30 (1808). [Plate 608]

Perennial, glabrous, 30–60 cm. Stems erect or ascending, branched from base, corymbose above, subangular. Lower leaves broadly triangular in outline, 3-pinnatisect, segments long-petiolulate, ultimate lobes long, linear, acute; upper leaves broadly sheathed, with blade 3-sect into linear lobes. Umbels long-peduncled; rays 8–12, up to 5 cm.; umbellets usually 10–16-flowered. Bracts and bracteoles few, caducous, lanceolate. Flowers rather long-pedicelled. Petals scarcely or not at all radiating, white with brown middle nerve. Fruiting pedicels usually longer than the fruit, stellately spreading, thick, rigid. Styles somewhat longer than the depressed-conical stylopodium, deflexed. Fruit 5–6 mm., cylindrical-prismatic, somewhat incurved, prominently ribbed. Fl. March–May.

Hab.: Fields and batha. Philistean Plain, Shefela, Judean Mts. Rare.

Area: E. Mediterranean.

2. Bunium elegans (Fenzl) Freyn, Oesterr. Bot. Zeitschr. 42 : 83 (1892). *B. elegans* (Fenzl) Freyn et var. *typicum* Wolff, in Pflznr. 90 (IV, 228) : 189 (1927). *Carum elegans* Fenzl, Pugill. 16 (1842); Boiss., Fl. 2 : 883 (1872). [Plate 609]

Perennial herb, glabrous, 20–40 cm. Stems erect, dichotomously branched. Branches erect or spreading. Lower leaves 10–25 cm., long-petioled, ovate-triangular in outline, 2–3-pinnatisect, segments divided into divaricate, short, linear lobes; upper leaves divided into long, filiform lobes. Umbels long-peduncled, 5–12-rayed; rays almost equal, 2–5 cm.; umbellets many-flowered. Bracts and bracteoles few, linear-subulate. Pedicels unequal, filiform, not thickening in fruit. Petals up to 2 mm., white with dark nerve. Stylopodium 0.5 mm., depressed, one half to one fourth as long as the deflexed or spreading styles. Fruit about 4 mm., shorter than the pedicel, oblong-prismatic; mericarps with 5 prominent ribs. Fl. March–May.

Hab.: Among winter crops. Philistean Plain, Samaria, Judean Mts., Golan, Gilead, Ammon. Uncommon.

Area: W. Irano-Turanian and E. Mediterranean.

3. Bunium pestalozzae Boiss., Diagn. ser. 1, 10 : 24 (1849).

Perennial, glabrous, 10–60 cm. Stems sparsely dichotomous-branched from base, corymbose above, slender, flexuous, terete, striate. Lower leaves long-petioled, ovate in outline, 2-pinnatisect, ultimate segments long, broadly linear, acute; upper leaves 3–5-sect into narrowly linear segments, or reduced to inflated sheaths. Umbels long-peduncled, 4–6(–8)-rayed; rays somewhat unequal, the posterior ray 1–2 cm. Bracts 0 or 1–2, minute. Umbellets usually 10-flowered. Bracteoles 5–7, lanceolate, acute, white-margined. Styles somewhat longer than the depressed-conical stylopodium, deflexed. Fruiting pedicels shorter than the fruit, not thickening, angular. Fruit oblong-linear, glaucescent, with obsolete calyx teeth at apex; mericarps linear, somewhat incurved, with white filiform ribs; oil ducts 3 in each furrow. Fl. May–June.

Hab.: Steppes, rocks, fields on sandy soil. Golan (after Evenari, in Opphr. et Evenari, Bull. Soc. Bot. Genève ser. 2, 31 : 329, 1941). Very rare.

Area: E. Mediterranean.

33. PITURANTHOS Viv.

Perennial herbs to dwarf shrubs. Stems green-glaucous, almost leafless. Leaves mostly basal, undivided or subternately divided, with oblong-linear to filiform lobes; uppermost leaves usually reduced to sheaths. Umbels small, terminal or axillary. Bracts and bracteoles often caducous. Flowers hermaphrodite. Calyx teeth obsolete. Petals greenish-white, ovate or orbicular, slightly notched or entire, with a rather long inflexed point. Stylopodium conical or depressed-conical with undulate margin; styles short, deflexed. Fruit laterally compressed, ovoid or globular, hairy or setulose; carpophore 2-parted; ribs of mericarp 5, filiform, prominent; oil ducts solitary in each furrow, commissural ducts 2.

About 10 species in Trop. Africa and in adjacent deserts of N. Africa and W. Asia.

Literature: H. Wolff, *Pityranthus* Viv., in: *Pflznr.* 90 (IV, 228) : 97–105 (1927).

1. Stems flexuous. Fruit globular, 1.5 mm., short-hirtellous. Umbels 6–10-rayed. Bracts and bracteoles persistent. **1. P. tortuosus**
– Stems straight. Fruit oblong, 2–3 mm., long-hirsute. Umbels 3–4(–5)-rayed. Bracts and bracteoles caducous. **2. P. triradiatus**

1. Pituranthos tortuosus (Desf.) Benth. ex Aschers. et Schweinf., Mém. Inst. Eg. 2 : 80 (1887; *"Pityranthus"*); Dinsmore in Post, Fl. Syr. Pal. Sin. ed. 2, 1 : 517 (1932; *"tortuosa"*). *Bubon tortuosum* Desf., Fl. Atl. 1 : 257, t. 73 (1798). *Deverra tortuosa* (Desf.) DC., Prodr. 4 : 143 (1830); Boiss., Fl. 2 : 860 (1872). [Plate 610]

Shrubby perennial, aromatic, glabrous, 30–60 cm. Stems erect, dichotomously and somewhat divaricately branched, flexuous, striate-furrowed, bluish-green or whitish, leafless. Leaves caducous; basal leaves 5–10 cm., ovate or suborbicular in outline, 2-pinnatisect into stiff and divergent, oblong to linear-subulate, acute lobes; sheathing petiole short, broad, broadly scarious-margined; lower cauline leaves with broad sheaths and very short, ternatisect or -partite blades; upper leaves less divided, often reduced to sheaths with filiform-subulate apices. Umbels mainly terminal, long-peduncled; rays 6–10, 1–2 cm., almost equal. Bracts and bracteoles persistent, oblong or ovate, scarious-margined. Flowers semiclosed. Petals glabrous or slightly puberulent beneath along the green nerve. Styles much longer than the depressed stylopodium. Fruit 1.5 mm., usually shorter than the pedicel, ovoid to almost globular, hirtellous. Fl. April–May (–September).

Hab.: Deserts; mainly in depressions or wadis. Philistean Plain, Judean Desert, Negev, Dead Sea area, Arava Valley, Moav, Edom. Locally fairly common.

Area: E. Saharo-Arabian (Palestine to Libya).

Strongly aromatic; very much appreciated as a condiment.

2. Pituranthos triradiatus (Hochst. ex Boiss.) Aschers. et Schweinf., Mém. Inst. Eg. 2 : 80 (1887; *"Pityranthus"*). *Deverra triradiata* Hochst. ex Boiss., Fl. 2 : 861 (1872). [Plate 611]

Spartoid shrub, glaucous, glabrous, 30–80 cm. or more. Adult stems erect, sparingly and alternately branched, straight, striate-furrowed, leafless, ending in a loose panicle. Leaves soon vanishing; basal leaves in clusters, 4–5 cm., with scarious-margined sheath, blade 2- or 3-ternately divided, segments few, about 1 cm., linear, deeply grooved; lower cauline leaves pinnately divided into few linear lobes; upper cauline leaves reduced to linear-subulate blades 1–3 cm. long or more, borne on short and broad, scarious-margined sheaths. Umbels mainly axillary, short- and thick-peduncled, 3–4(–5)-rayed, appressed to stem. Bracts and bracteoles caducous, the latter ovate, hooded, with broad membranous margins. Flowers semiclosed. Petals pubescent beneath, with a broad green nerve and narrow membranous margin. Styles as long as the conical stylopodium or shorter. Fruit (2–)3 mm., ellipsoidal-oblong, long-hirsute on and between ribs; the outer fruits on pedicels as long as or longer than the fruit, the inner fruits almost sessile. Fl. June–November.

Hab.: In depressions and wadis of stony deserts. Negev, Arava Valley, Edom. Less common than the former species.

Area: E. Saharo-Arabian (Palestine to Egypt).

34. Pimpinella L.

Annual or perennial herbs, sometimes shrubby. Basal leaves often undivided or 1-pinnatisect with incised or dentate segments. Umbels mostly terminal, many-rayed. Bracts and bracteoles frequently 0, rarely 1 or 3–5. Flowers hermaphrodite and staminate. Calyx teeth mostly obsolete. Petals sometimes slightly radiating, mostly white, obcordate or obovate, notched with inflexed apex, often papillose or hairy outside. Stylopodium depressed or conical; styles mostly long, erect or deflexed. Fruit slightly compressed laterally, ovoid to almost globular, rounded to cordate at base, usually narrowed at commissure; carpophore 2-fid; mericarps with filiform, rather prominent or sometimes obsolete ribs; oil ducts (1–)2–3(–5–6) in each furrow. Seeds with convex back, inner face plane.

About 150 species, mainly in temperate zones of the Old World.

Literature: H. Wolff, *Pimpinella* L., in: *Pflznr.* 90 (IV, 228): 219–319, 1927.

1. Bracts and bracteoles more than 1. Low, much-branched biennials or perennials   2
 – Bracts and bracteoles or bracteoles only 0 or 1   3
2. Fruit covered with bristles.   **2. P. corymbosa**
 – Fruit covered with warts or papillae.   **3. P. olivieri**
3(1). Tall biennials or perennials (50–100 cm.). Rays of umbel very unequal, up to 7 cm., contracted in fruit. Lower leaves 10–20 cm., pinnatisect into large, serrate or pinnatifid or pinnatipartite segments (1 cm. broad or more).   **1. P. peregrina**
 – Annual, usually low plants. Rays of umbels and lower leaves not as above   4
4. Fruit 3–5 mm.   **4. P. anisum**
 – Fruit 1–2 mm.   5
5. Fruit with long, spreading, straight or curved bristles. Stylopodium elongated-conical in fruit. Stems usually patulous-hairy to villose.   **5. P. eriocarpa**
 – Fruit covered with short, appressed (rarely curved or erect) hairs. Stylopodium mammillary-conical in fruit.   **6. P. cretica**

1. Pimpinella peregrina L., Sp. Pl. 264 (1753); Boiss., Fl. 2 : 867 (1872). *P. peregrina* L. var. *pauciradiata* Evenari in Opphr. et Evenari, Bull. Soc. Bot. Genève ser. 2, 31 : 336 (1941). [Plate 612]

Biennial or perennial herb, tall, hairy or glabrous, 50–100 cm. Stems solitary, erect, branched above, furrowed-striate. Basal leaves more or less long-petioled, with a long sheath at base and an ovate-orbicular, undivided blade; lower cauline leaves oblong in outline, pinnatisect, segments 3–5 pairs, 1 cm. broad or more, cuneate or cordate-ovate, serrate or incised or pinnatifid, the terminal ones 3-sect or 3-lobed; upper leaves pinnatisect into linear-lanceolate and cuneate, sharply incised segments; uppermost leaves strongly reduced, finely dissected. Umbels long-peduncled, many-rayed; rays very unequal, puberulent, contracted in fruit, the longest ray 4–7 cm. Involucre and involucel 0. Pedicels hairy. Petals white, sparsely hairy beneath. Stylopodium long-conical; styles long, erect-spreading. Fruit 1.5–2 mm., broadly ovoid to pyriform, densely covered with spreading white hairs. Fl. March–July.

Hab.: Batha and maquis. Sharon Plain, Upper and Lower Galilee, Mt. Carmel, Judean Mts., Golan, Gilead, Ammon. Locally fairly common.

Area: N. Mediterranean, with extensions towards the adjacent W. Irano-Turanian and S.E. Euro-Siberian borderlands.

2. Pimpinella corymbosa Boiss., Ann. Sci. Nat. Bot. ser. 3, 1 : 131 (1844) et Fl. 2 : 869 (1872). *P. corymbosa* Boiss. var. *pauciradiata* Nab., Publ. Fac. Sci. Univ. Masaryk 35 : 122 (1923). [Plate 613]

Perennial, tomentellous-canescent, usually woody at base, 20–50 cm. Stems intricately branched from the leafy base, thick, rigid, furrowed. Branches corymbose, contracted. Basal leaves 10–15 cm., long-petioled, oblong in outline, 1-pinnatisect, segments obovate, cuneate, with oblong lobes or teeth; upper leaves short-petioled or sessile on sheaths, blades 2-pinnatisect into remote, short and narrow, linear-cuneate segments; uppermost leaves very reduced. Umbels long-peduncled, (3–4–)5–15(–20)-rayed. Bracts and bracteoles 3–5, short, linear-lanceolate, white-margined. Petals white with purple base, ovate to quadrangular, puberulent beneath or glabrous. Stylopodium much shorter than the styles, depressed. Fruit 1.5–2 mm., ovoid, bristly; ribs rather prominent. Fl. April–June.

Hab.: Semisteppe batha and abandoned fields. S. Judean Mts., C. Negev, Golan, Gilead, Ammon, Moav. Rather rare.

Area: W. Irano-Turanian.

Characteristic of semisteppe batha.

3. Pimpinella olivieri Boiss., Ann. Sci. Nat. Bot. ser. 3, 1 : 132 (1844) et Fl. 2 : 870 (1872). [Plate 614]

Perennial, tomentellous, usually woody at base, 30–50 cm. Stems dichotomously or trichotomously branched from base, furrowed. Basal leaves oblong-lanceolate in outline, 2–3-pinnatisect, ultimate segments lanceolate, lobulate or incised; upper leaves ovate-lanceolate, ultimate segments oblong-linear, cuneate or truncate at base, entire or slightly serrate; uppermost leaves strongly reduced. Umbels 5–8(–10)-rayed; rays unequal, the longest one 3–4 cm. Bracts and bracteoles 3–5, short, linear. Petals puberulent beneath. Stylopodium short-conical, much shorter than the deflexed styles. Fruit 2 mm., ovoid-subglobular, covered with papillae or tubercles; ribs prominent. Fl. May–June.

Hab.: Stony ground. Moav. Rare.

Area: W. Irano-Turanian.

The specific rank of *P. olivieri*, which differs from *P. corymbosa* only in a few characteristics (e.g. the tuberculate-papillose fruit, the narrower leaves and the smaller number of rays), is still questionable.

4. Pimpinella anisum L., Sp. Pl. 264 (1753); Boiss., Fl. 2 : 866 (1872). [Plate 615]

Annual, aromatic, pubescent or puberulent, 10–60 cm. Stems erect, branched from base, terete, furrowed. Basal leaves petiolate, orbicular-reniform, undivided, dentate or incised-lobed; lower cauline leaves ovate-orbicular in outline and 3-lobed or ternately divided into ovate or obovate segments cuneate at base and incised-dentate at margin; upper cauline leaves short-petioled or sessile on the narrow sheaths, mostly pinnatisect into linear-lanceolate lobes. Umbels 7–15-rayed; rays puberulent. Bracts

0 or 1, filiform. Bracteoles usually few or 0, caducous. Petals white, ciliate at margin and bristly beneath. Stylopodium somewhat depressed; styles short, erect-spreading. Fruit 3–5 mm., ovoid-oblong, appressed-bristly, often with prominent ribs. Inner face of seed concave. Fl. April–June.

Hab.: Cultivated and escaped. Judean Mts.

Area: Origin probably E. Mediterranean.

5. Pimpinella eriocarpa Banks et Sol. in Russ., Nat. Hist. Aleppo ed. 2, 2 : 249 (1794; *"eriocarpos"*); Boiss., Fl. 2 : 867 (1872). [Plate 616]

Dwarf annual, hairy, 6–20 cm. Stems erect, dichotomously much branched, somewhat angulate, furrowed, patulous-pubescent. Basal leaves about 1 cm. across, long-petioled, ovate-orbicular, usually undivided, crenate-dentate; the others divided into 3 ovate to oblong serrate segments; upper leaves sessile on scarious sheaths, usually 3–5-partite into oblong or lanceolate-linear, cuneate, dentate-serrate segments. Umbels small, pedunculate, (3–)4–10-rayed; rays 1–1.5 cm., sparingly patulous-bristly. Involucre and involucel 0. Petals minute, slightly radiating, white, bristly beneath. Stylopodium elongated, conical, much shorter than the persistent, recurved styles. Fruit 1–1.5 mm., oblong-pyriform, beset with long, patulous or somewhat incurved, white bristles; ribs prominent. Fl. March–April.

Hab.: Steppes and stony hills. Judean Desert, N. Negev, Lower Jordan Valley, Dead Sea area, Moav. Uncommon.

Area: W. Irano-Turanian.

Among our specimens there are some which could be referred to *P. schweinfurthii* Aschers., Verh. Bot. Ver. Prov. Brandenb. 21 : 67 (1880); the latter deviates only slightly from *P. eriocarpa*.

6. Pimpinella cretica Poir. in Lam., Encycl. Suppl. 1 : 684 (1811). [Plates 617, 617 a]

Annual, glabrous or short-puberulent, 10–80 cm. Stems branched from base, slender, terete, striate. Basal and lower cauline leaves long-petioled, orbicular to ovate-orbicular or somewhat cordate at base, undivided, crenate-dentate; middle and upper cauline leaves ternately divided into orbicular or obovate-cuneate, incised or crenulate segments; uppermost leaves 1–3 cm., sessile, with sheaths about 1 cm. long and blades undivided or 3-fid into lanceolate-cuneate or oblong to linear, entire or incised segments. Umbels terminal and axillary, rather short-peduncled, 4–20-rayed. Involucre and involucel 0. Petals not or only slightly radiating, white, deeply 2-fid, glabrous or hairy outside. Stylopodium mammillary-conical, much shorter than the divergent styles. Fruit 1–1.5 mm., ovoid or pyriform, covered with short, appressed or somewhat spreading, more or less curly, curved or straight hairs; ribs of mericarp 5, filiform, obsolete or conspicuous. Fl. March–April.

1. Petals glabrous.   var. **cretica**
– Petals hairy outside   2
2. Fruit usually covered with appressed straight hairs.   var. **lasiopetala**
– Fruit covered with more or less curved, not appressed hairs.   var. **petraea**

Var. **cretica**. *P. cretica* Poir., l.c.; Boiss., Fl. 2 : 866 (1872). [Plate 617]. Umbels many-rayed. Petals glabrous. Fruit with straight, short, appressed hairs, rarely with rather long, not appressed bristles (f. *deserti-judaici* Zoh. f. nov.).

Hab.: Stony places, roadsides and batha. Acco Plain, Sharon Plain, Philistean Plain, Upper and Lower Galilee, Mt. Carmel, Esdraelon Plain, Mt. Gilboa, Samaria, Judean Mts., Judean Desert, Hula Plain, Upper and Lower Jordan Valley, Golan, Gilead, Ammon. Very common.

Var. **lasiopetala** Feinbr., Repert. Sp. Nov. 29 : 134 (1931). As above, but with hairy petals.

Hab.: As above. Gilead, Ammon, Moav.

Var. **petraea** (Nab.) Zoh. (comb. et stat. nov.). *P. petraea* Nab., Publ. Fac. Sci. Univ. Masaryk 35 : 122, t. 13, f. 2 (1923). [Plate 617 a]. Stems puberulent, 50–80 cm. Lower leaves orbicular-cordate; cauline leaves ternately divided, with up to 2.5 cm. broad, petiolulate, ovate-orbicular terminal segment; uppermost leaves 3-partite or 3-fid into oblong-lanceolate, entire or lobed segments. Umbels 4–10-rayed. Petals slightly radiating, bristly. Fruit densely covered with patulous-ascending bristles.

Hab.: Wadis and among stones. Dead Sea area, Arava Valley, Moav. Rare.

Area of species: E. Mediterranean, with slight extensions into the territories of adjacent regions.

The above division of the fairly polymorphic and common *P. cretica* should be regarded tentative.

Var. *petraea* is a weak variety which could equally well be referred to both *P. cretica* and *P. puberula* (DC.) Boiss., Ann. Sci. Nat. Bot. ser. 3, 1 : 129 (1844); it is perhaps more justified to include it within *P. cretica*, because the latter has also representative varieties in the Sudanian territory of Palestine. The true *P. puberula*, despite the record by Dinsmore in Post, Fl. Syr. Pal. Sin. ed. 2, 1 : 519 (1932), has not been observed in Palestine.

P. moabitica Post, Bull. Herb. Boiss. 3 : 156 (1895), recorded from Moav and the Dead Sea area, is, according to our findings, doubtless identical with *P. cretica* Poir. var. *petraea* (Nab.) Zoh., collected in the same region. Post, l.c., has probably established his *P. moabitica* on specimens deprived of their almost orbicular and undivided lower leaves.

35. SCALIGERIA DC.

Perennial herbs, moderately branched. Stems striate, leafy mainly at base. Leaves pinnatisect or undivided. Umbels terminal and axillary. Involucre of few to many narrow bracts or 0. Bracteoles scarious or coloured. Flowers hermaphrodite and staminate. Calyx teeth obsolete. Petals white, obovate, notched with inflexed apex. Stylopodium conical or discoid, shorter than the deflexed styles. Fruit somewhat compressed laterally, ovoid, globular or cylindrical, with 5 prominent ribs; oil ducts solitary and broad, or 3–5 and filiform in each furrow, sometimes interrupted; commissural ducts 2. Inner face of seed plane to somewhat concave, 2-grooved.

About 22 species, mainly in the Middle East and in Middle Asia.

1. Rays of umbel (5–)6–12(–20). Root tuber fusiform.   1. S. napiformis
– Rays of umbel (2–)3(–4). Root tuber globular.   2. S. hermonis

1. Scaligeria napiformis (Willd. ex Spreng.) Grande, Bull. Ort. Bot. Nap. 4 : 188 (1913). *Bunium napiforme* Willd. ex Spreng., Sp. Umb. 95 (1818); Greuter in Greuter et Rech. f., Boissiera 13 : 94 (1967). *S. cretica* (Urv.) Boiss., Diagn. ser. 1, 10 : 52 (1849) *nom. illegit.* et Fl. 2 : 875 (1872). *B. creticum* Mill., Gard. Dict. ed. 8, no. 2 (1768). *B. creticum* Urv., Mém. Soc. Linn. Paris 1 : 287 (1822) *nom. illegit.* [Plate 618]

Perennial, glabrous, 30–60 cm. Roots thick, fusiform. Stems dichotomously branched, grooved. Leaves mainly basal, long-petioled, triangular in outline, somewhat ternately 2–3-pinnatisect into petiolulate, ovate-cuneate, often 3–5-lobed or -dentate segments; cauline leaves of few linear or lanceolate lobes, borne on broadly scarious-margined sheaths; the uppermost leaves very much reduced. Umbels long-peduncled, (5–)6–12(–20)-rayed; rays mostly equal, 2–6 cm. Involucre 0. Bracteoles 1–4, linear-subulate. Stylopodium elongated-conical. Fruit about 1.5 mm., much shorter than the pedicel, ovoid to globular; ribs or mericarp thickened above. Fl. April–May.

Hab.: Batha, maquis and rocks; mostly in shade. Upper and Lower Galilee, Mt. Carmel, Samaria, Judean Mts., Hula Plain. Locally fairly common.

Area: E. Mediterranean.

2. Scaligeria hermonis Post in Post et Autran, Bull. Herb. Boiss. 1 : 399 (1893); Post, Fl. Syr. Pal. Sin., Add. 14 (1883–1896) et ed. 2, 1 : 522 (1932). [Plate 619]

Tall perennial, glabrous, 0.6–1.2 m., with tuberous and fibrous roots. Stems branched dichotomously, mainly above, grooved, almost leafless. Basal leaves caducous, long-petioled, with broad sheath at base and 2-pinnatisect blade; segments petiolulate, ovate to oblong, incised, pinnatisect or pinnatipartite into oblong-cuneate lobulate lobes; cauline leaves reduced to sheaths terminating in 1–3 pinnatisect segments, ultimate lobes long, linear, 1–2 mm. broad; uppermost leaves strongly reduced. Umbels long-peduncled, (2–)3(–4)-rayed; rays equal, 3–6 cm., filiform. Bracts 1–2, linear-lanceolate. Bracteoles (3–)4–8. Stylopodium depressed-conical, much shorter than the caducous styles. Fruit 2 mm., as long as or shorter than the pedicel, globular-ellipsoidal; ribs of mericarp filiform, fairly prominent. Fl. April–May.

Hab.: Among shady rocks and in oak forests. Upper and Lower Galilee, Esdraelon Plain, Mt. Gilboa, Golan, Gilead. Uncommon.

Area: E. Mediterranean.

36. BERULA Koch

Perennial aquatic herbs, glabrous. Stems erect, leafy. Leaves mostly (1–)3–4-pinnatisect, with coarsely dentate segments. Umbels terminal and axillary. Involucre and involucel present. Flowers hermaphrodite and staminate. Calyx teeth conspicuous. Petals white or yellowish, obcordate to orbicular with narrowed base, notched and inflexed at apex. Stylopodium short-conical; styles many times as long as the stylopodium, erect, becoming deflexed. Fruit laterally compressed, usually ovoid; carpophore undivided; ribs of mericarp more or less prominent; oil ducts 3 or more in each furrow. Seeds 5-angled or orbicular in cross section, inner face almost plane.

Three species in the N. temperate regions.

1. Berula erecta (Huds.) Coville, Contr. U.S. Nat. Herb. 4 : 115 (1893). *Sium erectum* Huds., Fl. Angl. 103 (1762). *B. angustifolia* (L.) Mert. et Koch in Röhling, Deutschl. Fl. ed. 3, 2 : 433 (1826); Boiss., Fl. 2 : 889 (1872). *S. angustifolium* L., Sp. Pl. ed. 2, 1672 (1763). [Plate 620]

Perennial, glabrous, 30–60(–100) cm. Stems stoloniferous, erect or decumbent, abundantly branched, hollow, stout, furrowed. Basal leaves submerged, long-petioled, 3–4-pinnatisect with segments mostly opposite, sessile, ovate-oblong, incised and serrate; cauline leaves 7–25 cm., 1-pinnatisect, segments 5–14 pairs, 1.5–6 cm., sessile, oblong-lanceolate to ovate-cuneate, acute to acuminate, irregularly serrate to lobed. Umbels opposite the leaves, pedunculate, many-rayed; rays 2–5 cm. Bracts 5 or more, 1–2 cm., deflexed, leaf-like, lanceolate, sometimes 3-fid. Bracteoles about 4–6 mm., deflexed. Flowers 1–2 mm., shorter than the pedicels. Petals white. Fruit about 1.5 mm., shorter than the pedicel, ovoid to globular; ribs filiform. Fl. June–September.

Hab.: Swamps and ditches. Hula Plain, Upper Jordan Valley, Ammon. Rare.
Area: Mainly W. and C. Euro-Siberian and N. Mediterranean.

37. CRITHMUM L.

Perennial maritime herbs, rhizomatous, woody at base. Stems much branched. Leaves succulent, 1–2-pinnatisect or ternately divided. Umbels terminal or axillary, many-rayed. Involucre and involucel present. Flowers hermaphrodite. Calyx teeth very short or obsolete. Petals minute, yellow or yellowish-green, entire with inflexed apex. Stylopodium short-conical; styles very short. Fruit slightly compressed laterally or dorsally, ovoid-oblong to ellipsoidal; carpophore filiform, 2-parted; mericarps with 5 prominent, acute primary ribs; furrows shallow and broad; oil ducts several in each furrow; pericarp thick, spongy, separating from the endocarp which is adnate to the semi-terete seed. Seeds with convex dorsal and plane ventral face.

One species in the Atlantic, Mediterranean, Macaronesian and Black Sea coastal areas.

1. Crithmum maritimum L., Sp. Pl. 246 (1753); Boiss., Fl. 2 : 977 (1872). [Plate 621]

Perennial shrubby herb, glabrous, 30–60 cm. Rootstock thick, elongated, terete. Stems dichotomously branched from base, solid, grooved. Leaves fleshy, ternately 1–2-pinnatisect, segments 1–7 × 0.3–2 cm., linear-lanceolate or oblong, acute, short-acuminate, entire, tapering at base; upper leaves strongly reduced, subsessile, ternately divided. Umbels rather large, long- and thick-peduncled, (8–)10–20(–30)-rayed; rays 2–6 cm., grooved. Bracts and bracteoles fleshy, deflexed, linear to ovate-lanceolate, acute, narrowly membranous-margined. Flowers 1.5–2 mm. across. Stylopodium short-conical, about as long as or longer than the styles. Fruit 5–6 mm., ovoid-oblong to ellipsoidal, corky, green to purplish. 2n = 22. Fl. May–September.

Hab.: Cliffs and rocks along the sea shore. Coastal Galilee, Acco Plain, Sharon Plain, Philistean Plain. Uncommon.

Area: Mediterranean and W. and S. Euro-Siberian.

Leaves eaten as a salad and pickled in vinegar.

38. Oenanthe L.

Perennial or biennial herbs, aquatic or paludinous, glabrous. Stems hollow. Leaves mostly 1–3-pinnatisect. Umbels (in ours) terminal and axillary, few- or several-rayed. Involucre 0 or of few or several bracts. Bracteoles many. Flowers hermaphrodite and staminate. Calyx teeth usually persistent, lanceolate, acute. Petals often radiating, white or pinkish, obovate, notched with inflexed apex. Stylopodium slightly convex to conical; styles long. Fruit terete, oblong, ovoid, top-shaped or globular, crowned with the persistent, mostly erect styles; carpophore 0; pericarp corky; mericarps separating late or not at all; ribs of mericarp 5, broad, obtuse, the lateral ribs broader than the dorsal; interspaces sometimes elevated and rib-shaped; oil ducts solitary in each furrow, commissural ducts 2. Inner face of seed plane.

About 40 species, mainly in temperate regions of the Old World.

1. Umbellets all pedunculate   2
– Central umbellet sessile, fertile, the others pedunculate, sterile.   **4. O. prolifera**
2. Fruit obconical, much shorter than the styles. Fruiting umbels mostly 3-rayed; fruiting umbellets globular.   **1. O. fistulosa**
– Fruit cylindrical, somewhat longer than or as long as the styles. Fruiting umbels 5–10- or more-rayed; fruiting umbellets semiglobular   3
3. Segments of lower leaves ovate, those of upper ones linear.   **2. O. pimpinelloides**
– Segments of lower and upper leaves all linear.   **3. O. silaifolia**

1. Oenanthe fistulosa L., Sp. Pl. 254 (1753); Boiss., Fl. 2 : 955 (1872). [Plate 622]

Perennial aquatic, glabrous, 40–80 cm. Roots with fusiform to ovoid tubers. Stems erect, hollow, furrowed, stoloniferous at base and constricted at nodes. Leaves all of the same shape, long-petioled, the lower ones 2–3-pinnatisect, the upper 1–2-pinnatisect; ultimate lobes short and rather crowded, oblong to linear or filiform in submerged leaves, obtuse and mucronulate. Terminal umbels with thick peduncles, (2–)3(–5)-rayed, rays 1–2 cm., thick and hollow, with fertile flowers; staminate umbels lateral, on longer and thinner peduncles, overtopping the fertile ones, 4–6-rayed. Bracts 0 or 1–2. Bracteoles several, narrowly membranous-margined. Petals radiating. Fruiting umbellets 1–1.3 cm. across, globular. Fruit 3–4 mm., top-shaped, shorter than the divergent, persistent and somewhat spiny styles and crowned with the triangular-acuminate calyx teeth. Fl. April–May.

Hab.: Swamps and river banks. Sharon Plain, Hula Plain. Rare.

Area: W. Euro-Siberian and Mediterranean.

Toxic.

2. Oenanthe pimpinelloides L., Sp. Pl. 255 (1753); Boiss., Fl. 2 : 958 (1872) [incl. *O. angulosa* Griseb., Spicil. Fl. Rumel. 1 : 354 (1843)]. [Plate 623]

Perennial swamp plant, glabrous, 60–80 cm. Roots fibrous, thin, each ending in an ovoid or globular tuber 0.4–1 cm. across. Stems erect, branched above, solid, thin, strongly furrowed-angulate. Basal leaves few, often submerged, 1-pinnatisect with segments cut into linear lobes; lower cauline leaves triangular-ovate in outline, 2–3-pinnatisect with segments cut into ovate-cuneate, crenate, incised or pinnatifid ultimate lobes; ultimate lobes of intermediate leaves oblong-linear; upper leaves undivided or cut into a few long, linear, entire lobes. Fertile umbels terminal, long-peduncled, (4–)5–10-rayed, rays somewhat thickened in fruit; staminate umbels on slenderer peduncles, overtopping the fertile ones. Involucre sometimes of linear-subulate bracts. Bracteoles many, deflexed, subulate or filiform. Petals radiating. Fruiting umbellets 5–7 mm., compact, head-like with flat top. Fruit about 4 mm., cylindrical, borne on a thickened pedicel cup-shape above, ripe fruit with the conspicuous calyx teeth and the somewhat divergent long styles, and with a callose dentate basal ring. Fl. April–May.

Hab.: Swamps and heavy soil. Sharon Plain, Hula Plain, Gilead. Rare.

Area: S. Euro-Siberian and Mediterranean.

3. Oenanthe silaifolia M.B., Fl. Taur.-Cauc. 3 : 232 (1819) p.p. quoad descr. et syn. [*O. peucedanifolia* Sm., Engl. Bot. 5, t. 348 (1796)]; Thell. in Hegi, Ill. Fl. Mitteleur. 5(2): 1258 (1926). *O. media* Griseb., Spicil. Fl. Rumel. 1 : 352 (1843); Boiss., Fl. 2 : 958 (1872). [Plate 624]

Perennial swamp herb, glabrous, 40–80 cm., with thickened, fusiform, obovoid or oblong tubers. Stems erect, sparsely branched above, hollow, angular, furrowed. Leaves all of similar shape, 1–4-pinnatisect, with ultimate lobes 1–3 cm., linear; lobes of the upper leaves longer. Fertile umbels long-peduncled, 6–12-rayed, rays 2–4 cm., thickened in fruit; staminate umbels on slender peduncles, overtopping the fertile ones. Bracts 0 or 1. Umbellets head-like, many-flowered, very compact, about 1 cm. thick, convex. Bracteoles numerous, lanceolate-subulate, appressed. Petals radiating. Fruit 2–3(–4) mm., longer than the pedicel, angular, cylindrical to top-shaped, crowned with the minute calyx teeth and the rigid erect styles. Fl. April–June.

Hab.: Swamps. Esdraelon Plain, Samaria, Hula Plain, Golan. Uncommon.

Area: N. Mediterranean, with extensions into the W. Euro-Siberian territories.

We accept Thellung's view (l.c.) that there is no objection to keeping the name *O. silaifolia* on the basis of the original description and Smith's synonym, in spite of Simon's contending (in Rouy, Rev. Bot. Syst. 1 : 69, 70, 1903 — fide Thell., l.c.) that the original herbarium sheet contains elements of two different species.

4. Oenanthe prolifera L., Sp. Pl. 254 (1753); Boiss., Fl. 2 : 959 (1872). [Plate 625]

Perennial, somewhat shrubby, glabrous, 50–80 cm., with fibrous, cylindrical or almost club-shaped roots. Stems erect, branched above, thick, furrowed. Leaves all of the same shape, very broadly sheathed, 2–3-pinnatisect; ultimate lobes ovate-cuneate, deeply incised or crenately dentate. Peduncles long, thickening in fruit. Umbels 3–8 in an umbel-like whorl; staminate umbels 1 or more beneath the whorl of fertile umbels; all umbels with few or many bracts and bracteoles; peripheral umbellets of fertile umbels 5–7, staminate or abortive, borne on flattened, (fasciated) woody rays irregularly split at apex, the central umbellet single, large, sessile, fertile, many-flowered.

Petals radiating. Style short, persistent. Fruiting umbellets very compact, hemispherical, convex above. Fruit 3–5 mm., sessile, obovoid or top-shaped to pyriform, prominently and obtusely ribbed; calyx teeth inconspicuous. Fl. February–May.

Hab.: Swamps. Acco Plain, Sharon Plain, Philistean Plain, Upper Galilee, Esdraelon Plain, Hula Plain, Upper Jordan Valley, Golan. Locally fairly common.

Area: E. Mediterranean.

Visiani (Fl. Dalm. 3 : 38, 1850–1852) and some other authors believe that this species should be synonymized with *O. crocata* L., Sp. Pl. 254 (1753), and regarded as a teratological form of the latter. This seems to me an unbased assumption. First, *O. crocata* differs markedly from *O. prolifera* not only in the structure of the whole umbellar system but also in the fruit form, the styles, the mericarpal ribs, etc. Secondly, I have been observing the species for 40 years in various parts of Palestine and have found it genetically constant; nor could I anywhere discover a form which could be looked upon as its "normal original form". Indeed, *O. prolifera* is strictly an E. Mediterranean species; thus the localities recorded for this species by Linnaeus from Apulia and Sicily are no doubt erroneous, as no authors dealing with the floras of Sicily and Apulia record this species (or form). This is why Boissier insisted on retaining the name *O. prolifera* for the E. Mediterranean species, and there is no reason to abolish this binomial.

39. FOENICULUM Mill.

Perennial herbs, sometimes woody at base, rarely annuals. Leaves 2–4-pinnatisect into long, mostly filiform lobes. Umbels terminal and axillary, long-peduncled, many-rayed. Involucre and involucel usually 0. Flowers usually hermaphrodite. Calyx teeth obsolete. Petals yellow, ovate, shallowly notched with inflexed apex. Stylopodium short-conical; styles short, recurved. Fruit ovoid-oblong; carpophore 2-parted; mericarps with 5 prominent ribs, the marginal ribs slightly broader; oil ducts large, 1 in each furrow, commissural ducts 2–4. Inner face of seed plane to concave.

About 5 species, mainly Mediterranean, some cultivated.

1. Foeniculum vulgare Mill., Gard. Dict. ed. 8, no. 1 (1768); Hill, Brit. Herb. 414 (1756) *nom. inval. F. officinale* All., Fl. Ped. 2 : 25 (1785); Boiss., Fl. 2 : 975 (1872). [Plate 626]

Perennial herb, green-glaucous, 0.7–1.5 (–2) m. Roots fusiform. Stems erect, mostly solid, terete, finely grooved. Leaves up to 60 cm., ovate-triangular in outline, 3–4-pinnatisect; lower leaves withering before flowering, long-petioled; upper leaves sessile, sheaths 1–5 cm. long; ultimate lobes of all leaves linear-filiform or linear, mucronate at apex, often remote, divaricate; blade of uppermost leaves very reduced or 0. Umbels 6–25-rayed; rays unequal. Flowers small. Styles very short. Fruit 4–6 × 2–3 mm., brownish or greyish-yellow; mericarps 5-angled or semiorbicular in cross section; ribs prominent, obtusely carinate. Fl. July–November.

Hab.: Wadi banks, batha and stony hillsides. Acco Plain, Sharon Plain, Philistean Plain, Upper and Lower Galilee, Mt. Carmel, Esdraelon Plain, Mt. Gilboa, Samaria, Shefela, Judean Mts., N. Negev, Hula Plain, Upper Jordan Valley, Beit Shean Valley, Lower Jordan Valley, Dead Sea area, Moav, Edom. Common.

Area: Mediterranean and Irano-Turanian (elsewhere introduced).

In Palestine this species is rather uniform in its habit. It is always perennial and reaches a height of 2 m. The number of rays in the umbels vary in a single individual from 6 to 25, so there is no room for f. *pauciradiatum* (*F. officinale* All. f. "*pauciradiata*" Nab., Publ. Fac. Sci. Univ. Masaryk 35 : 127, 1923).

F. vulgare is a leading plant in the summer aspect of some hemicryptophytic batha communities. The cultivated fennel also belongs to this species.

Widely used as a substitute for dill in flavouring and conserving pickles; the green stems are eaten by villagers; also known as an officinal plant ("oleum et fructus foeniculi").

The records of *F. piperitum* (Bernard. da Ucria) Sweet, Hort. Brit. 187 (1826) from Palestine seem to be erroneous.

Trib. PEUCEDANEAE. Flowers and commissural face of seeds as in the preceding tribe. Fruit compressed dorsally; lateral ribs of mericarp usually much broader than the dorsal ones, often forming wings. Seeds half-elliptical in cross section.

40. ANETHUM L.

Annual herbs with erect branched stems, aromatic. Leaves 2–4-pinnatisect with linear or filiform ultimate lobes. Umbels usually long-peduncled; rays few to many, equal. Involucre 0 or of 1–2 bracts. Involucel present or 0. Flowers usually hermaphrodite. Calyx teeth obsolete. Petals yellow, almost orbicular, notched with inflexed apex. Stylopodium depressed-conical; styles shorter. Fruit dorsally compressed, lenticular; carpophore filiform, 2-parted to base; ribs 5, filiform, the 3 dorsal ribs acutely keeled, the 2 lateral ribs confluent with the dilated, wing-like margin; oil ducts solitary, occupying the entire furrow, commissural ducts 2. Seeds half-elliptical in cross section.

Three species, from the Mediterranean countries to India.

1. All leaves with filiform lobes. Involucel 0. Umbels 15–30-rayed.   **1. A. graveolens**
– Leaves, at least the upper ones, dissected into linear lobes. Involucel with 5 linear bracteoles. Umbels 7–10-rayed.   **2. A. chryseum**

1. Anethum graveolens L., Sp. Pl. 263 (1753); Boiss., Fl. 2 : 1026 (1872). [Plate 627]

Annual, strongly aromatic, somewhat glaucous, glabrous, 30–60 cm. Stems erect, branched above, furrowed. Leaves 10–30 cm., ovate to oblong in outline, 3–4-pinnatisect; lower leaves petiolate, upper leaves borne on membranous-margined sheaths; lobes filiform, ending in a short bristle. Umbels 15–30-rayed; rays 3–7 cm., almost equal. Involucre and involucel 0. Styles short, erect at anthesis, later deflexed. Fruit 3–6 mm., elliptical, rarely orbicular; ribs prominent, the marginal ribs winged. Fl. April–June.

Hab.: Cultivated and escaped. Philistean Plain, Shefela, W. and N. Negev.
Area: Origin probably in S.W. Asia.

Leaves used for flavouring, seeds for pickling; also known in folk medicine.

2. Anethum chryseum Boiss. et Heldr. ex Boiss., Diagn. ser. 1, 10 : 32 (1849) et Fl. 2 : 1026 (1872).

Annual or biennial, 0.6–1.9 m. Stems corymbosely branched above, striate, glabrous. Lower leaves 2–3-pinnatisect, ultimate lobes linear, acute; upper leaves ternately pinnatisect, segments 1–2 cm., linear; all leaves scabridulous. Umbels 7–10-rayed; rays 1–4 cm. Involucre 0 or of 1–2 bracts. Bracteoles 5, shorter than the pedicels, linear. Fruit (immature) ellipsoidal, prominently ribbed. Fl. May–July.

Hab.: In cultivated and abandoned fields. Acco Plain. Very rare.

Area : E. Mediterranean.

41. CAPNOPHYLLUM Gaertn.

Glabrous annuals with erect, slightly branched stems. Leaves 2–4-pinnatisect. Umbels usually opposite the leaves, few-rayed. Involucre and involucel present or 0. Calyx teeth small, triangular-lanceolate. Petals white, ovate-oblong, slightly notched with inflexed apex. Stylopodium subconical. Fruit somewhat compressed dorsally, ovoid-oblong to ellipsoidal, thick-margined, crowned with calyx teeth and short divergent styles, hardly separating into mericarps; carpophore 2-parted; mericarps with thick prominent ribs; dorsal ribs acute, lateral ribs thick, corky, all transversely wrinkled-scabrid; oil ducts almost obsolete, solitary under the ribs. Inner face of seed almost plane.

Some 3 or 4 species in the Canary Islands and the Mediterranean and S. African regions.

1. Capnophyllum peregrinum (L.) Lag., Amen. Nat. Esp. 1, 2 : 93 (1821); Lange in Willk. et Lange, Prodr. Fl. Hisp. 3 : 33 (1874). *Tordylium peregrinum* L., Mant. 55 (1767). *Krubera peregrina* (L.) Hoffm., Gen. Umb. 104, 168, t. 1 B, f. 14 (1814); "*K. peregrina* (L.) Boiss.", Boiss., Fl. 2 : 1027 (1872). [Plate 628]

Glabrous annual, 15–50. Stems dichotomously branched, solid, rigid, somewhat flexuous, angular-furrowed. Leaves 10–20 cm., ovate-oblong in outline; lower leaves long-petioled with broad-sheathed base, 3-pinnatisect, ultimate lobes 2–5 mm., crowded, oblong-linear, obtuse and mucronulate, entire or 2–3 fid. Peduncles unequal in length, thick. Umbels terminal and axillary, opposite the leaves; rays 2–5, short, thick and rigid. Bracts few or 0, caducous, linear-subulate. Bracteoles several, persistent, lanceolate, as long as or longer than the thick and rigid pedicels. Fruit 5–7 × 3 mm., ovoid-oblong to ellipsoidal; mericarps strongly ribbed, rugose, hardly separating at maturity. Fl. March–June.

Hab.: Among winter crops (obligatory weed); heavy alluvial soils. Sharon Plain, Philistean Plain, Upper and Lower Galilee, Mt. Carmel, Esdraelon Plain, Mt. Gilboa, Samaria, Shefela, Hula Plain, Upper Jordan Valley, Golan, Gilead. Not rare.

Area : Mediterranean.

42. FERULA L.

Perennial herbs. Leaves often very large, mostly finely 2–5-pinnately or -ternately dissected, usually with narrow lobes. Flowering branches corymbose, terminating in opposite or whorled compound umbels; central umbel of whorl often sessile or short-peduncled. Involucre and involucel 0 or of few, often caducous bracts. Flowers of the central umbel hermaphrodite, fertile, those of the lateral ones mostly staminate. Calyx teeth mostly obsolete. Petals yellow, whitish- or yellowish-green, oblong or ovate, entire with inflexed apex. Stylopodium depressed-conical with lobed margin. Fruit large, dorsally compressed, flat, ovate or elliptical; carpophore 2-parted; ribs of mericarp 5, the 3 dorsal ribs filiform, the lateral ones confluent with the mostly inflated wing-like margin of the mericarp; oil ducts superficial, solitary or 2–4 or numerous in each furrow, sometimes obscure. Seeds plane on either face.

About 130 species mainly in C. and S.W. Asia.

Literature: E. P. Korovin, *Generis Ferula (Tourn.) L. Monographia Illustrata*, Acad. Sci. UzRSS, Taschkent, 1947.

1. Fruit 0.8–1 cm. across. Leaves 4-pinnatisect; lobes filiform or narrowly linear, usually 1.5–5 cm. long; sheaths of leaves very inflated. Umbels 20–40-rayed. Mediterranean plants up to 1.5(–2) m. tall.   **5. F. communis**
 – Fruit and / or leaves not as above   2
2. Oil ducts between dorsal ribs of mericarp solitary, broad   3
 – Oil ducts between dorsal ribs 2 or more, filiform   6
3. Low plants (20–40 cm.). Stems almost leafless, branching from lower part into many successive whorls of umbelliferous branches. Leaves scabrous-bristly, all radical or basal, withering before anthesis. Fruit linear-elliptical, 1–1.2 × 0.3–0.5 cm.
                                                                         1. F. biverticillata
 – Plants not as above   4
4. Leaves and stems grey-velvety with dense grey papillose hairs. Plants of E. Transjordan.   **4. F. blanchei**
 – Leaves and stems green or glaucous, glabrous or sparingly scabridulous   5
5. Fruit 7–9 × 3–4 mm. Ultimate lobes of lower leaves oblong, usually 1–2(–5) mm.; sheaths of leaves (2–)5–6(–7) × 1.5–2 cm. Umbels (3–5–)6–10-rayed. Desert plants.
                                                                                  3. F. daninii
 – Fruit 1–1.2 × 0.5–0.6 cm. Ultimate lobes of lower leaves linear to filiform, usually 0.5–2 cm.; sheaths of leaves (8–)9–12(–15) × 5–6 cm. Umbels 10–30-rayed. Non-desert plants.   **2. F. samariae**
6(2). Fruits 6–7 × 3–4 mm.; visible dorsal ribs of mericarp often 4 (one of the lateral ribs at some distance from the margin and not confluent with it), transversely wrinkled. Umbels 4–6(–9)-rayed. Stems slender, about 5–7 mm. thick. Tall desert plants.
                                                                               8. F. negevensis
 – Fruit larger; visible dorsal ribs 3, not transversely wrinkled. Umbels usually many-rayed. Stems 1–2 cm. thick   7
7. Mediterranean plants. Stems up to 2 m. tall or more and 2 cm. thick. Leaves up to 80 cm.; ultimate lobes of leaves oblong, 2–4 × 1.5–2 mm.; sheaths not inflated but appressed to stem. Fruit bluish when ripe, elliptical.   **6. F. tingitana**
 – Desert plants. Stems (40–)80–100 cm. Segments of leaves di- or trichotomously

branched; lobes linear, arcuate, 2–5 mm. long, callose at apex. Fruit yellowish-green when ripe, elliptical to suborbicular. **7. F. sinaica**

Sect. PEUCEDANOIDES Boiss., Fl. 2 : 983 (1872). Subgen. *Peucedanoides* (Boiss.) Korovin, Ferula Monogr. 9 (1947). Oil ducts usually solitary in the furrows.

1. Ferula biverticillata Thiéb., Bull. Soc. Bot. Fr. 82 : 190 (1935). [Plate 629]

Perennial, 20–40 cm. Roots thick, fusiform. Stems fibrous at base, erect, striate, divaricately branched from below the middle into several branches each with 2–4 whorls of inflorescences. Leaves up to 35 cm. (incl. the long petioles), falling before anthesis, mainly confined to the lower part of stem, ovate in outline, 3–4-pinnatisect, densely or sparingly scabrous-bristly, segments ovate or oblong in outline, 2–3-pinnatipartite, ultimate lobes short, oblong or linear, mucronate; upper leaves reduced to short acuminate sheaths, not inflated, appressed to stem. Inflorescences verticillately or corymbosely branched; fertile umbels 4–14-rayed. Involucre 0 or of few bracts. Involucel 0. Petals yellow. Stylopodium depressed-conical, much shorter than the deflexed styles. Fruit 1–1.2 × 0.3–0.5 cm., as long as or somewhat longer than the pedicel, linear-elliptical; mature mericarps somewhat curved; the 3 dorsal ribs prominent, thick, the lateral ribs at the very narrowly winged margin; oil ducts solitary in each furrow, commissural ducts 4. Fl. April–July. Fr. September.

Hab.: Fields; alluvial and loess soil, and stony ground. Sharon Plain, Philistean Plain, Mt. Carmel, Esdraelon Plain, Mt. Gilboa, C. Negev. Rare.

Area: E. Mediterranean.

2. Ferula samariae Zoh. et P. H. Davis, Kew Bull. 1947 : 91 (1947). [Plate 630]

Perennial, glabrous, 1–1.5(–2) m. Roots vertical, thick. Stems single, up to about 1 cm. thick, fibrous at base, erect, subverticillately branched above, grooved, green. Branches up to 20 cm. long, 2–3 mm. thick. Lower leaves up to 50 cm., flaccid, withering after flowering, broadly ovate in outline, 4-pinnatisect with ultimate lobes 0.5–1.5 cm. long, divaricate, glabrous or very sparsely scabrous; upper leaves reduced to membranous, stiff, very inflated, ovate-oblong, yellowish sheaths (8–)9–12(–15) × 5–6 cm., terminating in a few segments cut into long linear-filiform lobes. Inflorescences of verticillate branches, each ending with a short-peduncled or sessile 10–30-rayed fertile central umbel and 2 or more long-peduncled staminate lateral umbels; rays of fertile umbel 2–4 cm., elongating in fruit. Involucre obsolete. Bracteoles minute, triangular or triangular-lanceolate. Calyx teeth very short, triangular. Petals yellow. Fruit 1–1.2 × 0.5–0.6 cm., longer than the pedicel, elliptical; dorsal ribs thick, lateral ribs marginal, margin thick and dilated, 1 mm. broad or more, wing-like; oil ducts solitary in each furrow, commissural ducts 2. Fl. March–April.

Hab.: Hard limestone cliffs. Mt. Gilboa, Samaria (endemic). Rather rare.

Area: E. Mediterranean.

3. Ferula daninii Zoh.* [Plate 631]

Perennial, green, glabrous or very sparingly papillose, 30–80 cm. Stems single, erect,

---

* See Appendix at end of this volume.

sparsely branched from about the middle, slender, striate, turning brown. Lower leaves 20–40 cm., petiolate with appressed sheaths, mostly ternately divided into 3-pinnatisect oblong segments, terminal segments 1–3(–5) cm., ovate-oblong in outline, ultimate lobes 1–3-fid (rarely entire), with revolute margins, glabrous or sparingly scabrous; cauline leaves with inflated sheaths (2–)5–6(–7) × 1.5–2 cm. and less divided blades, ultimate lobes 0.3–1.2 cm., linear; uppermost leaves reduced to sheaths and to a few segments. Inflorescences of verticillate or opposite branches bearing a subsessile central fertile umbel and long-peduncled fertile or sterile lateral umbels; rays (3–5–)6–10, 3–10 cm. Involucre of 2 or more subulate bracts. Bracteoles 1 or more. Petals yellow. Fruiting pedicels about as long as the fruit. Fruit 7–9 × 3–5 mm., elliptical, whitish, crowned with obsolete calyx teeth, depressed-conical stylopodium and deflexed styles much longer than the stylopodium; mericarps with prominent dorsal ribs and pellucid margins about one third as broad as the rest of the mericarp; oil ducts solitary, occupying the entire furrow, commissural ducts 2. Fl. April–May. Fr. May–June.

Hab.: Steppes; rocky and marly ground. C. Negev (endemic). Rather rare.

Area: N. Irano-Turanian.

4. Ferula blanchei Boiss., Fl. 2 : 987 (1872). [Plate 632]

Perennial, grey-velvety, 30–50 cm. Roots very thick. Stems thick, about 1 cm., fibrous at base, erect, verticillately branched above, finely striate. Leaves crowded mainly at base of stems, grey-velvety with white papillose hairs; lower leaves triangular-ovate in outline, subternately divided into 2–3-pinnatisect segments, ultimate segments ovate-oblong, cut into 2–3-fid lobes; cauline leaves with short, not inflated sheaths 2–3 × 1–1.5 cm. and blades 5–12 cm., 2-pinnatisect into oblong-ovate, obtuse lobes; uppermost leaves reduced to sheaths. Inflorescences of several corymbose or verticillate branches each ending with a sessile or pedunculate 7–16-rayed fertile central umbel and 2 or more long-peduncled mostly staminate lateral umbels. Involucre 0. Involucel of 1 or more caducous, subulate bracteoles. Petals yellow, hairy. Fruiting pedicels much longer than the fruit. Fruit about 1.2 cm., almost orbicular; mericarps with a margin half as broad as the seed-bearing part; dorsal ribs prominent, close to one another, marginal ribs distant; oil ducts solitary in each furrow, commissural ducts 4. Fl. spring.

Hab.: Stony deserts. Ammon, Moav. Very rare.

Area: W. Irano-Turanian (Palestine, Syria, Iraq).

This species is reportedly identical with *F. orbicularis* Post et Beauv. ex Zoh., Palest. Journ. Bot. Jerusalem ser., 2 : 171 (1941).

Sect. FERULA. Sect. *Euferula* Boiss., Fl. 2 : 983 (1872). Subgen. *Euferula* (Boiss.) Korovin, Ferula Monogr. 9 (1947). Oil ducts usually 2–3 (or more) in each furrow.

5. Ferula communis L., Sp. Pl. 246 (1753); Boiss., Fl. 2 : 991 (1872). [Plate 633]

Tall perennial, 1–2 m. Stems single, 2–3 cm. thick, corymbosely or verticillately branched above, hollow, terete, striate. Lower leaves 30–60 cm., long-petioled, green, triangular-ovate in outline, with many 3–4-pinnatisect segments, ultimate lobes usually 1.5–5 cm., very rarely 0.5–1 cm., linear-filiform; upper leaves smaller, with membranous, inflated, broad, oblong sheaths and blades reduced to a few segments only; uppermost leaves without blades. Inflorescences of several branches subtended by 2 caducous, oblong bracts 2–3 cm. long, each branch terminating with a subsessile or short-peduncled, usually 20–40-rayed, fertile central umbel and 2 or more long-peduncled staminate lateral umbels; rays of fertile umbel 3–10 cm. Involucre and involucel 0. Petals yellow. Fruiting pedicels about as long as the fruit. Fruit (1–)1.2–2 × 0.8–1 cm., obovate or elliptical, rarely ovate-orbicular, brown; dorsal ribs of mericarp filiform, prominent, lateral ribs contiguous with the margin; margin 2 mm. broad or more, wing-like; oil ducts 3 (2 or 1) in each furrow, commissural ducts 2–6. Fl. March–May. Fr. June.

Hab.: Semisteppe bathas; stony, calcareous ground. Sharon Plain, Philistean Plain, Upper and Lower Galilee, Mt. Gilboa, Samaria, Shefela, Judean Mts., Judean Desert, N. Negev, Hula Plain, Upper Jordan Valley, Beit Shean Valley, Lower Jordan Valley, Golan, Gilead, Ammon, Moav, Edom. Fairly common.

Area: Mediterranean.

The local specimens of this species can scarcely be divided into clear-cut varieties, so that there is no room for maintaining var. *rigidula* Post, Fl. Syr. Pal. Sin. 359 (1883–1896). Seeds used in folk medicine as a remedy for kidney stones.

6. Ferula tingitana L., Sp. Pl. 247 (1753); Boiss., Fl. 2 : 992 (1872). [Plate 634]

Tall perennial, 2–3 m. Roots fusiform. Stems single, thick, up to 2 cm. in diam., fibrous at base, paniculately corymbose above, furrowed, green and turning brown. Lower leaves up to 80 cm. or more, long-petioled, glaucous-green, triangular-ovate in outline, blade 3–4-pinnatisect, segments oblong, ultimate lobes short, 2–4 × 1.5–2 mm., oblong, obtuse, mucronulate, scabridulous, with slightly revolute margin; upper leaves reduced to a narrow (not inflated) sheath up to 1.5 cm. long, ending in a short 3-pinnatisect blade. Inflorescences of many branches, terminal and axillary, subtended by caducous, membranous, oblong bracts; umbels mostly 8–15-rayed; rays 3–6 cm., elongating in fruit; central umbel short-peduncled, fertile; lateral umbels long-peduncled, staminate. Involucre and involucel 0. Petals yellow. Fruiting pedicel about as long as the fruit. Fruit 0.8–1.2 × 0.5–0.7 cm., elliptical, bluish at maturity; dorsal ribs of mericarp 3, filiform, prominent, lateral near margin; wings one fourth as broad as the seed-bearing part; oil ducts 3 in each furrow, commissural ducts 4. Fl. May. Fr. June.

Hab.: Batha; among rocks. Upper and Lower Galilee, Mt. Carmel, Esdraelon Plain, Samaria, Shefela, Upper and Lower Jordan Valley. Less common than the former species.

Area: S. Mediterranean.

Contains ammoniacum (gum ammoniac) used industrially in porcelain cements; formerly medicinal.

7. Ferula sinaica Boiss., Diagn. ser. 1, 10 : 40 (1849) et Fl. 2 : 987 (1872). [Plates 635, 636]

Perennial, glaucescent, (40–)80–100 cm. Roots fusiform. Stems 1–1.5 cm., thick, corymbosely branching above, terete, finely striate, brownish. Lower leaves 15–20 cm., triangular-ovate in outline, ternately divided into 3–4-pinnatisect segments; primary and secondary rhachis somewhat flattened; ultimate lobes di- or trichotomously branched, lobules 0.3–1 × 0.05–0.2 cm., arcuate, linear, with revolute margin and acute callose apex; upper leaves with membranous, oblong, longitudinally grooved sheaths 4–6(–8) × 1.3 cm., blade 8–12 cm. long and segments less dissected than in lower leaves. Inflorescences of many branches, each ending with a short- or long-peduncled 7–12-rayed fertile central umbel and 2 or more long-peduncled, staminate, lateral umbels; branches subtended by 2 bracts. Involucre 0. Involucel minute. Petals yellow. Styles long, deflexed. Fruit 0.8–1.2 × 0.6–0.8 cm., somewhat longer than the pedicel, elliptical to suborbicular; ribs rather prominent, marginal ribs extended into wings much narrower than the rest of the mericarp; oil ducts 2–3 in each furrow, commissural ducts 4. Fl. March–May.

Var. **sinaica**. *F. sinaica* Boiss., l.c. [Plate 635]. Fruit obovate to suborbicular. Central umbel rather long-peduncled.
    Hab.: Deserts; sandy ground. Edom. Rare.

Var. **eigii** Zoh.* [Plate 636]. Fruit elliptical. Central umbel very short-peduncled.
    Hab.: Deserts; gravelly or rocky ground. Ammon. Rare.
    Area of species: W. Irano-Turanian.

8. Ferula negevensis Zoh.* [Plate 637]

Perennial, 1–2 m. or more. Roots thick, fusiform. Stems single, slender, 5–7 mm. thick, fibrous at base, branched above, finely striate. Lower leaves 10–25 cm., ovate-oblong in outline, 3–4-pinnatisect, ultimate segments ovate-oblong, 1–3-pinnatipartite, lobes simple or 2–4-fid, 2–4 mm., linear, oblong or obovate, obtuse, scabridulous or papillose; upper leaves very much reduced to an inflated, coriaceous sheath 2–4 (–6) × 2 cm. and a blade of a few segments 1–2 cm. long. Inflorescences forked repeatedly; branches ending with 1–3 superposed fertile umbels and accompanied by a long-peduncled staminate lateral umbel; rays of fertile umbel 4–6 (–9). Petals yellow. Fruit about 6–7 × 3–4 mm., as long as or somewhat longer than the pedicel, broadly elliptical; mericarps with 4 visible dorsal ribs, the fifth concealed by the winged margin, ribs transversely wrinkled; wings not equally broad at both margins; oil ducts 2–3 in each furrow. Fl. April–May.
    Hab.: Steppes. C. Negev. Rare.
    Area: W. Irano-Turanian.

43. FERULAGO Koch

Perennial herbs, mostly tall, sparingly branched, glabrous. Leaves 2–3-pinnatisect. Inflorescences much branched, bearing whorled or opposite, long-peduncled umbels; central umbel fertile, lateral umbels staminate. Involucre and involucel present. Flowers hermaphrodite and staminate in different umbels. Calyx teeth present. Petals yellow, suborbicular or ovate, almost entire with inflexed apex. Fruit dorsally compressed,

---

* See Appendix at end of this volume.

oblong to ellipsoidal; carpophore deeply 2-parted; ribs of mericarp prominent, the 3 dorsal ones thick, sometimes wing-like, the lateral ribs confluent with the thick or winged margin of the mericarp; oil ducts numerous, the dorsal ones covered by the ribs, the commissural ducts superficial. Seeds fairly flat, shallowly concave on inner face.

About 50 species, mainly in S.W. Asia.

1. Ferulago syriaca Boiss., Diagn. ser. 1, 10 : 38 (1849); Boiss., Fl. 2 : 1002 (1872). [Plate 638]

Perennial, glaucescent, glabrous, 1–1.5 m. Stems corymbosely branched above, terete, finely striate. Lower leaves 20–40 cm., ovate-oblong in outline, ternately 2–3-pinnatisect, divisions long-petiolulate, the ultimate lobes linear or oblong, acute, mucronate, scabrid, 0.6–1 cm., with revolute margin and prominent nerve; upper leaves few, less divided. Umbels 4–12-rayed; rays 3–8 cm.; staminate umbels lateral, beneath the central fertile one. Bracts and bracteoles 3–7 mm., ovate-triangular. Calyx teeth minute, triangular. Stylopodium much shorter than the styles, depressed-conical. Fruiting pedicels about as long as the fruit. Fruit 0.8–1 × 0.5–0.6 cm., broadly ellipsoidal; mericarps with thick projecting ribs, the lateral ribs not much broader than the dorsal ones. Fl. May–June.

Hab.: Batha and maquis. Upper Galilee, Mt. Carmel, Judean Mts. Uncommon.

Area : E. Mediterranean.

44. PEUCEDANUM L.

Predominantly tall perennial herbs. Leaves 2–4-ternatisect or -pinnatisect. Inflorescences divaricately branched, umbels many, with few to several rays. Involucre or involucel or both present. Flowers hermaphrodite and staminate. Calyx teeth sometimes obsolete. Petals white, yellowish-green, yellow or reddish, broadly ovate or obovate, often notched with inflexed apex. Stylopodium broadly conical, surrounded by the margin of the calyx. Fruit dorsally compressed, flat, often notched at base or also at apex; carpophore filiform, 2-parted; mericarps with 3 dorsal approximate ribs and 2 remote lateral ribs contiguous with the winged margin; oil ducts 1(–2–3) in each furrow, commissural ducts 2–6. Seeds flat.

About 120 species, mainly in Eurasia.

1. Peucedanum spreitzenhoferi Dingl., Flora 66 : 210 (1883); Boiss., Fl. Suppl. 267 (1888). *P. junceum* (Boiss.) Mout., Fl. Djeb. Druze 161, t. 14, f. 3 (1953) non Humb. et Bonpl. ex Schult. in Roem. et Schult., Syst. Veg. 6 : 572 (1820). *Johrenia juncea* Boiss., Diagn. ser. 1, 10 : 33 (1849) et Fl. 2 : 1013 (1872). [Plate 639]

Perennial, almost leafless, green, glabrous, 1–2 m. Roots fusiform. Stems erect, divaricately branched from the middle, slender, striate. Lower leaves caducous, 20–30 cm., ovate-oblong in outline, 2–3-pinnatisect into long-petiolulate, oblong-lanceolate divisions; ultimate segments pinnatipartite or pinnatisect into oblong, mucronate, serrate or incised lobes; upper leaves reduced to ovate-lanceolate sheaths with or without a few segments. Umbels many, axillary and terminal, the latter long-peduncled;

rays 3–8, 1–5 cm., very slender. Involucre 0, rarely of 1 bract. Bracteoles 1–5, minute, lanceolate, broadly scarious-margined. Petals minute, yellow. Fruit 3–7 mm., obovate, broadly elliptical to orbicular, glabrous; winged margins about half as broad as the fruit-bearing part; ribs filiform; oil ducts solitary in each furrow, filiform. Fl. May–September.

Hab.: Waste places, roadsides and devastated batha. Sharon Plain, Upper Galilee, Esdraelon Plain, Mt. Gilboa, Samaria, Judean Mts., C. Negev, Hula Plain, Edom. Fairly common.

Area: E. Mediterranean.

45. Tordylium L.

Annual or biennial herbs, branched, pubescent. Stems leafy. Leaves 1–3-pinnatisect. Umbels (in ours) unequally few-rayed. Bracts few of 0. Bracteoles several. Flowers hermaphrodite and staminate. Calyx teeth triangular, sometimes irregularly elongated. Petals white, obovate, cuneate or clawed; the outer petal larger, often deeply 2-parted into one large and one minute lobe. Stylopodium conical, with undulate margin; styles deflexed. Fruits mostly of two kinds, i.e. some with flattened (dorsally compressed) mericarps and some with urceolate (single) mericarps, the flattened ones with broad, inflated, wrinkled or tuberculate margin; rarely mericarps all alike; carpophore 2-parted; dorsal ribs of mericarp equidistant, filiform, lateral ones confluent with the margin; oil ducts 1–3 in each furrow, rarely numerous, filiform, commissural ducts 2–10. Seeds flat.

About 6 species, mainly in the Mediterranean and Middle-Eastern countries.

1. Bracteoles erect, oblanceolate-spatulate, much longer than the umbellets. Flowers small. Petals slightly radiating. Fruit densely hairy, margin strongly wrinkled.
   2. T. syriacum
— Bracteoles reflexed, linear to subulate, shorter than the umbellets. Flowers rather large. Petals strongly radiating. Fruit not as above. **1. T. aegyptiacum**

1. Tordylium aegyptiacum (L.) Lam., Tabl. Encycl. 2: t. 193 (1792) et 336 (1819). [Plates 640, 641]

Annual, patulous-hirsute or papillose, 30–60 cm. Stems erect, dichotomously branched from near the base, terete, sulcate. Leaves (5–)10–20 cm., appressed- to patulous-pubescent, ovate-oblong in outline; the lower leaves long-petioled, 1-pinnatisect into ovate-oblong, deeply incised or partite segments, lobes simple or 3–4-lobuled; cauline leaves 2(–3)-pinnatisect with ultimate segments pinnatipartite into oblong, incised or lobulate, acute lobes; uppermost leaves largely reduced, with short, broad sheaths and small, 1-pinnatisect blades. Umbels many, long-peduncled, unequally (6–)7–15-rayed; the longest rays 5–10 cm., scabrous or papillose. Bracts and bracteoles linear to subulate, the former sometimes 2-fid, the latter shorter than the umbellets. Flowers rather large. Petals strongly radiating, the outer petal deeply 2-parted. Fruiting umbels with connivent rays. Outer fruits (0.4–)0.5–1 cm., orbicular- to elliptical-discoid, glabrous or tuberculate or papillose, somewhat notched at base and apex, with margin almost as broad as the seed-bearing part; inner part of margin pellucid, outer part inflated, white, sometimes bullate; ribs filiform; oil ducts solitary in each furrow, the 3 dorsal ones approximate, the lateral ones marginal, commissural ducts 2, approximate, parallel; inner fruits (2–)3–5 mm., urceolate. Fl. March–May.

Var. **aegyptiacum**. *T. aegyptiacum* (L.) Lam., l.c.; Boiss., Fl. 2 : 1030 (1872). *T. aegyptiacum* (L.) Lam. var. *laevis* Zoh., Palest. Journ. Bot. Jerusalem ser., 2 : 172 (1941) et var. *glabrum* Evenari in Opphr. et Evenari, Bull. Soc. Bot. Genève ser. 2, 31 : 338 (1941). *Hasselquistia aegyptiaca* L., Cent. Pl. 1 : 9 (1775) excl. syn. et Amoen. Acad. 4 : 270 (1759). [Plate 640]. Leaves 10–20 cm., appressed-puberulent. Umbels 7–15-rayed; the longest rays up to 10 cm. Outer fruits 0.8–1 cm., orbicular-discoid; inner fruits 3–5 mm., urceolate.

Hab.: Cultivated and fallow fields and waste places; heavy and light soils. Acco Plain, Coast of Carmel, Sharon Plain, Philistean Plain, Upper and Lower Galilee, Mt. Carmel, Esdraelon Plain, Mt. Gilboa, Samaria, Shefela, Judean Mts., Judean Desert, N. Negev, Hula Plain, Upper and Lower Jordan Valley, Golan, Gilead, Ammon. Common.

Area: E. Mediterranean and W. Irano-Turanian.

Var. **palaestinum** (Zoh.) Zoh. (comb. et stat. nov.). *T. palaestinum* Zoh., l.c. 171, ff. 24–26. [Plate 641]. Leaves 5–15 cm., patulous- to appressed-pubescent. Umbels 6–12-rayed; the longest rays up to 7 cm. Outer fruits 4–6 mm., almost orbicular-discoid to broadly elliptical-discoid; inner fruits 2–3 mm., urceolate.

Hab.: Fields. Acco Plain, Esdraelon Plain. Very rare.

Area: E. Mediterranean.

2. Tordylium syriacum L., Sp. Pl. 239 (1753); Boiss., Fl. 2 : 1030 (1872). *Hasselquistia syriaca* (L.) Boiss., Ann. Sci. Nat. Bot. ser. 3, 1 : 346 (1844). [Plate 642]

Annual, 10–30 cm. Stems erect, sparingly branched, hirsute-scabrous. Lower leaves 2–4 × 1.5–2 cm., undivided, ovate, dentate, the others 1-pinnatisect, segments ovate to cuneate-obovate, crenate or coarsely dentate, the terminal one much longer. Umbels few, long-peduncled; rays few, short and thickened, often contracted. Bracts linear, setaceous. Bracteoles 0.6–2 × 0.1–0.4 cm., much longer than the umbellet, erect, oblanceolate-spatulate. Flowers small. Petals slightly radiating. Outer fruits of umbel 0.8–1 cm., discoid-orbicular or -ovate, densely papillose-hairy, with margin about as broad as or broader than the seed-bearing part; inner part of margin pellucid, outer part inflated, white, strongly wrinkled; oil ducts solitary in each furrow, the 3 dorsal ones approximate, the lateral ones marginal, commissural ducts 2, approximate, parallel; inner fruits urceolate, few or sometimes 0. Fl. March–April.

Hab.: Batha and fallow fields. Coastal Galilee, Upper Galilee, Mt. Carmel. Rather rare.

Area: E. Mediterranean.

46. AINSWORTHIA Boiss.

Annual or perennial herbs, hairy or strigulose. Leaves undivided or 1-pinnatisect. Umbels several- to many-rayed, with filiform bracts and bracteoles. Flowers hermaphrodite and staminate, showy. Calyx teeth obsolete. Petals white, those of the inner flowers orbicular but oblique, those of the outer flowers larger, strongly radiating, unequally 2-parted into one long-obovate or long-elliptical lobe and one minute lateral lobe at the base of the former. Fruit either dorsally compressed, discoid, orbicular-ovate to broadly elliptical, with margin pithy, inflated, not wrinkled, or fruits dimorphic, some discoid and some urceolate; carpophore 2-parted; mericarps with equidistant filiform ribs, or with lateral ribs somewhat remote from the others; oil ducts solitary in each furrow. Seeds flat.

Four to five species in the E. Mediterranean countries.

1. Peripheral petals of outer flowers 0.5–1 cm. Fruits uniform, 2–4 mm.
   1. A. trachycarpa
– Peripheral petals of outer flowers much smaller. Fruits dimorphic, both discoid and urceolate; the former 5–7 mm.   **2. A. cordata**

1. Ainsworthia trachycarpa Boiss., Diagn. ser. 1, 10 : 43 (1849) et Fl. 2 : 1035 (1872). [Plate 643]

Annual, pubescent, 20–60 cm. Stems erect, moderately branched, angular-furrowed, retrorsely hispidulous and scabrous. Lower leaves long-petioled, mostly undivided, blade usually 3–8 × 2.5 cm., ovate-cordate, crenate or slightly lobed; upper leaves 1-pinnatisect into 3–5 ovate, doubly crenate segments, the terminal segment much longer than the lateral ones. Umbels mostly terminal, long-peduncled, many-rayed; rays 1–3 cm., unequal. Bracts many, deflexed, rigid, filiform-setaceous, scabrous-hispidulous. Bracteoles longer than the pedicels, rigid, filiform, hispidulous. Radiating petals 0.5–1 cm., very unequally 2-parted. Styles conspicuous, deflexed. Fruit 2–4 mm., discoid, ovate-orbicular, minutely warty, with inflated margin half as broad as the seed-bearing part; oil ducts filiform, lateral ones remote, commissural ducts 2, approximate. Fl. March–June.

Hab.: Fallow fields, roadsides, batha and cleared maquis. Coastal Galilee, Acco Plain, Sharon Plain, Philistean Plain, Upper and Lower Galilee, Mt. Carmel, Esdraelon Plain, Mt. Gilboa, Samaria, Judean Mts., Judean Desert, Hula Plain, Upper and Lower Jordan Valley, Golan, Gilead, Ammon. Common.

Area: E. Mediterranean, with slight extensions towards W. Irano-Turanian borderlands.

2. Ainsworthia cordata (Jacq.) Boiss., Ann. Sci. Nat. Bot. ser. 3, 1 : 343 (1844) emend. Alava, Not. Roy. Bot. Gard. Edinb. 31 : 116, f. 2, 3 (1971). *Hasselquistia cordata* Jacq., Hort. Bot. Vindob. 2 : 91 (1772). *A. carmeli* Boiss., Diagn. ser. 1, 10 : 44 (1849) et Fl. 2 : 1035 (1872). [Plate 644; under *A. carmeli* Boiss.]

Annual, hairy, 40–80 cm. Stems erect, sparingly branched, slender, angular, hispidulous, scabrous. Lower leaves undivided, long-petioled, cordate-ovate, blade 4–8 cm., doubly crenate; upper leaves either undivided and ovate-oblong or very often 3-sect into ovate segments, the terminal segment petiolulate, cordate; uppermost leaves reduced to an oblong, cuneate blade. Umbels mostly terminal, very long-peduncled, with few unequal rays; rays very conspicuously bristly-feathery with bristles much longer than the width of the ray. Bracts and bracteoles many, deflexed, setaceous, plumose-bristly, the bracteoles as long as or longer than the umbellets. Radiating petals 2–3 mm., unequally 2-parted, larger lobe broadly ovate. Fruits usually dimorphic, discoid and urceolate; the former larger, 5–7 mm., orbicular or broadly elliptical, sparsely tuberculate to smooth, with a smooth margin as broad as the seed-bearing part, outer part of margin white, slightly inflated; oil ducts filiform, the dorsal ones approximate, the lateral ones somewhat remote, commissural ducts 2, approximate. Fl. April–June.

Hab.: Maquis and batha, or other shady places. Upper and Lower Galilee, Mt. Carmel, Mt. Gilboa, Samaria, Upper Jordan Valley (endemic). Uncommon.

Area: E. Mediterranean.

47. SYNELCOSCIADIUM Boiss.

Tall, hairy, annual herbs, branched mostly above. Stems erect, thick, leafy mainly at base. Leaves 1-pinnatisect. Umbels terminal and axillary, very unequally rayed. Involucre and involucel present. Flowers hermaphrodite and staminate. Calyx teeth unequally long, lanceolate, caducous in fruit. Petals radiating, white, strigulose below, outer petals equally 2-parted. Stylopodium elongated, conical; styles erect, becoming indurated. Fruit dorsally compressed, with a broad margin; carpophore 2-parted; mericarps with very slender, scarcely visible ribs; dorsal ribs equidistant, lateral ones remote, close to margin; oil ducts solitary in each furrow, conspicuous, filiform, commissural ducts 2, approximate. Inner face of seed plane.

One species in Palestine and Syria.

1. Synelcosciadium carmeli (Labill.) Boiss., Ann. Sci. Nat. Bot. ser. 3, 1 : 346 (1844) et Fl. 2 : 1050 (1872). *Heracleum carmeli* Labill., Ic. Pl. Syr. Dec. 5 : 3, t. 1 (1812). [Plate 645]

Tall annual, setose or retrorsely hispid or appressed-bristly, 0.6–1.5 m. Stems erect, dichotomously branched above, rather thick, stiff, angular-striate, leafy mainly at base. Leaves densely covered with short appressed bristles, 1-pinnatisect into 2–3 pairs of sessile segments; segments of lower leaves 3–5 × 2–3 cm., ovate to oblong, coarsely dentate or lobed, lobes triangular-ovate, acute or acuminate; segments of upper leaves oblong-linear; uppermost leaves reduced to short-petioled, simple or 2-fid segments. Umbels many, 3–7-rayed, very contracted in fruit; rays bristly, very unequal, the longest up to 5–8 cm., the shortest almost 0. Bracts and bracteoles 4–5(–6) × 0.3–1 cm., linear-subulate, bristly, scarious-margined. Petals radiating, white, strigose below. Fruit 7–8 mm., orbicular to very broadly elliptical, retuse, appressed-strigulose, margin brighter, conspicuous but much narrower than the seed-bearing part; styles persistent; ribs of mericarp filiform, often concealed by the hairy cover; oil ducts conspicuous, filiform. Fl. April–June.

Hab.: Roadsides and batha; especially common in lower altitudes. Sharon Plain, Upper and Lower Galilee, Mt. Carmel, Mt. Gilboa, Samaria, Judean Mts., Dan Valley, Hula Plain, Upper Jordan Valley, Golan, Gilead, Ammon. Rather common.

Area: E. Mediterranean (Palestine to Syria).

Ducrosia flabellifolia Boiss., Ann. Sci. Nat. Bot. ser. 3, 1 : 342 (1844), has been reported from Transjordan by Mouterde, Nouv. Fl. Lib. Syr. 2: 654 (1970).

48. ZOSIMA Hoffm.

Perennial, pubescent or tomentose herbs with thick fusiform roots. Stems leafy only at base. Leaves 2–3-pinnatisect. Umbels terminal, long-peduncled, many-rayed. Bracts usually few. Bracteoles many. Flowers hermaphrodite and staminate. Calyx teeth minute. Petals white or yellowish-white, obovate, notched with long inflexed apex, pubescent. Stylopodium usually depressed, about as long as the styles. Fruit dorsally compressed, inner part of margin pellucid, outer part of margin inflated; carpophore 2-parted; ribs slender, the lateral ones remote and marginal; oil ducts solitary in each furrow and occupying the whole furrow, commissural ducts 2, approximate. Seeds flat or slightly convex at back.

About 10 species, mainly in S.W. Asia.

1. Zosima absinthiifolia (Vent.) Link, Enum. Hort. Berol. Alt. 1 : 274 (1821; "Zosimia apsinthifolia"); Boiss., Fl. 2 : 1037 (1872; "Zozimia absinthifolia (Vent.) DC."). *Heracleum absinthiifolium* Vent., Choix Pl. t. 7 (1803). [Plate 646]

Perennial, greyish-pubescent to tomentose, 20–50 cm., with a thick tap root. Stems short, furrowed, densely covered at base with the fibrous sheaths of dead leaves, sometimes stems almost 0 and then peduncles arising from the base. Leaves almost all basal, oblong-lanceolate in outline, 2-pinnatisect, segments of secondary order 4–7, ovate or oblong, dissected into oblong obtuse lobes. Umbels on long stout peduncles; rays 4–10 cm., angular, crisp-pubescent. Bracts few, linear to lanceolate, crisp-puberulent. Bracteoles many, shorter than the pedicels or as long. Petals white or yellowish-green, pubescent. Stylopodium depressed-cupuliform, with undulate margin. Fruit 0.8–1 × 0.5–1 cm., about as long as the hairy pedicel, orbicular to broadly elliptical or somewhat obovate, retuse at apex, covered with long hairs or glabrescent; mericarps with 3 approximate filiform ribs on the seed-bearing part and 2 thick ones near the margin. Fl. March–April.

Hab.: Steppes and deserts, on stony or silty ground, often as an associate of Artemisietum herbae-albae. Central Negev, Moav, Edom. Rare.

Area: W. Irano-Turanian.

Very aromatic; fleshy roots and leaves used as a pot herb.

49. MALABAILA Hoffm.

Perennial herbs, hairy. Stems mostly simple or dichotomously branched above. Leaves undivided or 1–3-pinnatisect. Umbels mostly terminal, long-peduncled, almost equally rayed. Involucre and involucel present or 0. Flowers hermaphrodite or staminate. Calyx teeth obsolete. Petals yellow, ovate, notched with inflexed apex. Stylopodium depressed-conical, undulate at margin. Fruit dorsally compressed, orbicular to obovate or broadly elliptical, with a broad wing pellucid in its inner part and inflated at margin; ribs of mericarp filiform, the dorsal ones equidistant, the lateral ones marginal; oil ducts solitary in each furrow, conspicuous, commissural ducts 2, approximate.

About 10 species, mainly in S.W. and C. Asia.

1. Malabaila secacul (Mill.) Boiss., Diagn. ser. 1, 10 : 42 (1849) et Fl. 2 : 1057 (1872; "*sekakul*"). *Tordylium secacul* Mill., Gard. Dict. ed. 8, no. 5 (1768). *Pastinaca secacul* (Mill.) Banks et Sol. in Russ., Nat. Hist. Aleppo ed. 2, 2 : 249 (1794). [Plate 647; under *M. sekakul* (Banks et Sol.) Boiss.]

Perennial, pubescent, with fusiform roots, 20–60 cm. Stems often simple, rarely dichotomously branched above, striate. Leaves 10–20 cm., triangular or oblong in outline, 1–2(–3)-pinnatisect into oblong divisions; segments often decurrent at base; ultimate segments incised to pinnatipartite into ovate, obtuse, crenate or lobulate lobes; upper leaves much reduced, with blade shorter than the sheath. Umbels (6–)10–15-rayed; rays 3–10 cm., scabrous. Involucre 0. Involucel of 1 or few bracteoles or 0, shorter than bristly pedicel. Flowers numerous in each umbellet. Petals crisp-pubescent. Fruit 0.7–1.2 cm., narrowly notched at apex, glabrous or hirtellous; wing broader than the seed-bearing part, its inflated margin as broad as its inner pellucid part; ribs inconspicuous, filiform; the 2 dorsal oil ducts narrower than the lateral ones, commissural ducts approximate. Fl. February–May.

Hab.: Steppes, fields, rarely batha. Upper Galilee, Mt. Gilboa, Samaria, Judean Mts., Judean Desert, W., N. and C. Negev, Hula Plain, Lower Jordan Valley, Golan, Gilead, Ammon, Moav, Edom. Fairly common.

Area: W. Irano–Turanian.

Most variable in size, degree of leaf dissection, indumentum, and size and shape of fruit. Further study is needed for a better knowledge of this rather common species.

Roots edible.

Trib. DAUCEAE. Flowers as in preceding tribe. Crystalline layer in fruit parenchyma 0. Fruit compressed dorsally or laterally; mericarps with 5 primary filiform ribs and 4 secondary prominent ribs often extending into wings or prickly crests.

50. EXOACANTHA Labill.

Annual herb, spiny, branched, with pinnatisect lower and undivided upper leaves. Umbels many-rayed; rays unequal, very thick and hollow, central rays very short or 0. Bracts and bracteoles spiny, the latter very unequal, the outermost bracteole much longer than the others. Flowers hermaphrodite, minute. Calyx with obsolete teeth. Petals subequal, white or pink, notched with inflexed apex. Stylopodium depressed, with entire margin; styles much longer than the stylopodium. Fruiting umbels contracted and crowned by the horizontal spines of the involucel. Pedicels thickened in fruit, incurved, arranged in dense clusters along the inner side of the rays. Fruit laterally subcompressed; carpophore 0; mericarps angular, ovoid; primary and secondary ribs all prominent, corky, obtuse, the primary dorsal ribs thicker than the rest; oil ducts solitary in each furrow, commissure broad, flat, with 4 ducts. Seeds cylindrical.

One species in Palestine, Syria and S. Turkey.

1. Exoacantha heterophylla Labill., Ic. Pl. Syr. Dec. 1 : 10, t. 2 (1791); Boiss., Fl. 2 : 1069 (1872). [Plate 648]

Annual, whitish, glabrous, glossy, 20–40 cm. Stems erect, profusely branched from base, often corymbose, angular. Radical leaves soon wilting, pinnatisect with 1–2 pairs of remote, ovate to oblong, acutely dentate or incised segments, the terminal segment much larger than the others; cauline leaves pinnatisect into 2 to 3 pairs of incised or pinnatipartite, obovate-cuneate segments; the uppermost leaves 5–12 cm., 3–partite into linear-lanceolate segments. Umbels usually on long thick angular peduncles; rays 1–2 cm., white. Bracts 1–5 cm., spreading or deflexed, canaliculate, spiny, with a white nerve. Outer bracteoles (spines) 2–6 cm., canaliculate; inner bracteoles 0.5–1 cm. Petals white or pink. Fruit 1 mm., broadly ovoid to almost globular, prominently ribbed, borne on a thick deflexed pedicel longer than the fruit. Fl. April–June.

Hab. : Fields; heavy soil (obligatory weed). Acco Plain, Sharon Plain, Philistean Plain, Upper and Lower Galilee, Esdraelon Plain, Samaria, Shefela, Judean Mts., Dan Valley, Upper Jordan Valley, Golan, Ammon. Uncommon.

Area : E. Mediterranean.

51. ARTEDIA L.

Annual herbs, glabrous, showy. Stems erect, branched. Leaves 3-pinnatisect into filiform lobes. Umbels large, many-rayed; central umbellet sterile. Bracts and bracteoles large, 1-pinnatisect into filiform lobes. Flowers hermaphrodite and staminate. Calyx teeth obsolete. Petals strongly radiating, white; the outer petals deeply cut into 2 unequal lobes, one minute and lateral, near the base of the longer one; inner petals minute, ovate, retuse with inflexed apex. Fruit dorsally compressed, orbicular or ovate; carpophore 2-parted; mericarps flat, with broad white wings cleft into obovate-spatulate lobes separated by rounded sinuses; ribs 5, the 3 dorsal ribs filiform, the lateral ones confluent with the margin; commissure with a longitudinal median rib and with prominent and transverse wrinkles; oil ducts solitary beneath the secondary ribs. Seeds flat.

One species, mainly in the E. Mediterranean countries.

1. **Artedia squamata** L., Sp. Pl. 242 (1753); Boiss., Fl. 2 : 1070 (1872). [Plate 649]

Annual, glabrous, 20–60 cm. Stems erect, moderately branched, striate. Lower leaves oblong in outline, (2–)3-pinnatisect; lobes short (about 1 cm. or less), filiform or setaceous, divaricate; upper leaves with a narrow, strongly nerved sheath and a reduced blade. Umbels long-peduncled; rays rather short, spreading, forming a plane upper surface. Bracts and bracteoles pinnately dissected into many setaceous lobes, the former with sheathing petioles, deflexed. Flowers very showy. Petals of outer umbellets radiating. Fruit 1–1.5 × 1–1.3 cm., almost orbicular; lobes of wings longer than the glabrous, rarely sparsely villose, seed-bearing part. Fl. March–May.

Hab.: Batha and fallow fields. Sharon Plain, Philistean Plain, Upper and Lower Galilee, Mt. Carmel, Esdraelon Plain, Samaria, Shefela, Judean Mts., Upper and Lower Jordan Valley, Golan, Gilead, Ammon, Moav. Locally fairly common.

Area: E. Mediterranean.

52. Daucus L.

Annual or biennial herbs, hispid or bristly. Stems mostly erect, branched. Leaves 2–4-pinnatisect. Umbels terminal and axillary, often showy. Bracts and bracteoles mostly dissected or 3-fid. Flowers hermaphrodite and staminate. Calyx teeth minute or obsolete. Petals mostly unequal, often radiating, white, yellowish-white or reddish, obovate, notched with inflexed apex. Styles shorter or longer than the slightly convex to conical stylopodium. Fruit dorsally subcompressed, ovoid to oblong or cylindrical; carpophore rigid, undivided, bristly; mericarps dorsally convex; primary ribs 5, filiform, short-setulose; secondary ribs 4, stout and more prominent than the primary ones, winged or broadly keeled, cleft into 1 row of prickles (very rarely prickles reduced to tubercles); oil ducts solitary under each secondary rib; commissural ducts 2. Inner face of seed flat.

About 60 species, most of them in Europe, Africa and W. Asia; a few also in N. America and Australia.

Literature: A. Thellung, Daucus-Studien, *Repert. Sp. Nov.* 23 : 147–159 (1926). M. Onno, Die Wildformen von *Daucus* Sect. *Carota, Beih. Bot. Centralbl.* 56, 2 : 83–136 (1936).

1. Umbels axillary all along the stem and more or less appressed to it on short, thick peduncles; rays 3–6. Petals not radiating. Mainly steppe and desert plants.
   4. D. subsessilis
 – Umbel mainly terminal, long-peduncled   2
2. Tall robust plants, 0.7–1.5 m. Terminal umbels 15–40-rayed; rays 5–10 cm., forming a plane, concave or convex surface 5–25 cm. in diam. Bracteoles at least partly pinnatisect or 3-fid, not scarious-margined. Fruit 1.5–3(–4) mm.; prickles on secondary ribs weak and short, bristle-like, mostly appressed to mericarp.   **6. D. carota**
 – Plants differing from above in all or most of the characters   3
3. Secondary ribs of mericarp with very long and weak bristles (not prickles), (2–)3(–4) times as long as the width of the seed-bearing part; base of bristles narrow, apex glochidiate. Bracts and bracteoles usually undivided, membranous with a green or brown nerve. Styles about half as long as the fruit. Plants of the Jordan Valley and Transjordan. Rare.   **7. D. jordanicus**

– Secondary ribs of mericarp with rigid prickles conspicuously broadened at base. Bracts and bracteoles mostly pinnatisect or 2–3-fid   **4**

4. Low (15–30 cm.) delicate plants with glabrous or slightly scabrous stems. Umbels short, 1–3 cm. in fruit, 3–6-rayed. Bracts pinnatifid, almost as long as the umbel or longer. Prickles on secondary ribs of mericarp up to 10, rarely more.

3. D. guttatus

– Taller plants, not as above   **5**

5. Bracts pinnatisect into 2–3 pairs of filiform segments. Bracteoles 3–5-fid. Plants yellowish. Prickles on secondary ribs of mericarp usually yellowish when ripe. Petals white, becoming yellow when dried. Weeds among winter crops.   **5. D. aureus**

– Bracts 2–3-fid, not pinnatisect. Plants not yellowish as above   **6**

6. Prickles on secondary ribs of mericarp with narrow-triangular base, very short-connate at base; primary ribs not prominent. Involucre much shorter than the umbel. Rays of umbel usually long, very unequal, the longest up to 6 cm. or more. Plants of light soils only.   **2. D. litoralis**

– Prickles on secondary ribs of mericarp often brown, with broad-triangular base, connate usually for one fourth to one third of their length; primary ribs prominent. Involucre usually as long as the umbel or longer. Rays of umbel usually short (up to 3 cm. or so), more or less equal. Plants of various soils.   **1. D. bicolor**

1. Daucus bicolor Sm. in Sibth. et Sm., Fl. Gr. Prodr. 1 : 184 (1806) et Fl. Gr. 3 : 64, t. 270 (1821). *D. broteri* Ten., Fl. Neap. Syll. App. 3 in Fl. Nap. 4 : (in folio) IV, (in octavo) 591 (1830) et Fl. Nap. 5 : 335, t. 222, f. 2 (1835–1838); Boiss., Fl. 2 : 1073 (1872). *D. broteri* Ten. var. *bicolor* (Sibth. et Sm.) Boiss., l.c. 1074. [Plate 650]

Annual, branched, scabrous-bristly, 15–60 cm. Stems erect or procumbent. Leaves oblong in outline, 2-pinnatisect into oblong, acute, entire or 2–3-fid, setulose lobes. Umbels 3–5 cm. across, terminal, 5–15-rayed, contracted in fruit; rays short, mostly 1.5–3 (–4) cm., equal or almost so. Bracts shorter than the fruiting umbel, spreading or deflexed, linear-subulate, mostly 3-fid. Bracteoles as long as or longer than the flowering umbellet, linear, undivided or 3-fid, scarious-margined. Central flowers of umbel sometimes sterile, violet. Petals white. Fruit 4–8 × 3–7 mm. (incl. prickles), ellipsoidal, mostly brown; primary ribs prominent, setulose; prickles on secondary ribs few (often 4–7), longer than the diameter of the seed-bearing part, somewhat remote, connate for one fourth to one third their length (very rarely almost free), base often broadly triangular, apex glochidiate. Fl. April–August.

Hab.: Batha, fields and roadsides. Acco Plain, Sharon Plain, Philistean Plain, Upper and Lower Galilee, Mt. Carmel, Esdraelon Plain, Mt. Gilboa, Samaria, Judean Mts., Judean Desert, Upper Jordan Valley. Fairly common.

Area: E. Mediterranean, with extensions into N. Mediterranean territories.

2. Daucus litoralis Sm. in Sibth. et Sm., Fl. Gr. Prodr. 1 : 185 (1806; "*littoralis*") et Fl. Gr. 3 : 65, t. 272 (1821); Boiss., Fl. 2 : 1074 (1872). [Plate 651]

Annual, glabrous, hirtellous or bristly (10–)30–50 cm. Stems branched from base. Branches erect, ascending, rarely procumbent. Leaves long-petioled, sheaths sometimes ciliate; blade oblong-lanceolate in outline, 2–3-pinnatisect, hirtellous-scabrous, segments ovate, cut into crowded, somewhat fleshy, oblong-lanceolate, acute, undivided or 1–3-fid lobes. Umbels terminal and axillary, long-peduncled, rarely sessile, (3–)5–10(–15)-rayed; rays very unequal, rigid; central umbellets often sessile, the longest (3–)6–15 cm. Bracts much shorter than the rays, undivided or 3-fid (or both in the same umbel), very rarely pinnatisect, setulose, with prominent nerve. Bracteoles shorter than the umbellet, oblong-lanceolate, entire, setulose-ciliate, broadly scarious-margined. Petals more or less radiating, white, yellowish, pinkish or purplish. Fruit ellipsoidal to ovoid; prickles on secondary ribs (4–)6–11, longer or shorter than the fruit-bearing part, free to short-connate at base, narrowly lanceolate to shortly triangular, glochidiate. Fl. March–April.

Exceedingly polymorphic. The following varieties have so far been distinguished:

1. Longer rays of umbel 10–15 cm.   var. **longiradiatus**
- Rays of umbel much shorter   2
2. Bracts 3-fid or pinnatisect into oblong or lanceolate somewhat succulent lobes. Plants yellowish-green. Umbels 6–15-rayed; rays 1.5–4 cm. Petals slightly radiating, sometimes purplish or yellowish. Procumbent desert plants.   var. **negevensis**
- Bracts mostly undivided   3
3. Prickles on secondary ribs of mericarp 4–7(–9), broadly triangular. Bracts broad. Umbels 3–6-rayed; rays short. Procumbent or ascending plants.   var. **forskahlei**
- Prickles on secondary ribs of mericarp (7–)8–12   4
4. Prickles triangular, shorter than the diameter of the seed-bearing part. Erect plants.   var. **gaillardotii**
- Prickles lanceolate, longer than the diameter of the seed-bearing part. Erect or procumbent plants.   var. **litoralis**

Var. **litoralis**. Erect or procumbent plants. Bracts mostly undivided, short-linear. Petals radiating, white to purplish. Prickles on secondary ribs of mericarp 7–12, longer than the diameter of the seed-bearing part, generally lanceolate, slightly broadened at base.

Hab.: Mainly sandy and loamy soils. Acco Plain, Sharon Plain, Philistean Plain, Edom. Fairly common.

Var. **negevensis** Plitm.* Procumbent yellowish-green plants. Sheaths of leaves ciliate. Umbels 6–15-rayed; rays 1.5–4 cm. Bracts 3-fid or pinnatisect. Petals slightly radiating, sometimes purplish or yellowish. Prickles on secondary ribs of mericarp 7–11.

Hab.: Deserts and sand flats. Sharon Plain, N. and C. Negev. Uncommon.

Var. **longiradiatus** Post, Fl. Syr. Pal. Sin. 371 (1883–1896). Erect plants. Rays of umbel (the longest ones) up to 15 cm. Bracts 2.5–3 cm., undivided. Bracteoles up to 2 cm. Petals conspicuously radiating, pinkish.

Hab.: Sandy ground. Acco Plain, Philistean Plain. Uncommon.

Scarcely a variety.

Var. **gaillardotii** Boiss., l.c. Stems erect. Umbels 6–9 (or more)-rayed. Prickles on secondary ribs of mericarp 9–10, mostly shorter than the diameter of the seed-bearing part.

Hab.: As above. Acco Plain, Sharon Plain. Uncommon.

* See Appendix at end of this volume.

Var. **forskahlei** Boiss., l.c. *Caucalis glabra* Forssk., Fl. Aeg.-Arab. 206 (1775). *D. glaber* (Forssk.) Thell., Mém. Soc. Sci. Cherbourg 38 : 407 (1911–1912) non *D. glaber* Opiz ex Celak., Arch. Naturw. Landes Böhm. 3 (Bot. Abth.) : 582 (1875). Stems procumbent or ascending. Umbels 3–6-rayed. Prickles on secondary ribs of mericarp 4–7 (–9), usually longer than the seed-bearing part.

Hab. : As above. Coast of Carmel, Sharon Plain, Philistean Plain, Arava Valley, deserts of Edom. Uncommon.

Area of species : Mediterranean, with extensions into the E. Saharo-Arabian territories.

The above varieties are not always sharply delimited, as there are intergrading forms between them resulting from hybridization in overlapping areas.

3. Daucus guttatus Sm. in Sibth. et Sm., Fl. Gr. Prodr. 1 : 184 (1806) et Fl. Gr. 3 : 63, t. 269 (1821). *D. setulosus* Guss. var. *brachylaenus* Boiss., Fl. 2 : 1075 (1872). [Plate 652]

Annual, minutely scabrous to glabrous, 15–20 cm. Stems erect, branched from base. Leaves oblong in outline, 2-pinnatisect into short, oblong-linear lobes; upper leaves 1-pinnatisect. Umbels terminal, small, 3–6-rayed, compact, contracted in fruit; rays 1–1.5 cm. Bracts almost as long as the longest rays, pinnatisect, setulose. Bracteoles as long as or shorter than the pedicels, linear-setaceous, undivided. Central flowers of umbellets fertile or sterile. Petals radiating, white. Fruit about 4 mm. (incl. prickles), broadly ellipsoidal; secondary ribs of mericarp with numerous prickles almost as long as the diameter of the seed-bearing part or longer, free almost to base, dilated at base, glochidiate at apex. Fl. April.

Hab. : Batha. Judean Mts., Upper Jordan Valley. Rare.

Area : N. Mediterranean.

4. Daucus subsessilis Boiss. ex Boiss., Fl. Suppl. 272 (1888). (*D. subsessilis* Boiss. in Sint. et Rigo, Pl. Cypr. exs. 347). [Plate 653]

Annual, erect, asperulous, 10–40 cm. Stems simple or branched from base. Branches unequal, thick and short, ascending. Leaves long-petioled, 5–10 × 3–5 cm., oblong in outline, 2–3-pinnatisect; ultimate lobes short, linear, acute, entire, setulose. Umbels axillary, with thick peduncles and few unequal rays. Bracts and bracteoles longer than the umbels or umbellets, pinnatisect. Petals not radiating, minute, white. Fruit about 5 × 4–6 (–7) mm. (incl. prickles), oblong; prickles on secondary ribs numerous, slender, twice as long as the width of the seed-bearing part or more, somewhat connate at base, lanceolate, darker at tip, with well-developed glochidia. Fl. March–May.

Hab. : Batha and deserts. Upper Galilee, Esdraelon Plain, Samaria, Shefela, Judean Mts., Judean Desert, C. Negev, Lower Jordan Valley, Dead Sea area, Gilead, Ammon, Moav. Uncommon.

Area : E. Mediterranean and W. Irano-Turanian.

5. Daucus aureus Desf., Fl. Atl. 1 : 242, t. 61 (1798). [Plate 654]

Annual, sparingly bristly, 30–80 cm. Stems erect, dichotomously branched from base or above, furrowed, leafy. Leaves (5–)10–25 cm., triangular-oblong in outline,

2–3-pinnatisect; segments divaricate, ovate or oblong, cut into linear or lanceolate, acute, glabrous or glabrescent lobes. Umbels terminal, long-peduncled, many-rayed; rays rigid, (2–)3–8 cm., contracted in fruit and nest-like. Bracts many, shorter than the fruiting umbels, deflexed in fruit, pinnatisect into linear or filiform segments 1 cm. long or more. Bracteoles shorter than the umbellets, partly 3–5-fid, partly undivided. Petals slightly radiating, white, yellow when drying. Fruit 5–8 × 3–6 mm. (incl. prickles), oblong; bristles of primary ribs thickened-bulbose at base; prickles on secondary ribs numerous, about 2–3 mm., very narrow, connate at base, lanceolate, white to yellowish when dry, sometimes reduced to protuberances; glochidia well developed; central fruit of umbellet and sometimes inner mericarps of fruit with very short prickles. Fl. April–July.

Var. **aureus**. *D. aureus* Desf., l.c.; Boiss., Fl. 2 : 1076 (1872). Mericarps with long prickles, mostly twice as long as the width of the seed-bearing part.

Hab.: Fields (obligatory weed). Acco Plain, Sharon Plain, Philistean Plain, Lower Galilee, Mt. Carmel, Esdraelon Plain, Upper Jordan Valley, Golan. Very common.

Var. **subinermis** Zoh.* Fruits with very short and thick protuberances or prickles.
Hab.: Fields. Esdraelon Plain. Rare.
Area of species : Mediterranean.

6. **Daucus carota** L., Sp. Pl. 242 (1753); Boiss., Fl. 2 : 1076 (1872). [Plate 655]
Annual or biennial, hispid, 0.7–1.5 m. Stems mostly erect, furrowed. Leaves oblong or ovate in outline, 2–3-pinnatisect, glabrous or hairy; segments of lower leaves mostly ovate, lanceolate-cuneate or rhombic, deeply cut into ovate-oblong or oblong, acute and mucronate lobes; segments of upper leaves with linear lobes. Flowering umbels 5–25 cm. in diam., terminal, borne on thickened hispid peduncles usually 20–60 cm.; rays numerous. Bracts as long as or shorter than the umbel, 1–2-pinnatisect, segments scarious-margined. Bracteoles as long as or longer than the umbellet, 3-fid to pinnatisect, more rarely undivided, ciliate-margined. Central flowers of umbel sterile. Petals radiating, white, those of central sterile flowers purplish. Fruit 1.5–3 (–4) × 2–3 mm. (incl. prickles), ovoid or oblong; prickles on secondary ribs numerous, longer (rarely shorter) than the width of the seed-bearing part and free almost to base; glochidia several to 0. Fl. April–August.

1. Terminal umbels (10–)12–20(–25) cm. across. Prickles on secondary ribs of mericarp with several glochidia at apex. ssp. **maximus**
– Terminal umbels (5–)8–10 cm. across. Prickles on secondary ribs of mericarp without or with 1–2 (rarely more) glochidia. ssp. **carota**

Subsp. **carota**. *D. carota* L. ssp. *carota* (L.) Thell. in Hegi, Ill. Fl. Mitteleur. 5 (2): 1514 (1926). Segments of lower leaves mostly ovate or lanceolate-cuneate, deeply cut into lobes remote from one another. Umbels 8–10 cm. across or less. Prickles of mericarp without or with 1–2 (very rarely more) glochidia at apex.

Hab.: Roadsides, fields and batha. Acco Plain, Sharon Plain, Philistean Plain, Mt. Carmel, Judean Mts. Uncommon.

* See Appendix at end of this volume.

Subsp. **maximus** (Desf.) Ball, Journ. Linn. Soc. Lond. Bot. 16 : 476 (1878). *D. maximus* Desf., Fl. Atl. 1 : 241 (1798) p.p.; Boiss., l.c.; Batt. in Batt. et Trab., Fl. Alg. 1 : 382 (1889). [Plate 655]. Segments of lower leaves ovate, ovate-lanceolate or rhombic, mucronate, cut into somewhat overlapping lobes. Umbels very large, (10–)12–20(–25) cm. across. Prickles of mericarp with several glochidia at apex.

Hab.: As above. Sharon Plain, Philistean Plain, Upper Galilee, Mt. Carmel, Esdraelon Plain, Mt. Gilboa, Shefela, Judean Mts., Upper Jordan Valley, Beit Shean Valley, Golan, Ammon. Common.

Area of species: Mediterranean, with extensions into W. Irano-Turanian territories.

The above taxa are not sharply distinguished from one another because of the many intermediate forms resulting from hybridization. *D. carota* L. in this country comprises, apart from the above varieties, additional forms on whose ranks future research will have to decide. Mericarps with strongly reduced prickles have been observed in both of the above subspecies.

The cultivated carrot, *D. carota* L. ssp. *sativus* (Hoffm.) Hay., Fl. Steierm. 1 : 1199 (1910); Thell., l.c. 1516, well distinguished by its yellow or whitish swollen tap root, rarely escapes from cultivation.

7. Daucus jordanicus Post, Journ. Linn. Soc. Lond. Bot. 24 : 431 (1888). [Plate 656]

Annual, glabrous or sparingly papillose, 25–50 cm. Stems slender, dichotomously branched. Leaves oblong in outline, 2–3-pinnatisect, ultimate lobes linear to filiform, setulose. Umbels terminal, long-peduncled, 6–12-rayed; rays somewhat unequal, the longest 4–8 cm. in fruit. Bracts unequal, linear-subulate, undivided (very rarely pinnatisect or 3-fid), the longest about half as long as the rays. Bracteoles shorter than the pedicels, ovate to oblong-lanceolate, acuminate, ciliate, very broadly scarious-margined. Petals radiating, white. Fruit 5–7 × 4–5 mm. (incl. prickles), much shorter than pedicel, oblong-ellipsoidal; prickles on secondary ribs numerous, much longer than the width of the seed-bearing part, free to the base, weak, setaceous, with minute glochidia at apex. Fl. April–May.

Hab.: Grassy places. Lower Jordan Valley, Gilead, Ammon, Moav, Edom. Rare.

Area: Mediterranean and Saharo-Arabian.

Daucus pulcherrimus (Willd.) Koch ex DC., Prodr. 4 : 210 (1830) [= *D. orientalis* (L.) Vines et Druce, Morison Herb. 131 (1914)], recorded by Bornmueller, Mitt. Thür. Bot. Ver. N.F., 30 : 76 (1913), from Palestine, has not been observed again. This species could not have been confused with any other, since it lacks an involucre.

Daucus pumilus (Gouan) Ball, Journ. Linn. Soc. Lond. Bot. 16 : 477 (1878), recorded by Rechinger f. (Ark. Bot. ser. 2, 2, 5 : 399, 1952), should be referred to *Pseudorlaya pumila* (L.) Grande, Nuov. Giorn. Bot. Ital. n.s., 32 : 86 (1925).

APPENDIX

DIAGNOSES PLANTARUM NOVARUM

Psoralea bituminosa L. var. **prostrata** Zoh. var. nov.

Planta prostrata vel ascendens, usque ad 40 cm. alta. Caules tenues. Foliola parva; foliorum inferiorum foliola usque ad 4 cm. diam., orbicularia vel ovata, obtusa vel truncata, foliorum superiorum usque ad 7 × 3 cm., elliptica vel lanceolata, acuta. Capitula 20–30-flora. Corolla alba vel ochroleuca vel rosea, raro violacea. Legumen (rostro 1.3–2 cm. longo incluso) 1.7–2.8 cm. longum.

Holotype: Palestine, Mt. Carmel, Yagur, 1929, *Naftolsky* 20836 (HUJ).

Var. **brachycarpa** Feldm. var. nov.

Erecta. Caules crassi. Foliorum inferiorum foliola ovato-elliptica, foliorum superiorum lanceolata vel lineari-lanceolata, 5–11 × 1.2–2 cm. Capitula 15–18-flora, fructifera paulo elongata. Calyx 1.3 cm. vel brevior. Legumen (rostro incluso) usque ad 1.4 cm. longum, nigrum, plerumque in calyce inclusum; rostrum circiter 8 mm. longum, basi dilatatum, rectum, flavum.

Holotype: Palestine, S.E. of Dead Sea, Ghor es Safi, 1925, *Eig* 84 (HUJ).

Var. **hulensis** Feldm. var. nov.

Dumulosa, erecta, 1.5–2 m. alta. Caules crassi, sulcati. Foliorum inferiorum foliola 4–6 × 3–5 cm., obcordata, foliorum superiorum lanceolata vel elliptica. Racemi spicati, 18–24-flori. Calyx 1–2.1 cm. longus, glaber. Corolla caerulea. Legumen parvum, (rostro 7–8 mm. longo incluso) 1.3–1.4 cm. longum, rectum.

Holotype: Palestine, Hula Plain, at foot of Bashan slopes, swamp near Gonen, 1952, *Feinbrun* 20873 (HUJ).

Astragalus cruciatus Link var. **biserialis** Zoh. var. nov.

Legumina 6–10 per capitulum, in duas series disposita, ut in var. *cruciato* longa.

Holotype: Palestine, Philistean Plain, Khan Yunis to Deir Belah, kurkar hills, 1942, *D. Zohary* 303 (HUJ).

Astragalus schimperi Boiss. var. **aravensis** Zoh. var. nov. Tab. 76.

Capitula 5–8-flora. Legumina erecta.

Holotype: Palestine, Arava Valley, 8 km. N. of Ein Rhadian, sand, 1950, *D. Zohary* 14801 (HUJ).

Var. **aradensis** Zoh. var. nov.

Legumina erecta, inter pilos patulos setiformes sparsissimos glabra.

Holotype: Palestine, E. Negev, about 4 km. E. of Dimona, calcareous grey and rocky soil, 1961, *Zohary* 9 (HUJ).

Astragalus hamosus L. var. **microcarpus** Zoh. var. nov.

Legumen multo minus quam in typo, non arcuatum (ut in *A. brachycerate*) sed hamosum.

Holotype: Palestine, Moav, Ziza to Qatrani, 1929, *Eig* and *Zohary* 154 (HUJ).

Astragalus bombycinus Boiss. var. **aravensis** Zoh. var. nov.

Legumen nigrescens, glabrum vel glabrescens.

Holotype: Palestine, Arava Valley, env. of Eilat, wadi bed, 1951, *Tadmor* 14918 (HUJ).

Hippocrepis multisiliquosa L. subsp. **cilatensis** Zoh. ssp. nov. Tab. 155.

Folia 2–6 cm. longa; stipulae minutae, fere liberae, ovato-triangulares; foliola 2–4-juga, 0.8–1 × 0.2–0.3 cm., obovata vel oblonga, basi cuneata, apice obtusa vel paulo retusa. Pedunculi foliis aequilongi vel longiores. Racemi 3–4-flori. Flores 5–6 mm. longi, pedicellis calyce multo brevioribus. Calyx campanulatus; dentes late triangulares, tubo paulo breviores, superiores caeteris multo breviores. Corolla alba, dense purpureo-venosa; vexillum carina et aliis paulo longius, fere orbiculare, apiculatum. Legumen circiter 8-articulatum, omnino hirtellum.

Holotype: Palestine, Arava Valley, Nahal Timna, sandy soil, 1966, *Zohary* 194 (HUJ).

Trigonella moabitica Zoh. sp. nov. Tab. 184

Annua, glauco-viridis, 10–25 cm. alta. Caules numerosi, erecti vel ascendentes, diffusi, glabri vel adpresse parce pubescentes. Stipulae breves, semisagittatae, foliorum inferiorum dentatae; foliola 0.3–1.2 × 0.3–0.6 cm., obovata vel oblonga vel obcordato-cuneata, dentata. Pedunculi tenues, folia aequantes vel eis longiores, in aristam 3 mm. longam abeuntes. Racemi capitulato-umbellati, 5–10-flori. Flores 5–7 mm. longi. Dentes calycini triangulari-lanceolati, tubo 2–3-plo breviores. Corolla flava; vexillum carina et aliis paulo longius, obovatum, retusum. Legumen 1–1.8 × 0.1–0.15 cm., compressum vel cylindricum, hamosum vel irregulariter semicirculare, apice attenuatum, breviter mucronatum, oblique et transverse nervatum. Semina plura, ca. 1.5 mm. longa, laevia.

Holotype: Palestine, Edom, Wadi-el-Hasa, near Qal'at-el-Hasa, 800 m., bed of wadi, 1936, *Eig, Zohary, Feinbrun* 283 (HUJ).

Trigonella berythea Boiss. et Bl. var. **leucantha** Zoh. var. nov.

A var. **berythca** floribus plerumque minoribus (0.8–1 cm. longis) differt. Corolla ochroleuca.

Holotype: Palestine, Judean Mts., Qiryat-Anavim, 1930, *Amdursky* 84 (HUJ).

Trifolium philistaeum Zoh. var. **filifolium** Zoh. var. nov.

Foliola omnia vel foliorum superiorum saltem filiformia, integra.

Holotype: Palestine, W. Negev, between Yad-Mordechai and Erez, sandy-limestone hill, 1962, *Plitmann* 11101 (HUJ).

Trifolium resupinatum L. var. **microcephalum** Zoh.

see Zohary and Heller, Israel Journ. Bot. 19 : 324 (1970).

Trifolium clusii Godr. et Gren. var. **gossypinum** Zoh.
see Zohary and Heller, Israel Journ. Bot. 19 : 325 (1970).

Trifolium tomentosum L. var. **lanatum** Zoh.
see Zohary and Heller, Israel Journ. Bot. 19 : 328 (1970).

Trifolium tomentosum L. var. **philistaeum** Zoh.
see Zohary and Heller, Israel Journ. Bot. 19 : 329 (1970).

Trifolium bullatum Boiss. et Hausskn. var. **macrosphaerum** Zoh.
see Zohary and Heller, Israel Journ. Bot. 19 : 331 (1970).

Trifolium meironense Zoh. et Lern. sp. nov. Tab. 263.

Annua, adpresse pubescens, 15–30 cm. alta. Caules plures, ascendentes. Folia alterna, ultima opposita; stipulae lineari-oblongae, basi membranaceae, longitudinaliter purpureo-nervatae, parte libera herbacea subulata; foliola lineari-elliptica vel oblonga, basi cuneata, apice mucronata, superne denticulata. Capitula 1–1.5(–2) × 1 cm., terminalia et axillaria, pedunculata, ovoideo-oblonga. Tubus calycinus cylindricus, 10-nervius, patule longe hirsutus; dentes inaequales, subulati vel aciculares, 1–3-nervii, longe pilosi, omnes (vel inferior saltem) apice purpurei; dens inferior tubo sesquilongior, caeteri tubo aequilongi vel breviores. Corolla calyce sesqui- vel duplo longior, pallide rosea. Capitulum fructiferum 1–1.8 × 0.6–1.2 cm., oblongo-conicum; calyx fructifer usque ad 5 mm. longus, tubo obconico, 10-nervio, dentibus basi triangularibus, parum patentibus vel erectis; faux calycina aperta, sed callosa et ciliata. Legumen membranaceum, superne coriaceum. Semen obovoideum vel pyriforme, lateraliter compressum.

Holotype : Palestine, Upper Galilee, Mt. Meiron, Adatir (grown in 1965 from seeds collected by *J. Katznelson,* from the above locality) 160 (HUJ).

Trifolium alexandrinum L. var. **serotinum** Zoh. et Lern. var. nov.

Planta e basi ramosa. Caules numerosi, plerumque crassi, fistulosi. Foliorum superiorum stipulae cum parte libera longe subulata. Capitula basi plerumque bracteis conspicuis vel minutis involucrata. Dens calycinus inferior caeteris conspicue longior; florum inferiorum dentes calycini apice oblique acuminati vel unilateraliter lobulati; calyx fructifer tubo herbaceo griseo non prominenter nervato, dentibus quam in typo minus divergentibus.

Holotype : Palestine, Lower Galilee, env. of Meskha, field border, alluvial basalt soil, 1963, *Zohary* 2104/9 (HUJ).

Lathyrus hierosolymitanus Boiss. var. **amphicarpus** Plitm. var. nov.

Rami nonnulli subterranei floriferi.

Holotype : Palestine, N. Negev, Wadi 'Ar'ere, 1965, *I. Gruenberg* 106701 (HUJ).

Var. luteus Plitm. var. nov.

Caules tenues, 15–30 cm. longi. Foliola 2–6 × 0.2–0.7 cm., graminiformia. Racemi 1–2-flori. Flores 0.9–1.1 cm., lutei.

Holotype: Palestine, Sharon Plain, Kefar Vitkin, 1954, *Jaffe* 106702 (HUJ).

Lathyrus gorgonei Parl. var. **lineatus** Plitm. var. nov.

Glabra vel glabrescens. Flores rubri, 2–2.5 cm. longi. Utraque leguminis valva nervo mediano prominenti longitudinaliter percursa.

Holotype: Palestine, Upper Jordan Valley, Tiberias, 1929, *R. Gabrielit* 107302 (HUJ).

Lathyrus cicera L. var. **negevensis** Plitm. var. nov. Tab. 306.

Legumen 2–4 × 0.6–0.9 cm., reticulato-venosum; utraque valva nervo mediano prominenti longitudinaliter percursa. Semina nonnumquam obsolete guttata.

Holotype: Palestine, N. Negev, km. 17 on Beersheba–Gaza road, 1949, *Zohary* 15537 (HUJ).

Lathyrus setifolius L. var. **sharonensis** Zoh. et Plitm. var. nov.

Folia quam in typo longiora, plerumque simpliciter cirrhosa. Flores 7–8 mm. longi. Legumen 1.5–2 cm. longum, glabrum. Semina quam in typo minora.

Holotype: Palestine, Sharon Plain, Herzliah env., heavy soil, 1926, *Zohary* and *Eig* 107501 (HUJ).

Sect. Lentiformia Zoh. sect. nov.

Annuae. Folia brevissime petiolata; foliorum inferiorum petioli aristati, superiorum simpliciter cirrhosi. Racemi uniflori. Flores minuti. Legumina 1(–2–3)-sperma, plerumque indehiscentia, in statu clauso secedentia.

Type species: *Lathyrus lentiformis* Plitm., Israel Journ. Bot. 14 : 90 (1965).

Erodium ciconium (L.) L'Hér. var. **macropetalum** Zoh. var. nov. Tab. 340 a.

Hirta vel glabrescens. Folia plerumque 1-pinnatipartita vel -secta; segmenta ovata, crenata vel lobata. Petala sepalis duplo longiora.

Holotype: Palestine, N. Negev, env. of Shoval, cultivated ground, 1966, *Zohary* 71 (HUJ).

Fagonia mollis Del. var. **hispida** Zoh. var. nov. Tab. 361 b.

Hispida, pilis glandulosis flavescentibus longis pilis glandulosis brevibus immixtis obsita. Foliola persistentia. Calyx semipersistens, demum membranaceus et capsulam adhaerens.

Holotype: Palestine, S. Negev, env. of Eilat, Nahal Shlomo, 1964, *Baum* and *Plitmann* 114 (HUJ).

Fagonia arabica L. var. **negevensis** Zoh. var. nov.

Spinae stipulares horizontales, foliis subduplo breviores; folia subhorizontalia, plerumque unifoliolata, brevissime petiolata; lamina usque ad 2 cm. longa, lineari-oblonga.

Holotype: Palestine, Arava Valley, Sedom–Eilat road near Nahal Zin junction, wadi, 1964, *Plitmann* 911 (HUJ).

Euphorbia arguta Banks et Sol. var. **dasycarpa** Plitm. var. nov.

Capsula hirsuta.

Holotype : Palestine, Sharon Plain, Binyamina to Caesarea, 1929, *Eig* 276 (HUJ).

Haplophyllum poorei C. C. Townsend subsp. **negevense** Zoh. et Danin ssp. nov. Tab. 429.

Caules eglandulosi. Folia semiamplexicaulia. Lobi calycini fere orbiculares, constanter griseo-virides. Corolla calyce 3–4-plo longior, pubescens. Filamenta apice abrupte angustata, eglandulosa; antherae pubescentes. Ovarium pilis et glandulis obsitum.

Holotype : Palestine, C. Negev, Ras Ramon, in fissures of hard limestone, 1965, *Danin* 2111 (HUJ).

Alcea galilaea Zoh. var. **rosea** Zoh. var. nov.

Petala rosea.

Holotype : Palestine, Upper Galilee, Safad, garden, 1925, *Naftolsky* 13112 (HUJ).

Viola pentadactyla Fenzl subsp. **hierosolymitana** Zoh. ssp. nov.

Corolla calyce brevior vel ei aequilonga (nec ut in typo duplo longior), alba vel ochroleuca (nec caerulea); calcar sepalorum appendicibus paulo (nec duplo) longius.

Holotype : Palestine, Judean Mts., env. of Jerusalem, 1942, *T. Kushnir* 57501 (HUJ).

Anisosciadium isosciadium Bornm. var. **idumaeum** Zoh. var. nov.

Flores exteriores omnes fertiles, sessiles, 2–3 dentibus calycinis exterioribus foliaceis latis instructi; flos centralis fertilis, dentibus calycinis carens, liber, floribus sterilibus propinquis non adnatus.

Holotype : Palestine, Edom, 9 km. N. of 'Aneze, ca. 1050 m., among stones of basalt, 1936, *Eig, Zohary, Feinbrun* 57195 (HUJ).

Ammi visnaga (L.) Lam. var. **longibracteatum** Zoh. var. nov.

Umbellae phyllis involucri, umbellulae phyllis involucelli superatae.

Holotype : Palestine, Hula Plain, env. of 'Amir-Khiam Walid, among rocks, 1941, *F. Weissmann* 510 (HUJ).

Ferula daninii Zoh. sp. nov. Tab. 631.

Perennis, viridis, glabra vel sparsissime papillosa, 30–80 cm. alta. Caules solitarii, erecti, superne parce ramosi, tenues, striati, demum brunnescentes. Folia inferiora 20–40 cm. longa, petiolata, vaginis adpressis praedita, plerumque ternatim in segmenta oblonga 3-pinnatisecta divisa, segmentis ultimis 1–3(–5) cm. longis, ambitu ovato-oblongis, laciniis ultimis 1–3-lobulatis, raro integris, margine revolutis, glabris vel sparse scabridis; foliorum caulinorum vaginae inflatae, (2–)5–6(–7) × 1.5–2 cm., laminae minus divisae, laciniis ultimis linearibus 0.3–1.2 cm. longis; folia suprema ad vaginas inflatas, apice segmenta pauca ferentes, reducta. Umbella centralis fertilis, subsessilis, laterales fertiles vel steriles, longipedunculatae; radii (3–5–)6–10, 3–10 cm. longi. Involucrum minute 2-bracteatum. Bracteolae 1 vel plures. Petala flava. Pedicelli fructiferi fructui subaequilongi. Fructus 7–9 × 3–5 mm., ellipticus, albidus, apice dentibus calycinis obsoletis, stylopodio conico-depresso et stylis deflexis, coronatus; mericarpia jugis dorsalibus prominentibus, margine pellucido semine triplo angustiore; vittae solitariae, valleculam totam implentes, vittae commissurales 2.

Holotype: Palestine, C. Negev, env. of Sde Boker, marly ground, wadi, N. exposure, 1967, *Danin* 110 (HUJ).

Ferula negevensis Zoh. sp. nov. Tab. 637.

Perennis, 1–2 m. alta vel altior. Radix crassa, fusiformis. Caules solitarii, 5–7 mm. diam., basi fibrosi, superne ramosi, tenuiter striati. Folia inferiora 10–25 cm. longa, ambitu ovato-oblonga, 3–4-pinnatisecta, segmentis ultimis ovato-oblongis, 1–3-pinnatipartitis, laciniis 2–4 mm. longis, linearibus, oblongis vel obovatis, obtusis, indivisis vel 2–4-fidis, scabridulosis vel papillosis; folia superiora ad vaginas coriaceas, inflatas, 2–4(–6) × 2 cm., apice segmenta pauca ferentes, reducta. Inflorescentia iterum atque iterum et furcatim ramosa; umbellae terminales fertiles 1–3, superpositae, 4–6(–9)-radiatae, laterales staminatae, longipedunculatae. Petala flava. Fructus 6–7 × 3–4 mm., pedicello aequilongus vel longior, late ellipticus; mericarpia jugis dorsalibus 4 distinctis, transverse rugosis (jugo quinto a margine alato occulto); alae inaequilatae; valleculae 2–3-vittatae.

Holotype: Palestine, C. Negev, Makhtesh Ramon near Ma'aleh Arad, Artemisietum herbae-albae, N. slope, 1963, *Lipkin* 101 (HUJ).

Daucus litoralis Sm. var. **negevensis** Plitm. var. nov.

Procumbens, flavido-viridis. Umbellae 6–15-radiatae; radii 1.5–4 cm. longi. Bracteae 3-fidae vel pinnatisectae. Petala paulo radiantia, interdum purpurascentia vel flavescentia. Mericarpiorum juga secundaria 7–11-aculeata.

Holotype: Palestine, N. Negev, Wadi Mishash, 1957, *Zohary* and *Waisel* 115 (HUJ).

Daucus aureus Desf. var. **subinermis** Zoh. var. nov.

Mericarpiorum aculei ad tubercula brevissima reducti.

Holotype: Palestine, Esdraelon Plain, betw. Kefar Yehoshua and Nahalal, 1929, *Eig* 77 (HUJ).

ADDENDA AND ERRATA

p. 7, line 8 from bottom, after Philistean Plain add Judean Mts.

p. 12, line 8 from bottom, description and Plate 19 referred to **Potentilla reptans** L. fit **P. kotschyana** Fenzl, Pugill. 6 (1842), so far not recorded for Palestine. In **P. reptans** L. the leaflets are dentate and not incised; it occurs in the Upper Galilee.

p. 16, line 10 from bottom, after Galilee add Samaria.

p. 16, line 2 from bottom, after (1812). insert [Plate 24]

p. 22, line 11 from bottom, read **3. Amygdalus orientalis** Duham., Arb. Arbust. 1 : 48 (1755); Mill., Gard. Dict. . . .

p. 28, line 8 from bottom, read *tortilis;* Brenan, Kew . . .

p. 29 line 11 from bottom, read *A. seyal* Del.

p. 47, line 17 from top, instead of **Retama** Boiss. read **Retama** Raf.

p. 53, line 4 from bottom, read Wadi el Asal

p. 60, line 5 from bottom (footnote excl.), after Var. **aravensis** Zoh. insert [Plate 76]

p. 62, line 4 from top, after Eig, l.c. insert [Plate 78]

p. 62, lines 22–25 from top, read **9. Astragalus hauarensis** Boiss., Diagn. ser. 1, 9 : 63 (1849); Boiss., Fl. 2 : 234 (1872) *pro syn. A. gyzensis* Del., Fl. Aeg. Ill. 70 no. 690 (1813) *nom. nud.* et Fl. Eg. Suppl. t. 64, f. 14 (1813) *inedit.;* Del. ex Bge., Mém. Acad. Sci. Pétersb. ser. 7, 11, 16 : 14 (1868) et 15, 1 : 16 (1869) p.p.; Boiss., Fl. l.c. p.p. non *A. gyzensis* auct. Fl. Ross. [Plate 80]

p. 67, line 18 from top, after Eig, l.c. insert [Plate 89]

p. 67, line 26 from top, after Eig, l.c. insert [Plate 89a]

p. 72, line 16 from top, instead of (incl. read (et

p. 84, line 9 from bottom, after (1800). insert [Plate 121]

p. 95, line 20 from top, instead of (Mauri ex Sanguinetti) Daveau, read (Mauri ex Sanguinetti) Sanguinetti, Fl. Rom. Prodr. Alt 581. (1864); Daveau, . . .

p. 99, lines 2 and 5 from top, after Boiss., l.c. 179 p.p. insert [Plate 146a] and [Plate 146] respectively.

p. 106, line 8 from bottom, read Heyn, l.c. 190).

p. 112, line 7 from top, read quoad syn. Linn. *Hedysarum alhagi* L., Sp. Pl. 745 (1753) p.p. excl. syn. Wheel. et pl. ex Tataria. *A. maurorum* DC., Prodr. 2 : 352 (1825);

p. 118, line 1 from top, read **6. Ononis viscosa** L. ssp. **breviflora** (DC.) Nym.

p. 121, line 19 from top, after (1811). insert [Plate 177]

p. 126, line 23 from top, after Calyx add teeth

p. 132, delete lines 16–17 from top.

p. 143, line 7 from top, after (1883–1896). insert [Plate 208]

p. 147, line 6 from top, after (1826). insert [Plate 214]

p. 147, line 20 from top, instead of Rhode read Rohde

p. 148, line 12 from bottom, after 1900. insert [Plate 216]

p. 149, line 13 from bottom, after Eig in herb. insert [Plate 217]

p. 150, line 13 from top, read **19. Medicago doliata** Carmign., Giorn. Pis. 12, 1 (1810) var. **muricata** (Benth.) Heyn in P. H. Davis, Fl. Turk. 3 : 507 (1970). *M. aculeata* Gaertn., Fruct. 2 : 349 (1791); *M. aculeata* Willd., etc. . . .

p. 150, and p. 151, lines 12 from bottom and 10 from top respectively, instead of *M. tuberculata* (L.) Willd., read *M. tuberculata* (Retz.) Willd.

p. 154, line 12 from bottom, read Ind. Kew. 2 : 199 (1895; *"sicula"*).

p. 162, line 8 from bottom, after (1847). insert [Plate 231]

p. 163, line 2 from top, instead of glabrous, read glabrous to glabrescent,

p. 164, line 16 from top, read non Nutt., Proc. Acad. Nat. Sci. Philad. 4 : 8 (1848) et Journ. Acad. Philad. ser. 2, 1 : 151 (1848).

p. 164, line 3 from bottom (footnote excl.), read **Trifolium grandiflorum** Schreb., Nov. Act. Acad. Leop.-Carol. 3 : 477 (1767); Gruenberg–Fertig and Stearn, Israel Journ. Bot. 21 (in press). *T. speciosum* Willd., ...

p. 165, lines 9–7 from bottom, read **6. Trifolium boissieri** Guss. ex Soyer-Willem. et Godr., Mém. Soc. Roy. Sci. Nancy 1846 : 220 (1847); Guss., Fl. Sic. Syn. 2 : 858 (1845; *"boisseri"*) *nom. prov.*; Boiss., Fl. 2 : 152 (1872). "*T. speciosum* Willd." sensu Boiss., Diagn. ser. 1, 2 : 33 (1843) et sensu Griseb., Spicil. Fl. Rumel. 1 : 37 (1843) non Willd., Sp. Pl. 3 : 1382 (1802); Gruenberg–Fertig and Stearn, Israel Journ. Bot. 21 (in press). [Plate 236]

p. 168, lines 15–16 from top, delete *T. leiocalycinum* Boiss. et Sprun. . . .

p. 169, line 19 from bottom, read *T. neglectum* C. A. Mey.

p. 171, line 5 from bottom (footnote excl.), after (1961). insert [Plate 245]

p. 175, line 7 from bottom, read Zoh. in P. H. Davis, Fl. Turk. 3 : 414 (1970).

p. 175, line 4 from bottom, after (1849). insert [Plate 248]

p. 179, line 11 from bottom, read Var. **desvauxii** (Boiss. et Bl.) Gib. et Belli, Mem. Accad. Sci. Torino ser. 2, 39 : 346 (1889) p.p.; Post, . . .

p. 187, line 3 from bottom, after excl. var. *β*. insert [Plate 268, f. 1]

p. 188, line 9 from top, after (1907). insert [Plate 268, f. 2]

p. 203, line 7 from bottom, after (1839). insert [Plate 291]

p. 206, line 11 from top, after (1857). insert [Plate 295, f. 1]

p. 206, line 16 from bottom, after (1849). insert [Plate 295, f. 3]

p. 207, line 2 from top, after (1814). insert [Plate 295, f. 2]

p. 210, between lines 3 and 4 from top, insert Ten species in the Mediterranean region and W. Asia.

p. 211, line 1 from top, after (1927). insert [Plate 300]

p. 214, line 12 from top, after As above. Add Sharon Plain,

p. 216, line 13 from bottom (footnote excl.), after Plitm.* insert [Plate 306]

p. 222, between lines 21 and 22 from top, insert Plate 315 does not represent the true *P. elatius* M.B. but a form which is probably intermediate between the latter and *P. syriacum* (Berg.) Lehm. The true *P. elatius* is distinguished by its entire leaflets and its peduncles 2-flowered and much longer than leaves.

p. 251, line 8 from bottom (footnote excl.), instead of *E. tristis,* read *F. tristis*

p. 266, line 11 from bottom, read excl. syn. [*Croton tinctorium γ Lam.*];

p. 324, line 5 from bottom (footnote excl.), after Golan add Upper Galilee.

INDEX

(Synonyms in italics)

My cordial thanks are given here to Mrs M. Bivas for reading the English text of both volumes and to Dr. E. D. Kollmann for his corrections of the Latin Diagnoses.

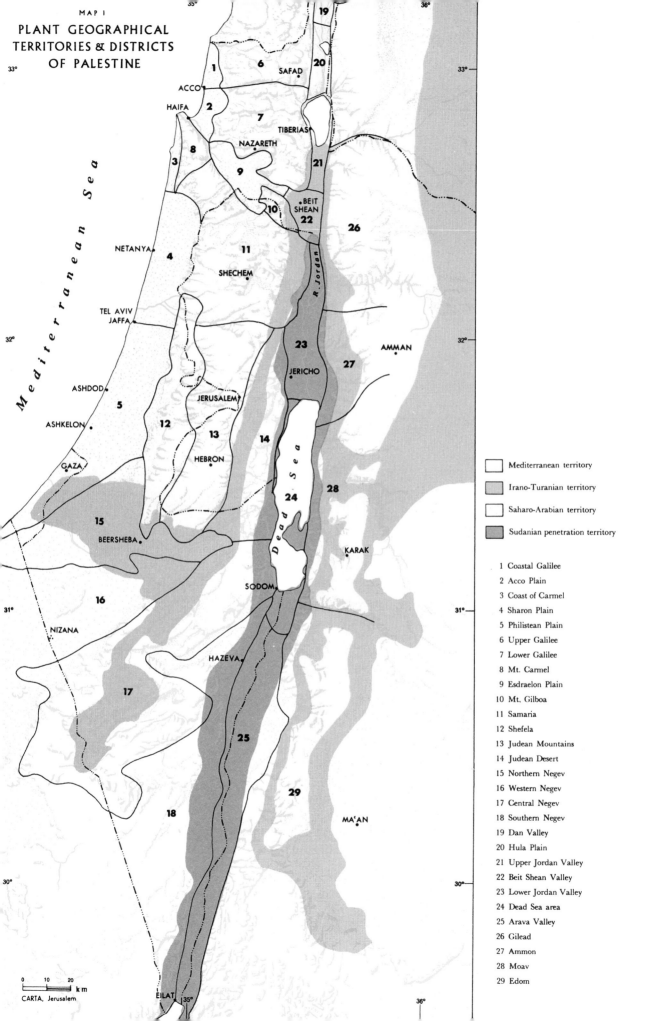

MAP I

PLANT GEOGRAPHICAL TERRITORIES & DISTRICTS OF PALESTINE

Mediterranean Sea

Dead Sea

R. Jordan

ACCO
HAIFA
SAFAD
TIBERIAS
NAZARETH
BEIT SHEAN
NETANYA
SHECHEM
TEL AVIV JAFFA
ASHDOD
ASHKELON
JERUSALEM
GAZA
HEBRON
JERICHO
AMMAN
BEERSHEBA
KARAK
SODOM
NIZANA
HAZEVA
MA'AN
EILAT

☐ Mediterranean territory

▨ Irano-Turanian territory

☐ Saharo-Arabian territory

▩ Sudanian penetration territory

1 Coastal Galilee
2 Acco Plain
3 Coast of Carmel
4 Sharon Plain
5 Philistean Plain
6 Upper Galilee
7 Lower Galilee
8 Mt. Carmel
9 Esdraelon Plain
10 Mt. Gilboa
11 Samaria
12 Shefela
13 Judean Mountains
14 Judean Desert
15 Northern Negev
16 Western Negev
17 Central Negev
18 Southern Negev
19 Dan Valley
20 Hula Plain
21 Upper Jordan Valley
22 Beit Shean Valley
23 Lower Jordan Valley
24 Dead Sea area
25 Arava Valley
26 Gilead
27 Ammon
28 Moav
29 Edom

CARTA, Jerusalem

0 10 20 km

MAP 2

PLANT GEOGRAPHICAL REGIONS REPRESEN

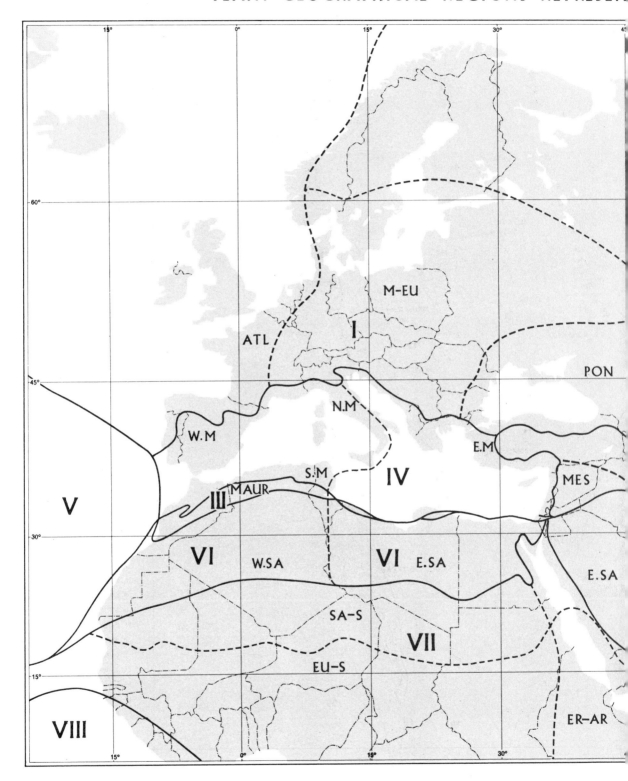

I   Euro-Siberian region

             West Euro-Siberian subregion
ATL   *Atlantic province*
BOR   *Boreal province*
M-EU   *Medio-European province*
PON   *Pontic province*

II   Sino-Japanese region

III   Irano-Turanian region

             West Irano-Turanian subregion
MAUR   *Mauritanian steppes province*
MES   *Mesopotamian province*
IR-AN   *Irano-Anatolian province*
M-AS   *Medio-Asiatic province*

             East Irano-Turanian subregion
C-AS   *Centro-Asiatic province*

IV   Mediterranean region

W.M   *West Mediterranean subregion*
N.M   *North Mediterranean part*
S.M   *South Mediterranean part*
E.M   *East Mediterranean subregion*

V   Macaronesian region

VI   Saharo-Arabian region

W.SA   *West Saharo-Arabian subregion*
E.SA   *East Saharo-Arabian subregion*

VII   Sudanian region

             West Sudanian subregion
SA-S   *Sahelo-Sudanian province*
EU-S   *Eu-Sudanian province*
E.S   *East Sudanian subregion*
NU-SI   *Nubo-Sindian province*
ER-AR   *Eritreo-Arabian province*

VIII   Guineo-Congolese region
IX   Indian region
X   Malaysian region